VW Golf
Owners Workshop Manual

Mark Storey

Models covered

(6416 - 416)

Hatchback & Estate ('Mk 7')

Petrol: 1.2 litre (1197cc), 1.4 litre (1395cc) & 2.0 litre (1984cc)
Diesel: 1.6 litre (1598cc) & 2.0 litre (1968cc)

Does NOT cover 1.0 litre 3-cylinder or 1.6/1.8 litre 4-cylinder petrol engines,
all-electric or hybrid models, convertible, Clubsport S, Golf R or dual fuel models
Does NOT cover facelifted Golf range introduced for 2017

© Haynes Publishing 2018

ABCDE
FGHIJ
KLMNO
PQRST

A book in the **Haynes Owners Workshop Manual Series**

Printed in Malaysia

Haynes Publishing
Sparkford, Yeovil, Somerset BA22 7JJ, England

ISBN **978 1 78521 416 5**

Haynes North America, Inc
859 Lawrence Drive, Newbury Park, California 91320, USA

British Library Cataloguing in Publication Data
A catalogue record for this book is available from the British Library.

*Printed using NORBRITE BOOK 48.8gsm (CODE: 40N6533) from NORPAC; procurement system certified under Sustainable Forestry Initiative
standard. Paper produced is certified to the SFI Certified Fiber Sourcing Standard (CERT - 0094271)*

Contents

LIVING WITH YOUR VW GOLF

Introduction to the VW Golf   Page   0•4

Safety first!   Page   0•5

Roadside Repairs

If your car won't start   Page   0•6

Jump starting   Page   0•7

Wheel changing   Page   0•8

Identifying leaks   Page   0•9

Towing   Page   0•9

Weekly Checks

Introduction   Page   0•10

Underbonnet check points   Page   0•10

Engine oil level   Page   0•11

Coolant level   Page   0•12

Brake (and clutch) fluid level   Page   0•12

Screen washer fluid level   Page   0•13

Wiper blades   Page   0•13

Tyre condition and pressure   Page   0•14

Battery   Page   0•15

Electrical systems   Page   0•15

Lubricants and fluids   Page   0•16

Tyre pressures   Page   0•16

MAINTENANCE

Routine maintenance and servicing

Petrol models   Page   1A•1

   Servicing specifications   Page   1A•2

   Maintenance schedule   Page   1A•3

   Maintenance procedures   Page   1A•7

Diesel models   Page   1B•1

   Servicing specifications   Page   1B•2

   Maintenance schedule   Page   1B•3

   Maintenance procedures   Page   1B•6

Contents

REPAIRS AND OVERHAUL

Engine and associated systems

1.2 and 1.4 litre petrol engine in-car repair procedures	Page **2A•1**
2.0 litre direct injection petrol engine in-car repair procedures	Page **2B•1**
1.6 and 2.0 litre diesel engine in-car repair procedures	Page **2C•1**
Engine removal and overhaul procedures	Page **2D•1**
Cooling, heating and air-conditioning systems	Page **3•1**
Petrol engine fuel systems	Page **4A•1**
Diesel engine fuel systems	Page **4B•1**
Emission control and exhaust systems – petrol models	Page **4C•1**
Emission control and exhaust systems – diesel models	Page **4D•1**
Starting and charging systems	Page **5A•1**
Ignition system – petrol engines	Page **5B•1**
Preheating system	Page **5C•1**

Transmission

Clutch – manual transmission	Page **6A•1**
Clutch – DSG transmission	Page **6B•1**
Manual transmission	Page **7A•1**
DSG semi-automatic transmission	Page **7B•1**
Driveshafts	Page **8•1**

Brakes and Suspension

Braking system	Page **9•1**
Suspension and steering systems	Page **10•1**

Body equipment

Bodywork and fittings	Page **11•1**
Body electrical systems	Page **12•1**
Wiring diagrams	Page **12•28**

REFERENCE

Dimensions and weights	Page **REF•1**
Conversion factors	Page **REF•2**
Buying spare parts	Page **REF•3**
Disconnecting the battery	Page **REF•3**
General repair procedures	Page **REF•4**
Vehicle identification numbers	Page **REF•5**
Jacking and vehicle support	Page **REF•5**
Tools and working facilities	Page **REF•6**
MOT test checks	Page **REF•8**
Fault finding	Page **REF•12**

Index

	Page **REF•21**

The Golf models covered by this manual date from January 2013 to December 2016. These are commonly known as the Mk7 (or 5G1) models. Note that a facelifted model (the Golf 7.5) was introduced in January 2017 and is not covered by this manual.

The Golf mark 7 is available in three body styles: 3 door hatchback, 5 door hatchback and an estate version. A convertible model (based on the Mk6 Golf) is also available, but is not covered by this manual. All versions are based on the modular 'MQB' Volkswagen group platform, that forms the basis for several models within the Volkswagen group.

Models are available with a range of petrol or diesel engines. Petrol engines range in size from 1.0 litres to 2.0 litres, but note that only the popular 1.2 litre, 1.4 and 2.0 litre petrol engines are covered by this manual. Diesel engines range in size from 1.6 litre to 2.0 litre. These are all 'Common Rail' (CR) engines. On CR engines the injectors are supplied with high pressure fuel from a reservoir (the 'common rail'). All the engines are of a well-proven design and, provided regular maintenance is carried out, are unlikely to give trouble.

Fully-independent front suspension is fitted, with a classic MacPherson strut layout, complete with an anti-roll bar on all models. All of the front suspension components (apart from the struts) are attached to a subframe assembly. The rear suspension uses trailing arms together with multi-link transverse arms on higher powered models (those with an output of greater than 90 Kw), whilst lower powered models (up to 89 Kw) have a simpler torsion beam axle fitted.

A five or six-speed manual gearbox is fitted, with a six or seven speed 'DSG' (Direkt-Schalt-Getriebe) semi-automatic transmission also available.

A wide range of standard and optional equipment is available within the model range to suit most tastes, including air conditioning (with manual or fully automatic climate control).

For the home mechanic, Golf models are straightforward vehicles to maintain, and most of the items requiring frequent attention are easily accessible.

Your Golf Manual

The aim of this manual is to help you get the best value from your vehicle. It can do so in several ways. It can help you decide what work must be done (even should you choose to get it done by a garage). It will also provide information on routine maintenance and servicing, and give a logical course of action and diagnosis when random faults occur. However, it is hoped that you will use the manual by tackling the work yourself. On simpler jobs it may even be quicker than booking the car into a garage and going there twice, to leave and collect it. Perhaps most important, a lot of money can be saved by avoiding the costs a garage must charge to cover its labour and overheads.

The manual has drawings and descriptions to show the function of the various components so that their layout can be understood. Tasks are described and photographed in a clear step-by-step sequence.

References to the 'left' and 'right' of the vehicle are in the sense of a person in the driver's seat facing forward.

Acknowledgements

Thanks are due to Draper Tools and AST tools, who provided some of the workshop tools, and to all those people at Sparkford who helped in the production of this manual.

This manual is not a direct reproduction of the vehicle manufacturer's data, and its publication should not be taken as implying any technical approval by the vehicle manufacturers or importers.

We take great pride in the accuracy of information given in this manual, but vehicle manufacturers make alterations and design changes during the production run of a particular vehicle of which they do not inform us. No liability can be accepted by the authors or publishers for loss, damage or injury caused by any errors in, or omissions from, the information given.

Working on your car can be dangerous. This page shows just some of the potential risks and hazards, with the aim of creating a safety-conscious attitude.

General hazards

Scalding

• Don't remove the radiator or expansion tank cap while the engine is hot.
• Engine oil, transmission fluid or power steering fluid may also be dangerously hot if the engine has recently been running.

Burning

• Beware of burns from the exhaust system and from any part of the engine. Brake discs and drums can also be extremely hot immediately after use.

Crushing

• When working under or near a raised vehicle, always supplement the jack with axle stands, or use drive-on ramps.
Never venture under a car which is only supported by a jack.
• Take care if loosening or tightening high-torque nuts when the vehicle is on stands. Initial loosening and final tightening should be done with the wheels on the ground.

Fire

• Fuel is highly flammable; fuel vapour is explosive.
• Don't let fuel spill onto a hot engine.
• Do not smoke or allow naked lights (including pilot lights) anywhere near a vehicle being worked on. Also beware of creating sparks (electrically or by use of tools).
• Fuel vapour is heavier than air, so don't work on the fuel system with the vehicle over an inspection pit.
• Another cause of fire is an electrical overload or short-circuit. Take care when repairing or modifying the vehicle wiring.
• Keep a fire extinguisher handy, of a type suitable for use on fuel and electrical fires.

Electric shock

• Ignition HT and Xenon headlight voltages can be dangerous, especially to people with heart problems or a pacemaker. Don't work on or near these systems with the engine running or the ignition switched on.

• Mains voltage is also dangerous. Make sure that any mains-operated equipment is correctly earthed. Mains power points should be protected by a residual current device (RCD) circuit breaker.

Fume or gas intoxication

• Exhaust fumes are poisonous; they can contain carbon monoxide, which is rapidly fatal if inhaled. Never run the engine in a confined space such as a garage with the doors shut.
• Fuel vapour is also poisonous, as are the vapours from some cleaning solvents and paint thinners.

Poisonous or irritant substances

• Avoid skin contact with battery acid and with any fuel, fluid or lubricant, especially antifreeze, brake hydraulic fluid and Diesel fuel. Don't syphon them by mouth. If such a substance is swallowed or gets into the eyes, seek medical advice.
• Prolonged contact with used engine oil can cause skin cancer. Wear gloves or use a barrier cream if necessary. Change out of oil-soaked clothes and do not keep oily rags in your pocket.
• Air conditioning refrigerant forms a poisonous gas if exposed to a naked flame (including a cigarette). It can also cause skin burns on contact.

Asbestos

• Asbestos dust can cause cancer if inhaled or swallowed. Asbestos may be found in gaskets and in brake and clutch linings. When dealing with such components it is safest to assume that they contain asbestos.

Special hazards

Hydrofluoric acid

• This extremely corrosive acid is formed when certain types of synthetic rubber, found in some O-rings, oil seals, fuel hoses etc, are exposed to temperatures above 400OC. The rubber changes into a charred or sticky substance containing the acid. *Once formed, the acid remains dangerous for years. If it gets onto the skin, it may be necessary to amputate the limb concerned.*
• When dealing with a vehicle which has suffered a fire, or with components salvaged from such a vehicle, wear protective gloves and discard them after use.

The battery

• Batteries contain sulphuric acid, which attacks clothing, eyes and skin. Take care when topping-up or carrying the battery.
• The hydrogen gas given off by the battery is highly explosive. Never cause a spark or allow a naked light nearby. Be careful when connecting and disconnecting battery chargers or jump leads.

Air bags

• Air bags can cause injury if they go off accidentally. Take care when removing the steering wheel and trim panels. Special storage instructions may apply.

Diesel injection equipment

• Diesel injection pumps supply fuel at very high pressure. Take care when working on the fuel injectors and fuel pipes.

Warning: Never expose the hands, face or any other part of the body to injector spray; the fuel can penetrate the skin with potentially fatal results.

Remember...

DO

• Do use eye protection when using power tools, and when working under the vehicle.

• Do wear gloves or use barrier cream to protect your hands when necessary.

• Do get someone to check periodically that all is well when working alone on the vehicle.

• Do keep loose clothing and long hair well out of the way of moving mechanical parts.

• Do remove rings, wristwatch etc, before working on the vehicle – especially the electrical system.

• Do ensure that any lifting or jacking equipment has a safe working load rating adequate for the job.

DON'T

• Don't attempt to lift a heavy component which may be beyond your capability – get assistance.

• Don't rush to finish a job, or take unverified short cuts.

• Don't use ill-fitting tools which may slip and cause injury.

• Don't leave tools or parts lying around where someone can trip over them. Mop up oil and fuel spills at once.

• Don't allow children or pets to play in or near a vehicle being worked on.

The following pages are intended to help in dealing with common roadside emergencies and breakdowns. You will find more detailed fault finding information at the back of the manual, and repair information in the main chapters.

If your car won't start and the starter motor doesn't turn

- ☐ If it's a model with automatic transmission, make sure the selector is in the P or N position.
- ☐ Open the bonnet and make sure that the battery terminals are clean and tight.
- ☐ Switch on the headlights and try to start the engine. If the headlights go very dim when you're trying to start, the battery is probably flat. Try jump starting using another car.

If your car won't start even though the starter motor turns as normal

- ☐ Is there fuel in the tank?
- ☐ Is there moisture on electrical components under the bonnet? Switch off the ignition, and then wipe off any obvious dampness with a dry cloth. Spray a water-repellent aerosol product (WD-40 or equivalent) on the fuel system electrical connectors like those shown in the photos. Note that diesel engines do not normally suffer from damp.

A Check the condition and security of the battery connections (under cover).

B Check the fuses in the fusebox located on the left-hand side of the engine compartment.

C Check the security of all the accessible electrical connectors

Check that electrical connections are secure (with the ignition switched off) and spray them with a water-dispersant spray like WD-40 if you suspect a problem due to damp.

Jump starting

HAYNES HiNT *Jump starting will get you out of trouble, but you must correct whatever made the battery go flat in the first place. There are three possibilities:*

1 *The battery has been drained by repeated attempts to start, or by leaving the lights on.*

2 *The charging system is not working properly (alternator drivebelt slack or broken, alternator wiring fault or alternator itself faulty).*

3 *The battery itself is at fault (electrolyte low, or battery worn out).*

When jump-starting a car, observe the following precautions:

Caution: Remove the key in case the central locking engages when the jump leads are connected.

✔ Before connecting the booster battery, make sure that the ignition is switched off.

✔ Ensure that all electrical equipment (lights, heater, wipers, etc) is switched off.

✔ Take note of any special precautions printed on the battery case.

✔ Make sure that the booster battery is the same voltage as the discharged one in the vehicle.

✔ If the battery is being jump-started from the battery in another vehicle, the two vehicles MUST NOT TOUCH each other.

✔ Make sure that the transmission is in neutral (or PARK, in the case of automatic transmission).

HAYNES HiNT *Budget jump leads can be a false economy, as they often do not pass enough current to start large capacity or diesel engines. They can also get hot.*

1 Connect one end of the red jump lead to the positive (+) terminal of the flat battery.

Connect the other end of the red lead to the positive (+) terminal of the booster battery.

2 Connect the other end of the red lead to the positive (+) terminal of the booster battery.

3 Connect one end of the black jump lead to the negative (-) terminal of the booster battery.

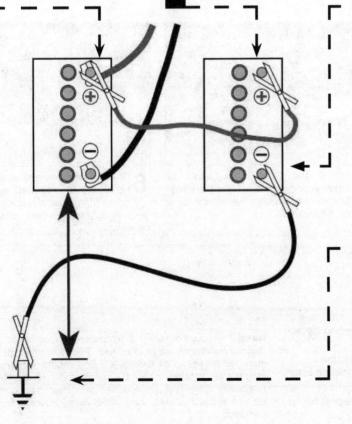

4 Connect the other end of the black jump lead to the earth bracket provided or to a bolt or bracket on the engine block.

5 Make sure that the jump leads will not come into contact with the fan, drive-belts or other moving parts of the engine.

6 Start the engine using the booster battery and run it at idle speed. Switch on the lights, rear window demister and heater blower motor, then disconnect the jump leads in the reverse order of connection. Turn off the lights etc.

Wheel changing

⚠️ *Warning: Do not change a wheel in a situation where you risk being hit by other traffic. On busy roads, try to stop in a lay-by or a gateway. Be wary of passing traffic while changing the wheel – it is easy to become distracted by the job in hand.*
Note: Some models do not have a spare wheel supplied as standard, instead a compressor and bottle of tyre sealant is supplied. It is possible to obtain and use a spare wheel.

Preparation

☐ When a puncture occurs, stop as soon as it is safe to do so.
☐ Park on firm level ground, if possible, and well out of the way of other traffic.
☐ Use hazard warning lights if necessary.
☐ If you have one, use a warning triangle to alert other drivers of your presence.

☐ Apply the handbrake and engage first or reverse gear (or Park on models with automatic transmission).
☐ Chock the wheel diagonally opposite the one being removed – a couple of large stones will do for this.

☐ If the ground is soft, use a flat piece of wood to spread the load under the jack.
☐ Where fitted the spare wheel is located in the floor beneath the load area. Lift up the cover to access the wheel and tool kit.

Changing the wheel

1 Use the wire hook to remove the wheel bolt caps (some models) or wheel trim. Use the wheel brace to slacken each of the wheel bolts by half a turn.

2 Use the special adapter when slackening the locking wheel bolts.

3 Locate the jacking point. A triangular dimple is pressed into the sill (A). Alternatively locate the reinforced section of the sill (B)

4 Make sure the jack is located on firm ground, and engage the jack head correctly with the sill. Then raise the jack until the wheel is raised clear of the ground.

5 Unscrew the wheel bolts (using the adapter provided) and remove the wheel. Place the wheel under the vehicle sill in case the jack fails.

6 Fit the spare wheel and screw in the bolts. Lightly tighten the bolts with the wheel brace then lower the car to the ground. Securely tighten the wheel bolts in a diagonal sequence.

Finally...

☐ Remove the wheel chock.

☐ Check the tyre pressure on the wheel just fitted. If it is low, or if you don't have a pressure gauge with you, drive slowly to the next garage and inflate the tyre to the correct pressure.

☐ The wheel bolts should be slackened and tightened to the specified torque at the earliest possible opportunity (see Chapter Section).

☐ Have the damaged tyre or wheel repaired as soon as possible, or another puncture will leave you stranded.

Note: *The spare wheel is a temporary 'space-saver' spare wheel. Special conditions apply to its use. This type of spare wheel is only intended for use in an emergency, and should not remain fitted any longer than it takes to get the punctured tyre repaired. While the temporary wheel is in use, ensure it is inflated to the correct pressure, do not exceed 50mph, and avoid harsh acceleration, braking or cornering.*

Using the puncture repair kit

 Warning: Do not use the puncture repair kit in a situation where you risk being hit by other traffic. On busy roads, try to stop in a lay-by or a gateway. Be wary of passing traffic while repairing the puncture – it is easy to become distracted by the job in hand.

☐ When a puncture occurs, stop as soon as it is safe to do so.
☐ Park on firm level ground, if possible, and well out of the way of other traffic.
☐ Use hazard warning lights if necessary.

☐ If you have one, use a warning triangle to alert other drivers of your presence.
☐ Apply the handbrake and engage first or reverse gear (or Park on models with automatic transmission).

☐ Where supplied the sealant and compressor are fitted in the spare wheel well beneath the load area.

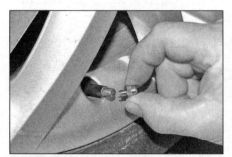

1 With the valve at the lowest point, remove the valve with the provided tool

2 Shake the sealant bottle and empty the entire contents into the tyre

3 Fit the compressor and inflate the tyre to a maximum of 2.5 Bar. If the pressure is low, drive the vehicle a metre to distribute the fluid and try again. If the pressure will not hold the tyre is beyond repair. If all is well drive for 10 minutes and check the pressure again. Replace the tyre at the earliest opportunity DO NOT exceed 50 mph.

Towing

When all else fails, you may find yourself having to get a tow home – or of course you may be helping somebody else. Long-distance recovery should only be done by a garage or breakdown service. For shorter distances, DIY towing using another car is easy enough, but observe the following points:

Use a proper tow-rope – they are not expensive. The vehicle being towed must display an ON TOW sign in its rear window.

Always turn the ignition key to the 'on' position when the vehicle is being towed, so that the steering lock is released, and the direction indicator and brake lights work.

The towing eye is kept inside the spare wheel (see Wheel changing). To fit the eye, unclip the access cover from the relevant bumper and screw the eye firmly into position **(see illustration)**.

Before being towed, release the handbrake and select neutral on the transmission.

Note that greater-than-usual pedal pressure will be required to operate the brakes, since the vacuum servo unit is only operational with the engine running.

The driver of the car being towed must keep the tow-rope taut at all times to avoid snatching.

Make sure that both drivers know the route before setting off.

Only drive at moderate speeds and keep the distance towed to a minimum. Drive smoothly and allow plenty of time for slowing down at junctions.

Flip open the cover

Fit the towing eye...

...and fully tighten with the wheel brace

Identifying leaks

Puddles on the garage floor or drive, or obvious wetness under the bonnet or underneath the car, suggest a leak that needs investigating. It can sometimes be difficult to decide where the leak is coming from, especially if an engine undershield is fitted. Leaking oil or fluid can also be blown rearwards by the passage of air under the car, giving a false impression of where the problem lies.

 Warning: Most automotive oils and fluids are poisonous. Wash them off skin, and change out of contaminated clothing, without delay.

 The smell of a fluid leaking from the car may provide a clue to what's leaking. Some fluids are distinctively coloured. It may help to remove the engine undershield, clean the car carefully and to park it over some clean paper overnight as an aid to locating the source of the leak. Remember that some leaks may only occur while the engine is running.

Sump oil

Engine oil may leak from the drain plug...

Oil from filter

...or from the base of the oil filter.

Gearbox oil

Gearbox oil can leak from the seals at the inboard ends of the driveshafts.

Antifreeze

Leaking antifreeze often leaves a crystalline deposit like this.

Brake fluid

A leak occurring at a wheel is almost certainly brake fluid.

Introduction

There are some very simple checks which need only take a few minutes to carry out, but which could save you a lot of inconvenience and expense.

These checks require no great skill or special tools, and the small amount of time they take to perform could prove to be very well spent, for example:

☐ Keeping an eye on tyre condition and pressures, will not only help to stop them wearing out prematurely, but could also save your life.

☐ Many breakdowns are caused by electrical problems. Battery-related faults are particularly common, and a quick check on a regular basis will often prevent the majority of these.

☐ If your car develops a brake fluid leak, the first time you might know about it is when your brakes don't work properly. Checking the level regularly will give advance warning of this kind of problem.

☐ If the oil or coolant levels run low, the cost of repairing any engine damage will be far greater than fixing the leak, for example.

Underbonnet check points

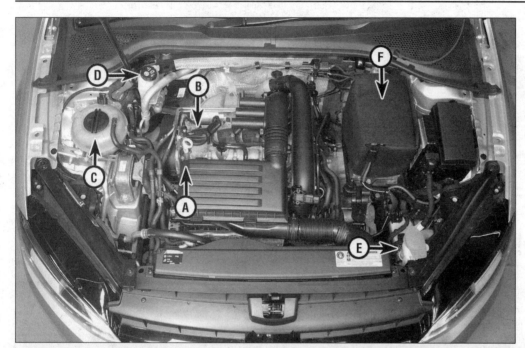

◀ 1.4 litre petrol engine

A *Engine oil level dipstick*

B *Engine oil filler cap*

C *Coolant expansion tank*

D *Brake (and clutch) fluid reservoir*

E *Screen washer fluid reservoir*

F *Battery*

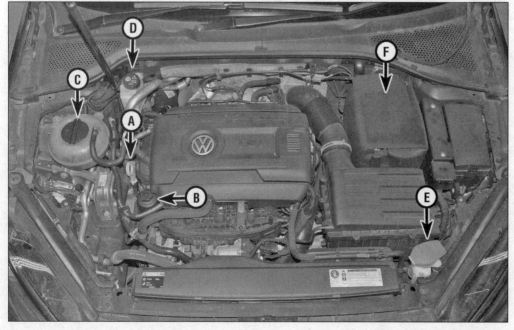

◀ 2.0 litre petrol engine

A *Engine oil level dipstick*

B *Engine oil filler cap*

C *Coolant expansion tank*

D *Brake (and clutch) fluid reservoir*

E *Screen washer fluid reservoir*

F *Battery*

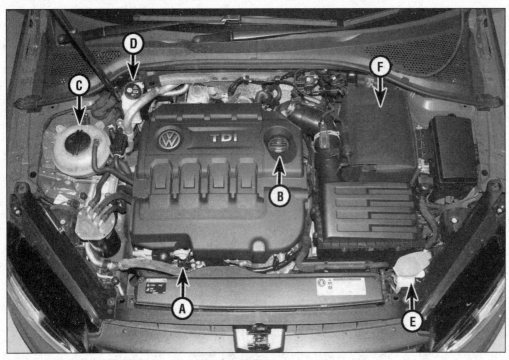

◀ 1.6 litre diesel engine

A *Engine oil level dipstick*
B *Engine oil filler cap*
C *Coolant expansion tank*
D *Brake (and clutch) fluid reservoir*
E *Screen washer fluid reservoir*
F *Battery*

Engine oil level

Before you start
✔ Make sure that the car is on level ground.
✔ Check the oil level before the car is driven, or at least 5 minutes after the engine has been switched off.

> **HAYNES HiNT**
> *If the oil is checked immediately after driving the vehicle, some of the oil will remain in the upper engine components, resulting in an inaccurate reading on the dipstick.*

The correct oil
Modern engines place great demands on their oil. It is very important that the correct oil for your car is used (see *Lubricants and fluids*).

Car care
● If you have to add oil frequently, you should check whether you have any oil leaks. Place some clean paper under the car overnight, and check for stains in the morning. If there are no leaks, then the engine may be burning oil.
● Always maintain the level between the upper and lower dipstick marks (see photo 2). If the level is too low, severe engine damage may occur. Oil seal failure may result if the engine is overfilled by adding too much oil.

1 The dipstick is located at the front of the engine (see *Underbonnet check points*); the dipstick is often brightly coloured or has a picture of an oil-can on the top for identification. Withdraw the dipstick.

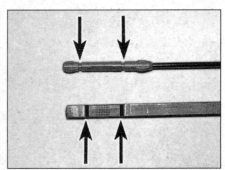

2 The oil level on the end of the dipstick, which should be between the upper (MAX) mark and lower (MIN) mark (two versions shown, but all are similar).

3 Oil is added through the filler cap aperture, unscrew the cap.

4 Top-up the level; a funnel may help to reduce spillage. Add the oil slowly, checking the level on the dipstick often. Don't overfill (see *Car care*).

Coolant level

Warning: Do not attempt to remove the expansion tank pressure cap when the engine is hot, as there is a very great risk of scalding. Do not leave open containers of coolant about, as it is poisonous.

Car care

● With a sealed-type cooling system, adding coolant should not be necessary on a regular basis. If frequent topping-up is required, it is likely there is a leak. Check the radiator, all hoses and joint faces for signs of staining or wetness, and rectify as necessary.

● It is important that antifreeze is used in the cooling system all year round, not just during the winter months. Don't top up with water alone, as the antifreeze will become diluted.

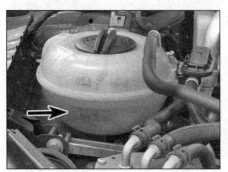

1 The coolant level must be checked with the engine cold; the coolant level should be between the MAX and MIN marks on the expansion tank.

2 If topping-up is necessary, remove the pressure cap (see Warning) from the expansion tank. Slowly unscrew the cap to release any pressure present in the cooling system, and remove the cap.

3 Add a mixture of water and antifreeze to the expansion tank until the coolant level is between the level marks. Once the level is correct, securely refit the cap.

Brake (and clutch) fluid level

Warning: Brake fluid can harm your eyes and damage painted surfaces, so use extreme caution when handling and pouring it.
Warning: Do not use fluid that has been standing open for some time, as it absorbs moisture from the air, which can cause a dangerous loss of braking effectiveness.

Before you start

✔ Make sure that your car is on level ground.

Safety first!

● If the reservoir requires repeated topping-up this is an indication of a fluid leak somewhere in the system, which should be investigated immediately.
● If a leak is suspected, the car should not be driven until the braking system has been checked. Never take any risks where brakes are concerned.

1 The upper (MAX) fluid level marking is on the side of the reservoir, which is located at the rear of the engine compartment. Remove the air intake pipe to improve access. First wipe clean the area around the filler cap with a clean cloth.

2 If topping-up is necessary, unscrew the cap and remove it along with the rubber seal.

3 Carefully add fluid, avoiding spilling it on the surrounding paintwork. Use only the specified hydraulic fluid. After filling to the correct level, refit the cap and diaphragm and tighten it securely. Wipe off any spilt fluid.

Screen washer fluid level

● Screenwash additives not only keep the windscreen clean during bad weather, they also prevent the washer system freezing in cold weather – which is when you are likely to need it most. Don't top-up using plain water, as the screenwash will become diluted, and will freeze in cold weather.

 Warning: On no account use engine coolant antifreeze in the screen washer system – this may damage the paintwork.

1 The washer fluid reservoir is located at the front left-hand side of the engine compartment. To check the fluid level, open the cap and then look down the clear filler neck.

2 If topping-up is necessary, add water and a screenwash additive in the quantities recommended on the bottle.

Wiper blades

Note: *Checking and removing the rear wiper blade is essentially the same as the front.*

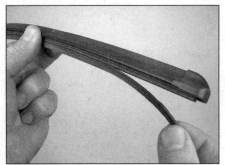

1 Check the condition of the wiper blades: if they are cracked or show signs of deterioration, or if the glass swept area is smeared, renew them. For maximum clarity of vision, wiper blades should be renewed annually.

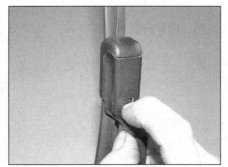

2 To remove a windscreen wiper blade, turn the ignition on, then turn the ignition off, and press the wiper switch stalk down once. This places the arms in the 'service' position. Lift the wiper from the screen and press the securing clip …

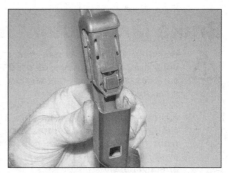

3 … slide the blade upwards from the end of the wiper arm, taking care not to allow the wiper arm to spring back and damage the windscreen. When completed, return the blades to the park position by pressing the wiper switch stalk again.

Tyre condition and pressure

It is very important that tyres are in good condition, and at the correct pressure - having a tyre failure at any speed is highly dangerous. Tyre wear is influenced by driving style - harsh braking and acceleration, or fast cornering, will all produce more rapid tyre wear. As a general rule, the front tyres wear out faster than the rears. Interchanging the tyres from front to rear ("rotating" the tyres) may result in more even wear. However, if this is completely effective, you may have the expense of replacing all four tyres at once!

Remove any nails or stones embedded in the tread before they penetrate the tyre to cause deflation. If removal of a nail does reveal that the tyre has been punctured, refit the nail so that its point of penetration is marked. Then immediately change the wheel, and have the tyre repaired by a tyre dealer.

Regularly check the tyres for damage in the form of cuts or bulges, especially in the sidewalls. Periodically remove the wheels, and clean any dirt or mud from the inside and outside surfaces. Examine the wheel rims for signs of rusting, corrosion or other damage. Light alloy wheels are easily damaged by "kerbing" whilst parking; steel wheels may also become dented or buckled. A new wheel is very often the only way to overcome severe damage.

New tyres should be balanced when they are fitted, but it may become necessary to re-balance them as they wear, or if the balance weights fitted to the wheel rim should fall off. Unbalanced tyres will wear more quickly, as will the steering and suspension components. Wheel imbalance is normally signified by vibration, particularly at a certain speed (typically around 50 mph). If this vibration is felt only through the steering, then it is likely that just the front wheels need balancing. If, however, the vibration is felt through the whole car, the rear wheels could be out of balance. Wheel balancing should be carried out by a tyre dealer or garage.

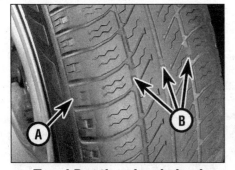

1 *Tread Depth - visual check*
The original tyres have tread wear safety bands (B), which will appear when the tread depth reaches approximately 1.6 mm. The band positions are indicated by a triangular mark on the tyre sidewall (A).

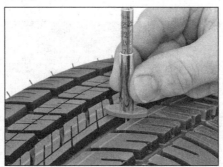

2 *Tread Depth - manual check*
Alternatively, tread wear can be monitored with a simple, inexpensive device known as a tread depth indicator gauge.

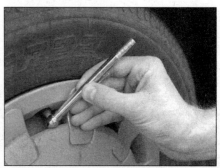

3 *Tyre Pressure Check*
Check the tyre pressures regularly with the tyres cold. Do not adjust the tyre pressures immediately after the vehicle has been used, or an inaccurate setting will result.

Tyre tread wear patterns

Shoulder Wear

Underinflation (wear on both sides)
Under-inflation will cause overheating of the tyre, because the tyre will flex too much, and the tread will not sit correctly on the road surface. This will cause a loss of grip and excessive wear, not to mention the danger of sudden tyre failure due to heat build-up.
Check and adjust pressures
Incorrect wheel camber (wear on one side)
Repair or renew suspension parts
Hard cornering
Reduce speed!

Centre Wear

Overinflation
Over-inflation will cause rapid wear of the centre part of the tyre tread, coupled with reduced grip, harsher ride, and the danger of shock damage occurring in the tyre casing.
Check and adjust pressures

If you sometimes have to inflate your car's tyres to the higher pressures specified for maximum load or sustained high speed, don't forget to reduce the pressures to normal afterwards.

Uneven Wear

Front tyres may wear unevenly as a result of wheel misalignment. Most tyre dealers and garages can check and adjust the wheel alignment (or "tracking") for a modest charge.
Incorrect camber or castor
Repair or renew suspension parts
Malfunctioning suspension
Repair or renew suspension parts
Unbalanced wheel
Balance tyres
Incorrect toe setting
Adjust front wheel alignment
Note: *The feathered edge of the tread which typifies toe wear is best checked by feel.*

Battery

Caution: Before carrying out any work on the vehicle battery, read the precautions given in 'Safety first!' at the start of this manual.

✔ Make sure that the battery tray is in good condition, and that the clamp is tight. Corrosion on the tray, retaining clamp and the battery itself can be removed with a solution of water and baking soda. Thoroughly rinse all cleaned areas with water. Any metal parts damaged by corrosion should be covered with a zinc-based primer, then painted.

✔ If the battery is flat, and you need to jump start your vehicle, see Roadside repairs.

 Battery corrosion can be kept to a minimum by applying a layer of petroleum jelly to the clamps and terminals after they are reconnected.

1 The battery is located on the left-hand side of the engine compartment. Open the cover to gain access to the battery terminals. The exterior of the battery should be inspected periodically for damage such as a cracked case or cover.

2 Check the battery lead clamps for tightness to ensure good electrical connections, and check the leads for signs of damage.

3 If corrosion (white, fluffy deposits) are evident, remove the cables from the battery terminals, clean them with a small wire brush, then refit them. Automotive stores sell a tool for cleaning the battery post …

4 … as well as the battery cable clamps.

Electrical systems

✔ Check all external lights and the horn. Refer to Chapter Section for details if any of the circuits are found to be inoperative.

✔ Visually check all accessible wiring connectors, harnesses and retaining clips for security, and for signs of chafing or damage.

 If you need to check your brake lights and indicators unaided, back up to a wall or garage door and operate the lights. The reflected light should show if they are working properly.

1 If a single indicator light, brake light, sidelight or headlight has failed, it is likely that a bulb has blown, and will need to be renewed. Refer to Chapter 12, Section 5 for details. If both brake lights have failed, it is possible that the switch has failed (see Chapter 9, Section 18).

2 If more than one indicator or tail light has failed, it is likely that either a fuse has blown or that there is a fault in the circuit. Fuses are located in a fusebox behind the glovebox (shown with glovebox removed) and in a fusebox on the left-hand side of the engine compartment.

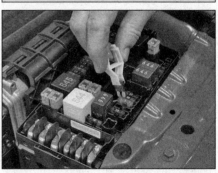

3 To renew a blown fuse, simply pull it out and fit a new fuse of the correct rating (see *Wiring diagrams*). If the fuse blows again, it is important that you find out why – a complete checking procedure is given in Chapter 12, Section 2.

Lubricants and fluids

Note: *Using lubricants and fluids that do not meet the VW standard may invalidate the warranty*

Standard (distance/time) service interval: . . . .   Multigrade (high-lubricity) engine oil, viscosity SAE 5W/40. Eg. Castrol Edge.

Petrol engines:
Fixed service intervals. . . . .   VW 502 00
LongLife service intervals . . . .   VW 504 00

Diesel engines:
Engines with fixed service intervals . . . .   VW 507 00
Engines with flexible service intervals. . . . .   VW 507 00

Cooling system. . . . .   VW additive G12 plus-plus (TL-VW 774 G) or G12 plus (TL-VW 774 F) – antifreeze and corrosion protection

Manual transmission . . . .   Synthetic gear oil, viscosity SAE 75W VW G52

DSG semi-automatic transmissions. . . . .   G 052 145

Braking system. . . . .   Hydraulic fluid to SAE J1703F or DOT 4

Tyre pressures

Note: *The recommended tyre pressures for each vehicle are given on a sticker attached to the inside of the fuel filler flap or the drivers side B-pillar. The pressures given are for the original equipment tyres – the recommended pressures may vary if any other make or type of tyre is fitted; check with the tyre manufacturer or supplier for latest recommendations. The following pressures are typical.*

All models	Front	Rear
Normal load	2.1 bars (29 psi)	2.1 bars (29 psi)
Full load	2.4 bars (33 psi)	2.8 bars (41 psi)
Emergency spare wheel	4.2 bars (61 psi)	

Chapter 1A
Routine maintenance and servicing – petrol models

Contents

Section number

Air filter element renewal – petrol models 28
Airbag unit check 23
Antifreeze check 12
Auxiliary drivebelt check – petrol models. 11
Auxiliary drivebelt renewal – petrol models 30
Battery check 21
Brake (and clutch) fluid renewal – petrol models 32
Brake hydraulic circuit check 13
Brake pad check 7
Component location – petrol models. 3
Coolant renewal – petrol models 33
Driveshaft gaiter check. 19
DSG transmission oil renewal 17
Engine management self-diagnosis memory fault check 25
Engine oil and filter renewal – petrol models 6
Exhaust system check 9
Headlight beam adjustment 14

Section number

Hinge and lock lubrication 22
Hose and fluid leak check 10
Introduction 4
Maintenance schedule – petrol models 2
Manual transmission oil level check. 16
Pollen filter element renewal 15
Regular maintenance 5
Resetting the service interval display. 8
Road test and exhaust emissions check 27
Servicing specifications – petrol models 1
Spark plug renewal. 29
Steering and suspension check 20
Sunroof check and lubrication 26
Timing belt renewal 31
Underbody protection check 18
Windscreen/tailgate/headlight washer system check 24

Degrees of difficulty

Easy, suitable for novice with little experience	**Fairly easy,** suitable for beginner with some experience	**Fairly difficult,** suitable for competent DIY mechanic	**Difficult,** suitable for experienced DIY mechanic	**Very difficult,** suitable for expert DIY or professional

1   Servicing specifications – petrol models

Lubricants and fluids
Refer to *Lubricants and fluids* on page 0•16

Engine codes*
1.2 litre petrol engine:	CJZA, CJZB and CYVB
1.4 litre petrol engine	CPTA, CHPA, CMBA, CXSA, CPVA, CZEA, CZDA, CZCA and CPVB
2.0 litre petrol engine	CHHA, CHHB, CJXE and CXDA

*See '*Vehicle identification*' at the end of this manual for the location of the engine code markings.

Capacities

Engine oil – including filter (approximate)
1.2 litre and 1.4 litre engines	4.0 litres
2.0 litre engines	5.7 litres

Cooling system (approximate)
All engines	8.0 litres

Transmission
Manual transmission*:
Type 0AF (5 speed)	2.0 litres
Type 02S (6 speed)	1.9 litres
Type 02Q (6 speed)	2.3 litres

DSG transmission
0D9 (6 speed)	5.2 litres
0CW (7 Speed)	1.9 litres

Fuel tank (approximate)
All models	50 litres

Washer reservoirs
Models with headlight washers	5.5 litres
Models without headlight washers	3.0 litres

Cooling system
Antifreeze mixture:
40% antifreeze	Protection down to -25°C
50% antifreeze	Protection down to -35°C

Note: *Refer to antifreeze manufacturer for latest recommendations.*

Ignition system

Spark plugs:	Type	Electrode gap
1.2 litre (All engine codes)	04E 905 601	0.70 to 0.80 mm
1.4 litre (CPTA, CHPA, CPVA, CZEA, CZDA and CPVB)	04E 905 612	0.65 to 0.75 mm
1.4 litre (CMBA, CXSA and CZCA)	04E 905 601	0.70 to 0.80 mm
2.0 litre (CHHA and CHHB)	06K 905 611	N/A
2.0 litre (CJXE and CXDA)	06K 905 601	N/A

Brakes
Brake pad lining minimum thickness:
Front	2.0 mm
Rear	2.0 mm

Torque wrench settings

	Nm	lbf ft
Manual gearbox drain/filler plug plug (0AF transmission only):		
Spline head type bolt	25	18
Hex head bolt	30	22
Manual gearbox drain plug (02S transmission only)	35	25
Manual gearbox filler/level plug	30	22
Oil filter (models with a canister type filter)	20	15
Oil filter cap (models with a paper filter and plastic cap))	25	18
Pivot pin bolt (02S transmission only)	25	18
Reversing light switch	20	15
Roadwheel bolts	120	89
Spark plugs:		
1.2 and 1.4 litre engines	22	16
2.0 litre engines	30	22
Sump drain plug*	30	22

Do not re-use

2 Maintenance schedule – petrol models

The maintenance intervals in this manual are provided with the assumption that you, not the dealer, will be carrying out the work. These are the minimum intervals recommended by us for vehicles driven daily. If you wish to keep your vehicle in peak condition at all times, you may wish to perform some of these procedures more often. We encourage frequent maintenance, since it enhances the efficiency, performance and resale value of your vehicle.

When the vehicle is new, it should be serviced by a dealer service department (or other workshop recognised by the vehicle manufacturer as providing the same standard of service), in order to preserve the warranty. The vehicle manufacturer may reject warranty claims if you are unable to prove that servicing has been carried out as and when specified, using only original equipment parts or parts certified to be of equivalent quality.

Depending on the model specification service intervals will either be at standard times (or distance) or set to 'LongLife' service intervals. On models set to the LongLife display, the service interval is variable according to the number of starts, length of journeys, vehicle speeds, brake pad wear, bonnet opening frequency, fuel consumption, oil level and oil temperature, however the vehicle must be serviced at least every two years. Note that if the variable (LongLife) service interval is being used, the engine must only be filled with the recommended long-life engine oil (see *Lubricants and fluids*).

All Golf models are equipped with a Service Interval Display (SID) indicator in the instrument panel. When a service date is approaching a message will appear in the message centre or a spanner symbol will appear in the instrument panel. The message or spanner symbol will also show the distance (or time) to the next service and will count down as the due date approaches. A minus symbol or a 'Service – - days ago' (on models with a message centre) will be shown when the due date (or mileage) has passed. Note that on models on Longlife service intervals that have the battery disconnected for a long time the service interval will not be correctly calculated. Where this is the case the vehicle should be serviced at the standard intervals.

After completing a service, Volkswagen technicians use a the factory diagnostic tool to reset the service display to the next service interval, and a print-out is put in the vehicle service record. The display can be reset by the owner as described in Section 8.

Every 250 miles
☐ Refer to Weekly checks

Every 10 000 miles or 12 months, whichever comes first
☐ Renew the engine oil and filter (Section 6)

Note: *Frequent oil and filter changes are good for the engine. We recommend changing the oil at least once a year.*

☐ Check the front and rear brake pad thickness (Section 7)
☐ Reset the service interval display (Section 8).

Every 20 000 miles or 2 years, whichever comes first
In addition to the items listed above, carry out the following:
☐ Check the condition of the exhaust system and its mountings (Section 9)
☐ Check all under bonnet components and hoses for fluid and oil leaks (Section 10)
☐ Check the condition of the auxiliary drivebelt (Section 11)
☐ Check the coolant antifreeze concentration (Section 12)
☐ Check the brake hydraulic circuit for leaks and damage (Section 13)
☐ Check the headlight beam adjustment (Section 14)
☐ Renew the pollen filter element (Section 15)
☐ Check the underbody protection for damage (Section 18)
☐ Check the condition of the driveshaft gaiters (Section 19)
☐ Check the steering and suspension components for condition and security (Section 20)
☐ Check the battery condition and security (Section 21)
☐ Lubricate all hinges and locks (Section 22)
☐ Check the condition of the airbag unit(s) (Section 23)
☐ Check the operation of the windscreen/tailgate/headlight washer system(s) (as applicable) (Section 24)
☐ Check the engine management self-diagnosis memory for faults (Section 25)
☐ Carry out a road test and check exhaust emissions (Section 27)

Every 40 000 miles or 4 years, whichever comes first
Note: *Many dealers perform these tasks at every second service.*
☐ Renew the air filter element (Section 28)
☐ Check the condition of the auxiliary drivebelt (Section 11)
☐ Renew the DSG transmission oil (where applicable) (Section 17).

Every 60 000 miles or 4 years
☐ Renew the timing belt and tensioner roller as described in Chapter 2A Section 7.

Note: *Volkswagen do not have a specific belt change interval. The condition of the belt should be checked at a maximum of 150,000 miles. However the cautious owner should consider replacing the belt at 60,000 miles (or every 4 years whichever occurs sooner). It is strongly recommended that the interval be further reduced on vehicles that are subjected to intensive use, ie, mainly short journeys or a lot of stop-start driving. The actual belt renewal interval is very much up to the individual owner, but bear in mind that severe engine damage will result if the belt breaks.*

Note: *It is increasingly considered best practice to always replace the idlers and tensioner whenever the timing belt is replaced. Note also that most manufacturers will not guarantee a belt unless the tensioners and rollers have been replaced at the same time.*

Every 2 years
☐ Renew the brake (and clutch) fluid (Section 32)
☐ Renew the coolant* (Section 33)

Note: **This work is not included in the service schedule and should not be required if the recommended G12 Plus (Purple colour) coolant antifreeze/inhibitor is used. G12 Plus can be mixed with older versions (G11 and G12).*

3 Component location – petrol models

Underbonnet view of a 1.4 litre

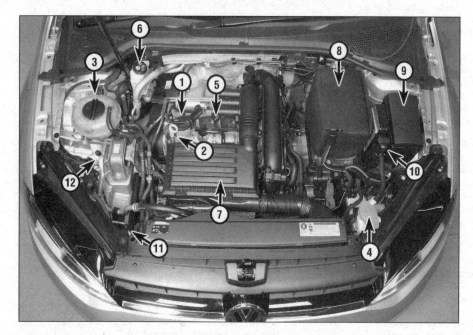

1 Engine oil filler cap
2 Engine oil dipstick
3 Coolant expansion tank
4 Windscreen/headlight washer
   fluid reservoir
5 Ignition coils
6 Brake master cylinder fluid
   reservoir
7 Air filter housing
8 Battery (under cover)
9 Fusebox
10 ECU (Electronic Control Unit)
11 AC charge port
12 AC charge port

Front underbody view of a 1.4 litre

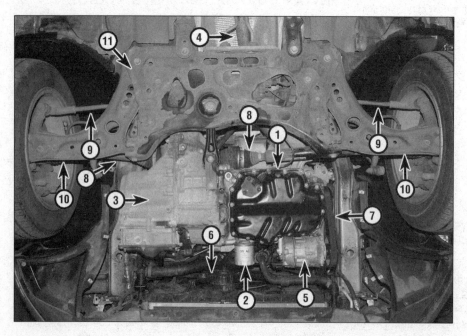

1 Sump drain plug
2 Oil filter
3 DSG transmission
4 Exhaust front pipe
5 Air conditioning compressor
6 Radiator and electric cooling
   fans
7 Auxiliary drivebelt
8 Driveshafts
9 Steering track rods
10 Front suspension lower arms
11 Front subframe

Rear underbody view (torsion beam axle)

1 Fuel tank
2 Rear exhaust silencer
3 Coil springs
4 Shock absorbers
5 Beam axle

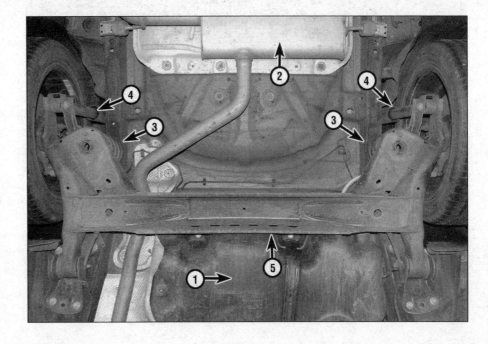

Rear underbody view (multi link axle)

1 Fuel tank
2 Subframe
3 Anti-roll bar
4 Trailing arms
5 Lower transverse links
6 Track rods
7 Upper transverse links

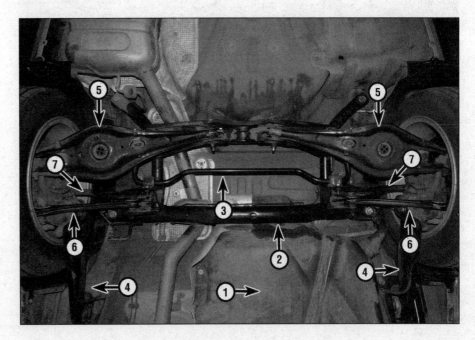

Underbonnet view of a 2.0 litre (engine cover removed)

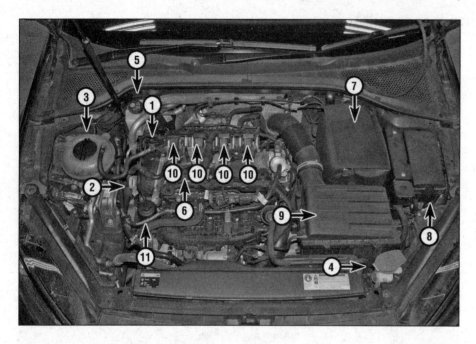

1 Oil filler cap
2 Oil dipstick
3 Coolant expansion reservoir
4 Windscreen/headlight washer fluid reservoir
5 Brake master cylinder fluid reservoir
6 EVAP control solenoid
7 Battery (under cover)
8 Fusebox
9 Air filter
10 Ignition coils
11 Oil filter

Front underbody view of a 2.0 litre

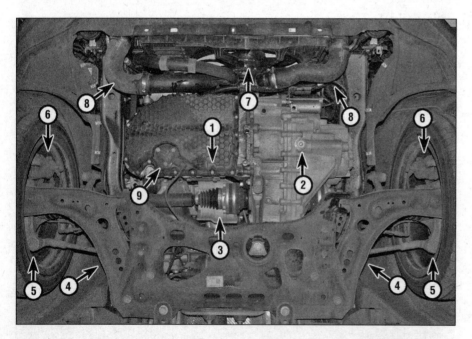

1 Engine oil drain plug
2 Transmission oil drain plug
3 Driveshaft inner CV joint
4 Track control arms
5 Track rod ends
6 Front brake calipers
7 Radiator and cooling fans
8 Charge air pipes
9 Oil level/temperature sensor

4 Introduction

1 This Chapter is designed to help the home mechanic maintain his/her vehicle for safety, economy, long life and peak performance.

2 The Chapter contains a master maintenance schedule, followed by Sections dealing specifically with each task in the schedule. Visual checks, adjustments, component renewal and other helpful items are included. Refer to the accompanying illustrations of the engine compartment and the underside of the vehicle for the locations of the various components.

3 Servicing your vehicle will provide a planned maintenance programme, which should result in a long and reliable service life. This is a comprehensive plan, so maintaining some items but not others will not produce the same results.

4 As you service your vehicle, you will discover that many of the procedures can – and should – be grouped together, because of the particular procedure being performed, or because of the proximity of two otherwise unrelated components to one another. For example, if the vehicle is raised for any reason, the exhaust can be inspected at the same time as the suspension and steering components.

5 The first step in this maintenance programme is to prepare yourself before the actual work begins. Read through all the Sections relevant to the work to be carried out, then make a list and gather all the parts and tools required. If a problem is encountered, seek advice from a parts specialist, or a dealer service department.

5 Regular maintenance

1 If, from the time the vehicle is new, the routine maintenance schedule is followed closely, and frequent checks are made of fluid levels and high-wear items, as suggested throughout this manual, the engine will be kept in relatively good running condition, and the need for additional work will be minimised.

2 It is possible that there will be times when the engine is running poorly due to the lack of regular maintenance. This is even more likely if a used vehicle, which has not received regular and frequent maintenance checks, is purchased. In such cases, additional work may need to be carried out, outside of the regular maintenance intervals.

3 If engine wear is suspected, a compression test (refer to the relevant Part of Chapter 2) will provide valuable information regarding the overall performance of the main internal components. Such a test can be used as a basis to decide on the extent of the work to be carried out. If, for example, a compression test indicates serious internal engine wear, conventional maintenance as described in this Chapter will not greatly improve the performance of the engine, and may prove a waste of time and money, unless extensive overhaul work is carried out first.

4 The following series of operations are those most often required to improve the performance of a generally poor-running engine:

Primary operations

a) *Clean, inspect and test the battery (See 'Weekly checks').*
b) *Check all the engine-related fluids (See 'Weekly checks').*
c) *Check the condition and tension of the auxiliary drivebelt (Section 11).*
d) *Renew the spark plugs (Section 29).*
e) *Check the condition of the air filter, and renew if necessary (Section 28).*
f) *Check the condition of all hoses, and check for fluid leaks (Section 10).*

5 If the above operations do not prove fully effective, carry out the following secondary operations:

Secondary operations

6 All items listed under Primary operations, plus the following:
a) *Check the charging system (see Chapter 5A Section 4).*
b) *Check the ignition system (see Chapter 5B).*
c) *Check the fuel system (see Chapter 4A).*

6 Engine oil and filter renewal – petrol models

1 Frequent oil and filter changes are the most important maintenance procedures which can be undertaken by the DIY owner. As engine oil ages, it becomes diluted and contaminated, which leads to premature engine wear.

2 Before starting this procedure, gather all the necessary tools and materials. Also make sure that you have plenty of clean rags and newspapers handy, to mop-up any spills. Ideally, the engine oil should be warm, as it will drain better, and more built-up sludge will be removed with it. Take care, however, not to touch the exhaust or any other hot parts of the engine when working under the vehicle. To avoid any possibility of scalding, and to protect yourself from possible skin irritants and other harmful contaminants in used engine oils, it is advisable to wear gloves when carrying out this work. Access to the underside of the vehicle will be greatly improved if it can be raised on a lift, driven onto ramps, or jacked up and supported on axle stands (see *Jacking and vehicle support*). Whichever method is chosen, make sure that the vehicle remains level, or if it is at an angle, that the drain plug is at the lowest point. Undo the retaining screws and remove the engine undertray(s), then also remove the engine top cover where applicable **(see illustrations)**.

3 Using a socket and wrench or a ring spanner, slacken the drain plug about half a turn. On 2.0 litre models fitted with a plastic

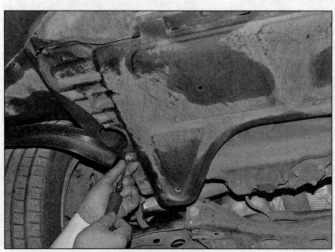

6.2a Unscrew and...

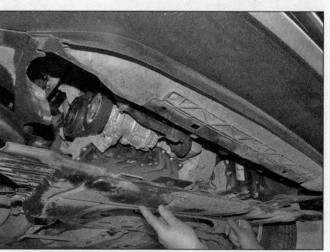

6.2b ...remove the engine undershield

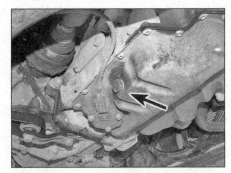

6.3a The engine oil drain plug location on the sump (1.2 and 1.4 litre engines)…

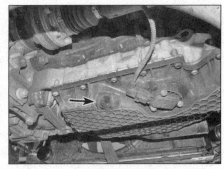

6.3b …and on the 2.0 litre engine with a plastic sump

6.3c The sealing plug for models with a plastic sump and a choice of special tools for releasing it

Keep the drain plug pressed into the sump while unscrewing it by hand the last couple of turns. As the plug releases, move it away sharply so the stream of oil issuing from the sump runs into the container, not up your sleeve.

sump the drain plug is also a plastic item with a bayonet type fitting. Remove the plastic drain plug with a screwdriver or the widely available special tool **(see illustrations)**. Position the draining container under the drain plug, then remove the plug completely (see Haynes Hint). On early models the seal is integral with the drain plug and the drain plug must be renewed. Later models have a sealing ring that can be replaced.

4 Allow some time for the old oil to drain, noting that it may be necessary to reposition the container as the oil flow slows to a trickle. On 2.0 litre model to ensure all the all drains from the filter housing release the oil filter before fitting the new drain plug.

5 After all the oil has drained, clean the area around the drain plug opening, and fit the new

plug. Tighten threaded plugs to the specified torque.

6 Move the container into position under the oil filter/engine **(see illustrations)**.
a) On 1.2 and 1.4 litre a canister-type filter is located from below on the front of the cylinder block.
b) On 2.0 litres engines a filter element is located from above at the right-hand end of the engine close to the timing chain.

7 To remove the canister-type oil filter, use an oil filter removal tool **(see illustrations)** and slacken the filter initially, then unscrew it by hand the rest of the way. Empty the oil in the filter into the container.

8 To remove the renewable element type oil filter, unscrew and remove the cap and remove the element and sealing ring **(see illustrations)**.

6.6a Engine oil filter location on 1.2 and 1.4 litre engines…

6.6b …and on 2.0 litre engines

6.7a Using a socket type tool to slacken the filter

6.7b As soon as the filter is slackened remove it by hand

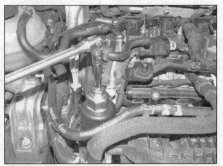

6.8a Unscrew and…

6.8b …remove the cap and filter element together

6.10a Clean the filter mounting...

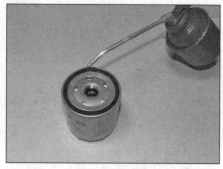

6.10b..and apply a thin film of oil to the filter sealing ring before fitting

6.10c A torque wrench will be required to tighten the filter to the specified torque

9 Clean the filter housing and cap as necessary. On canister-type filters, check the old filter to make sure that the rubber sealing ring has not stuck to the engine. If it has, carefully remove it.

10 To fit the canister-type oil filter, apply a light coating of clean engine oil to the sealing ring on the new filter, then screw it into position on the engine **(see illustrations)**. Tighten the filter firmly by hand and then tighten it to the specified torque. Note that Volkswagens requirement to tighten the filter to a specified torque is unusual for canister type oil filters. The standard method is to simply tighten the filter by hand.

11 On 2.0 litre engines remove the filter from the housing. Remove the O-ring type seal, clean the threads on the housing, fit a new seal and lubricate it with clean engine oil. Fit the filter to the housing and screw the assembly back onto the engine. Tighten the cap to the specified torque **(see illustrations)**.

12 Remove the dipstick, and then unscrew the oil filler cap from the cylinder head cover. Fill the engine, using the correct grade and type of oil (see Lubricants and fluids Section). A funnel may help to reduce spillage. Pour in half the specified quantity of oil first **(see illustrations)**, then wait a few minutes for the oil to run to the sump (see *Weekly checks*). Continue adding oil a small quantity at a time until the level is above the minimum mark on the dipstick – ideally the level will be between

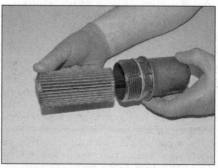

6.11a Remove the old filter and...

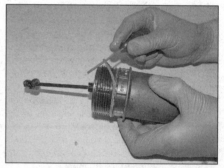

6.11b ...sealing ring

6.11c Fit a new filter and seals and then lubricate the seals and threads of the housing

6.11d Fit the new filter and housing...

6.11e ...and tighten to the specified torque

6.12a If not already done so, remove the engine cover – where fitted

6.12b Add oil to bring the level above the minimum mark on the dipstick. Do not overfill

the maximum and minimum mark. Refit the filler cap.

Caution: Because the front of the vehicle is still raised at this point, do not overfill the engine with oil. The level on the dipstick will increase when the vehicle is lowered to the ground.

13 Start the engine and run it for a few minutes; check for leaks around the oil filter seal and the sump drain plug. Note that there may be a few seconds delay before the oil pressure warning light goes out when the engine is started, as the oil circulates through the engine oil galleries and the new oil filter before the pressure builds-up.

⚠️ *Warning: Do not increase the engine speed above idling while the oil pressure light is illuminated, as considerable damage can be caused to the engine and turbocharger.*

14 If all is well, refit the engine undershield. Lower the vehicle to the ground and where fitted replace the engine cover.

15 Finally, recheck the level on the dipstick, and add more oil to bring the level up to the maximum mark on the dipstick.

16 Dispose of the used engine oil safely, with reference to General repair procedures in the Reference section of this manual.

7.1 The outer brake pads can be observed through the holes in the wheels

7 Brake pad check

1 The outer brake pads can be checked (on most models) without removing the wheels, by observing the brake pads through the holes in the wheels **(see illustration)**. If necessary, remove the wheel trim. The thickness of the pad lining must not be less than the dimension given in the Specifications.

2 If the outer pads are worn near their limits, it is worthwhile checking the inner pads as well. Apply the handbrake then jack up the vehicle and support it on axle stands (see *Jacking and vehicle support*). Remove the roadwheels.

3 Use a steel rule to check the thickness of the brake pads, and compare with the minimum thickness given in the Specifications **(see illustrations)**.

4 For a comprehensive check, the brake pads should be removed and cleaned. The operation of the caliper can then also be checked, and the condition of the brake disc itself can be fully examined on both sides. Refer to Chapter 9.

5 If any pad's friction material is worn to the specified minimum thickness or less, all four pads at the front or rear, as applicable, must be renewed as a set. If there is any doubt as to the condition of the brake pads (and the brake discs) always err on the side of caution and replace them.

6 On completion of the check, refit the road wheels and lower the vehicle to the ground.

8 Resetting the service interval display

1 After all necessary maintenance work has been completed the service interval display must be reset. The Service Interval Display (SID) can only be reset on models that are on

fixed service intervals. Models that are factory set to variable service intervals must have the SID reset using diagnostic equipment. A Volkswagen dealer will have the factory scan tool, but many independent garages will also have an aftermarket tool capable of resetting the SID.

2 To continue with the 'variable' or 'longlife' service intervals which take into consideration the number of starts, length of journeys, vehicle speeds, brake pad wear, bonnet opening frequency, fuel consumption, oil level and oil temperature, the display must be reset by a Volkswagen dealership (or suitably equipped garage) using a diagnostic tool.

3 For the home mechanic it is recommended that models have the service schedule changed from 'variable' to 'fixed' either by a Volkswagen dealer or suitably equipped garage.

4 To reset the SID:
● Turn the ignition off.
● Press and hold down the odometer button in the centre of the instrument panel.
● Turn the ignition on (whilst still holding down the button).
● Rotate the button to the right (clockwise) for approximately 1 second.
● Release the button and turn the ignition off.
● The service message will disappear. Note that on some models the message will clear when the engine is restarted.

9 Exhaust system check

1 With the engine cold (at least an hour after the vehicle has been driven), check the complete exhaust system from the engine to the end of the tailpipe. The exhaust system is most easily checked with the vehicle raised on a hoist, or supported on axle stands, so that the exhaust components are readily visible

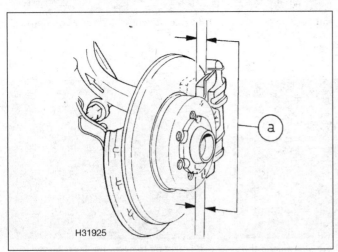

7.3a The thickness (a) of the brake pad linings must not be less than the specified amount

7.3b Specialist tools are available that can easily measure the remaining friction material

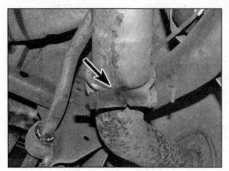

9.2a A typical exhaust gas leak at a clamp...

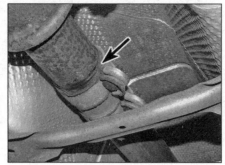

9.2b ...and at a sleeve type clamp

A leak in the cooling system will usually show up as white- or antifreeze-coloured deposits on the area adjoining the leak.

and accessible (see *Jacking and vehicle support*).

2 Check the exhaust pipes and connections for evidence of leaks, severe corrosion and damage. Make sure that all brackets and mountings are in good condition, and that all relevant nuts and bolts are tight. Leakage at any of the joints or in other parts of the system will usually show up as a black sooty stain in the vicinity of the leak **(see illustrations)**.

3 Rattles and other noises can often be traced to the exhaust system, especially the brackets and mountings. Try to move the pipes and silencers. If the components are able to come into contact with the body or suspension parts, secure the system with new mountings. Otherwise separate the joints (if possible) and twist the pipes as necessary to provide additional clearance.

10 Hose and fluid leak check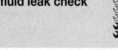

1 Visually inspect the engine joint faces, gaskets and seals for any signs of water or oil leaks. Pay particular attention to the areas around the camshaft cover, cylinder head, oil filter and sump joint faces. Bear in mind that, over a period of time, some very slight seepage from these areas is to be expected – what you are really looking for is any indication of a serious leak. Should a leak be found, renew the offending gasket or oil seal by referring to the appropriate Chapters in this manual.

2 Also check the security and condition of all the engine-related pipes and hoses. Ensure that all cable-ties or securing clips are in place and in good condition. Clips which are broken or missing can lead to chafing of the hoses, pipes or wiring, which could cause more serious problems in the future.

3 Carefully check the radiator hoses and heater hoses along their entire length. Renew any hose which is cracked, swollen or deteriorated. Cracks will show up better if the hose is squeezed. Pay close attention to the hose clips that secure the hoses to the cooling system components. Hose clips can pinch and puncture hoses, resulting in cooling system leaks.

4 Inspect all the cooling system components (hoses, joint faces, etc) for leaks (see **Haynes Hint**). Where any problems of this nature are found on system components, renew the component or gasket with reference to Chapter 3.

5 Where applicable, inspect the transmission fluid cooler hoses for leaks or deterioration.

6 With the vehicle raised, inspect the petrol tank and filler neck for punctures, cracks and other damage. The connection between the filler neck and tank is especially critical. Sometimes a rubber filler neck or connecting hose will leak due to loose retaining clamps or deteriorated rubber.

7 Carefully check all rubber hoses and metal fuel lines leading away from the petrol tank. Check for loose connections, deteriorated hoses, crimped lines, and other damage. Pay particular attention to the vent pipes and hoses, which often loop up around the filler neck and can become blocked or crimped. Follow the lines to the front of the vehicle, carefully inspecting them all the way. Renew damaged sections as necessary.

8 From within the engine compartment, check the security of all fuel hose attachments and pipe unions, and inspect the fuel hoses and vacuum hoses for kinks, chafing and deterioration.

9 Where applicable, check the condition of the power steering fluid hoses and pipes.

11 Auxiliary drivebelt check – petrol models

1 Apply the handbrake, then jack up the front of the vehicle and support it on axle stands (see *Jacking and vehicle support*).

2 Using a socket on the crankshaft pulley bolt, turn the engine slowly clockwise so that the full length of the auxiliary drivebelt can be examined. Look for cracks, splitting and fraying on the surface of the belt; check also for signs of glazing (shiny patches) and separation of the belt plies. Use a mirror to check the underside of the drivebelt **(see illustration)**. If damage or wear is visible, or if there are traces of oil or grease on it, the belt should be renewed (see Section 30).

12 Antifreeze check

1 The cooling system should be filled with the recommended G12 antifreeze and corrosion protection fluid – do not mix this antifreeze with any other type. Over a period of time, the concentration of fluid may be reduced due to topping-up (this can be avoided by topping-up with the correct antifreeze mixture – see Specifications) or fluid loss. If loss of coolant has been evident, it is important to make the necessary repair before adding fresh fluid.

2 With the engine cold, carefully remove the cap from the expansion tank. If the engine is not completely cold, place a cloth rag over the cap before removing it, and remove it slowly to allow any pressure to escape.

3 Antifreeze checkers are available from car accessory shops. Draw some coolant from the expansion tank and observe how many plastic balls are floating in the checker. Usually, 2 or 3 balls must be floating for the correct concentration of antifreeze, but follow the manufacturer's instructions.

4 If the concentration is incorrect, it will be necessary to either withdraw some coolant and add antifreeze, or alternatively drain the old coolant and add fresh coolant of the correct concentration (see Section 33).

11.2 Checking the underside of the auxiliary drivebelt with a mirror

13 Brake hydraulic circuit check

1 Check the entire brake hydraulic circuit for leaks and damage. Start by checking the master cylinder in the engine compartment. At the same time, check the vacuum servo unit and ABS units for signs of fluid leakage.
2 Raise the front and rear of the vehicle and support it on axle stands (see *Jacking and vehicle support*). Check the rigid hydraulic brake lines for corrosion and damage. Also check the brake pressure regulator in the same manner.
3 At the front of the vehicle, check that the flexible hydraulic hoses to the calipers are not twisted or chafing on any of the surrounding suspension components. Turn the steering on full lock to make this check. Also check that the hoses are not brittle or cracked.
4 Lower the vehicle to the ground after making the checks.

14 Headlight beam adjustment

1 Accurate adjustment of the headlight beam is only possible using optical beam-setting equipment, and this work should therefore

be carried out by a dealer or garage with the necessary facilities. All MOT test centres will have the required equipment.
2 Basic adjustments can be carried out in an emergency, and further details are given in Chapter 12 Section 9.

15 Pollen filter element renewal

1 The pollen filter is located in the heater unit and is accessed from inside the car, on the passenger's side.
2 Open the glovebox, reach up and push the limit stops **(see illustration)** out of the way, so that the entire glovebox can be lowered into the service position.
3 Release the upper locking tabs and remove the filter cover **(see illustrations)**.
4 Not the orientation and slide out the pollen filter **(see illustrations)**.
5 Clean out any debris from the housing as required.
6 Refitting is a reversal of removal.

16 Manual transmission oil level check

1 There is no requirement to check the manual transmission fluid level – the transmission is effectively sealed for life.

However the transmission should be checked for leaks. Full details of refilling and checking the transmission oil level are given in Chapter 7A Section 4.

17 DSG transmission oil renewal

Renewal

1 The DSG transmission oil renewal is described in Chapter 7B Section 6.

18 Underbody protection check

1 Raise and support the vehicle on axle stands (see *Jacking and vehicle support*). Using an electric torch or lead light, inspect the entire underside of the vehicle, paying particular attention to the wheel arches. Look for any damage to the flexible underbody coating, which may crack or flake off with age, leading to corrosion. Also check that the wheel arch liners are securely attached with any clips provided – if they come loose, dirt may get in behind the liners and defeat their purpose. If there is any damage to the underseal, or any corrosion, it should be repaired before the damage gets too serious.

19 Driveshaft gaiter check

1 With the vehicle raised and securely supported on stands, slowly rotate the roadwheel. Inspect the condition of the outer constant velocity (CV) joint rubber gaiters, squeezing the gaiters to open out the folds. Check for signs of cracking, splits or deterioration of the rubber, which may allow the grease to escape, and lead to water and grit entry into the joint. Also check the security and condition of the retaining clips. Repeat these checks on the inner joints **(see**

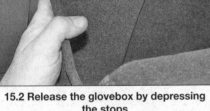
15.2 Release the glovebox by depressing the stops

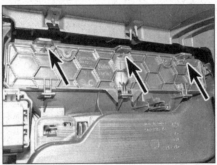
15.3a Release the tabs and...

15.3b ...remove the cover

15.4a Note the airflow direction (down)...

15.4b ...and then slide out the pollen filter

illustration). If any damage or deterioration is found, the gaiters should be renewed (see Chapter 8 Section 3).

2 At the same time, check the general condition of the CV joints themselves by first holding the driveshaft and attempting to rotate the wheel. Repeat this check by holding the inner joint and attempting to rotate the driveshaft. Any appreciable movement indicates wear in the joints, wear in the driveshaft splines, or a loose driveshaft retaining nut.

20 Steering and suspension check

1 Raise the front and rear of the vehicle, and securely support it on axle stands (see *Jacking and vehicle support*).

2 Visually inspect the track rod end balljoint dust cover, the lower front suspension balljoint dust cover, and the steering rack-and-pinion gaiters for splits **(see illustration)** chafing or deterioration. Any wear of these components will cause loss of lubricant, together with dirt and water entry, resulting in rapid deterioration of the balljoints or steering gear.

3 Check the power steering fluid hoses for chafing or deterioration, and the pipe and hose unions for fluid leaks. Also check for signs of fluid leakage under pressure from the steering gear rubber gaiters, which would indicate failed fluid seals within the steering gear.

4 Grasp the roadwheel at the 12 o'clock and 6 o'clock positions, and try to rock it **(see illustration)**. Very slight free play may be felt, but if the movement is appreciable, further investigation is necessary to determine the source. Continue rocking the wheel while an assistant depresses the footbrake. If the movement is now eliminated or significantly reduced, it is likely that the hub bearings are at fault. If the free play is still evident with the footbrake depressed, then there is wear in the suspension joints or mountings.

5 Now grasp the wheel at the 9 o'clock and 3 o'clock positions, and try to rock it as before **(see illustration)**. Any movement felt now may again be caused by wear in the hub bearings or the steering track rod balljoints. If the inner or outer balljoint is worn, the visual movement will be obvious.

6 Using a large screwdriver or flat bar, check for wear in the suspension mounting bushes by levering between the relevant suspension component and its attachment point. Some movement is to be expected as the mountings are made of rubber, but excessive wear should be obvious. Also check the condition of any visible rubber bushes, looking for splits, cracks or contamination of the rubber.

7 With the car standing on its wheels, have an assistant turn the steering wheel back-and-forth about an eighth of a turn each way. There should be very little, if any, lost

19.1 Check the condition of the driveshaft gaiters

20.4 Check for wear in the bearings by grasping the wheel top and bottom and trying to rock it

movement between the steering wheel and roadwheels. If this is not the case, closely observe the joints and mountings previously described, but in addition, check the steering column universal joints for wear, and the rack-and-pinion steering gear itself.

8 Check for any signs of fluid leakage around the front suspension struts and rear shock absorber. Should any fluid be noticed, the suspension strut or shock absorber is defective internally, and should be renewed. **Note:** *Suspension struts/shock absorbers should always be renewed in pairs on the same axle to ensure correct vehicle handling.*

9 The efficiency of the suspension strut/shock absorber may be checked by bouncing the vehicle at each corner. Generally speaking, the body will return to its normal position and stop after being depressed. If it rises and returns

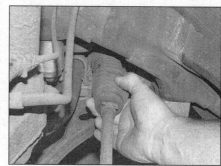

20.2 Check the rack gaiters for spilts

20.5 Check for wear in the bearings and ball joints by grasping the wheel at the sides and trying to rock it

on a rebound, the suspension strut/shock absorber is probably suspect. Examine also the suspension strut/shock absorber upper and lower mountings for any signs of wear.

21 Battery check

1 The battery is located on the left-hand side of the engine compartment. Open the cover **(see illustration)** to gain access to the battery.

2 Check that both battery terminals are securely attached **(see illustration)** and are free from corrosion. **Note:** *Before disconnecting the terminals from the battery, refer to Chapter 5A Section 3.*

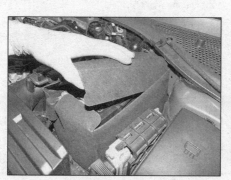

21.1 Open the cover

21.2 Check that the terminals are secure

21.3 Check that the battery clamp is secure (shown with cover removed)

3 Check the battery casing for signs of damage or cracking and check the battery retaining clamp bolt is securely tightened **(see illustration)**. If the battery casing is damaged in any way the battery must be renewed (see Chapter 5A Section 3).
4 On completion close the battery cover.

22 Hinge and lock lubrication

1 Lubricate the hinges of the bonnet, doors and tailgate with a light general-purpose oil. Similarly, lubricate all latches, locks and lock strikers. At the same time, check the security and operation of all the locks, adjusting them if necessary (see Chapter 11 Section 13).
2 Lightly lubricate the bonnet release mechanism and cable with a suitable grease.

23 Airbag unit check

1 The airbag system will perform a self-check when the ignition is turned on. The airbag warning light will illuminate and then go out after several seconds. If a system fault is found the airbag warning light will remain on and a fault code will be logged. The fault code can be read by a suitable diagnostic tool and appropriate action taken.
2 Inspect the exterior condition of the airbag(s) for signs of damage or deterioration. If an airbag shows signs of damage, it must be renewed (Chapter 12 Section 24). Note that it is not permissible to attach any stickers to the surface of the airbag, as this may affect the deployment of the unit.

24 Windscreen/tailgate/ headlight washer system check

1 Check that each of the washer jet nozzles are clear and that each nozzle provides a strong jet of washer fluid.
2 The tailgate jet should be aimed to spray at the centre of the screen, using a pin.

3 The windscreen washer nozzles should be aimed slightly above the centre of the screen using a small screwdriver to turn the jet eccentric.
4 The headlight inner jet should be aimed slightly above the horizontal centreline of the headlight, and the outer jet should be aimed slightly below the centreline. Volkswagen technicians use a special tool to adjust the headlight jet after pulling the jet out onto its stop.
5 Especially during the winter months, make sure that the washer fluid frost concentration is sufficient.

25 Engine management self-diagnosis memory fault check

1 This work should be carried out by a Volkswagen dealer or a diagnostic specialist using special equipment. Note however that simple diagnostic tools are now widely available. Most of the lower priced tools will only access the mandatory OBD (On Board Diagnostics) emissions related fault codes. The diagnostic socket is located below the facia, at the right-hand side **(see illustration)**. The 16 pin socket is often referred to as the Data Link Connector (or DLC).

26 Sunroof check and lubrication

1 Check the operation of the sunroof, and leave it in the fully open position.
2 Wipe clean the guide rails on each side of the sunroof opening, then apply lubricant to them. Volkswagen recommend VAG lubricant spray G 052 778.

27 Road test and exhaust emissions check

Instruments and electrical equipment

1 Check the operation of all instruments and electrical equipment including the air conditioning system.

25.1 The diagnostic socket (shown with diagnostic tool connected)

2 Make sure that all instruments read correctly, and switch on all electrical equipment in turn, to check that it functions properly.

Steering and suspension

3 Check for any abnormalities in the steering, suspension, handling or road 'feel'.
4 Drive the vehicle, and check that there are no unusual vibrations or noises which may indicate wear in the driveshafts, wheel bearings, etc.
5 Check that the steering feels positive, with no excessive 'sloppiness', or roughness, and check for any suspension noises when cornering and driving over bumps.

Drivetrain

6 Check the performance of the engine, clutch (where applicable), gearbox/transmission and driveshafts.
7 Listen for any unusual noises from the engine, clutch and gearbox/transmission.
8 Make sure the engine runs smoothly at idle, and there is no hesitation on accelerating.
9 Check that, where applicable, the clutch action is smooth and progressive, that the drive is taken up smoothly, and that the pedal travel is not excessive. Also listen for any noises when the clutch pedal is depressed.
10 On manual gearbox models, check that all gears can be engaged smoothly without noise, and that the gear lever action is smooth and not abnormally vague or 'notchy'.
11 On automatic transmission models, make sure that all gearchanges occur smoothly, without snatching, and without an increase in engine speed between changes. Check that all the gear positions can be selected with the vehicle at rest. If any problems are found, they should be referred to a Seat dealer.
12 Listen for a metallic clicking sound from the front of the vehicle, as the vehicle is driven slowly in a circle with the steering on full-lock. Carry out this check in both directions. If a clicking noise is heard, this indicates wear in a driveshaft joint, in which case renew the joint if necessary.

Braking system

13 Make sure that the vehicle does not pull to one side when braking, and that the wheels do not lock when braking hard.
14 Check that there is no vibration through the steering when braking.
15 Check that the handbrake operates correctly without excessive movement of the lever, and that it holds the vehicle stationary on a slope.
16 Test the operation of the brake servo unit as follows. With the engine off, depress the footbrake four or five times to exhaust the vacuum. Hold the brake pedal depressed, then start the engine. As the engine starts, there should be a noticeable 'give' in the brake pedal as vacuum builds-up. Allow the engine to run for at least two minutes, and then switch it off. If the brake pedal is depressed

28.2a Release the inlet duct...

28.2b ...the breather hose...

28.2c ...and the outlet duct

now, it should be possible to detect a hiss from the servo as the pedal is depressed. After about four or five applications, no further hissing should be heard, and the pedal should feel considerably harder.

17 Under controlled emergency braking, the pulsing of the ABS unit must be felt at the footbrake pedal.

Exhaust emissions check

18 Although not part of the manufacturer's maintenance schedule, this check will normally be carried out on a regular basis according to the country the vehicle is operated in. Currently in the UK, exhaust emissions testing is included as part of the annual MOT test after the vehicle is 3 years old. In Germany the test is made when the vehicle is 3 years old, then repeated every 2 years.

28 Air filter element renewal – petrol models

1.2 and 1.4 litre engines

1 Where fitted remove the engine cover.
2 Compress and slide back the hose clips from the air inlet and outlet ducts **(see illustrations)**.
3 Pull up the complete air filter housing from the ball headed pegs.
4 On the bench turn over the housing and remove the screws. Release the clips and lift off the cover. Remove the air filter **(see illustrations)**.
5 Fit the new filter element using a reversal

of the removal procedure. Lubricate the the locating pegs on the cover/housing with silicone grease or petroleum jelly **(see illustration)**.

2.0 litre engines

6 The air cleaner is located in front of the battery on the left-hand side of the engine compartment.
7 Remove the breather hose from the side of the filter **(see illustration)**.
8 Undo the screws and lift up the top cover of the air cleaner **(see illustration)**.
9 Lift up the lid and remove the filter element from the housing **(see illustration)**.
10 Fit the new filter element using a reversal of the removal procedure.

28.4a Remove the screws

28.4b ...unclip the cover and remove the filter

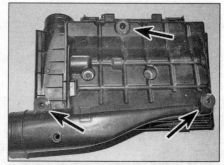

28.5 Lubricate the mounting points

28.7 Remove the hose

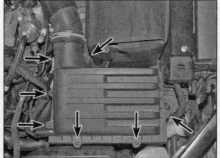

28.8 Undo the screws and lift up the cover

28.9 Remove the air filter

29 Spark plug renewal

1 The correct functioning of the spark plugs is vital for the correct running and efficiency of the engine. It is essential that the plugs fitted are appropriate for the engine (a suitable type is specified at the beginning of this Chapter). If this type is used and the engine is in good condition, the spark plugs should not need attention between scheduled renewal intervals. Spark plug cleaning is rarely necessary, and should not be attempted unless specialised equipment is available, as damage can easily be caused to the firing ends.

2 All petrol engine covered in this manual have one coil per cylinder, with the ignition coil fitted directly on top of the spark plug.

3 Where fitted, remove the engine top cover.

4 On 1.2 and 1.4 litre models remove the

29.6a Remove the mounting bolt…

29.7a Use a socket and extension…

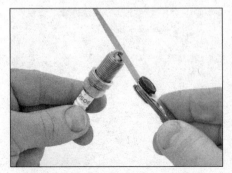

29.11 Check the electrode gap using a feeler gauge, but do not attempt to adjust it

29.5a Disconnect the wiring plugs (1.4 litre engine shown)

air inlet duct. On 1.4 litre engines with ACT (engine codes CPTA and CZEA) disconnect the wiring plugs from the control valves and pull off the small air hose.

5 Disconnect the wiring plugs from the ignition coils. On 2.0 litre models they must all be released together. Some 2.0 litre models

29.6b …and pull out the ignition coil

29.7b …and remove the spark plugs

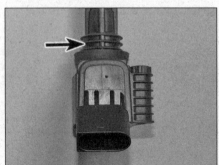

29.14 The vent holes correctly aligned

29.5b On 2.0 litre engines the connectors must be removed together

also have an earth connection to each coil that must be disconnected **(see illustrations)**.

6 In turn remove the bolt from each coil and pull up the coil to remove it **(see illustrations)**. Note that the coils form an almost airtight seal over the spark plug and in the cylinder head. In addition a tenacious silicon paste is also used. The best approach is to remove the coils when the engine is warm (NOT hot) and slowly pull and release each coil in stages.

7 Use a spark plug socket with an extension to remove the spark plugs **(see illustrations)**.

All engines

8 Examination of the spark plugs will give a good indication of the condition of the engine. If the insulator nose of the spark plug is clean and white, with no deposits, this is indicative of a weak mixture or too hot a plug (a hot plug transfers heat away from the electrode slowly, a cold plug transfers heat away quickly).

9 If the tip and insulator nose are covered with hard black-looking deposits, then this is indicative that the mixture is too rich. Should the plug be black and oily, then it is likely that the engine is fairly worn, as well as the mixture being too rich.

10 If the insulator nose is covered with light tan to greyish-brown deposits, then the mixture is correct and it is likely that the engine is in good condition.

11 The spark plug electrode gap is of considerable importance as, if it is too large or too small, the size of the spark and its efficiency will be seriously impaired. On engines covered in this manual the plug gaps should not be adjusted. The gap can be checked, but if the gap is outside the specifications the plugs should be replaced **(see illustration)**.

12 Before fitting the spark plugs, check that plug exterior surfaces and threads are clean.

13 Fit the spark plugs and tighten them to the specified torque.

14 Before refitting the ignition coils apply a small amount of silicon paste to the base of the ignition coil boot (VAG part number G 052 565 A1 or similar). Check that the vent holes in the rubber boot (where present) are in line with the wiring plug connector **(see illustration)**.

15 Refit the ignition coils using a reversal of the removal procedure.

30 Auxiliary drivebelt renewal – petrol models

1 The poly-vee drivebelt drives the alternator and where fitted the air conditioning compressor. Removal and refitting is essentially the same for all petrol engines covered by this manual.

2 On all engines, the drivebelt tension is adjusted automatically by a spring-tensioned idler.

Renewal

3 For improved access, apply the handbrake, then jack up the front of the vehicle and support it on axle stands (see *Jacking and vehicle support*). Remove the right-hand front roadwheel, then remove the lower section of the wing liner **(see illustration)**.

4 If the drivebelt is to be re-used, mark it for clockwise direction to ensure it is refitted the same way round **(see illustration)**.

5 Use a spanner on the pulley bolt (2.0 litre engines) or on the tensioner bolt (1.2 and 1.4 litre engines) and turn the tensioner to release the belt. Lock the tensioner in its released position by inserting a drill or bolt through the lug into the tensioner body **(see illustrations)**.

6 Note how the drivebelt is routed, then remove it from the crankshaft pulley, alternator pulley and air conditioning compressor pulley.

7 Locate the new drivebelt on the pulleys,

then release the tensioner. Check that the belt is located correctly in the multi-grooves in the pulleys.

8 Refit the lower section of the wing liner and roadwheel. Lower the vehicle to the ground. Refit the engine top cover.

31 Timing belt renewal

Renewal

1 Refer to Chapter 2A Section 7 for details.

32 Brake (and clutch) fluid renewal – petrol models

⚠️ **Warning: Brake hydraulic fluid can harm your eyes and damage painted surfaces, so use extreme caution when handling and pouring it. Do not use fluid that has been standing open for some time, as it absorbs moisture from the air. Excess moisture can cause a dangerous loss of braking effectiveness.**

1 The procedure is similar to that for the bleeding of the hydraulic system as described in Chapter 9 Section 2, except that the brake fluid reservoir should be emptied by syphoning, using a clean poultry baster or similar before starting, and allowance should be made for

the old fluid to be expelled when bleeding a section of the circuit. Since the clutch hydraulic system also uses fluid from the brake system reservoir, it should also be bled at the same time by referring to Chapter 6A Section 2.

2 Working as described in Chapter 9 Section 2, open the first bleed screw in the sequence, and pump the brake pedal gently until nearly all the old fluid has been emptied from the master cylinder reservoir.

> **HAYNES HiNT**
> *Old hydraulic fluid is often much darker in colour than the new, making it easy to distinguish the two.*

3 Top-up to the MAX level with new fluid, and continue pumping until only the new fluid remains in the reservoir, and new fluid can be seen emerging from the bleed screw. Tighten the screw, and top the reservoir level up to the MAX level line.

4 Work through all the remaining bleed screws in the sequence until new fluid can be seen at all of them. Be careful to keep the master cylinder reservoir topped-up to above the MIN level at all times, or air may enter the system and greatly increase the length of the task.

5 When the operation is complete, check that all bleed screws are securely tightened, and that their dust caps are refitted. Wash off all traces of spilt fluid, and recheck the master cylinder reservoir fluid level.

6 On models with manual transmission, once the brake fluid has been changed the clutch fluid should also be renewed. Referring to Chapter 6A Section 2, bleed the clutch until new fluid is seen to be emerging from the slave cylinder bleed screw, keeping the master cylinder fluid level above the MIN level line at all times to prevent air entering the system. Once the new fluid emerges, securely tighten the bleed screw then disconnect and remove the bleeding equipment. Securely refit the dust cap then wash off all traces of spilt fluid.

7 On all models, ensure the master cylinder fluid level is correct (see *Weekly checks*) and thoroughly check the operation of the brakes and (where necessary) clutch before taking the car on the road.

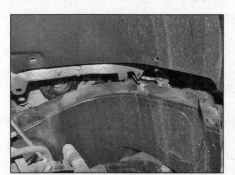

30.3 Remove the lower section of the wing liner

30.4 Mark the direction of rotation

30.5a The belt and tensioner on 1.2 and 1.4 litre engines with AC

30.5b Rotate the tensioner until the pin (or bolt) can be fitted (1.4 litre engine shown)

30.5c The tensioner locked in position on the 2.0 litre engine

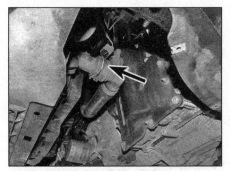

33.3a Releasing the bottom radiator hose...

33.3b ...to drain the coolant

33.10 A suitable coolant filling tool from Draper tools

33 Coolant renewal – petrol models

⚠ **Warning: Wait until the engine is cold before starting this procedure. Do not allow antifreeze to come in contact with your skin, or with the painted surfaces of the vehicle. Rinse off spills immediately with plenty of water. Never leave antifreeze lying around in an open container, or in a puddle in the driveway or on the garage floor. Children and pets are attracted by its sweet smell, but antifreeze can be fatal if ingested.**

Note: *This work is not included in the service schedule and should not be required if the recommended VAG G12/13 LongLife coolant antifreeze/inhibitor is used. However, if standard antifreeze/inhibitor is used, the work should be carried out at the recommended interval.*

Cooling system draining

1 With the engine completely cold, unscrew the expansion tank cap.

2 Firmly apply the handbrake then jack up the front of the vehicle and support it on axle stands (see *Jacking and vehicle support*). Undo the retaining screws and remove the engine undertray to gain access to the base of the radiator.

3 Position a suitable container beneath the radiator lower hose end fitting. Pull out the horse shoe type clip (or release the hose clip, depending on the model) and allow the coolant to drain into the container **(see illustrations)**.

4 On engines with engines with a liquid intercooler, to fully drain the system also disconnect one of the coolant hoses from the intercooler.

5 If the coolant has been drained for a reason other than renewal, then provided it is clean, it can be re-used.

6 Once all the coolant has drained, reconnect the bottom hose to the radiator. Where necessary, also reconnect the coolant hose to the intercooler. Refit the undertray, and tighten the retaining screws securely.

Cooling system flushing

7 A vehicle that has had the coolant system checked and is still using the original Volkswagen coolant should not require a flush of any description. If there is any evidence of contamination then a system flush should be considered. A wide range of proprietary chemical flushes for this purpose are widely available in the aftermarket.

8 Most of the cleaning/flushing chemicals on the market are simply added to the expansion tank and the engine is then run (or driven) for a prescribed length of time. The coolant and flushing chemical are then drained in the normal manner. The radiator top hose is then removed and the radiator back flushed with clean water. The cabin heater matrix is also back flushed after disconnecting the flow and return hoses from the bulkhead. There is generally no need to flush the engine, however where this is possible it should be considered. Once free of debris and contamination the system is refilled with fresh coolant as described below.

Cooling system filling

9 Before attempting to fill the cooling system, ensure that all hoses are securely connected and their retaining clips are in good condition. If the recommended Volkswagen coolant is not being used, ensure that a suitable antifreeze mixture is used all year round, to prevent corrosion of the engine components (see following sub-Section).

Note: *Volkswagen recommend that only distilled water should be used.*

10 Volkswagen recommend the use of a vacuum filling tool, to refill the coolant. Suitable machines are widely available in the aftermarket **(see illustration)**. However filling in the traditional manner is stll possible.

11 Remove the expansion tank filler cap and slowly fill the system with the coolant. Continue to fill the cooling system until bubbles stop appearing in the expansion tank. Help to bleed the air from the system by repeatedly squeezing the radiator bottom hose.

12 When no more bubbles appear, top the coolant level up to the MAX level mark. Do not then refit the cap to the expansion tank at this stage.

13 Turn the cabin heater to maximum and turn on the fan. Switch off the air conditioning.

14 Whilst watching the coolant level in the expansion tank, run the engine until warm air comes from the cabin heater and the thermostat has opened. A simple way to check is to spray clean water over the radiator. This will evaporate ('steam' will be produced) as the radiator heats up. Do not allow the fan to operate at this point.

15 Turn off the engine and check the coolant level, topping up if required. Refit the expansion tank cap and run the engine at a fast idle speed until the cooling fan cuts in. Wait for the fan to stop then switch the engine off and allow the engine to cool.

16 When the engine has cooled, check the coolant level with reference to *Weekly checks*. Top-up the level if necessary, and refit the expansion tank cap.

Antifreeze mixture

17 If the recommended Volkswagen coolant is not being used, the antifreeze should always be renewed at the specified intervals. This is necessary not only to maintain the antifreeze properties, but also to prevent corrosion which would otherwise occur as the corrosion inhibitors become progressively less effective.

18 Always use an ethylene-glycol based antifreeze which is suitable for use in mixed-metal cooling systems. The quantity of antifreeze and levels of protection are indicated in the Specifications.

19 Before adding antifreeze, the cooling system should be completely drained, preferably flushed, and all hoses checked for condition and security.

20 After filling with antifreeze, a label should be attached to the expansion tank, stating the type and concentration of antifreeze used, and the date installed. Any subsequent topping-up should be made with the same type and concentration of antifreeze.

Caution: Do not use engine antifreeze in the windscreen/tailgate washer system, as it will damage the vehicle paintwork. A screenwash additive should be added to the washer system in the quantities stated on the bottle.

Chapter 1B
Routine maintenance and servicing – diesel models

Contents

Section number

Air filter element renewal – diesel models 28
Airbag unit check 22
Antifreeze check 12
Auxiliary drivebelt check – diesel models 11
Auxiliary drivebelt renewal – diesel models 30
Battery check 20
Brake (and clutch) fluid renewal 32
Brake hydraulic circuit check 13
Brake pad check 7
Component locations 3
Coolant renewal 33
Driveshaft gaiter check 18
DSG transmission oil renewal 27
Engine management self-diagnosis memory fault check 24
Engine oil and filter renewal – diesel models 6
Exhaust system check 9
Fuel filter renewal – diesel models 29

Section number

Headlight beam adjustment 14
Hinge and lock lubrication 21
Hose and fluid leak check 10
Introduction 4
Maintenance schedule – diesel models 2
Manual transmission oil level check 16
Particulate filter ash deposit mass check 34
Pollen filter element renewal 15
Regular maintenance 5
Resetting the service interval display 8
Road test and exhaust emissions check 26
Servicing specifications 1
Steering and suspension check 19
Sunroof check and lubrication 25
Timing belt and tensioner roller renewal 31
Underbody protection check 17
Windscreen/tailgate/headlight washer system check 23

Degrees of difficulty

| **Easy,** suitable for novice with little experience | **Fairly easy,** suitable for beginner with some experience | **Fairly difficult,** suitable for competent DIY mechanic | **Difficult,** suitable for experienced DIY mechanic | **Very difficult,** suitable for expert DIY or professional |

1 Servicing specifications

Lubricants and fluids

Refer to *Lubricants, fluids and tyre pressures* on page 0•16

Engine codes*

Manufacturer's engine codes*:

1598 cc (1.6 litre)	CLHA, CLHB, CRKB, CXXA, CXXB and DBKA
1968 cc (2.0 litre)	CKFC, CRBC, CRLB, CRMB and CUNA

*See '*Vehicle identification*' at the end of this manual for the location of the engine code markings.

Capacities

Engine oil (including filter)

All versions except engine code CUNA	4.6 litres
Engine code CUNA	4.7 litres

Cooling system

All engines	8.0 litres

Transmission

Manual transmission: *

Type 0A4 (5 speed).	1.8 litres (refill capacity)
Type 02Q (6 speed).	2.3 litres

See Chapter 7A for application details

DSG transmission: *

Type 0D9 (6 speed).	5.2 litres (refill capacity)
Type OCW.	1.9 litres (only after overhaul)

See Chapter 7B for application details

Fuel tank (approximate

All models.	60 litres

Washer reservoirs

Models with headlight washers	5.5 litres
Models without headlight washers.	3.0 litres

Cooling system

Antifreeze mixture:

40% antifreeze	Protection down to -25°C
50% antifreeze	Protection down to -35°C

Note: *Refer to antifreeze manufacturer for latest recommendations.*

Brakes

Brake pad lining minimum thickness:

Front	2.0 mm
Rear	2.0 mm

Torque wrench settings

	Nm	lbf ft
Manual gearbox filler/drain plug:		
Multi-point socket head	30	22
Hexagon socket head.	45	31
OD9 transmission:		
Drain/filler plug	45	33
Oil filter cap	25	18
Oil filter drain plug	5	3
Roadwheel bolts.	120	89
Sump drain plug.	30	22

2 Maintenance schedule – diesel models

1 The maintenance intervals in this manual are provided with the assumption that you, not the dealer, will be carrying out the work. These are the minimum intervals recommended by us for vehicles driven daily. If you wish to keep your vehicle in peak condition at all times, you may wish to perform some of these procedures more often. We encourage frequent maintenance, since it enhances the efficiency, performance and resale value of your vehicle.

2 When the vehicle is new, it should be serviced by a dealer service department (or other workshop recognised by the vehicle manufacturer as providing the same standard of service), in order to preserve the warranty. The vehicle manufacturer may reject warranty claims if you are unable to prove that servicing has been carried out as and when specified, using only original equipment parts or parts certified to be of equivalent quality.

3 Depending on the model specification service intervals will either be at standard times (or distance) or set to 'LongLife' service intervals. On models set to the LongLife display, the service interval is variable according to the number of starts, length of journeys, vehicle speeds, brake pad wear, bonnet opening frequency, fuel consumption, oil level and oil temperature, however the vehicle must be serviced at least every two years. Note that if the variable (LongLife) service interval is being used, the engine must only be filled with the recommended long-life engine oil (see Lubricants and fluids 0 Section 6).

4 All Golf models are equipped with a Service Interval Display (SID) indicator in the instrument panel. When a service date is approaching a message will appear in the message centre or a spanner symbol will appear in the instrument panel. The message or spanner symbol will also show the distance (or time) to the next service and will count down as the due date approaches. A minus symbol or a 'Service – - days ago' (on models with a message centre) will be shown when the due date (or mileage) has passed. Note that on models on Longlife service intervals that have the battery disconnected for a long time the service interval will not be correctly calculated. Where this is the case the vehicle should be serviced at the standard intervals.

Every 250 miles
☐ Refer to 'Weekly checks'.

Every 10 000 miles or 12 months, whichever comes first
☐ Renew the engine oil and filter (Section 6)

Note: *Frequent oil and filter changes are good for the engine. We recommend changing the oil at least once a year.*

☐ Check the front and rear brake pad thickness (Section 7)
☐ Reset the service interval display (Section 8)

Every 20 000 miles or 2 years, whichever comes first
In addition to the items listed above, carry out the following:
☐ Check the condition of the exhaust system and its mountings (Section 9)
☐ Check all underbonnet components and hoses for fluid and oil leaks (Section 10)
☐ Renew the fuel filter* (Section 29)
☐ Check the condition of the auxiliary drivebelt (Section 11)
☐ Check the coolant antifreeze concentration (Section 12)

Every 20 000 miles or 2 years, whichever comes first (continued)
☐ Check the brake hydraulic circuit for leaks and damage (Section 13)
☐ Check the headlight beam adjustment (Section 14)
☐ Renew the pollen filter element (Section 15)
☐ Check the underbody protection for damage (Section 17)
☐ Check the condition of the driveshaft gaiters (Section 18)
☐ Check the steering and suspension components for condition and security (Section 19)
☐ Check the battery condition and security (Section 20)
☐ Lubricate all hinges and locks (Section 21)
☐ Check the condition of the airbag unit(s) (Section 22)
☐ Check the operation of the windscreen/tailgate/headlight washer system(s) (as applicable) (Section 23)
☐ Check the engine management self-diagnosis memory for faults (Section 24)
☐ Check the operation of the sunroof and lubricate the guide rails (Section 25)
☐ Carry out a road test and check exhaust emissions (Section 26)

*Only when using diesel fuel not conforming to DIN EN 590 or when using RME fuel (diester)

Every 40 000 miles or 4 years, whichever comes first
Note: *Many dealers perform these tasks at every second service.*
☐ Renew DSG transmission oil (Section 27)
☐ Renew the air filter element (Section 28)
☐ Renew the fuel filter* (Section 29)
☐ Check the condition of the auxiliary drivebelt (Section 30)

*Only when using diesel fuel conforming to DIN EN 590

Every 60 000 miles or 4 years
☐ Renew the timing belt and tensioner roller (Section 31)

Note: *Volkswagen recommend that the belt change interval should be reduced to every 75,000 miles if the vehicle is used in a dusty environment. The belt and tensioner renewal interval is very much up to the individual owner but, bearing in mind that severe engine damage will result if the belt breaks in use, we recommend a shorter interval.*
Note: *Always check with the vehicle manufacturer for the latest belt change intervals – they are often subject to change without notice.*
Note: *It is increasingly considered best practise to always replace the idlers, tensioner and coolant pump whenever the timing belt is replaced. Note also that most manufacturers will not guarantee a belt unless the tensioners and rollers have been replaced at the same time.*

Every 95 000 miles, then every 19 000 miles
☐ Check the particulate filter ash deposit mass (Section 34)

Every 2 years
☐ Renew the brake (and clutch) fluid (Section 32)
☐ Renew the coolant* (Section 33)

*This work is not included in the schedule and should not be required if the recommended G12 Plus LongLife coolant antifreeze/inhibitor is used.

3 Component location – diesel models

Underbonnet view of a 1.6 litre model (engine cover removed)

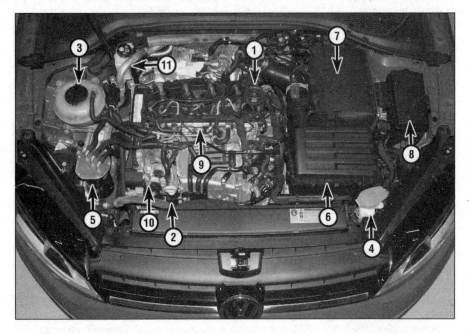

1 Engine oil filler cap
2 Engine oil dipstick
3 Coolant expansion reservoir
4 Windscreen/headlight/rear window washer fluid reservoir
5 Fuel filter
6 Air filter housing
7 Battery (under cover)
8 Fusebox
9 Common rail
10 High pressure pump
11 Brake fluid reservoir

Front underbody view (undershield removed)

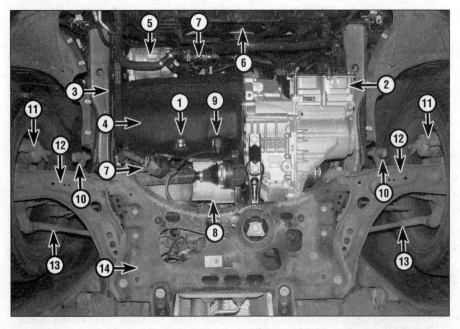

1 Sump drain plug
2 Mechatronic control (DSG)
3 Auxiliary belt
4 Sump insulator cover
5 Air conditioning compressor
6 Radiator and electric cooling fans
7 Electric coolant pumps
8 Driveshaft heat shield
9 Engine oil level/temperature sensor
10 Front anti-roll bar drop-links
11 Front brake calipers
12 Front suspension lower arms
13 Steering track rod arms
14 Front suspension subframe

Rear underbody view (torsion beam axle)

1 *Fuel tank*
2 *Rear silencer*
3 *Torsion beam*
4 *Shock absorbers*
5 *Coil springs*

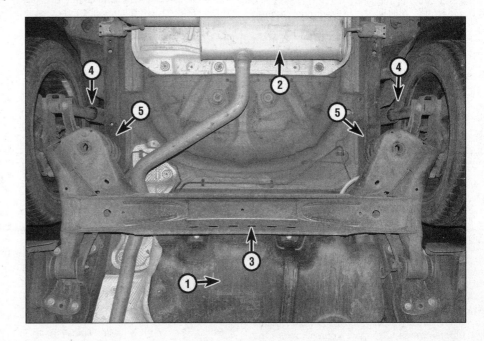

Rear underbody view (multi-link axle)

1 *Fuel tank*
2 *Subframe*
3 *Rear anti-roll bar*
4 *Rear trailing arm and bracket*
5 *Lower transverse links*
6 *Track control arms*
7 *Upper transverse links*

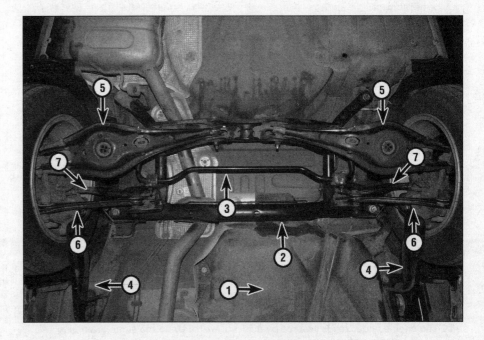

4 Introduction

1 This Chapter is designed to help the home mechanic maintain his/her vehicle for safety, economy, long life and peak performance.

2 The Chapter contains a master maintenance schedule, followed by Sections dealing specifically with each task in the schedule. Visual checks, adjustments, component renewal and other helpful items are included. Refer to the accompanying illustrations of the engine compartment and the underside of the vehicle for the locations of the various components.

3 Servicing your vehicle will provide a planned maintenance programme, which should result in a long and reliable service life. This is a comprehensive plan, so maintaining some items but not others, will not produce the same results.

4 As you service your vehicle, you will discover that many of the procedures can – and should – be grouped together, because of the particular procedure being performed, or because of the proximity of two otherwise unrelated components to one another. For example, if the vehicle is raised for any reason, the exhaust can be inspected at the same time as the suspension and steering components.

5 The first step in this maintenance programme is to prepare yourself before the actual work begins. Read through all the Sections relevant to the work to be carried out, then make a list and gather all the parts and tools required. If a problem is encountered, seek advice from a parts specialist, or a dealer service department.

5 Regular maintenance

1 If, from the time the vehicle is new, the routine maintenance schedule is followed closely, and frequent checks are made of fluid levels and high-wear items, as suggested throughout this manual, the engine will be kept in relatively good running condition, and the need for additional work will be minimised.

2 It is possible that there will be times when the engine is running poorly due to the lack of regular maintenance. This is even more likely if a used vehicle, which has not received regular and frequent maintenance checks, is purchased. In such cases, additional work may need to be carried out, outside of the regular maintenance intervals.

3 If engine wear is suspected, a compression test (refer to Chapter 2C Section 2) will provide valuable information regarding the overall performance of the main internal components. Such a test can be used as a basis to decide on the extent of the work to be carried out. If, for example, a compression test indicates serious internal engine wear, conventional maintenance as described in this Chapter will not greatly improve the performance of the engine, and may prove a waste of time and money, unless extensive overhaul work is carried out first.

4 The following series of operations are those most often required to improve the performance of a generally poor-running engine:

Primary operations

a) Clean and inspect the battery (see 'Weekly checks').
b) Check all the engine-related fluids (see 'Weekly checks').
c) Drain the water from the fuel filter (not all models) (Section 29).
d) Check the condition and tension of the auxiliary drivebelt (Section 11).
e) Check the condition of the air filter, and renew if necessary (Section 28).
f) Check the condition of all hoses, and check for fluid leaks (Section 10).

5 If the above operations do not prove fully effective, carry out the following secondary operations:

Secondary operations

6 All items listed under Primary operations, plus the following:

a) Check the charging system (see Chapter 5A Section 4).
b) Check the preheating system (see Chapter 5C Section 2).
c) Renew the fuel filter (Section 29) and check the fuel system (see Chapter 4B).

6 Engine oil and filter renewal – diesel models

1 Frequent oil and filter changes are the most important preventative maintenance procedures, which can be undertaken by the DIY owner. As engine oil ages, it becomes diluted and contaminated, which leads to premature engine wear.

2 Before starting this procedure, gather all the necessary tools and materials. Also make sure that you have plenty of clean rags and newspapers handy, to mop-up any spills. Ideally, the engine oil should be warm, as it will drain better, and more built-up sludge will be removed with it. Take care, however, not to touch the exhaust or any other hot parts of the engine when working under the vehicle. To avoid any possibility of scalding, and to protect yourself from possible skin irritants and other harmful contaminants in used engine oils, it is advisable to wear gloves when carrying out this work. Access to the underside of the vehicle will be greatly improved if it can be raised on a lift, driven onto ramps, or jacked up and supported on axle stands (see *Jacking and vehicle support*). Whichever method is chosen, make sure that the vehicle remains level, or if it is at an angle, that the drain plug is at the lowest point. Undo the retaining screws and remove the engine undertray **(see illustration)**.

3 Slacken the sump drain plug about half a turn. Position the draining container under the drain plug, and then remove the plug completely **(see illustration and Haynes Hint)**.

> **HAYNES HiNT** *Keep the drain plug pressed into the sump while unscrewing it by hand the last couple of turns. As the plug releases, move it away sharply so the stream of oil issuing from the sump runs into the container, not up your sleeve.*

4 Allow some time for the old oil to drain, noting that it may be necessary to reposition the container as the oil flow slows to a trickle.

5 After all the oil has drained, wipe off the drain plug with a clean rag, and fit a new sealing washer. Clean the area around the drain plug opening, and refit the plug. Tighten the drain plug to the specified torque **(see**

6.2 The engine undertray is secured by a number of screws

6.3 Undo the sump drain plug

6.5 Tighten the drain plug to the specified torque

6.6 The oil filter, obscured by the wiring loom and coolant hose

illustration). **Note:** *On some engines, the sealing washer is integral with the drain plug. On these engines, the drain plug must be renewed.*
6 Move the coolant hose to the side and then unclip the alternator wiring loom and move it to the side **(see illustration)**.

7 Place a container beneath the filter and unscrew the drain plug from the centre of the filter housing. Allow the oil to drain into the container.
8 When all the oil has drained, unscrew the oil filter housing and remove it together with the

filter element. Unclip the filter element from the cap and dispose of it **(see illustrations)**.
9 Remove the filter and O-ring seal from the cap **(see illustrations)** and then using a clean rag, wipe all oil and sludge from the inside of the filter housing and cap.

6.8a Use a 32 mm socket to unscrew the filter cap …

6.8b … and withdraw the filter and cap

6.9a Remove the filter from the cap…

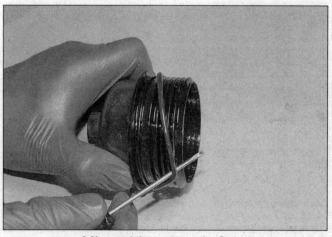

6.9b …and then remove the O-ring

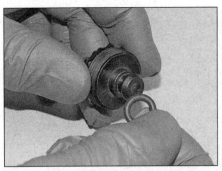

6.10a Fit the new seal to the drain plug...

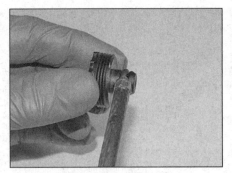

6.10b ...lubricate it and...

6.10c ...tighten it to the specified torque

6.10d Fit a new seal to the housing

6.10e Fit the new filter into the cap

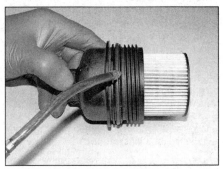

6.10f Lubricate the O-ring seal with clean
engine oil

10 The new filter will be supplied with a large sealing O-ring and a small O-ring for the central drain plug. Fit the new sealing ring(s) and then refit the assembly and tighten the cap to the specified torque. (The correct torque is shown on the cap) Make sure the filter element is engaged with the cap and the correct way up **(see illustrations)**.

11 Remove the old oil and all tools from under the car. Refit the wiring loom to the cable clip and move the coolant hose back into position.

12 Remove the dipstick, and then unscrew the oil filler cap from the cylinder head cover. Fill the engine, using the correct grade and type of oil (see *Lubricants and fluids*). A funnel may help to reduce spillage. Pour in half the specified quantity of oil first **(see illustration)**,

then wait a few minutes for the oil to run to the sump (see *Weekly checks*). Continue adding oil a small quantity at a time until the level is above the minimum mark on the dipstick – ideally the level will be between the maximum and minimum mark. Refit the filler cap.

Caution: Because the front of the vehicle is still raised at this point, do not overfill the engine with oil. The level on the dipstick will increase when the vehicle is lowered to the ground.

13 Start the engine and monitor the instrument panel warning lights – the oil pressure warning light should not come on. With the engine still running check for leaks around the oil filter housing, oil filter drain plug and the sump drain plug.

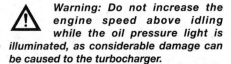 *Warning: Do not increase the engine speed above idling while the oil pressure light is illuminated, as considerable damage can be caused to the turbocharger.*

14 Switch off the engine, and wait a few minutes for the oil to settle in the sump once more.

15 Check around the sump drain plug for oil leaks. If all is well, refit the engine undershield. Lower the vehicle to the ground and fit the engine top cover.

16 Finally, recheck the level on the dipstick, and add more oil to bring the level up to the maximum mark on the dipstick.

17 Dispose of the used engine oil safely, with reference to General repair procedures in the Reference section of this manual.

7 Brake pad check

1 On some models the outer brake pads can be checked without removing the wheels, by observing the brake pads through the holes in the wheels **(see illustration)**. If necessary, remove the wheel trim. The thickness of the pad lining must not be less than the dimension given in the Specifications.

2 If the outer pads are worn near their limits, it is worthwhile checking the inner pads as well. Apply the handbrake then jack up vehicle and support it on axle stands (see *Jacking and vehicle support*). Remove the roadwheels.

6.12 Pour in half the specified quantity of
oil first, wait, then add enough oil to bring
the level to above the minimum mark on
the dipstick

7.1 On some models the outer brake pads
can be observed through the holes in the
wheels

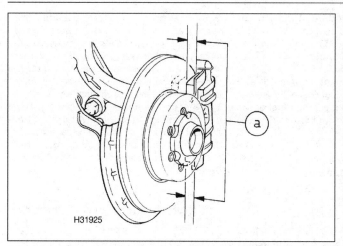

7.3a The thickness (a) of the brake pad linings must not be less than the specified amount

7.3b Specialist tools are also available to check the the friction material

3 Use a steel rule to check the thickness of the brake pads, and compare with the minimum thickness given in the Specifications **(see illustrations)**.

4 For a comprehensive check, the brake pads should be removed and cleaned. The operation of the caliper can then also be checked, and the condition of the brake disc itself can be fully examined on both sides. Refer to Chapter 9 Section 4 (front) or Chapter 9 Section 8 (rear).

5 If any pad's friction material is worn to the specified minimum thickness or less, all four pads at the front or rear, as applicable, must be renewed as a set. If there is any doubt as to the condition of the brake pads (and the brake discs) always err on the side of caution and replace them.

6 On completion of the check, refit the roadwheels and lower the vehicle to the ground.

8 Resetting the service interval display

1 After all necessary maintenance work has been completed the service interval display must be reset. The Service Interval Display (SID) can only be reset on models that are on fixed service intervals. Models that are factory set to variable service intervals must have the SID reset using diagnostic equipment. A Volkswagen dealer will have the factory scan tool, but many independent garages will also have an aftermarket tool capable of resetting the SID.

2 To continue with the 'variable' or 'longlife' service intervals which take into consideration the number of starts, length of journeys, vehicle speeds, brake pad wear, bonnet opening frequency, fuel consumption, oil level and oil temperature, the display must be reset by a Volkswagen dealership (or suitably equipped garage) using a diagnostic tool.

3 For the home mechanic it is recommended that models have the service schedule changed from 'variable' to 'fixed' either by a Volkswagen dealer or suitably equipped garage.

4 To reset the SID:
● Turn the ignition off.
● Press and hold down the odometer button in the centre of the instrument panel.
● Turn the ignition on (whilst still holding down the button).
● Wait until 'Reset oil change service' or 'Reset inspection' appears in the message centre.
● Release the button.
● Press button again once.
● The service message will disappear. Note that on some models the message will clear when the engine is restarted.
● Turn ignition off.

9 Exhaust system check

1 With the engine cold (at least an hour after the vehicle has been driven), check the complete exhaust system from the engine to the end of the tailpipe. The exhaust system is most easily checked with the vehicle raised on a hoist, or suitably supported on axle stands, so that the exhaust components are readily visible and accessible (see *Jacking and vehicle support*).

2 Check the exhaust pipes and connections for evidence of leaks, severe corrosion and damage. Make sure that all brackets and mountings are in good condition, and that all relevant nuts and bolts are tight. Leakage at any of the joints or in other parts of the system will usually show up as a black sooty stain in the vicinity of the leak **(see illustrations)**.

3 Rattles and other noises can often be traced to the exhaust system, especially the brackets and mountings. Try to move the pipes and silencers. If the components are able to come into contact with the body or suspension parts, secure the system with new mountings. Otherwise separate the joints (if possible) and twist the pipes as necessary to provide additional clearance.

10 Hose and fluid leak check

1 Visually inspect the engine joint faces, gaskets and seals for any signs of water or

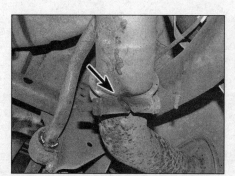

9.2a Typical minor exhaust leak from a clamp type fitting…

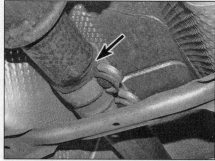

9.2b …and a sleeve type fitting

A leak in the cooling system will usually show up as white- or antifreeze coloured deposits on the area adjoining the leak.

oil leaks. Pay particular attention to the areas around the camshaft cover, cylinder head, oil filter and sump joint faces. Bear in mind that, over a period of time, some very slight seepage from these areas is to be expected – what you are really looking for is any indication of a serious leak. Should a leak be found, renew the offending gasket or oil seal by referring to the appropriate Chapters in this manual.

2 Also check the security and condition of all the engine-related pipes and hoses. Ensure that all cable ties or securing clips are in place and in good condition. Clips, which are broken or missing, can lead to chafing of the hoses, pipes or wiring, which could cause more serious problems in the future.

3 Carefully check the radiator hoses and heater hoses along their entire length. Renew any hose that is cracked, swollen or deteriorated. Cracks will show up better if the hose is squeezed. Pay close attention to the hose clips that secure the hoses to the cooling system components. Hose clips can pinch and puncture hoses, resulting in cooling system leaks.

4 Inspect all the cooling system components (hoses, joint faces, etc) for leaks (see Haynes Hint). Where any problems of this nature are found on system components, renew the component or gasket with reference to Chapter 3.

5 Where applicable, inspect the automatic transmission fluid cooler hoses for leaks or deterioration.

6 With the vehicle raised, inspect the fuel tank and filler neck for punctures, cracks and other damage. The connection between the filler neck and tank is especially critical. Sometimes a rubber filler neck or connecting hose will leak due to loose retaining clamps or deteriorated rubber.

7 Carefully check all rubber hoses and metal fuel lines leading away from the tank. Check for loose connections, deteriorated hoses, crimped lines, and other damage. Pay particular attention to the vent pipes and hoses, which often loop up around the filler

neck and can become blocked or crimped. Follow the lines to the front of the vehicle, carefully inspecting them all the way. Renew damaged sections as necessary.

8 From within the engine compartment, check the security of all fuel hose attachments and pipe unions, and inspect the fuel hoses and vacuum hoses for kinks, chafing and deterioration.

11 Auxiliary drivebelt check – diesel models

1 Apply the handbrake, then jack up the front of the vehicle and support it on axle stands (see *Jacking and vehicle support*).

2 Using a socket on the crankshaft pulley bolt, turn the engine slowly clockwise so that the full length of the auxiliary drivebelt can be examined. Look for cracks, splitting and fraying on the surface of the belt; check also for signs of glazing (shiny patches) and separation of the belt plies. If damage or wear is visible, or if there are traces of oil or grease on it, the belt should be renewed (see Section 30).

12 Antifreeze check

1 The cooling system should be filled with the recommended G12 antifreeze and corrosion protection fluid – do not mix this antifreeze with any other type. Over a period of time, the concentration of fluid may be reduced due to topping-up (this can be avoided by topping-up with the correct antifreeze mixture – see Section 1) or fluid loss. If loss of coolant has been evident, it is important to make the necessary repair before adding fresh fluid.

2 With the engine cold, carefully remove the cap from the expansion tank. If the engine is not completely cold, place a cloth rag over the cap before removing it, and remove it slowly to allow any pressure to escape.

15.2 Release the glovebox by depressing the stops

3 Antifreeze checkers are available from car accessory shops. Draw some coolant from the expansion tank and observe how many plastic balls are floating in the checker. Usually, 2 or 3 balls must be floating for the correct concentration of antifreeze, but follow the manufacturer's instructions.

4 If the concentration is incorrect, it will be necessary to either withdraw some coolant and add antifreeze, or alternatively drain the old coolant and add fresh coolant of the correct concentration (see Section 33).

13 Brake hydraulic circuit check

1 Check the entire brake hydraulic circuit for leaks and damage. Start by checking the master cylinder in the engine compartment. At the same time, check the vacuum servo unit and ABS units for signs of fluid leakage.

2 Raise the front and rear of the vehicle and support it on axle stands (see *Jacking and vehicle support*). Check the rigid hydraulic brake lines for corrosion and damage.

3 At the front of the vehicle, check that the flexible hydraulic hoses to the calipers are not twisted or chafing on any of the surrounding suspension components. Turn the steering on full lock to make this check. Also check that the hoses are not brittle or cracked.

4 Lower the vehicle to the ground after making the checks.

14 Headlight beam adjustment

1 Accurate adjustment of the headlight beam is only possible using optical beam-setting equipment, and this work should therefore be carried out by a Volkswagen dealer or service station with the necessary facilities. MOT test centres have this equipment.

2 Basic adjustments can be carried out in an emergency, and further details are given in Chapter 12 Section 10.

15 Pollen filter element renewal

1 The pollen filter is located in the heater unit and is accessed from inside the car, on the passenger's side.

2 Open the glovebox, reach up and push the limit stops (see illustration) out of the way, so that the entire glovebox can be lowered into the service position.

3 Release the upper locking tabs and remove the filter cover **(see illustrations)**.
4 Not the orientation and slide out the pollen filter **(see illustrations)**.
5 Clean out any debris from the housing as required.
6 Refitting is a reversal of removal.

16 Manual transmission oil level check

1 There is no requirement to check the manual transmission fluid level – the transmission is effectively sealed for life. However the transmission should be checked for leaks. Full details of refilling and checking the transmission oil level are given in Chapter 7A Section 4.

17 Underbody protection check

1 Raise and support the vehicle on axle stands (see *Jacking and vehicle support*). Using an electric torch or lead light, inspect the entire underside of the vehicle, paying particular attention to the wheel arches. Look for any damage to the flexible underbody coating, which may crack or flake off with age, leading to corrosion. Also check that the wheel arch liners are securely attached with any clips provided – if they come loose, dirt may get in behind the liners and defeat their purpose. If there is any damage to the under seal, or any corrosion, it should be repaired before the damage gets too serious.

18 Driveshaft gaiter check

1 With the vehicle raised and securely supported on stands, slowly rotate the

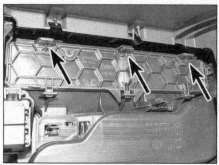

15.3a Release the tabs and...   15.3b ...remove the cover

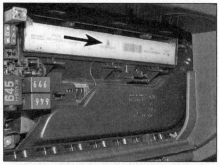
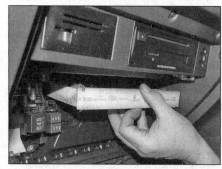

15.4a Note the airflow direction (down)...   15.4b ...and then slide out the pollen filter

roadwheel. Inspect the condition of the outer constant velocity (CV) joint rubber gaiters, squeezing the gaiters to open out the folds. Check for signs of cracking, splits or deterioration of the rubber, which may allow the grease to escape, and lead to water and grit entry into the joint. Also check the security and condition of the retaining clips. Repeat these checks on the inner joints **(see illustration)**. If any damage or deterioration is found, the gaiters should be renewed (see Chapter 8 Section 3).
2 At the same time, check the general condition of the CV joints themselves by first holding the driveshaft and attempting to rotate the wheel. Repeat this check by holding the inner joint and attempting

to rotate the driveshaft. Any appreciable movement indicates wear in the joints, wear in the driveshaft splines, or a loose driveshaft retaining nut.

19 Steering and suspension check

1 Raise the front and rear of the vehicle, and securely support it on axle stands (see *Jacking and vehicle support*).
2 Visually inspect the track rod end balljoint dust cover, the lower front suspension balljoint dust cover, and the steering rack-and-pinion gaiters for splits **(see illustration)** chafing or

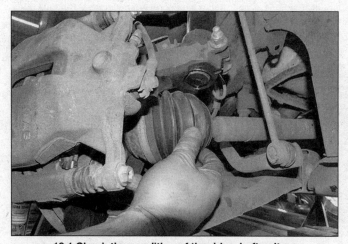

18.1 Check the condition of the driveshaft gaiters

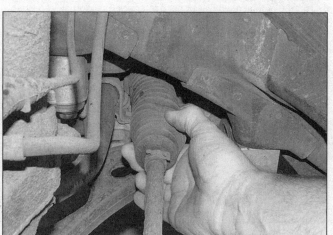

19.2 Check the rack gaiters for spilts

19.4 Check for wear in the bearings by grasping the wheel top and bottom and trying to rock it

19.5 Check for wear in the bearings and ball joints by grasping the wheel at the sides and trying to rock it

deterioration. Any wear of these components will cause loss of lubricant, together with dirt and water entry, resulting in rapid deterioration of the balljoints or steering gear.

3 Check the power steering fluid hoses for chafing or deterioration, and the pipe and hose unions for fluid leaks. Also check for signs of fluid leakage under pressure from the steering gear rubber gaiters, which would indicate failed fluid seals within the steering gear.

4 Grasp the roadwheel at the 12 o'clock and 6 o'clock positions, and try to rock it **(see illustration)**. Very slight free play may be felt, but if the movement is appreciable, further investigation is necessary to determine the source. Continue rocking the wheel while an assistant depresses the footbrake. If the movement is now eliminated or significantly reduced, it is likely that the hub bearings are at fault. If the free play is still evident with the footbrake depressed, then there is wear in the suspension joints or mountings.

5 Now grasp the wheel at the 9 o'clock and 3 o'clock positions, and try to rock it as before **(see illustration)**. Any movement felt now may again be caused by wear in the hub bearings or the steering track rod balljoints. If the inner or outer balljoint is worn, the visual movement will be obvious.

6 Using a large screwdriver or flat bar, check for wear in the suspension mounting bushes by levering between the relevant suspension

component and its attachment point. Some movement is to be expected as the mountings are made of rubber, but excessive wear should be obvious. Also check the condition of any visible rubber bushes, looking for splits, cracks or contamination of the rubber.

7 With the car standing on its wheels, have an assistant turn the steering wheel back-and-forth about an eighth of a turn each way. There should be very little, if any, lost movement between the steering wheel and roadwheels. If this is not the case, closely observe the joints and mountings previously described, but in addition, check the steering column universal joints for wear, and the rack-and-pinion steering gear itself.

8 Check for any signs of fluid leakage around the front suspension struts and rear shock absorber. Should any fluid be noticed, the suspension strut or shock absorber is defective internally, and should be renewed. **Note:** *Suspension struts/shock absorbers should always be renewed in pairs on the same axle to ensure correct vehicle handling.*

9 The efficiency of the suspension strut/shock absorber may be checked by bouncing the vehicle at each corner. Generally speaking, the body will return to its normal position and stop after being depressed. If it rises and returns on a rebound, the suspension strut/shock absorber is probably suspect. Examine also the suspension strut/shock absorber upper and lower mountings for any signs of wear.

20 Battery check

1 The battery is located on the left-hand side of the engine compartment. Open the cover **(see illustration)** to gain access to the battery.
2 Check that both battery terminals are securely attached **(see illustration)** and are free from corrosion. **Note:** *Before disconnecting the terminals from the battery, refer to Chapter 5A Section 3.*
3 Check the battery casing for signs of damage or cracking and check the battery retaining clamp bolt is securely tightened **(see illustration)**. If the battery casing is damaged in any way the battery must be renewed (see Chapter 5A Section 3).
4 On completion close the battery cover.

21 Hinge and lock lubrication

1 Lubricate the hinges of the bonnet, doors and tailgate with light general-purpose oil. Similarly, lubricate all latches, locks and lock strikers. At the same time, check the security and operation of all the locks, adjusting them if necessary (see Chapter 11 Section 13).
2 Lightly lubricate the bonnet release mechanism and cable with suitable grease.

22 Airbag unit check

1 The airbag system will perform a self-check when the ignition is turned on. The airbag warning light will illuminate and then go out after several seconds. If a system fault is found the airbag warning light will remain on and a fault code will be logged. The fault code can be read by a suitable diagnostic tool and appropriate action taken.

20.1 Open the cover

20.2 Check that the terminals are secure

20.3 Check that the battery clamp is secure (shown with cover removed)

2 Inspect the exterior condition of the airbag(s) for signs of damage or deterioration. If an airbag shows signs of damage, it must be renewed (Chapter 12 Section 24). Note that it is not permissible to attach any stickers to the surface of the airbag, as this may affect the deployment of the unit.

23 Windscreen/tailgate/ headlight washer system check

1 Check that each of the washer jet nozzles are clear and that each nozzle provides a strong jet of washer fluid.
2 The tailgate jet should be aimed to spray at the centre of the screen, using a pin.
3 The windscreen washer nozzles should be aimed slightly above the centre of the screen using a small screwdriver to turn the jet eccentric (see Chapter 12 Section 18).
4 The headlight inner jet should be aimed slightly above the horizontal centreline of the headlight, and the outer jet should be aimed slightly below the centreline. Volkswagon technicians use a special tool to adjust the headlight jet after pulling the jet out onto its stop.
5 Especially during the winter months, make sure that the washer fluid frost concentration is sufficient.

24 Engine management self-diagnosis memory fault check

1 This work should be carried out by a Volkswagen dealer or a diagnostic specialist using special equipment. Note however that simple diagnostic tools are now widely available. Most of the lower priced tools will only access the mandatory OBD (On Board Diagnostics) emissions related fault codes. The diagnostic socket is located below the facia, at the right-hand side **(see illustration)**. The 16 pin socket is often referred to as the Data Link Connector (or DLC).

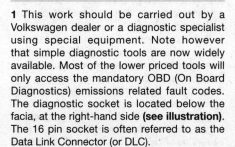

24.1 The diagnostic socket with a low cost diagnostic tool plugged in

25 Sunroof check and lubrication

1 Check the operation of the sunroof, and leave it in the fully open position.
2 Wipe clean the guide rails on each side of the sunroof opening, then apply lubricant to them. VW recommend VAG lubricant spray G 052 778.
3 Check that the drains are clear by carefully pouring clean water down each corner.

26 Road test and exhaust emissions check

Instruments and electrical equipment

1 Check the operation of all instruments and electrical equipment including the air conditioning system.
2 Make sure that all instruments read correctly, and switch on all electrical equipment in turn, to check that it functions properly.

Steering and suspension

3 Check for any abnormalities in the steering, suspension, handling or road 'feel'.
4 Drive the vehicle, and check that there are no unusual vibrations or noises, which may indicate wear in the driveshafts, wheel bearings, etc.
5 Check that the steering feels positive, with no excessive 'sloppiness', or roughness, and check for any suspension noises when cornering and driving over bumps.

Drivetrain

6 Check the performance of the engine, clutch (where applicable), gearbox/transmission and driveshafts.
7 Listen for any unusual noises from the engine, clutch and gearbox/transmission.
8 Make sure the engine runs smoothly at idle, and there is no hesitation on accelerating.
9 Check that, where applicable, the clutch action is smooth and progressive, that the drive is taken up smoothly, and that the pedal travel is not excessive. Also listen for any noises when the clutch pedal is depressed.
10 On manual gearbox models check that all gears can be engaged smoothly without noise, and that the gear lever action is smooth and not abnormally vague or 'notchy'.
11 On automatic (DSG) transmission models, make sure that all gearchanges occur smoothly, without snatching, and without an increase in engine speed between changes. Check that all the gear positions

can be selected with the vehicle at rest. If any problems are found, they should be referred to a dealer.
12 Listen for a metallic clicking sound from the front of the vehicle, as the vehicle is driven slowly in a circle with the steering on full-lock. Carry out this check in both directions. If a clicking noise is heard, this indicates wear in a driveshaft joint, in which case renew the joint if necessary.

Braking system

13 Make sure that the vehicle does not pull to one side when braking, and that the wheels do not lock when braking hard.
14 Check that there is no vibration through the steering when braking.
15 Check that the handbrake operates correctly and that it holds the vehicle stationary on a slope.
16 Test the operation of the brake servo unit as follows. With the engine off, depress the footbrake four or five times to exhaust the vacuum. Hold the brake pedal depressed, and then start the engine. As the engine starts, there should be a noticeable 'give' in the brake pedal as vacuum builds-up. Allow the engine to run for at least two minutes, and then switch it off. If the brake pedal is depressed now, it should be possible to detect a hiss from the servo as the pedal is depressed. After about four or five applications, no further hissing should be heard, and the pedal should feel considerably harder.
17 Under controlled emergency braking, the pulsing of the ABS unit must be felt at the footbrake pedal.

Exhaust emissions check

18 Although not part of the manufacturer's maintenance schedule, this check will normally be carried out on a regular basis according to the country the vehicle is operated in. Currently in the UK, exhaust emissions testing is included as part of the annual MOT test after the vehicle is 3 years old. In Germany the test is made when the vehicle is 3 years old, then repeated every 2 years.

27 DSG transmission oil renewal

1 Renewal of the DSG transmission oil is described in Chapter 7B Section 6.

28 Air filter element renewal – diesel models

1 The air cleaner is located in front of the battery in the left-hand front corner of the engine compartment.
2 Undo the cover retaining screws and lift

28.2 Undo the retaining screws

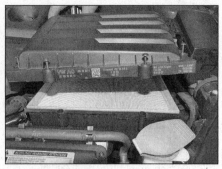

28.3a Lift up the cover…

28.3b …and remove the filter

the air cleaner cover, taking care not to put any strain on the intake ducting and air mass meter **(see illustration)**.
3 Lift the cover and remove the air filter **(see illustrations)**.

4 Remove any debris that may have collected inside the air cleaner.
5 Fit a new air filter element in position, ensuring that the edges are securely seated.
6 Refit the lid and tighten the screws.

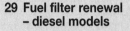

29 Fuel filter renewal – diesel models

Note: *Carry out this procedure at this interval only when using diesel fuel conforming to DIN EN 590 (standard fuel in the UK).*
1 The fuel filter is mounted in the right-hand front corner of the engine compartment.
2 Before removing the fuel filter, clean around the fuel pipes on the top of the filter housing to prevent any dirt entering the fuel system **(see illustration)**. Place some cloth around the filter housing to catch any fuel spillage.
3 Undo the screws and lift the cover complete with fuel hoses from the top of the filter housing and move it to one side **(see illustrations)**.
4 Withdraw the old filter element out from the housing and discard **(see illustration)**.
5 Use a pipette/syringe to draw out the dirty fuel and water residue from inside the fuel filter lower housing. Then insert the new filter element, pressing it down fully into position **(see illustrations)**.
6 To help the engine start easier (to prevent having to bleed the system), top up the filter housing with clean diesel, making sure that no dirt or water enters the system.
7 Start and run the engine at idle, then check around the fuel filter for fuel leaks. **Note:** *It may take a few seconds of cranking before the engine starts. If the engine does not start the system must be bleed using a vacuum tool or*

29.2 Place cloths or shop towels around the base of the filter

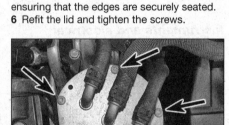

29.3a Remove the screws…

29.3b …lift off the cover…

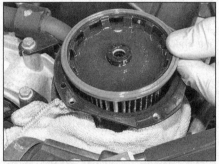

29.4 …and lift out the old filter element

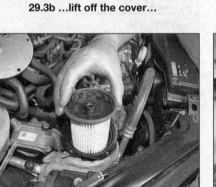

29.5a Use a pipette to draw out the old fuel…

29.5b … and insert the new filter element

29.5c There are two versions of the filter. Fit the correct one

29.7 Bleeding the fuel system with a vacuum pump

hand primer **(see illustration)**. *Identify the fuel return line from the injectors and remove it from the filter. Connect the vacuum pump or hand primer and draw fuel up to the filter. Reconnect the filter fuel line and start the vehicle.*

30 Auxiliary drivebelt renewal – diesel models

Check

1 See Section 11, for information on checking the condition of the drivebelt.
2 When the belt is removed, check all pulleys are free from any damage and are secure. Also check that the alternator and air-conditioning compressor are mounted securely.

Renewal

3 For improved access, apply the handbrake, and then jack up the front of the vehicle and support it on axle stands (see *Jacking and vehicle support*).
4 Remove the right-hand front roadwheel, then remove the lower section of the wing liner.
5 A small hex key, drill bit, bolt or the factory locking pin (T10060A) will be required to lock the tensioner in position, so that the belt can be removed.
6 If the belt is to be refitted mark the direction of rotation on the belt.
7 Fit a spanner to the tensioner, rotate it anti-clockwise and fit the locking pin **(see illustrations)**.
8 Lift off the drivebelt **(see illustration)**.

9 Fit the replacement belt, remove the locking pin and slowly release the spanner, allowing the tensioner to tighten the belt.
10 Check that the belt is correctly aligned in the pulley grooves (rotate the crankshaft if required) and then refit the lower section of the wing liner. Fit the wheel and lower the vehicle to the ground.

31 Timing belt and tensioner roller renewal

1 Refer to Chapter 2C Section 7 for details of renewing the timing belt and tensioner roller.

32 Brake (and clutch) fluid renewal

 Warning: Brake hydraulic fluid can harm your eyes and damage painted surfaces, so use extreme caution when handling and pouring it. Do not use fluid that has been standing open for some time, as it absorbs moisture from the air. Excess moisture can cause a dangerous loss of braking effectiveness.

1 The procedure is similar to that for the bleeding of the hydraulic system as described in Chapter 9 Section 2, except that the brake fluid reservoir should be emptied by siphoning, using an old, clean antifreeze tester or similar before starting, and allowance should be made for the old fluid to be expelled when bleeding a section of the circuit. Since the clutch hydraulic system also uses fluid from the brake system reservoir, it should also be bled at the same time by referring to Chapter 6A Section 2.
2 Working as described in Chapter 9 Section 2, open the first bleed screw in the sequence, and pump the brake pedal gently until nearly all the old fluid has been emptied from the master cylinder reservoir.
3 Top-up to the MAX level with new fluid, and continue pumping until only the new fluid remains in the reservoir, and new fluid can be seen emerging from the bleed screw. Tighten the screw, and top the reservoir level up to the MAX level line.

4 Work through all the remaining bleed screws in the sequence until new fluid can be seen at all of them. Be careful to keep the master cylinder reservoir topped-up to above the MIN level at all times, or air may enter the system and greatly increase the length of the task.
5 When the operation is complete, check that all bleed screws are securely tightened, and that their dust caps are refitted. Wash off all traces of spilt fluid, and recheck the master cylinder reservoir fluid level.
6 On models with manual transmission, once the brake fluid has been changed the clutch fluid should also be renewed. Referring to Chapter 6A Section 2, bleed the clutch until new fluid is seen to be emerging from the slave cylinder bleed screw, keeping the master cylinder fluid level above the MIN level line at all times to prevent air entering the system. Once the new fluid emerges, securely tighten the bleed screw then disconnect and remove the bleeding equipment. Securely refit the dust cap then wash off all traces of spilt fluid.
7 On all models, ensure the master cylinder fluid level is correct (see *Weekly checks*) and thoroughly check the operation of the brakes and (where necessary) clutch before taking the car on the road.

33 Coolant renewal

Note: *This work is not included in the service schedule and should not be required if the recommended VAG G12 LongLife coolant antifreeze/inhibitor is used. However, if standard antifreeze/inhibitor is used, the work should be carried out at the recommended interval.*

 Warning: Wait until the engine is cold before starting this procedure. Do not allow antifreeze to come in contact with your skin, or with the painted surfaces of the vehicle. Rinse off spills immediately with plenty of water. Never leave antifreeze lying around in an open container, or in a puddle in the driveway or on the garage floor. Children and pets are attracted by its sweet smell, but antifreeze can be fatal if ingested.

30.7a Slacken the belt...

30.7b ...and fit the locking pin

30.8 Remove the belt. Note the direction of rotation mark

Cooling system draining

1 With the engine completely cold, unscrew the expansion tank cap.

2 Firmly apply the handbrake then jack up the front of the vehicle and support it on axle stands (see *Jacking and vehicle support*). Undo the retaining screws and remove the engine undertray(s) to gain access to the base of the radiator.

3 Remove the retaining clip and disconnect the bottom hose from the radiator to drain the coolant **(see illustration)**. Repeat the procedure on the lower intercooler hose.

4 Release the clamps and disconnect the hoses from the electric coolant circulation pumps, located at the front and rear of the cylinder block **(see illustration)**.

5 Draining the coolant from the radiators is straightforward, however due to the complex cooling system, draining the coolant from all the hoses and components will require further dismantling. Where an airline is available, disconnecting one or more hoses from the intercooler and/or the cabin heater matrix hose and blowing compressed air through the hoses will assist in draining the cooling system.

6 If the coolant has been drained for a reason other than renewal, then provided it is clean, it can be re-used, though this is not recommended.

7 Once all the coolant has drained reconnect the hoses. Refit the undertray(s), tighten the retaining screws securely.

Cooling system flushing

8 A vehicle that has had the coolant system checked and is still using the original Volkswagen coolant should not require a flush of any description. If there is any evidence of contamination then a system flush should be considered. A wide range of proprietary chemical flushes for this purpose are widely available in the aftermarket.

9 Most of the cleaning/flushing chemicals on the market are simply added to the expansion tank and the engine is then run (or driven) for a prescribed length of time. The coolant and flushing chemical are then drained in the normal manner. The radiator top hose is then removed and the radiator back flushed with clean water. The cabin heater matrix is also back flushed after disconnecting the flow and return hoses from the bulkhead. There is generally no need to flush the engine, however where this is possible it should be considered. Once free of debris and contamination the system is refilled with fresh coolant as described below.

Cooling system filling

10 Before attempting to fill the cooling system, ensure that all hoses are securely connected and their retaining clips are in good condition. If the recommended Volkswagen coolant is not being used, ensure that a suitable antifreeze mixture is used all year round, to prevent corrosion of the engine components (see following sub-Section).
Note: *Volkswagen recommend that only distilled water should be used.*

11 The recommended refill method is to use a vacuum type coolant filling tool **(see illustration)**. The tool vacuums the cooling system and then the vacuum is used to draw the coolant into the system. This method ensures there are no airlocks in the cooling system.

12 It is also possible to fill the cooling system manually, by adding coolant slowly through the coolant reservoir.

13 Remove the expansion tank filler cap and slowly fill the system with the coolant **(see illustration)**. Continue to fill the cooling system until bubbles stop appearing in the expansion tank. Help to bleed the air from the system by repeatedly squeezing the radiator bottom hose.

14 When no more bubbles appear, top the coolant level up to the MAX level mark. Do not refit the cap to the expansion tank.

15 Run the engine at a fast idle speed until the cooling fan cuts in. Watch for air bubbles rising in the coolant reservoir. Wait for the fan to stop then switch the engine off and allow the engine to cool.

16 When the engine has cooled, check the coolant level with reference to *Weekly checks*. Top-up the level if necessary, and refit the expansion tank cap.

Antifreeze mixture

17 If the recommended Volkswagen coolant is not being used, the antifreeze should always be renewed at the specified intervals. This is necessary not only to maintain the antifreeze properties, but also to prevent corrosion, which would otherwise occur as the corrosion inhibitors become progressively less effective.

18 Always use an ethylene-glycol based antifreeze which is suitable for use in mixed-metal cooling systems. The quantity of antifreeze and levels of protection are indicated in the Specifications.

19 Before adding antifreeze, the cooling system should be completely drained, preferably flushed, and all hoses checked for condition and security.

20 After filling with antifreeze, a label should be attached to the expansion tank, stating the type and concentration of antifreeze used, and the date installed. Any subsequent topping-up should be made with the same type and concentration of antifreeze.

Caution: Do not use engine antifreeze in the windscreen/tailgate washer system, as it will damage the vehicle paintwork. A screenwash additive should be added to the washer system in the quantities stated on the bottle.

34 Particulate filter ash deposit mass check

1 Eventually, the amount of ash deposited in the particle filter by the filtration process will cause a blockage, and engine running problems. VW state that the maximum amount of ash is 60g. At this point, the particle filter must be renewed. Unfortunately, the mass of the ash can only be established using dedicated diagnostic equipment, connected to the vehicle through the diagnostic plug under the drivers side of the facia. Consequently, this task should be performed by a dealer or suitably equipped specialist.

33.3 Drain the coolant

33.4 Disconnect the hose from the electric pump

33.11 A suitable coolant filling tool

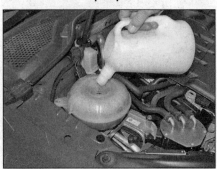

33.13 Slowly refill the coolant reservoir

Chapter 2 Part A
1.2 and 1.4 litre petrol engine in-car repair procedures

Contents

Section number

Camshaft housing – removal and refitting 4
Camshaft oil seals – renewal 11
Camshafts – inspection 9
Compression test – description and interpretation 2
Crankshaft oil seals – renewal 16
Crankshaft pulley – removal and refitting 5
Cylinder head – removal, inspection and refitting 12
Engine assembly and valve timing marks –
    general information and usage 3
Engine mountings – inspection and renewal 17
Engine oil cooler – removal and refitting 18

Section number

Flywheel – removal, inspection and refitting 15
General Information 1
Hydraulic tappets/roller rocker fingers – removal, inspection
    and refitting. 10
Oil level/temperature sender – removal and refitting 20
Oil pressure warning light switch – removal and refitting. 19
Oil pump – removal and refitting 14
Sump – removal and refitting 13
Timing belt – removal and refitting. 7
Timing belt covers – removal and refitting 6
Timing belt tensioner and sprockets – removal and refitting 8

Degrees of difficulty

| Easy, suitable for novice with little experience | Fairly easy, suitable for beginner with some experience | Fairly difficult, suitable for competent DIY mechanic | Difficult, suitable for experienced DIY mechanic | Very difficult, suitable for expert DIY or professional |

Specifications

General

1.2 litre engines

Manufacturers engine codes* . . . . CJZA, CJZB and CYVA
Maximum power output:
  Engine code CJZB . . . . 63 kW at 4300 to 5300 rpm
  Engine code CJZA . . . . 77 kW at 4500 to 5500 rpm
  Engine code CYVB . . . . 81 kW at 4600 to 5600 rpm
Maximum torque output:
  Engine code CJZB . . . . 160 Nm at 1400 to 3500 rpm
  Engine code CJZA and CYVB . . . . 175 Nm at 1400 to 4000 rpm
Bore . . . . 71.0 mm
Stroke . . . . 75.6 mm
Compression ratio . . . . 10.5 : 1
Compression pressure:
  Minimum compression pressure . . . . Approximately 7.0 bar
  Maximum difference between cylinders . . . . Approximately 3.0 bar
Firing order . . . . 1 -3 -4 -2
Number 1 cylinder location . . . . Timing belt end

General (continued)

1.4 litre engines

Manufacturer's engine codes*	CPTA, CHPA, CMBA, CXSA, CPVA, CZEA and CZDA
Maximum power output:	
Engine codes CMBA, CXSA and CPVA	90 kW at 5000 to 6000 rpm
Engine codes CZCA and CPVB	92 kW at 5000 to 6000 rpm
Engine codes CPTA and CHPA	103 kW at 4500 to 6000 rpm
Engine codes CZEA and CZDA	110 kW at 5000 to 6000 rpm
Maximum torque output:	
Engine codes CMBA, CXSA, CPVA, CZCA and CPVB	200 Nm at 1400 to 4000 rpm
Engine codes CPTA, CHPA, CZEA and CZDA	250 Nm at 1500 to 3500 rpm
Bore	74. mm
Stroke...	80.0 mm
Compression ratio:	
Engine codes CPTA, CHPA, CMBA, CXSA and CPVA...........	10.5 : 1
Engine codes CZEA, CZDA, CZCA and CPVB.................	10.0 : 1
Compression pressures:	
Minimum compression pressure	Approximately 7.0 bar
Maximum difference between cylinders.....................	Approximately 3.0 bar
Firing order..	1 – 3 – 4 – 2
No 1 cylinder location....................................	Timing belt end

*See 'Vehicle identification' at the end of this manual for the location of the engine code markings

Lubrication system

Oil pump type..	Gear type, crankshaft driven on 1.2 and chain-driven from crankshaft on 1.4 litre engines
Oil pressure (oil temperature 80°C):	
At idle	0.6 bar (minimum)
At 2000 rpm	1.5 bar (minimum)
At 4500 rpm (for 1.2 litre engines or 3800 rpm for 1.4 litre engines) .	2.8 bar (minimum)

Torque wrench settings

	Nm	lbf ft
Ancillary (alternator, etc) bracket mounting bolts..................	45	33
Auxiliary drivebelt tensioner securing bolt*		
Stage 1..	20	15
Stage 2..	Angle-tighten a further 90°	
Big-end bearing cap bolts*:		
Stage 1..	30	22
Stage 2..	Angle-tighten a further 90°	
Camshaft actuator bolts (ACT engines only)	8	6
Camshaft cover bolts:		
Stage 1..	10	7
Stage 2..	Angle-tighten a further 180°	
Camshaft sprocket bolts*:		
Exhaust sprocket (non VVT engines)		
Stage 1..	50	37
Stage 2..	Angle-tighten a further 90°	
Exhaust sprocket (VVT engines)		
Stage 1..	50	37
Stage 2..	Angle-tighten a further 135°	
Inlet sprocket bolt		
Stage 1..	50	37
Stage 2..	Angle-tighten a further 135°	
Camshaft sprocket plug (Inlet)*	20	15
Camshaft sprocket cover bolts (Exhaust VVT engines)*:		
Stage 1..	8	6
Stage 2..	Angle-tighten a further 45°	
Coolant pump bolts:		
Stage 1..	10	7
Stage 2..	Loosen one revolution	
Stage 3..	10	7
Stage 4..	12	9
Coolant pump sprocket bolt*:		
Stage 1..	20	15
Stage 2..	Angle-tighten a further 90°	

Torque wrench settings (continued)

	Nm	lbf ft
Crankshaft oil seal/ oil pump housing bolts (1.2 litre engines)		
Stage 1 (upper 6 bolts)*	8	6
Stage 2	Angle-tighten a further 90°	
Lower bolts (bottom right)	20	15
Crankshaft flange/end cover bolts (1.4 litre engines)*:		
Stage 1 (all bolts)	8	6
Stage 2 (2 lower right-hand bolts)	20	15
Stage 3 (all bolts)	Angle-tighten a further 90°	
Crankshaft position sensor wheel-to-crankshaft bolts	10	7
Crankshaft sprocket bolt*:		
Stage 1	150	110
Stage 2	Angle-tighten a further 180°	
Cylinder head bolts*:		
Stage 1	40	30
Stage 2	Angle-tighten a further 90°	
Stage 3	Angle-tighten a further 90°	
Stage 4	Angle-tighten a further 90°	
Engine mountings:		
RH engine mounting*:		
Mounting to engine bracket:		
Stage 1	60	44
Stage 2	Angle-tighten a further 90°	
Mounting to body:		
Stage 1	40	30
Stage 2	Angle-tighten a further 90°	
Mounting to body (horizontal bolt)		
Stage 1	20	15
Stage 2	Angle-tighten a further 90°	
Bracket to engine:		
Stage 1	7	5
Stage 2	40	30
Stage 3	Angle-tighten a further 90°	
LH engine mounting*:		
Mounting to body:		
Stage 1	50	37
Stage 2	Angle-tighten a further 90°	
Mounting to transmission:		
Stage 1	60	44
Stage 2	Angle-tighten a further 90°	
Rear pendulum mounting*:		
To transmission:		
Stage 1	50	37
Stage 2	Angle-tighten a further 90°	
To subframe:		
Stage 1	130	96
Stage 2	Angle-tighten a further 90°	
Flywheel*:		
Stage 1	60	44
Stage 2	Angle-tighten a further 90°	
Inlet manifold to head	8	6
Oil cooler bolts*:		
Stage 1	8	6
Stage 2	Angle-tighten a further 90°	
Oil drain plug	30	22
Oil level/temperature sender bolts	8	6
Oil pick-up pipe-to-oil pump bolts (1.2 litre engines)	8	6
Oil pick-up pipe to oil pump bolts (1.4 litre engines)*		
Stage 1	5	4
Stage 2	Angle-tighten a further 90°	
Oil pressure switch	20	15
Oil pump bolts (1.4 litre engines)	10	7
Oil spray jet/pressure relief valve bolts	27	20
Roadwheel bolts	120	89
Sump bolts (1.2 litre engines)*:		
Stage 1	8	6
Stage 2	Angle-tighten a further 90°	
Sump bolts (1.4 litre engines)*	12	9

Torque wrench settings (continued)

	Nm	lbf ft
Sump bolts (upper sump 1.4 litre engines only)*:		
Stage 1	8	6
Stage 2	Angle-tighten a further 90°	
Thermostat cover bolts (large cooling circuit)	8	6
Thermostat cover (to coolant pump)	8	6
Timing belt outer cover bolts	8	6
Timing belt rear cover bolts:		
Small bolts	10	7
Large bolt	23	17
Timing belt tensioner bolt.................................	25	18
Timing belt idler pulley bolt	45	33
Timing TDC pin blanking plug	30	22
Turbocharger to cylinder head nuts*	14	10
Turbocharger heat shield bolts (main bolts)	25	18

*Do not re-use

1 General Information

How to use this Chapter

1 This Part of Chapter 2 describes those repair procedures that can reasonably be carried out on the engine while it remains in the vehicle. If the engine has been removed from the vehicle and is being dismantled as described in Part D, any preliminary dismantling procedures can be ignored.

2 Note that while it may be possible physically to overhaul certain items while the engine is in the vehicle, such tasks are not usually carried out as separate operations, and usually require the execution of several additional procedures (not to mention the cleaning of components and of oilways); for this reason, all such tasks are classed as major overhaul procedures, and are described in Part D of this Chapter.

Engine description

3 Throughout this Chapter, engines are identified by the manufacturer's code letters. A listing of all engines covered, together with their code letters, is given in the Specifications.

4 The engines covered in this Part of the Chapter are of water-cooled, double-overhead camshaft (DOHC), in-line four-cylinder design. The engine family is designated EA211 by VAG (Volkswagen Audi Group). The engines have an aluminium alloy cylinder block fitted with grey cast-iron cylinder liners, and an aluminium alloy cylinder head. The exhaust manifold is integrated into the cylinder head. The engine is transversely mounted at the front of the vehicle, with the transmission unit on its left-hand end.

5 The crankshaft is of five-bearing type, but note that the crankshaft must not be removed due to the design of the bearing pedestals. Removing the bearing caps will distort the pedestals and damage the bearings.

6 The camshafts are mounted in a modular camshaft carrier and are driven by a toothed timing belt from the crankshaft sprocket. Variable Valve Timing (VVT) is fitted to the inlet camshaft o all versions. Models with an output greater than 103 kW also have VVT fitted to the exhaust camshaft. Repair to the camshafts is not possible. If a fault develops the entire housing (module) is replaced.

7 1.4 litre engines with codes CPTA and CHPA have 'Active Cylinder Management' (confusingly termed 'ACT' by Volkswagen). On these engines actuators slide the camshaft lobes away from the rocker arms on the middle two cylinders (cylinders two and three) enabling the engine to run on two cylinders. This improves fuel consumption and reduces overall emissions.

8 The valves are closed by coil springs, and the valves run in guides pressed into the cylinder head. The camshafts actuate the valves by roller rocker fingers supported by hydraulic tappets.

9 On 1.4 litre engines the oil pump is driven via a chain from a sprocket on the crankshaft. The output of the chain driven oil pump is variable, with the output controlled by the engine management system. 1.2 litre engines have a 'duocentric' oil pump driven directly by the crankshaft. Oil is drawn from the sump through a strainer, and then forced through an externally-mounted, renewable filter. From there, it is distributed to the cylinder head, where it lubricates the camshaft journals and hydraulic tappets, and also to the crankcase, where it lubricates the main bearings, connecting rod big-ends, gudgeon pins and cylinder bores. A coolant-fed oil cooler is fitted to all engines.

10 Engine coolant is circulated by a pump, driven by the timing belt. For details of the cooling system, refer to Chapter 3.

Operations with engine in car

11 The following operations can be performed without removing the engine:

a) Compression pressure – testing.
b) Camshaft cover – removal and refitting.
c) Crankshaft pulley – removal and refitting.
d) Timing belt covers – removal and refitting.
e) Timing belt – removal, refitting and adjustment.
f) Timing belt tensioner and sprockets – removal and refitting.
g) Camshaft oil seal – renewal.
h) Camshaft and hydraulic tappets – removal, inspection and refitting.
i) Cylinder head – removal and refitting.
j) Cylinder head and pistons – decarbonising.
k) Sump – removal and refitting.
l) Oil pump – removal, overhaul and refitting.
m) Crankshaft oil seals – renewal.
n) Engine/transmission mountings – inspection and renewal.
o) Flywheel/driveplate – removal, inspection and refitting.

Note: It is possible to remove the pistons and connecting rods (after removing the cylinder head and sump) without removing the engine. However, this is not recommended. Work of this nature is more easily and thoroughly completed with the engine on the bench, as described in Chapter 2D Section 12.

2 Compression test –
description and interpretation

Caution: The following work may insert fault codes in the engine management ECU. These fault codes must be cleared by a VW dealer or suitably equipped repairer.

Note: A suitable compression tester will be required for this test.

1 When engine performance is down, or if misfiring occurs which cannot be attributed to the ignition or fuel systems, a compression test can provide diagnostic clues as to the engine's condition. If the test is performed regularly it can give warning of trouble before any other symptoms become apparent.

2 The engine must be fully warmed-up to normal operating temperature, the battery must be fully-charged and the spark plugs must be removed (Chapter 1A Section 29). The aid of an assistant will be required.

3 Disable the ignition system either by disconnecting the wiring plugs from the coils (see Chapter 5B Section 3) or install a remote starter switch to the starter motor.

4 Referring to Chapter 4A Section 4, disconnect the wiring from the fuel injectors.

5 Fit a compression tester to the No 1 cylinder spark plug hole. The type of tester which screws into the plug thread is preferred.

6 Have the assistant hold the throttle wide open and crank the engine for several seconds on the starter motor. **Note:** *The throttle will not operate until the ignition is switched on. After one or two revolutions, the compression pressure should build-up to a maximum figure and then stabilise. Record the highest reading obtained.*

7 Repeat the test on the remaining cylinders, recording the pressure in each.

8 All cylinders should produce very similar pressures. Any difference greater than that specified indicates the existence of a fault. Note that the compression should build-up quickly in a healthy engine. Low compression on the first stroke, followed by gradually increasing pressure on successive strokes, indicates worn piston rings. A low compression reading on the first stroke, which does not build-up during successive strokes, indicates leaking valves or a blown head gasket (a cracked head could also be the cause). Deposits on the undersides of the valve heads can also cause low compression.

9 If the pressure in any cylinder is reduced to the specified minimum or less, carry out the following test to isolate the cause. Introduce a teaspoonful of clean oil into that cylinder through its spark plug hole and repeat the test.

10 If the addition of oil temporarily improves the compression pressure, this indicates that bore or piston wear is responsible for the pressure loss. No improvement suggests that leaking or burnt valves, or a blown head gasket, may be to blame.

11 A low reading from two adjacent cylinders is almost certainly due to the head gasket having blown between them and the presence of coolant in the engine oil will confirm this.

3.0 A full set of aftermarket timing tools from AST tools

12 If one cylinder is about 20 percent lower than the others and the engine has a slightly rough idle, a worn camshaft lobe could be the cause.

13 If the compression reading is unusually high, the combustion chambers are probably coated with carbon deposits. If this is the case, the cylinder head should be removed and decarbonised.

14 On completion of the test, refit the spark plugs, and reconnect the ignition coils.

15 Have any fault codes cleared by a Volkswagen dealer or suitably equipped garage.

3 Engine assembly and valve timing marks – general information and usage

Note: *A set of specific timing tools will be required to set the engine at TDC (Top Dead Centre). These are available in the aftermarket* **(see illustration)** *or directly from Volkswagen.*

General information

1 TDC is the highest point in the cylinder that each piston reaches as it travels up and down when the crankshaft turns. Each piston reaches TDC at the end of the compression stroke and again at the end of the exhaust stroke, but TDC generally refers to piston

3.6 Remove the charge air and inlet air ducts

position on the compression stroke. No 1 piston is at the timing belt end of the engine.

2 Positioning No 1 piston at TDC is an essential part of many procedures, such as timing belt removal and camshaft removal.

3 The design of the engines covered in this Chapter is such that piston-to-valve contact may occur if the camshaft or crankshaft is turned with the timing belt removed. For this reason, it is important to ensure that the camshaft and crankshaft do not move in relation to each other once the timing belt has been removed from the engine.

Setting No 1 cylinder to TDC and checking the timing

4 Jack up and support the front of the vehicle (see *Jacking and vehicle support*), remove the engine undershield and then drain the coolant as described in Chapter 1A Section 33. Note that there is no need to completely drain the coolant, the level only requires lowering to below the coolant pump.

5 Remove the air filter housing as described in Chapter 4A Section 3.

6 Remove the air inlet pipes from the transmission end of the engine **(see illustration)**.

7 Disconnect the evaporative emissions (EVAP) hose and then remove the crankcase breather hose from the left-hand end of the engine **(see illustrations)**.

3.7a Disconnect the EVAP hose and...

3.7b ...then remove the breather hose

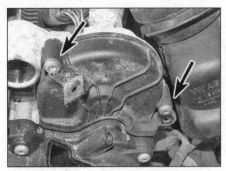

3.9a Remove the screws and...

3.9b ...lift off the cover

3.10 Remove the cover

8 Remove the upper cover from the thermostat housing and secure it to the side (1.4 litre engines). On 1.2 litre engines remove the coolant hose and air inlet duct. Where required disconnect the wiring plugs from the coolant temperature sensor and the charge air (boost pressure) sensor.

9 Unclip the wiring loom from the coolant pump drivebelt sprocket and then remove the coolant pump drivebelt cover **(see illustrations)**.

10 Unscrew the bolts and remove the cover from the inlet camshaft **(see illustration)**.

11 Remove the spark plug from cylinder number 1. If desired, to make the engine easier to turn, remove all of the spark plugs as described in Chapter 1A Section 29.

12 Insert a long screwdriver into the spark plug hole of number 1 cylinder and then rotate the engine (via the crankshaft pulley bolt) in

the normal direction, until the the piston is at the bottom of the stroke (BDC – Bottom Dead Centre).

13 Turn the crankshaft in the normal direction of rotation (clockwise when looking at the crankshaft pulley) until the screwdriver has risen by 30 mm **(see illustration)**.

14 Remove the blanking plug from the right-hand rear of the cylinder block and insert the crankshaft locking tool T10340 (or equivalent) into the block **(see illustration)**. Slowly rotate the crankshaft in the normal direction until it stops against the locking pin.

15 Note that if the pin can not be fully inserted, remove it and rotate the engine another 90 degrees in the normal direction and refit the pin. Turn the engine further clockwise until the crankshaft stops against the pin.

16 Next check the position of the camshaft

sprockets. Looking through the exhaust camshaft sprocket, check the the grooves directly behind the sprocket are level and above and imaginary line drawn through the centre of the sprocket. On engine codes CPTA and CZEA the hole in the sprocket must be in the 12 O'clock position and aligned with the hole in the camshaft housing.

17 Next check the position of the inlet camshaft grooves, again they should be just above the horizontal.

Note: *If the camshafts are not aligned as shown, then the engine is set at TDC on number 4 cylinder. Remove the crankshaft timing pin, rotate the engine one revolution and repeat the alignment procedure.*

18 This is the basic check of the correct timing. The timing can be verified by fitting the timing tool (T10494 for all 1.4/1.2 litre engines and tool T10504/2 for engine with 'ACT' technology) to the inlet and exhaust camshafts **(see illustrations)**. If the tool can not be fitted it is permissible to slightly depress the timing belt (using special tool T10487 or an equivalent) between the inlet and exhaust camshaft sprockets to correct any minor alignment issues. The timing belt upper cover must be removed as described in Section 6 first.

19 Remove the timing tools on completion and then refit the removed components. Refill the cooling system as described in Chapter 1A Section 33.

3.13 Raise the piston by 30 mm

3.14 Remove the blanking plug

3.18a Fit the camshaft setting tool all engines, except...

3.18b ...those with ACT technology, where a different tool is required

4 Camshaft housing –
removal and refitting

Note: *The camshafts are housed in a single combined valve cover and camshaft carrier. The camshafts can not be removed from the housing. If there is a fault with the camshafts (such as worn lobes, or excessive end float for example) then the complete housing and camshafts must be replaced.*

Removal

1 Drain the coolant (Chapter 1A Section 33) and then remove the coolant pump as described in Chapter 3 Section 7.

4.7a Unbolt the inlet elbow from the turbocharger

4.7b Unbolt (and move to the side) the coolant pipes

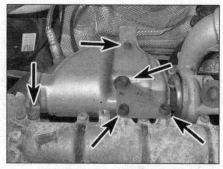

4.8a Unbolt and then...

4.8b ...remove the heat shield

4.9a Disconnect the wiring plug from the VVT control solenoid and...

4.9b ...unbolt the ground wire

2 Remove the air filter housing as described in Chapter 4A Section 3.

3 Remove the ignition coils as described in Chapter 5B Section 3.

4 Remove the timing belt from the camshaft sprockets as described in Section 7 – there is no need to completely remove the timing belt at this stage

5 Fit the camshaft locking tool to the coolant pump sprocket and the inlet camshaft (as described in Section 3). Fitting the tool will lock the camshafts in position.

6 Disconnect the wiring plug and fuel lines from the high pressure fuel pump (Chapter 4A Section 4).

7 Remove the inlet duct from the rear of the engine and then remove the turbocharger coolant hoses (see illustrations).

8 Unbolt and remove the heat shield from the top of the turbocharger (see illustrations).

9 On models fitted with 'ACT' disconnect the wiring plugs from the actuators. On all models disconnect the wiring plugs from the camshaft position sensors and the VVT control valve(s). Unbolt the ground wire (see illustrations).

Release (and unbolt) the wiring loom from the retaining brackets and then move the wiring loom to the side.

10 Remove the dipstick and then unbolt the housing in the reverse order (15 to 1) to that shown (see illustration 4.15).

11 Remove the housing and store it on a clean surface. Recover the gasket (see illustrations).

Refitting

12 Thoroughly clean the mating surfaces of the camshaft housing and the cylinder head.

4.11a Remove the camshaft housing and...

4.11b ...then recover the gasket

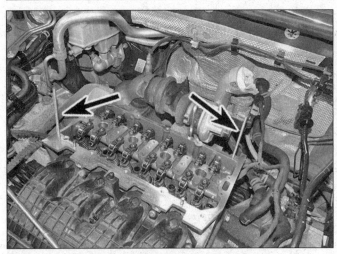

4.13 Fit guide studs to the cylinder head

4.14 Lower the new gasket over the studs

13 Fit guide studs to the cylinder head. These can be fabricated from bolts with their heads cut off and a slot filed into the end of the stud for removal **(see illustration)**.

14 Fit a new gasket **(see illustration)**, check that the cam followers are all correctly located and then lower the housing into position.

15 Tighten the new bolts progressively to the specified torque in sequence **(see illustration)**.

16 The remainder of refitting is a reversal of removal, but consider fitting a new timing belt and always fit a new coolant pump belt.

Rotate the engine at least twice in the normal direction to check the valve timing. Refill the coolant as described in Chapter 1A Section 33.

5 Crankshaft pulley – removal and refitting

Removal

1 Raise the front right-hand side of the vehicle, and support the vehicle securely on axle stands (see *Jacking and vehicle support*). Remove the road wheel.

2 Remove the lower section of the wing liner **(see illustration)**.

3 If necessary (for any later work to be carried out), turn the crankshaft using a socket or spanner on the crankshaft sprocket bolt until the relevant timing marks align (see Section 3).

4 Remove the auxiliary drivebelt as described in Chapter 1A Section 30.

Caution: The bolt is difficult to release, due to the high torque and angle setting required. A home made tool can be fabricated, but the use of the correct tool (AST 5144 for example) is highly recommended.

5 Use a large peg wrench (or the special tool T10475) to counterhold the pulley and then remove the bolt **(see illustrations)**. Dispose of the bolt, a new one will be required for refitting.

Refitting

6 Clean the mounting surface of both the pulley and the crankshaft. Refit the pulley to the sprocket, lubricate the new bolt and fit it.

7 Tighten the new bolt to the specified torque.

8 The refitting of the remaining components is a reversal of removal.

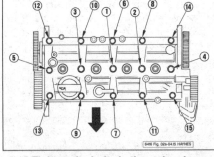

4.15 Tighten the bolts in the order shown

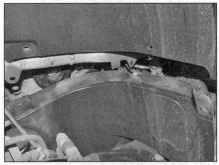

5.2 Remove the wing liner

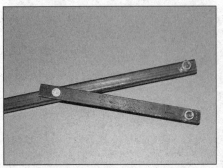

5.5a A large adjustable peg wrench will be required to counterhold the pulley

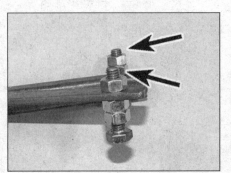

5.5b Adapt the tool, so that the bolts engage with the shallow slots in the pulley

5.5c Counterhold the pulley with the tool and slacken the bolt

6.1 Unclip the fuel lines

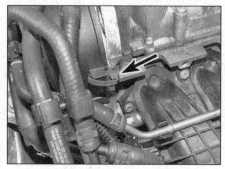

6.2a Release the front clip...

6.2b ...the rear clip...

6.2c ...and lift off the cover

6.5a Remove the bolts...

6.5b ...and remove the lower the cover

6 Timing belt covers – removal and refitting

Note: *The centre cover is the engine support bracket. Removal is described in Section 7 (Timing belt).*

Upper cover

Removal

1 Unclip the fuel lines from the cover and move them to the side (see illustration).
2 Remove the bolt from the coolant pipe bracket, release the retaining clips and lift off the cover (see illustrations).

7.9 Remove the engine mounting

Refitting

3 Refitting is a reversal of removal.

Lower cover

Removal

4 Remove the crankshaft pulley as described in Section 5.
5 Unscrew the securing bolts, and withdraw the cover from the front of the engine (see illustrations).

Refitting

6 Refitting is a reversal of removal.

7 Timing belt – removal and refitting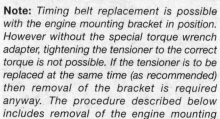

Note: *Timing belt replacement is possible with the engine mounting bracket in position. However without the special torque wrench adapter, tightening the tensioner to the correct torque is not possible. If the tensioner is to be replaced at the same time (as recommended) then removal of the bracket is required anyway. The procedure described below includes removal of the engine mounting bracket.*
Caution: *The timing tools are alignment tools, they are not designed to hold the crankshaft or camshafts in position*

whilst the sprocket and pulley bolts are removed. Always use a counterhold tool to release and tighten the sprocket bolts and crankshaft pulley bolt.

Removal

1 Remove the air filter housing as described in Chapter 4A Section 3.
2 Remove the inlet and outlet pipes from the turbocharger (see illustration 3.6).
3 Remove the timing belt upper cover, with reference to Section 6.
4 Jack up and support the front of the vehicle (see Jacking and support 13). Remove the wheel and then the lower section of the right-hand wing liner.
5 Slacken the crankshaft pulley bolt as described in Section 5. Do not remove the bolt at this stage.
6 Turn the crankshaft to position No 1 piston at TDC, as described in Section 3 and install the timing tools.
7 Remove the crankshaft pulley, with reference to Section 5. Before finally removing the pulley, check that No 1 piston is still positioned at TDC (Section 5).
8 Remove the timing belt lower cover as described in Section 6.
9 Using a block of wood (to spread the load) place a jack under the engine sump and support the engine. Unbolt the right-hand engine mounting from the engine bracket and inner wing (see illustration).

7.10 Remove the tensioner

7.11 Remove the upper bolt and pivot the alternator away from the engine bracket

7.12a Unbolt the coolant hose

10 Unbolt and remove the auxiliary drivebelt tensioner **(see illustration)**.
11 Slacken the lower alternator mounting bolt, remove the upper bolt and then pivot the alternator away from the engine bracket **(see illustration)**.
12 Unbolt and remove the engine bracket from the engine block – 3 bolts. Lower the bracket from the engine, raising and lowering the engine on the jack as required to allow the bracket to pass down and out of the engine bay **(see illustrations)**.
13 Using an adjustable peg spanner (or the factory tool T10172) counterhold the inlet sprocket and remove the blanking plug. Next slacken (but do not remove) the sprocket retaining bolt **(see illustrations)**. On models with VVT on the exhaust camshaft, remove the cover (5 bolts). On all engines (whilst counterholding the sprocket), slacken (but do

not remove) the exhaust camshaft sprocket retaining bolt.
14 If the timing belt is to be refitted, mark its running direction.
15 Loosen the timing belt tensioner securing nut to release the tensioner. Push back the tensioner and tighten the locking nut. Remove the timing belt from the sprockets.
16 If further work is anticipated, turn the crankshaft a quarter-turn (90°) anti-clockwise to position Nos 1 and 4 pistons slightly down their bores from the TDC position. This will eliminate any risk of piston-to-valve contact if the crankshaft or camshaft is turned whilst the timing belt is removed.

Refitting

17 Although not mandatory the fitting of a new tensioner and idler is highly recommended. If they are not to be replaced,

they should be turned by hand and checked for play and abnormal noise.
18 Fit the new tensioner, checking that the tab on the rear fits into the slot on the cylinder head **(see illustration)**. Fit a new idler pulley.
19 Check that the camshaft locking tool is correctly fitted. If the crankshaft was lowered, then turn the crankshaft a quarter-turn (90°) clockwise to reposition the engine at TDC (the TDC timing pin should be in place).
20 Fit new bolts to the camshaft sprockets and tighten the bolts, so that the sprockets rotate freely without any play.
21 Remove the crankshaft sprocket and clean the mounting surface. Refit the sprocket.
22 Fit the timing belt around the crankshaft sprocket, the idler, the tensioner and the camshaft sprockets **(see illustration)**.

7.12b Lower the bracket out of the engine bay

7.13a Remove the blanking plug…

7.13b …and then slacken the sprocket bolt

7.13c Repeat the procedure on the exhaust camshaft sprocket (non VVT engine shown)

7.18 The tang on the tensioner must engage correctly in the cylinder head

7.22 Fit the new belt

23 The timing belt must now be tensioned as follows.

24 Using a 30 mm spanner turn the tensioner so that the indicator is 10 mm to the right of the adjustment window. Next turn the tensioner back, so that it lies in the middle of the adjustment window **(see illustrations)**.

25 Hold the tensioner in this position and tighten the locking nut to the specified torque.

26 Using the peg spanner to counterhold the camshaft sprockets, tighten the new bolts to 50 Nm.

27 Remove the timing tools from the crankshaft and the camshafts.

28 Fit the lower timing belt cover and tighten the bolts.

29 Clean the mounting surface of both the crankshaft pulley and the crankshaft sprocket. Fit the crankshaft sprocket with the new bolt and tighten the bolt using the counterhold tool and socket to the specified torque.

30 Turn the crankshaft two revolutions in the normal direction of rotation and refit the timing tools as described in Section 3. Slightly depressing the new belt between the camshaft sprockets is is permissible if the camshaft locking tool does not fit easily. If the tool does not fit the timing is incorrect and the installation procedure must be repeated.

31 Using the counterhold, tighten the camshaft sprockets to the second stage of the tightening procedure. Note that the final angle tightening is different for the inlet and exhaust camshafts on engines with VVT on the inlet only.

32 Fit a new blanking plug and seal to the inlet camshaft. On models with VVT on the exhaust camshaft, fit new bolts (and seal) to the cover and tighten the bolts to the specified torque.

33 Refit the engine bracket, alternator bolts and the engine mounting.

34 Fit the remaining components in reverse order to removal.

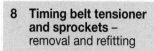

8 Timing belt tensioner and sprockets – removal and refitting

Camshaft sprockets

Removal

1 Remove the timing belt as described in Section 7.

2 The camshaft must be held stationary as the sprocket bolt is slackened. This can be achieved by making up a tool, and using it to hold the sprocket stationary by means of the holes in the sprocket face. The tool fits easily into the exhaust camshaft sprocket on engines that only have VVT on the inlet camshaft. On the inlet camshaft (and the exhaust camshaft on models with VVT on both camshafts) the only location points are shallow holes in the face of the VVT hubs. A factory tool is available to overcome this problem (T10172) but is also possible to

7.24a Over tighten the tensioner by 10 mm…

7.24b …and then adjust the tensioner to the correct central position

fabricate a similar tool **(see illustrations)**. If a home made tool is used an assistant will be required to keep the tool locked in place, whilst the bolt is slackened.

3 Unscrew the sprocket bolt and withdraw it, then withdraw the sprocket from the end of the camshaft **(see illustrations)**.

4 Repeat the procedure for the other sprocket. Discard the bolts as new ones must be used.

Refitting

5 Prior to refitting, check the camshaft oil seals for signs of leakage, and if necessary renew the seal as described in Section 11.

6 Follow the timing belt replacement procedure as described in Section 7 and then tighten the sprocket bolt to the specified torque. Prevent the sprocket from turning using the method

used on removal. Note that there are different angle settings depending on the engine code (see the Specifications of this Chapter).

Crankshaft sprocket

Removal

7 Remove the crankshaft pulley (Section 5) and the timing belt as described in Section 7.

8 Slide the crankshaft sprocket off the crankshaft.

Refitting

⚠ **Warning: Do not turn the crankshaft, as the pistons may hit the valves.**

9 Clean both surfaces of the sprocket and refit it.

10 Refit the timing belt as described in Section 7.

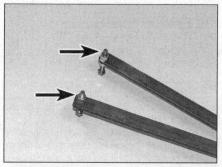
8.2a Adjust the depth of the bolts and file them as required to ensure a snug fit

8.2b Use the tool to counterhold the sprocket

8.3a Remove the bolt and…

8.3b …remove the sprocket

8.15 The tang must engage with the cylinder head

8.19 Remove the idler

10.3 Lift out the tappets and rocker fingers

11 Clean the front surface of the sprocket again and the rear surface of the crankshaft pulley. Due to the unique design of the sprocket and crankshaft pulley it is essential that both mounting surfaces are thoroughly cleaned before installation.

12 Refit the remaining components in reverse order.

Tensioner assembly

Removal

13 Remove the timing belt as described in Section 7.

14 Unscrew the bolt and then withdraw the tensioner assembly from the engine.

Refitting

15 Offer the tensioner assembly into position over the mounting stud, ensuring that the tang on the tensioner backplate engages with the corresponding cut-out in the cylinder head **(see illustration)**.

16 Refit the bolt, but do not fully tighten the nut at this stage.

17 Refit and tension the timing belt as described in Section 7.

Idler pulley

Removal

18 Remove the timing belt as described in Section 7.

19 Slacken the bolt and remove the tensioner as a complete assembly **(see illustration)**. Note that on some models the bolt is held captive in the idler by an O-ring seal.

Refitting

20 Refitting is a reversal of removal.

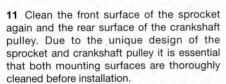

9 Camshafts – inspection

Note: *Due to the method of construction, the camshafts can not be removed from the camshaft housing. The camshafts are removed with the camshaft housing as described in Section 4.*

Inspection

1 Visually inspect the camshaft for evidence of wear on the surfaces of the lobes and journals. Normally their surfaces should be smooth and have a dull shine; look for scoring, erosion or pitting and areas that appear highly polished, indicating excessive wear. Accelerated wear will occur once the hardened exterior of the camshaft has been damaged, so always renew worn items. **Note:** *If these symptoms are visible on the tips of the camshaft lobes, check the corresponding tappet/rocker finger, as it may be worn as well.*

2 If the machined surfaces of the camshaft appear discoloured or blued, it is likely that it has been overheated at some point, probably due to inadequate lubrication.

3 If there are any faults found with the camshafts the complete camshaft housing assembly must be replaced.

10 Hydraulic tappets/roller rocker fingers – removal, inspection and refitting

Removal

1 Remove the camshaft housing, as described in Section 4.

2 As the components are removed, keep them in strict order, so that they can be refitted in their original locations. Accelerated wear leading to early failure will result if the tappets and rocker fingers are interchanged.

3 Note the fitted position, then lift out the rocker finger complete with the hydraulic tappets **(see illustration)**.

4 Carefully unclip the tappets from the rocker fingers. It is advisable to store the tappets (in the correct order) upright in an oil bath whilst they are removed from the engine. Make a note of the position of each tappet, as they must be refitted in their original locations on reassembly.

Inspection

5 Check the cylinder head bore contact surfaces and the hydraulic tappets for signs of scoring or damage. Also, check that the oil holes in the tappets are free from obstructions.

If significant scoring or damage is found, it may be necessary to renew the cylinder head and the complete set of tappets.

6 Check the valve, tappet and camshaft contact faces of the rockers for wear or damage, and also check the rockers for any signs of cracking. Renew any worn or damaged rockers.

7 Inspect the camshaft, as described in Section 9.

Refitting

8 Smear some clean engine oil onto the sides of the hydraulic tappets, and offer them into position in their original bores in the cylinder head. Push them down until they are seated correctly and lubricate the upper surface of the tappet.

9 Oil the rocker contact faces of the tappets, and the tops of the valve stems, then refit the rockers to their original locations, ensuring that the rockers are securely clipped onto the tappets.

10 Lubricate the camshaft lobe contact surfaces and refit the camshaft housing as described in Section 4.

11 Camshaft oil seals – renewal

Note: *The oil seals are a PTFE (Teflon) type and are fitted dry, without using any grease or oil. These have a wider sealing lip and have been introduced instead of the coil spring type oil seal.*

1 Remove the timing belt as described in Section 7.

2 Remove the camshaft sprocket as described in Section 8. Note that there is also a seal behind the coolant pump sprocket. This is replaced using the same method as for the camshaft oil seals.

3 Drill two small holes into the existing oil seal, diagonally opposite each other. Take great care to avoid drilling through into the seal housing or camshaft sealing surface. Thread two self-tapping screws into the holes and, using a pair of pliers, pull on the heads of the screws to extract the oil seal.

4 Alternatively (and where possible) protect

11.4 Lever out the seal

11.6 Fit the new seal

11.7 Drive the seal home with a suitable socket

the cylinder head and lever out the seal **(see illustration)**.

5 Clean out the seal housing and the sealing surface of the camshaft by wiping it with a lint-free cloth. Remove any swarf or burrs that may cause the seal to leak.

6 Carefully push the seal over the camshaft until it is positioned above its housing **(see illustration)**.

7 Using a hammer and a socket of suitable diameter, drive the seal squarely into its housing **(see illustration)**. **Note:** *Select a socket that bears only on the hard outer surface of the seal, not the inner lip which can easily be damaged. Remove the adhesive tape from the end of the camshaft after the seal has been located correctly.*

8 Refit the camshaft sprocket with reference to Section 8.

9 Refit and tension the timing belt as described in Section 7.

12 Cylinder head – removal, inspection and refitting

Note: *The cylinder head must be removed with the engine cold. New cylinder head bolts and a new cylinder head gasket will be required on refitting.*

Removal

1 Disconnect the battery as described in Chapter 5A Section 3.

2 Drain the cooling system as described in Chapter 1B Section 33 and then remove the coolant hoses from the coolant pump.

3 Remove the timing belt from the camshaft sprockets as described in Section 7. There is no need to completely remove the belt at this point, so the engine mounting bracket can be left in place.

4 Remove the camshaft housing as described in Section 4 and then remove the hydraulic tappets and rocker fingers. Store them in the correct cylinder order.

5 Remove the inlet manifold as described in Chapter 4A Section 8.

6 Disconnect the wiring plugs from the fuel injectors, the fuel pressure sensor and the oil pressure sensor. If the cylinder head is

to reworked, then remove the fuel rail and injectors at this point. Alternatively remove the cylinder head complete with the fuel rail and fuel pump.

7 Jack up and support the front of the vehicle (see *Jacking and vehicle support*).

8 Remove the heat shield from above the right-hand driveshaft **(see illustration)**.

9 Release the clamp from the catalytic converter, remove the converter support bracket and seperate the convertor from the turbocharger. Secure the converter to the bulkhead with cable ties.

10 Anticipating some oil spillage, disconnect the oil supply and oil return pipes from the turbocharger.

11 Disconnect the wiring plugs from the turbocharger control module and from the coolant temperature sensor.

12 Remove the upper rear bolt from the engine support bracket. Support the engine on a jack (using a block of wood to spread the load) and remove the engine mounting to improve access. Refit the mounting after the bolt is removed. Remove the jack from the sump.

13 Progressively slacken the cylinder head bolts, by one turn at a time, in the reverse order to that shown **(see illustration 12.28)**. Remove the cylinder head bolts and dispose of them – new bolts must be fitted.

14 With all the bolts removed, lift the cylinder head from the block, together with the turbocharger. If the cylinder head is stuck, tap it with a soft-faced mallet to break the joint. Do not insert a lever into the gasket joint.

15 Lift the cylinder head gasket from the block.

Inspection

16 Dismantling and inspection of the cylinder head is covered in Chapter 2D Section 6.

Refitting

17 The mating faces of the cylinder head and block must be perfectly clean before refitting the head.

18 Use a scraper to remove all traces of gasket and carbon, also clean the tops of the pistons. Take particular care with the aluminium surfaces, as the soft metal is easily damaged.

19 Make sure that debris is not allowed to enter the oil and water passages – this is particularly important for the oil circuit, as carbon could block the oil supply to the camshaft and crankshaft bearings. Using adhesive tape and paper, seal the water, oil and bolt holes in the cylinder block. To prevent carbon entering the gap between the pistons and bores, smear a little grease in the gap. After cleaning a piston, rotate the crankshaft so that the piston moves down the bore, then wipe out the grease and carbon with a cloth rag. Clean the other piston crowns in the same way.

20 Check the head and block for nicks, deep scratches and other damage. If slight, they may be removed carefully with a file. More serious damage may be repaired by machining, but this is a specialist job.

21 If warpage of the cylinder head is suspected, use a straight-edge to check it for distortion, as described in Part D of this Chapter.

22 Ensure that the cylinder head bolt holes in the crankcase are clean and free of oil. Syringe or soak up any oil left in the bolt holes. This is most important in order that the correct bolt tightening torque can be applied, and to prevent the possibility of the block being cracked by hydraulic pressure when the bolts are tightened.

23 Ensure that the crankshaft has been turned to position Nos 1 and 4 pistons slightly down their bores from the TDC position (refer to timing belt refitting in Section 7). This will

12.8 Remove the heat shield

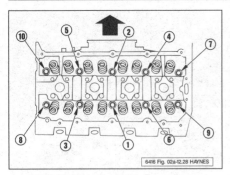

12.28 Tighten the bolts in sequence

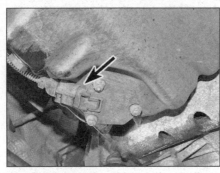

13.4 Disconnect the wiring connector from the oil level/temperature sender

eliminate any risk of piston-to-valve contact as the cylinder head is refitted.

24 Where applicable, refit the turbocharger to the cylinder head with reference to Chapter 4C Section 4.

25 Ensure that the cylinder head locating dowels are in place in the cylinder block, then fit a new cylinder head gasket over the dowels, ensuring that the part number is uppermost. Where applicable, the OBEN/TOP marking should also be uppermost. Note that VW recommend that the gasket is only removed from its packaging immediately prior to fitting.

26 Lower the cylinder head into position on the gasket, ensuring that it engages correctly over the dowels.

27 Fit the new cylinder head bolts, and screw them in as far as possible by hand.

28 Working progressively, in sequence, tighten all the cylinder head bolts to the specified Stage 1 torque **(see illustration)**.

29 Again working progressively, in sequence, tighten all the cylinder head bolts through the specified Stage 2 angle.

30 Tighten all the cylinder head bolts through the specified Stage 3 angle.

31 Finally, tighten all the cylinder head bolts, in sequence, through the specified Stage 4

angle.

32 Refit the camshaft housing as described in Section 4.

33 Refit and tension the timing belt as described in Section 7. The replacement of the timing belt is highly recommended.

34 Refit the auxiliary drivebelt as described in Chapter 1A Section 30.

35 If the fuel pump was removed, install the cam follower (tappet), fit a new O-ring seal and then refit the pump using new bolts (Chapter 4A Section 4).

36 If the fuel rail and injectors have been removed, fit new seals to the injectors (Chapter 4A Section 4) and then refit the the fuel rail

37 Refit the inlet manifold as described in Chapter 4A Section 8.

38 Fill the turbocharger with fresh oil though the oil supply pipe. Reconnect the turbocharger supply pipe and return line using new seals.

39 Reconnect the catalytic converter using a new gasket and clamp (Chapter 4C Section 6).

40 Refit the spark plugs and ignition coils.

41 Reconnect all wiring plugs. Secure the loom to the retaining clips and brackets.

42 Refill the cooling system as described in Chapter 1A Section 33.

13 Sump – removal and refitting

Note: *VAG sealant (D 176 404 A2 or equivalent) will be required to seal the sump on refitting.*

Removal

1 Apply the handbrake, then jack up the front of the vehicle and support securely on axle stands (see *Jacking and vehicle support*).

2 Remove the securing screws and withdraw the engine undertray(s).

3 Drain the engine oil and remove the oil filter as described in Chapter 1A Section 6.

4 Disconnect the wiring connector from the oil level/temperature sender in the sump **(see illustration)**.

5 Unscrew and remove the bolts securing the sump to the cylinder block/upper sump. On 1.2 litre engines remove the bolts securing the sump to the bell housing. The sump is bonded to the engine block with a liquid gasket (or upper sump on 1.4 litre engines). Removal can be difficult due to the adhesive nature of the sealant, especially on models with a pressed steel sump.

6 On 1.2 litre engines a levering point is provided at the rear of the engine block and this should be used to partially release the sump. On 1.4 litre engines the sump must be carefully levered down at the transmission end **(see illustrations)**. As soon as comes free at any point a sharp knife can be used to further release the sealant. VW list a special knife tool (T10561) for this purpose.

Refitting

7 Begin refitting by thoroughly cleaning the mating faces of the sump and cylinder block. Ensure that all traces of old sealant are removed.

13.6a Gently prise the sump free...

13.6b ...and then lower it from the engine

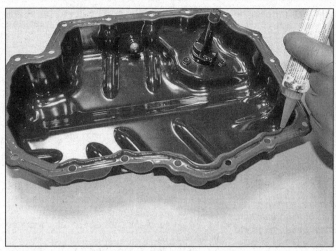

13.8 Apply the sealant around the inside of the bolt holes (1.4 litre engine shown)

13.9a Fit guide studs to the engine

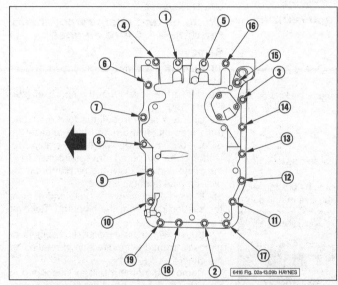

13.9b Tighten the bolts in sequence (1.2 litre engines)

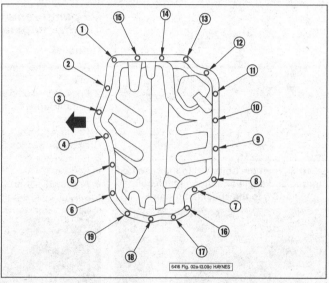

13.9c Tighten the bolts in sequence (1.4 litre engines)

8 Ensure that the cylinder block mating face of the sump is free from all traces of old sealant, oil and grease, and then apply a 2.0 to 3.0 mm thick bead of silicone sealant (VAG D 176 404 A2 or equivalent) to the sump (see illustration). Note that the sealant should be run around the inside of the bolt holes in the sump. The sump must be fitted within 5 minutes of applying the sealant.

9 Fit guide studs to the to the opposite corners of the and then offer the sump up to the block (or lower sump on 1.4 litre engines). Fit the bolts, noting that new bolts should be used on 1.2 litre engines and tighten the bolts in sequence until contact is made (see illustrations). Fully tighten the bolts to the specified torque and on 1.2 litre engines tighten the bolts to the second stage angle setting.

10 On 1.2 litre engines, refit the sump to bell housing bolts, and tighten them to the specified torque.

11 Refit the wiring connector to the oil level/temperature sender, then refit the engine undertray(s), and lower the vehicle to the ground.

12 Allow at least 30 minutes from the time of refitting the sump for the sealant to dry, then refill the engine with oil, with reference to Chapter 1A Section 6.

Upper sump – 1.4 litre engines

Removal

13 Remove the AC compressor from the mounting bracket as described in Chapter 3 Section 12. Do not disconnect the refrigerant lines.

14 Remove the lower sump as described above.

15 Remove the oil pump as described in Section 14.

16 Remove the upper sump to bell housing bolts.

17 Loosen the upper sump bolts in the

reverse order (19 to 1) to that shown (see illustration 13.21).

18 The upper sump is secured in place with a liquid gasket the same as the main sump. Carefully lever the upper sump from the engine block without damaging the face of the sump or the engine block. Remove the oil baffle.

Refitting

19 Ensure that the cylinder block mating face of the upper sump is free from all traces of old sealant, oil and grease, and then apply a 2.0 mm thick bead of silicone sealant (VAG D 176 404 A2 or equivalent) to the upper sump. Note that the sealant should be run around the inside of the bolt holes in the upper sump. The upper sump must be fitted within 5 minutes of applying the sealant.

20 Check that the dowel pin is correctly located and then refit the baffle plate.

21 Fit the upper sump and tighten the new

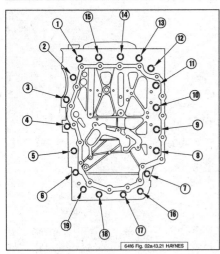

13.21 Tighten the bolts in the specified sequence

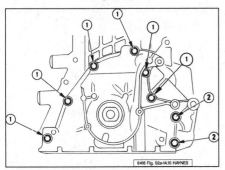

14.10 Tighten the bolts 1-6 to the specified torque and angle and then tighten bolts 7 and 8 to the specified torque

14.14 Remove the cover

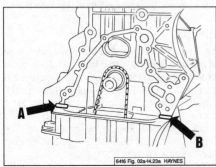

14.23a Apply a thin bead of sealant to the areas shown (A and B)

bolts in sequence **(see illustration)** to the specified torque.

22 Fit the upper sump to transmission bolts and tighten to the specified torque.

23 Refit the oil pump and lower (main) sump. Wait a minimum of 30 minutes and refill the engine oil.

24 Refit the remaining components in the reverse order of removal.

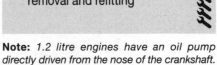

14 Oil pump – removal and refitting

Note: *1.2 litre engines have an oil pump directly driven from the nose of the crankshaft. 1.4 litre engines have a chain driven oil pump bolted to the upper sump.*

Note: *Individual parts are not available for the oil pumps. If they are worn or faulty they must be replaced as a complete assembly.*

Oil pump removal and refitting – 1.2 litre engines

Removal

1 Remove the timing belt as described in Section 7.

2 Remove the sump as described in Section 13.

3 Unbolt and remove the auxiliary belt tensioner.

4 Remove the alternator as described in Chapter 5A Section 5.

5 Remove the crankshaft oil seal as described in Section 16.

6 Anticipate some oil spillage by placing shop towels below the pump. Remove the oil pump

14.15 Remove the bolts

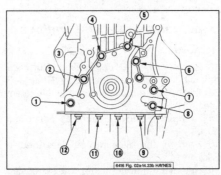

14.23b Tighten the bolts in sequence, noting that bolts 7 and 8 have a higher torque value

mounting bolts and pull the oil pump off the dowel pins. Slide the pump off the crankshaft nose and remove it.

7 Remove the gasket.

Refitting

8 Clean and inspect the mounting surface and then fit a new gasket. Locate the gasket over the dowel pins.

9 Rotate the pump, so that the notches in the pump drive are aligned with the slots in the crankshaft nose.

10 Fit the pump and secure it in place with new bolts.Tighten the bolts in the correct order to the specified torque. Note that the upper bolts have a torque and angle setting and must be replaced **(see illustration)**.

11 Fit a new crankshaft oil seal as described in Section 16.

12 Install the sump (Section 13) and the alternator (Chapter 5A Section 5) and then fit the remaining components in the reverse order to removal.

Oil pump and chain removal and refitting – 1.4 litre engines

Removal

13 Remove the sump as described in Section 13.

14 Unclip the cover from the sprocket **(see illustration)**.

15 Unscrew and remove the four mounting bolts **(see illustration)** and then release the oil pump from the dowels in the crankcase. Unhook the oil pump drive sprocket from the chain and withdraw the oil pump and oil pick-up pipe from the engine.

16 If desired, unscrew the bolts and remove the suction pipe from the oil pump. Recover the O-ring seal.

17 If the drive chain requires replacement or removal, first mark the direction of rotation on the chain.

18 Remove the timing belt as described in Section 7 and then unbolt the AC compressor and secure it to the side as described in Chapter 3 Section 12. Do not disconnect the refrigerant lines.

19 Remove the crankshaft pulley for the timing chain and then unbolt and remove the oil seal housing complete with the crankshaft oil seal.

20 Unhook the chain from the crankshaft sprocket – note that the the sprocket is not removable.

Refitting

21 If the drive chain was removed, then fit a new chain and then refit the oil pump with a new seal. Tighten the bolts to the specified torque.

22 Refit the sump as described in Section 13.

23 When refitting the crankshaft oil seal housing, apply liquid gasket as shown and then apply a thin bead to the upper sump flange. Note that it is not possible to apply a 2 mm bead as the crankshaft and the dowel pins on the engine block do not allow the housing to be dropped into position. It must slide up to the block. Tighten the new bolts to the specified torque **(see illustrations)**.

Fit a new crankshaft oil seal as described in Section 16.

24 Refit the remaining components in the reverse order of removal.

15 Flywheel – removal, inspection and refitting

Note: *New flywheel securing bolts will be required on refitting.*

Removal

1 Remove the gearbox (see Chapter 7A Section 3 or Chapter 7B Section 2) and where fitted the clutch (Chapter 6A Section 5).
2 The flywheel bolts are offset to ensure correct fitment. Unscrew the bolts while holding the flywheel stationary. Temporarily insert a bolt in the cylinder block, and use a screwdriver to hold the flywheel or make up a holding tool **(see illustrations)**.
3 Lift the flywheel from the crankshaft **(see illustration)**.

Inspection

4 Check the flywheel for wear and damage. Examine the starter ring gear for excessive wear to the teeth. If any wear is found the complete flywheel must be replaced. If the clutch friction face is discoloured or scored excessively, it may be possible to regrind it, but this work should also be entrusted to an automotive machine shop.
5 Where a dual mass flywheel is fitted

the following guidelines may help decide if replacement is required. If in doubt, a professional inspection is recommended. The dual-mass flywheel should be checked as follows:

Warpage

6 Place a straight edge across the face of the drive surface, and check by trying to insert a feeler gauge between the straight edge and the drive surface **(see illustration)**. The flywheel will normally warp like a bowl – ie. Higher on the outer edge. If the warpage is more than 0.40 mm, the flywheel may need replacing.

Free rotational movement

7 This is the distance the drive surface of the flywheel can be turned independently of the flywheel primary element, using finger effort alone. Move the drive surface in one direction and make a mark where the locating pin aligns with the flywheel edge. Move the drive surface in the other direction (finger pressure only) and make another mark **(see illustration)**. The total of free movement should not exceed 20.0 mm. If it's more, the flywheel may need replacing.

Total rotational movement

8 This is the total distance the drive surface can be turned independently of the flywheel primary element. Insert two bolts into the clutch pressure plate/damper unit mounting holes, and with the crankshaft/flywheel held stationary, use a lever/pry bar between the

bolts and use some effort to move the drive surface fully in one direction – make a mark where the locating pin aligns with the flywheel edge. Now force the drive surface fully in the opposite direction, and make another mark. The total rotational movement should not exceed 44.00 mm. If it does, have the flywheel professionally inspected.

Lateral movement

9 The lateral movement (up and down) of the drive surface in relation to the primary element of the flywheel, should not exceed 2.0 mm. If it does, the flywheel may need replacing. This can be checked by pressing the drive surface down on one side into the flywheel (flywheel horizontal) and making an alignment mark between the drive surface and the inner edge of the primary element. Now press down on the opposite side of the drive surface, and make another mark above the original one. The difference between the two marks is the lateral movement **(see illustration)**.
10 There should be no cracks in the drive surface of the flywheel. If cracks are evident, the flywheel will need replacing.

Refitting

11 Refitting is a reversal of removal, bearing in mind the following points.
a) *Ensure that the engine to transmission plate is in place before fitting the flywheel.*
b) *Use new bolts when refitting the flywheel and coat the threads of the bolts with locking fluid before inserting them. Tighten the securing bolts to the specified torque.*

15.2a Tool used to hold the flywheel stationary

15.2b Unscrew the securing bolts…

15.3 …and remove the flywheel

15.6 Flywheel warpage check – see text

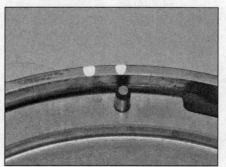

15.7 Flywheel free rotational movement check alignment marks – see text

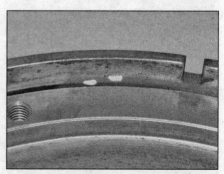

15.9 Flywheel lateral movement check marks – see text

16 Crankshaft oil seals – renewal

Note: *The oil seals are a PTFE (Teflon) type and are fitted dry, without using any grease or oil. These have a wider sealing lip and have been introduced instead of the coil spring type oil seal.*

Timing belt end oil seal

Note: *If the oil seal housing/oil pump is removed, VAG sealant (D 176 404 A2, or equivalent) will be required to seal the housing on refitting.*

1 Remove the timing belt as described in Section 7, and the crankshaft sprocket with reference to Section 8.

2 To remove the seal without removing the housing Or oil pump on 1.2 litre engines), drill two small holes diagonally opposite each other, insert self-tapping screws, and pull on the heads of the screws with pliers.

3 If the oil pump (1.2 litre engines) or the housing (1.4 litre engines) has been removed the new seal can be fitted on the bench, before refitting the oil pump or housing.

4 Thoroughly clean the oil seal seating in the housing or oil pump.

5 Wind a length of tape around the end of the crankshaft to protect the oil seal lips as the seal is fitted.

6 Fit a new oil seal to the housing, pressing or driving it into position using a socket or tube of suitable diameter. Ensure that the socket or tube bears only on the hard outer ring of the seal, and take care not to damage the seal lips. Press or drive the seal into position until it is seated on the shoulder in the housing. Make sure that the closed end of the seal is facing outwards.

Flywheel end oil seal

Note: *In these engines, the seal, sealing flange and sender wheel are a complete unit. Special*

16.7a Remove the intermediate plate from the dowels …

16.7b … and from behind the top of the crankshaft seal housing

16.8a Undo the crankshaft speed sensor retaining bolt

16.8b Sealing flange bolts

tools are required to refit the sealing flange, and press the sender wheel onto the end of the crankshaft. It is not possible to accurately fit these parts without the tools, which may be available from VAG (part no. T10134) and are available from aftermarket automotive tool specialists. E.g. Draper tools).

7 Remove the flywheel as described in Section 15, then prise the intermediate plate from the locating dowels on the cylinder block and unhook it from behind the top of the seal housing **(see illustrations)**.

8 Undo the bolt securing the crankshaft speed sensor and remove it from the seal housing,

then undo the bolts securing the sealing flange to the cylinder block **(see illustrations)**.

9 Insert three 6 x 35 mm bolts into the threaded holes in the sealing flange. Tighten the bolts gradually and evenly, and press the sealing flange, and sender wheel from the crankshaft/cylinder block **(see illustrations)**. The seal, sender wheel and sealing flange are supplied as a complete unit.

10 Ensure the mating face of the cylinder block is clean and free from debris. The new sealing flange/seal/sender wheel assembly is supplied with a sealing lip support ring, which serves as a fitting sleeve, and must not

16.9a Screw in three 6 x 35 mm bolts …

16.9b …and draw the sealing flange and sender wheel from place

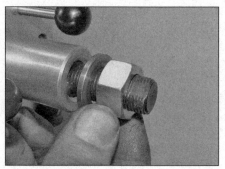

16.11a Rotate the nut until its level with the end of the flat clamping surface...

16.11b ...then clamp it in a vice

16.12a Rotate the nut until the inner part of the tool ...

be removed prior to installation. Equally, the sender wheel must not be separated from the assembly.

11 If using the VW tool, proceed as follows. If using an aftermarket tool specialist's product, follow the instructions supplied with the tool. Rotate the large spindle nut until it's level with the end of the clamping surface of the spindle, then clamp the spindle in a vice **(see illustrations)**.

12 Press the tool housing downwards until it rests on the nut and washer. Rotate the nut until the inner part of the tool is at the same height as the housing **(see illustrations)**.

13 Remove the seal securing clip. The hole on the sender wheel must align with the marking on the sealing flange **(see illustrations)**.

14 Place the flange outer side down on a clean, flat surface, then press the seal guide fitting sleeve (supplied ready fitted), housing, and sender wheel downwards until all the components are flat on the surface. In this position the upper edge of the sender wheel should be level with the edge of the sealing flange **(see illustrations)**.

15 Place the sealing flange on the assembly tool, so the pin locates in the hole in the sender wheel **(see illustration)**.

16 Push the sealing flange and guide fitting sleeve against the tool whilst tightening the 3 knurled screws. Ensure the pin is still located in the sender wheel **(see illustration)**.

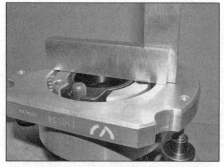

16.12b ...is flush with the flat surface of the housing

16.13a Remove the securing clip ...

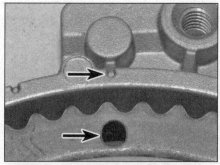

16.13b ...the hole in the sender wheel should align with the marking on the flange

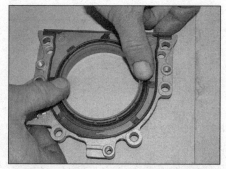

16.14a Press the assembly downwards on a clean, flat surface...

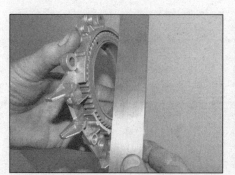

16.14b ...so the upper edge of the sender wheel is level with the edge of the flange

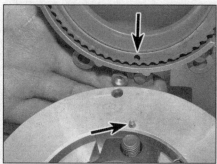

16.15 Fit the flange to the tool, ensuring the pin locates in the hole

16.16 With the pin engaged in the hole, tighten the 3 knurled screws to secure the flange to the tool

16.18a Unscrew the nut to the end of the thread ...

16.18b ...and push the spindle in as far as possible

16.19 Hand-tighten the hex bolts to secure the tool to the crankshaft

17 Ensure the end of the crankshaft is clean, and is locked at TDC on No. 1 cylinder as described in Section 3.

18 Unscrew the large nut to the end of the spindle threads, then press the spindle inwards as far as possible **(see illustrations)**.

19 Align the flat side of the assembly with the sump flange, then secure the tool to the crankshaft using the integral Allen bolts **(see illustration)**. Only hand tighten the bolts.

20 Insert two M7x 35 mm bolts to guide the sealing flange to the cylinder block **(see illustration)**.

21 Using hand pressure alone, push the tool assembly onto the crankshaft until the seal guide fitting sleeve contacts the crankshaft flange, then push the guide pin (black knob) into the hole in the crankshaft. This is to ensure the sender wheel reaches its correct installation position **(see illustration)**.

22 Rotate the large nut until it makes contact with the tool housing, then tighten it to 35 Nm. After tightening this nut, a small air gap must still be present between the sealing flange and cylinder block **(see illustrations)**.

23 Unscrew the large nut; the two M7 x 35 Nm screws, the three knurled screws and the Allen bolts securing the tool to the crankshaft. Remove the tool, and pull the seal guide fitting sleeve from place (if it didn't come out with the tool) **(see illustration)**.

24 Use a vernier caliper or feeler gauge to measure the fitted depth of the sender wheel in relation to the crankshaft flange **(see illustration)**. The correct depth is 0.5 mm.

25 If the gap is correct, fit the sealing flange bolts and tighten them to the specified torque.

26 If the gap is too small, re-attach the tool to the sealing flange and crankshaft, then refit the two M7 x 35 mm guide bolts to the flange. Tighten the large spindle nut to 40 Nm, remove the tool and re-measure the air gap. If the gap is still too small, re-attach the tool and tighten the spindle nut to 45 Nm. Re-measure the gap. When the gap is correct, refit the flange retaining bolts, and tighten them to the specified torque.

27 The remainder of refitting is a reversal of removal.

16.20 Use two M7 x 35 mm bolts to guide the sealing flange

16.21 Push the black knob into the hole in the crankshaft

16.22a After tightening the spindle nut to 35 Nm ...

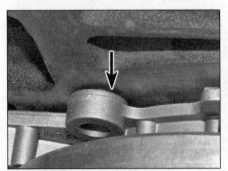

16.22b ...there should be an air gap between the sealing flange and the cylinder block

16.23 Remove the tool and seal fitting guide sleeve

16.24 Measure the fitted depth of the sender wheel in relation to the end of the crankshaft

17.7 Disconnect the level sensor wiring plug

17.8 Unclip the reservoir and move it to the side

17.9a Remove the bolts…

17 Engine mountings – inspection and renewal

Inspection

1 If improved access is required, jack up the front of the vehicle, and support it securely on axle stands (see *Jacking and vehicle support*). Remove the engine undertray(s).
2 Check the mounting rubbers to see if they are cracked, hardened or separated from the metal at any point; renew the mounting if any such damage or deterioration is evident.
3 Check that all the mountings are securely tightened; use a torque wrench to check if possible.
4 Using a large screwdriver or a crowbar, check for wear in the mounting by carefully levering against it to check for free play. Where this is not possible, enlist the aid of an assistant to move the engine/transmission back-and-forth, or from side-to-side, whilst you observe the mounting. While some free play is to be expected, even from new components, excessive wear should be obvious. If excessive free play is found, check first that the fasteners are correctly secured, then renew any worn components as described in the following paragraphs.

Renewal

Right-hand mounting

5 Support the engine on a trolley jack under the sump. Use a block of wood between the

17.9b …and then lift out the mounting

sump and the head of the jack, to prevent any damage to the sump.
6 Unclip the fuel lines from the coolant reservoir.
7 Disconnect the level sensor wiring plug **(see illustration)**.
8 Unclip the coolant reservoir and move it to one side **(see illustration)**.
9 Unscrew the bolts securing the mounting to the body and then unscrew the bolts securing it to the engine bracket. Withdraw the mounting from the engine compartment **(see illustrations)**.
10 Refitting is a reversal of removal, bearing in mind the following points.
a) Use new securing bolts.
b) Align the mounting as shown **(see illustration)**.
c) Tighten all fixings to the specified torque.

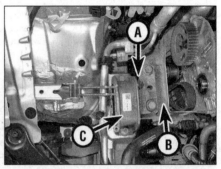

17.10 Align the mounting so that the gap (A) = 10 mm with the bracket (B) parallel to the lower bracket (C)

Left-hand mounting

Note: *New mounting bolts will be required on refitting.*
11 Support the transmission on a trolley jack with a block of wood placed between the head of the jack and the transmission to spread the load.
12 Remove the air filter (Chapter 1A Section 28) and the turbocharger inlet and outlet ducts.
13 Remove the battery and battery tray, as described in Chapter 5A Section 3.
14 On models fitted with a security cover remove the shear bolts and lift off the metal cover. Disconnect the wiring plugs from the ECU. Unclip the ECU from the bracket **(see illustrations)** and remove it from the vehicle.

17.14a Disconnect the wiring plugs

17.14b Remove the ECU

17.14c Bag up the ECU wiring plugs to protect them from contamination

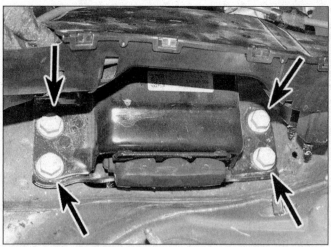

17.15 Lift up the loom to access the mounting bolts

17.16 Remove the bolts

17.17 Remove the bracket from the transmission

17.20 The rear torque arm

15 Unbolt the ECU mounting bracket and then unclip the wiring loom sufficiently to expose the transmission mounting bolts **(see illustration)**.
16 Remove the mounting to body bolts and then remove the bolts securing the mounting to the transmission bracket **(see illustration)**.
17 Lift out the mounting and then where required, unbolt and remove the bracket from the transmission **(see illustration)**. Removal of the bracket is essential for transmission removal.
18 Refitting is a reversal of removal, bearing in mind the following points:
a) Use new mounting bolts.
b) Tighten all fixings to the specified torque.

Rear mounting (torque arm)

19 Apply the handbrake, then jack up the front of the vehicle and support securely on axle stands (see *Jacking and vehicle support*).
20 Working under the vehicle, unscrew and remove the bolt securing the mounting to the subframe **(see illustration)**.

21 Unscrew the two bolts securing the mounting to the transmission, then withdraw the mounting from under the vehicle.
22 Refitting is a reversal of removal, but use new mounting securing bolts, and tighten all fixings to the specified torque.

18 Engine oil cooler – removal and refitting

Removal

1 The oil cooler is mounted at the front of the engine block, hidden by the inlet manifold.
2 Drain the coolant and remove the inlet manifold as described in Chapter 4A Section 8.
3 Anticipating some spillage, remove the bolts **(see illustration)** and lift of the oil cooler. Recover the O-ring seals.

Refitting

4 Refitting is a reversal of removal, bearing in mind the following points:
a) Use new seals.
b) Use new bolts.

19 Oil pressure warning light switch – removal and refitting

Note: *1.2 litre engines have a pressure regulating valve in the oil pump. The valve is not replaceable. Pressure is constantly regulated to 3.5 Bar. 1.4 litre engines have variable oil pressure, adaptable according to engine load and speed.1.2 litre engines have a single oil pressure switch, fitted below the inlet manifold. I.4 litre engines have an additional (2.5 Bar) switch mounted at the rear of the engine and an oil pressure regulating valve mounted low on the rear of the engine block.*

18.3 Remove the bolts

19.1 Oil pressure switch (shown with inlet manifold removed)

Note: *Volkswagen insist that the oil pressure switches must be replaced if removed.*

Removal

1 If replacing the front (0.3 to 0.6 Bar) oil switch, unclip the EVAP control solenoid from the side of the inlet manifold and then disconnect the wiring plug **(see illustration).**
2 Anticipating some oil spillage, unscrew the switch and remove it.
3 Where a rear (2.15 to 2.95 bar) switch is fitted (1.4 litre engines only), jack up and support the front of the vehicle (see *Jacking and vehicle support*).
4 Where required remove the engine undershield and the unbolt the heat shield from above the right-hand driveshaft.
5 Disconnect the wiring and anticipating some oil spillage, unscrew the switch.

Refitting

6 Dispose of the switch – a new one must be fitted.
7 Fit the new switch, complete with the seal, and tighten it to the specified torque.

8 Reconnect the wiring and refit the other components. If raised, lower the vehicle, then check and top-up the engine oil if required.

20 Oil level/temperature sender – removal and refitting

Removal

1 The oil level/temperature sender is fitted to bottom of the sump **(see illustration).**
2 Drain the engine oil as described in Chapter 1A Section 6.
3 Disconnect the wiring connector and wipe clean the area around the sender.
4 Undo the three retaining bolts and remove the sender.

Refitting

5 Examine the sealing washer for signs of damage or deterioration and if necessary renew.

6 Refit the sender and tighten the retaining bolts to the specified torque.
7 Securely reconnect the wiring connector then refill the engine with oil, with reference to Chapter 1A Section 6.
8 On completion, check and, if necessary, top-up the engine oil as described in *Weekly checks*.

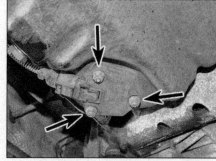

20.1 Oil level/temperature sender – located in the base of the sump

Notes

Chapter 2 Part B
2.0 litre direct injection petrol engine in-car repair procedures

Contents

Section number

Balancer shafts – removal and refitting 7
Camshafts and camshaft cover – removal, inspection and
   refitting 8
Crankshaft oil seals – renewal 9
Crankshaft pulley – removal and refitting. 5
Cylinder compression test 3
Cylinder head – removal and refitting. 10
Engine mountings – inspection and renewal 17
Engine valve timing marks – general information, setting TDC
   and chain checking 2

Section number

Flywheel – removal, inspection and refitting 12
General Information 1
Hydraulic tappets – operational check. 11
Oil cooler – removal and refitting 16
Oil pressure switches and oil control valves –
   general information, removal and refitting 15
Oil pump – removal, inspection and refitting 14
Sump – removal and refitting 13
Timing chain and balancer shaft chain – removal and refitting 6
Timing chain covers – removal and refitting. 4

Degrees of difficulty

Easy, suitable for novice with little experience 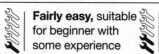	Fairly easy, suitable for beginner with some experience	Fairly difficult, suitable for competent DIY mechanic	Difficult, suitable for experienced DIY mechanic	Very difficult, suitable for expert DIY or professional

Specifications

General

Manufacturer's engine codes*	CHHA, CHHB, CJXE and CXDA
Maximum power output:	
Engine codes CHHA.	169 kW at 4700 to 6200 rpm
Engine code CHHB	162 kW at 4500 to 6200 rpm
Engine codes CJXE	195 kW at 5350 to 6600 rpm
Engine code CXDA	162 kW at 4300 to 6200 rpm
Bore	82.5 mm
Stroke.	92.8 mm
Compression ratio:	
Engine codes CHHA, CHHB and CXDA.	9.6 : 1
Engine code CJXE	9.3 : 1
Compression pressures:	
Minimum compression pressure:	Approximately 7.0 bar
Maximum difference between cylinders.	Approximately 3.0 bar
Firing order	1 – 3 – 4 – 2
No 1 cylinder location.	Timing chain end

*See 'Vehicle identification' at the end of this manual for the location of the engine code markings.

Camshafts

Camshaft endfloat	N/A
Camshaft bearing running clearance	0.24 to 0.06 mm
Camshaft run-out	0.04 mm

Lubrication system

Oil pump type.	Gear type, chain-driven from crankshaft
Oil pressure (oil temperature 80°C):	
At idling.	0.85 to 1.6 bar
At 2000 rpm	1.2 to 1.6 bar

Torque wrench settings

	Nm	lbf ft
Ancillaries bracket to engine block bolts*:		
Stage 1	20	15
Stage 2	Angle-tighten a further 90°	
Auxiliary drivebelt tensioner bolts*:		
Stage 1	8	6
Stage 2	Angle-tighten a further 45°	
Balancer shaft timing chain tensioner bolt	85	63
Balancer shaft chain guide bolts	20	15
Balancer shaft idler gear bolt*:		
Stage 1	10	7
Stage 2	25	18
Stage 3	Angle-tighten a further 90°	
Balancer shaft housing bolts*:		
Stage 1	4	3
Stage 2	Angle-tighten a further 45°	
Balancer shaft idler gear bolt*:		
Stage 1	25	18
Stage 2	Angle-tighten a further 90°	
Big-end bearing caps bolts*:		
Stage 1	45	33
Stage 2	Angle-tighten a further 90°	
Camshaft bearing saddle bolts (steel bolts):		
Stage 1	3	2
Stage 2	9	7
Camshaft bearing saddle (aluminium bolts)*:		
Stage 1	4	3
Stage 2	Angle-tighten a further 180°	
Camshaft cover bolts*:		
Stage 1	8	6
Stage 2	Angle-tighten a further 90°	
Camshaft control valve bolt	9	7
Camshaft position sensor bolt	9	7
Camshaft timing bolts (VVT) bolts**	35	26
Crankcase breather bolts	9	7
Crankshaft oil seal housing bolts (transmission end)	9	7
Crankshaft pulley bolt*:		
Stage 1	150	110
Stage 2	Angle-tighten a further 90°	
Crankshaft sensor pick-up ring bolts*:		
Stage 1	10	7
Stage 2	Angle-tighten a further 90°	
Crankshaft sensor bolt*:		
Stage 1	4	2
Stage 2	Angle-tighten a further 45°	
Cylinder head bolts*:		
Stage 1	40	30
Stage 2	Angle-tighten a further 90°	
Stage 3	Angle-tighten a further 90°	
Cylinder head bolts (timing chain end)*:		
Stage 1	8	6
Stage 2	Angle-tighten a further 90°	
Engine mountings:		
RH engine mounting:		
Mounting to body bolts*:		
Stage 1	40	30
Stage 2	Angle-tighten a further 90°	
Mounting to body horizontal bolt*:		
Stage 1	20	15
Stage 2	Angle-tighten a further 90°	
Mounting to bracket bolts*:		
Stage 1	60	44
Stage 2	Angle-tighten a further 90°	
Bracket to engine bolts*:		
Stage 1	7	5
Stage 2	40	30
Stage 3	Angle-tighten a further 90°	

Torque wrench settings (continued)

	Nm	lbf ft
Engine mountings: (continued)		
LH engine mounting:		
Mounting to body:		
Stage 1	50	37
Stage 2	Angle-tighten a further 90°	
Mounting to bracket*:		
Stage 1	60	44
Stage 2	Angle-tighten a further 90°	
Bracket to transmission*:		
Stage 1	60	44
Stage 2	Angle-tighten a further 90°	
Rear mounting link:		
To transmission*:		
Stage 1	50	37
Stage 2	Angle-tighten a further 90°	
To subframe*:		
Stage 1	130	96
Stage 2	Angle-tighten a further 90°	
Flywheel mounting bolts*:		
Stage 1	60	44
Stage 2	Angle-tighten a further 90°	
Knock sensor*:		
Stage 1	8	6
Stage 2	Angle-tighten a further 90°	
Main bearing cap bolts*:		
Stage 1	65	48
Stage 2	Angle-tighten a further 90°	
Main bearing cap side bolts (tighten after main bolts)*:		
Stage 1	20	15
Stage 2	Angle-tighten a further 90°	
Oil cooler bolts*:		
Stage 1	8	6
Stage 2	Angle-tighten a further 45°	
Oil filter housing	25	18
Oil jets	27	20
Oil level sensor bolts	9	7
Oil pump bolts*:		
Stage 1	8	6
Stage 2	Angle-tighten a further 90°	
Oil pump baffle bolts*:		
Stage 1	4	2
Stage 2	Angle-tighten a further 45°	
Oil pump suction pipe bolts*:		
Stage 1	4	2
Stage 2	Angle-tighten a further 45°	
Oil pump chain tensioner bolt	9	7
Oil pressure control valve bolt*:		
Stage 1	4	2
Stage 2	Angle-tighten a further 90°	
Roadwheel bolts	120	89
Sump bolts (steel sump)*:		
Stage 1	8	6
Stage 2	Angle-tighten a further 45°	
Sump bolts (plastic sump)*:		
Stage 1	8	6
Stage 2	Angle-tighten a further 90°	
Sump bolts (upper sump) *:		
Stage 1	8	6
Stage 2 (outer bolts at transmission end only)	Angle-tighten a further 180°	
Stage 3 (outer bolts within lower sump area only)	Angle-tighten a further 45°	
Stage 4 (centre bolt at transmission end only)	Angle-tighten a further 180°	
Stage 5 (centre bolts within the the lower sump area only)	Angle-tighten a further 90°	
Timing chain cover (upper)	9	7

Torque wrench settings (continued)

	Nm	lbf ft
Timing chain (lower cover)*:		
Steel bolts:		
Stage 1	8	6
Stage 2	Angle-tighten a further 45°	
Aluminium bolts:		
Stage 1	4	2
Stage 2	Angle-tighten a further 45°	
Timing chain tensioner bolts*:		
Stage 1	4	2
Stage 2	Angle-tighten a further 90°	
Timing chain guide bolts	20	15

* Do not re-use
** Caution: Left-hand threads

1 General Information

How to use this Chapter

1 This Part of Chapter 2 describes those repair procedures that can reasonably be carried out on the engine while it remains in the vehicle. If the engine has been removed from the vehicle and is being dismantled as described in Part D, any preliminary dismantling procedures can be ignored.

2 Note that while it may be possible physically to overhaul certain items while the engine is in the vehicle, such tasks are not usually carried out as separate operations, and usually require the execution of several additional procedures (not to mention the cleaning of components and of oilways); for this reason, all such tasks are classed as major overhaul procedures, and are described in Part D of this Chapter.

Engine description

3 Throughout this Chapter, engines are identified by the manufacturer's code letters. A listing of all engines covered, together with their code letters, is given in the Specifications.

4 The engines are water-cooled, double overhead camshaft (DOHC), in-line four-cylinder direct injection units, with aluminium cylinder blocks and cylinder heads. All are mounted transversely at the front of the vehicle, with the transmission bolted to the left-hand end of the engine.

5 The crankshaft is of five-bearing type, and thrust washers are fitted to the centre main bearing to control crankshaft endfloat.

6 The cylinder head carries the double camshafts. It also houses the intake and exhaust valves, which are closed by single coil springs, and which run in guides pressed into the cylinder head. The camshaft actuates the valves by cam followers and hydraulic tappets mounted in the cylinder head. The cylinder head contains integral oilways which supply and lubricate the tappets.

7 The timing chain drives the camshafts. A hydraulic tensioner is fitted to the chain.

Variable valve timing is fitted to the inlet camshaft and exhaust camshaft. The exhaust camshaft has two different camshaft lift profiles mounted on a sliding shaft. The profile is selected by solenoids that slide the appropriate camshaft lobe into position as dictated by the engine management system.

8 The valves are operated from the camshafts through roller rocker arms and hydraulic adjusters – the valve clearances are adjusted automatically.

9 The engine coolant pump is driven by toothed belt, with the drive supplied by the front balancer shaft. Coolant temperature is controlled by a rotary valve (part of the coolant pump housing). An electric coolant pump is also fitted to provide rapid heating to the cabin heater matrix.

10 Lubricant is circulated under pressure by a pump, driven by a chain from the crankshaft. Oil is drawn from the sump through a strainer, and then forced through an externally-mounted, renewable filter. From there, it is distributed to the cylinder head, where it lubricates the camshaft journals and hydraulic tappets, and also to the crankcase, where it lubricates the main bearings, connecting rod big-ends, gudgeon pins and cylinder bores. The oil pressure is variable depending on engine load and demand. An oil cooler is fitted next to the oil filter.

11 Balancer shafts are fitted to the cylinder block. The two contra-rotating shafts are chain driven from the crankshaft.

Operations with engine in car

12 The following operations can be performed without removing the engine:
a) Compression pressure – testing.
b) Auxiliary drivebelt – removal and refitting.
c) Camshafts – removal and refitting.
d) Camshaft oil seals – renewal.
e) Coolant pump – removal and refitting (refer to Chapter 3 Section 7).
f) Crankshaft oil seal – renewal.
g) Crankshaft pulley – removal and refitting.
h) Cylinder head – removal and refitting*.
i) Engine mountings – inspection and renewal.
j) Balancer shafts – removal and refitting.
k) Oil pump and pick-up assembly – removal and refitting.

l) Sump (upper and lower) – removal and refitting.
m) Timing chain and cover – removal, inspection and refitting.
n) Flywheel – removal and refitting
* Cylinder head dismantling procedures are detailed in Chapter 2D Section 6.
Note: It is possible to remove the pistons and connecting rods (after removing the cylinder head and sump) without removing the engine. However, this is not recommended. Work of this nature is more easily and thoroughly completed with the engine on the bench, as described in Chapter 2D Section 9.

2 Engine valve timing marks
– general information, setting TDC and chain checking

General information

1 The crankshaft and camshaft sprockets are driven by the timing chain, and rotate in phase with each other. When the the timing chain is removed during servicing or repair, it is possible for the shafts to rotate independently of each other, and the correct phasing is then lost.

2 The design of the engines covered in this Chapter is such that piston to valve contact will occur if the crankshaft is turned with the timing chain removed. For this reason, it is important that the correct phasing between the camshafts and crankshaft is preserved whilst the timing chain is off the engine. This is achieved by setting the engine in a reference condition (known as Top Dead Centre or TDC) before the timing chain is removed, and then preventing the shafts from rotating until the chain is refitted. Similarly, if the engine has been dismantled for overhaul, the engine can be set to TDC during reassembly to ensure that the correct shaft phasing is restored.

3 TDC is the highest position a piston reaches within its respective cylinder – in a four-stroke engine, each piston reaches TDC twice per cycle; once on the compression stroke, and once on the exhaust stroke. In general, TDC normally refers to No 1 cylinder on the compression stroke. Note that the cylinders

2.4a The crankshaft pulley TDC marks correctly aligned

2.4b A dial gauge and adapter can also be used to confirm TDC

are numbered one to four, starting from the timing chain end of the engine.

4 The crankshaft pulley has one or two marks which, when aligned with reference marks on the timing chain lower cover, indicates that No 1 cylinder (and hence also No 4 cylinder) is at TDC. Note that it is possible to incorrectly align the marks, as the lower (4 o'clock position) mark is the only one clearly visible with the engine in the vehicle **(see illustrations)**.

5 The camshaft sprockets are also equipped with timing marks **(see illustration)** – when these are aligned with marks on the camshaft cover, No 1 cylinder is at TDC compression.

Setting TDC on No 1 cylinder

6 Before starting work, make sure that the ignition is switched off.

7 Pull the engine top cover upwards from its fasteners.

8 If a very precise check of the timing is needed, remove the number 1 spark plug as described in Chapter 1A Section 29.

9 Remove the timing chain upper cover as described in Section 4.

10 Jack up and support the front of the vehicle (see *Jacking and vehicle support*) and then remove the lower section of the right-hand front wing liner.

11 Turn the engine clockwise with a spanner on the crankshaft pulley until the timing mark on the outer circumference of the crankshaft pulley aligns with the mark on the timing chain cover. With this aligned, the timing marks on the camshafts should align with the marks on the camshaft cover.

12 If an exact check of the timing is required, rotate the engine until the timing marks are approaching the correct TDC position. At this point a dial gauge and adapter will be required. Arrange the dial gauge so the long extension fits in the number 1 spark plug hole and then rotate the engine until the dial gauge stops moving. At this point the number 1 piston will be exactly at TDC. If TDC is missed, rotate the engine and try again – do not be tempted to turn the engine backwards. Next check that the camshaft and crankshaft marks are aligned as described earlier.

Chain checking

13 If there is a concern with noise from the timing chain area or fault code has been set that relates to camshaft or crankshaft position sensors than it is possible to inspect the timing chain 'stretch' through an inspection window in the lower timing chain cover.

14 Jack up and support the front of the vehicle (see *Jacking and vehicle support*).

Remove the wheel and the lower section of the right-hand wing liner.

15 Reach up and remove the blanking plug from the inspection window. Using a socket on the crankshaft pulley bolt turn the engine in the normal direction of rotation (clockwise) whilst looking at the timing chain tensioner (a mirror is useful here). Turn the engine until the tensioner is at maximum extension and then count the number of notches visible on the tensioner. There should be no more than 6 notches visible **(see illustration)**. If 7 or more notches are visible the chain must be replaced (see Section 6).

3 Cylinder compression test

1 When engine performance is down, or if misfiring occurs which cannot be attributed to the ignition or fuel systems, a compression test can provide diagnostic clues as to the engine's condition. If the test is performed regularly, it can give warning of trouble before any other symptoms become apparent.

2 The engine must be fully warmed-up to normal operating temperature, the battery must be fully charged, and all the spark plugs must be removed (refer to Chapter 1A Section 29). The aid of an assistant will also be required. Remove the engine cover.

3 Remove the spark plugs as described in Chapter 1A Section 29.

4 Disable the injectors by disconnecting the wiring plugs.

5 Fit a compression tester to the No 1 cylinder spark plug hole. A screw in type of tester must be used.

6 Have an assistant hold the throttle wide open. Crank the engine on the starter motor several seconds. After one or two revolutions, the compression pressure should build-up to a maximum figure, and then stabilise. Record the highest reading obtained.

2.5 The camshaft TDC marks

2.15 Check the extension of the timing chain tensioner

4.1 Remove the cover

4.2a Disconnect the fuel supply line...

4.2b ...and the fuel vapour line

7 Repeat the test on the remaining cylinders, recording the pressure in each. Keep the throttle wide open.

8 All cylinders should produce very similar pressures; a difference of more than 3 bars between any two cylinders indicates a fault. Note that the compression should build-up quickly in a healthy engine. Low compression on the first stroke, followed by gradually-increasing pressure on successive strokes, indicates worn piston rings. A low compression reading on the first stroke, which does not build-up during successive strokes, indicates leaking valves or a blown head gasket (a cracked head could also be the cause).

9 Refer to the Specifications of this Chapter, and compare the recorded compression figures with those stated by the manufacturer.

10 On completion of the test, refit the spark plugs, injector wiring plugs and engine cover. Note that in some cases, disconnecting the wiring plugs from the coils and injectors and then cranking the engine may cause fault codes to be stored by the engine management ECM – have these codes erased by means of a suitable diagnostic tool/fault code reader. See your Volkswagen dealer or suitably equipped garage. Note that low cost fault code readers are now widely available, see Chapter 4A Section 1 for details.

---

4 Timing chain covers – removal and refitting

Top cover

Removal

1 Remove the engine cover (**see illustration**).

2 Anticipating some coolant spillage, remove the coolant hose and then disconnect the fuel lines (**see illustrations**). Seal the openings in the fuel lines.

3 Disconnect the wiring plugs and then unbolt and remove the VVT (Variable Valve Timing) control valves (**see illustrations**).

4 Unbolt and remove the dipstick (**see illustration**).

5 Remove the bolts and lift off the cover (**see illustration**).

Refitting

6 Refitting is a reversal of removal. Replace the gasket and the control valve seals. Fit a new O-ring to the dipstick.

Lower cover

Note: *The lower cover will be destroyed when removed. A new cover must always be fitted.*

Note: *The main reason for removing the lower timing chain cover will be to replace the timing chains (as described in Section 6). Whilst not essential it is highly recommended that the engine is removed to remove the lower cover and replace the timing chains. This may at first seem unnecessary, but the marked links on*

4.3a Unbolt and then...

4.4 Remove the dipstick

both the chains and the sprockets are difficult to see and the consequences of incorrectly fitting a replacement timing chain may destroy the engine. Removal of the engine and transmission is relatively straightforward once the AC system has been degassed with suitable equipment.

Removal

7 Jack up and support the front of the vehicle – see *Jacking and vehicle support* and then remove the engine undershield.

8 Drain the engine oil as described in Chapter 1A Section 6.

9 Remove the right-hand wheel and then remove the lower section of the front wing liner.

10 Remove the auxiliary drivebelt and then

4.3b ...remove the control valves

4.5 Remove the upper timing chain cover

4.10 Remove the belt tensioner

4.13 Remove the control valve

unbolt and remove the belt tensioner (see illustration).

11 Remove the crankshaft pulley as described in Section 5.

12 Support the engine under the sump with a trolley jack, using a block of wood to spread the load. Take particular care to locate the jack so that the oil level sensor is not damaged. Remove the engine mounting bracket as described in Section 17.

13 Anticipating some oil spillage, disconnect the wiring plug and then unbolt the oil pressure control valve (see illustration).

14 If not already done so, remove the dipstick by unbolting it.

15 Remove the cover bolts (8 or 15 depending on the version) and then lever off the cover (see illustrations). Note that the cover is held in place with an adhesive type gasket sealant. Removal without distorting the cover is virtually impossible.

Refitting

16 Thoughtly clean all the gasket material from the engine.

4.15a Remove the bolts, lever off and…

4.15b …remove the cover

17 Check that the dowel pins are in position and then apply a 2 – 3 mm bead of sealant to the new cover. Install the cover within 5 minutes and then fit the new bolts. Tighten the bolts to the first stage torque (see illustrations). Note there are different torque settings for the type of bolt (aluminium or steel).

18 Tighten all the bolts to the second angle stage except the bolts 3 and 6 (15 bolt cover) or 1 and 4 (8 bolt cover). These are the bolts that hold the crankshaft pulley tool and are only fully tightened after the crankshaft pulley has been installed – see Section 5.

19 Where removed, fit a new inspection

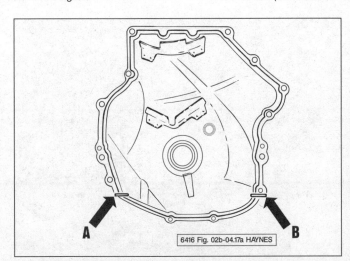

4.17a Apply a 2-3mm bead of sealant to the cover. Note the extra sealant (A) where the cover meets the upper sump to block joint

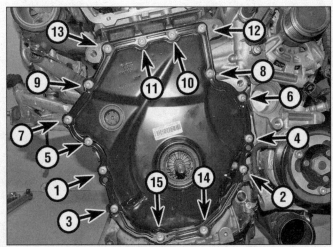

4.17b Tighten the bolts in the order shown

5.0 A comprehensive set of aftermarket tools from AST tools

5.4 Slacken the bolt, but DO NOT remove it

5.5 Fit the special tool

window plug and then fit a new crankshaft oil seal as described in Section 9.

20 Refit the oil pressure control valve, using a new O-ring.

21 Refit the crankshaft pulley, belt tensioner and the auxiliary drivebelt.

22 Refit the dipstick (with a new O-ring) and the engine mounting, using new bolts.

23 Refit the wing liner and wheel. Lower the vehicle to the ground and then refill the oil as described in Chapter 1A Section 6.

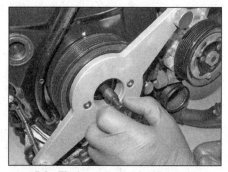

5.6a Fit the sprocket locking tool

5 Crankshaft pulley – removal and refitting

Caution: The crankshaft pulley bolt also locks the timing chain triple sprocket to the crankshaft. If the bolt is removed without the special tools, then the sprocket can rotate on the crankshaft. This will alter the timing and could lead to engine damage. The factory tools required are T10531, but they are also available in the aftermarket (see illustration). Always check the timing as described in Section 2 after removing and refitting the crankshaft pulley.

Removal

1 Jack up and support the front of the vehicle (see *Jacking and vehicle support*). Remove the wheel and the lower section of the wing liner.

2 Remove the auxiliary drivebelt as described in Chapter 1A Section 30.

3 Turn the crankshaft pulley to the TDC position – align the mark on the pulley as described in Section 2.

4 Slacken the bolt using a counterhold tool

(T10355 or similar). Alternatively remove the starter motor and lock the flywheel ring gear with a prybar. Note that the engine must remain at TDC **(see illustration)**.

5 Remove the bolt at the 7 o'clock and the 2 o'clock from the lower cover. Dispose of the bolts – new ones must be used. Install the special tool and lock the crankshaft pulley in position **(see illustration)**.

6 Remove the crankshaft pulley bolt completely and then install the locking tool from the special tool kit. Tighten the crankshaft sprocket locking tool and then remove the crankshaft pulley complete with the special tool **(see illustrations)**.

7 If the engine requires turning without the crankshaft pulley fitted then install the turning tool and locking collar. Note that the flat on the turning tool will be horizontal with the engine at TDC **(see illustration)**.

Refitting

8 Remove the locking/turning tool and collar – not the centre lock tool though – and check that the engine is still at TDC.

9 The replacement of the crankshaft oil seal is recommended at this point as described in Section 9.

10 Fit the crankshaft pulley and lock it it

5.6b Remove the crankshaft pulley and note the position of the TDC groove in the pulley

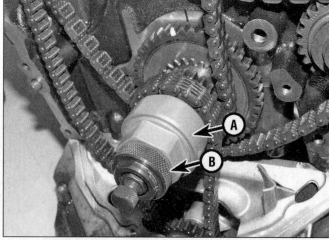

5.7 Install the turning tool (A) and the locking collar (B). Shown with lower timing chain cover removed

place by installing the turning tool so that the hexagon face is against the crankshaft pulley and then fit the locking collar The crankshaft pulley must fit correctly on the timing chain sprocket.

11 Fit the crankshaft pulley holding tool (T10531/1) and bolt it to the timing chain cover.

12 Remove the locking collar, turning tool and locking shaft. Lubricate the new bolt O-ring, fit the new bolt and install the bolt hand tight **(see illustrations)**.

13 Remove the crankshaft pulley holding/locking tool.

14 Using the counterhold tool (T10355 or equivalent) tighten the new bolt to the specified torque.

15 If the lower timing chain cover has been removed, fit new bolts to the timing chain cover and tighten them to the specified torque and angle – see Section 4. Note the different torque settings, depending on the material the bolt is made from (steel or aluminium).

16 Refit the remaining components in reverse order to removal.

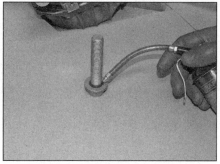

5.12a Lubricate the O-ring seal...

5.12b ...and fit the new bolt hand tight

6 Timing chain and balancer shaft chain – removal and refitting

General information

1 The primary function of the timing chain is to drive the camshafts. Unlike models that have the camshaft driven by toothed belt, the chain driven 2 litre engine does not have chain replacement interval. Replacement will only be required if the chain has 'stretched' (see the checking procedure in Section 2). If other major engine work has been undertaking, it would be prudent to replace the chain (including the tensioner and the chain guides).

Removal

Note: *The timing chain can be replaced with the engine in the vehicle, but it is highly recommended that the engine is removed to replace the timing chains. This may at first seem unnecessary, but the marked links on both the chains and the sprockets are difficult to see and the consequences of incorrectly fitting a replacement timing chain may destroy the engine. Removal of the engine and transmission is relatively straightforward once the AC system has been degassed with suitable equipment. The replacement procedure below is described with the engine removed from the vehicle.*

2 Set the engine at TDC (Top Dead Centre) as described in Section 2. Counterhold the crankshaft sprocket and slacken the pulley bolt a half turn.

3 Remove the auxiliary drivebelt with reference to Chapter 1A Section 30 and then unbolt the belt tensioner from the front of the engine.

4 Remove the engine mounting bracket as described in Section 17.

5 Remove the timing chain upper cover as described in Section 4.

6 Remove the crankshaft pulley (Section 5) and then remove the timing chain lower cover as described in Section 4.

7 With the a socket on the crankshaft turning tool, release the timing valve centre bolts using special socket T10352/2 (or aftermarket equivalent). Note that these bolts have left-hand threads – turn clockwise to remove them **(see illustration)**.

8 Unbolt and remove the bearing saddle from the camshafts **(see illustration)**.

9 Remove the 2 front centre bolts from below the camshafts sprockets and install the special tool T40243. Use the tool to slowly compress the timing chain hydraulic tensioner. When the tensioner is fully compressed insert the tensioner locking pin (T40267) **(see illustrations)**.

10 Install the camshaft locking tool (T40271/2 or equivalent) to the inlet camshaft sprocket

6.7 Remove both valve timing control valves. Note both have LEFT-HAND threads

6.8 Remove the bearing support saddle

6.9a Remove the bolts...

6.9b ...install the tool...

6.9c ...compress and lock the tensioner with the special tool

6.10 Lock the inlet camshaft with the special tool

6.11 Install the locking tool to the exhaust camshaft

6.12 Remove the upper guide rail

(see illustration). Slightly turn the camshaft sprocket if required using the special tool (T40266).

11 The second camshaft locking tool (T4027/1) must now be installed to the exhaust camshaft sprocket. If necessary, remove the bolt from the tensioner and then lower the tensioner. Using the special tool

(T40266) turn the exhaust camshaft sprocket clockwise sufficiently to install the camshaft locking tool (T4027/1) (see illustration).

12 Depress the locking tab and remove the upper guide rail (see illustration).

13 Unbolt and remove the hydraulic chain tensioner (see illustration). Dispose of the bolts – new ones must be used.

14 Depress the tensioning spring of the oil pump chain tensioner, insert a suitable locking pin such as a drill bit or section of welding rod (or the special VAG pin T40011) (see illustrations). Unbolt and remove the tensioner.

15 Unbolt and remove the camshaft chain front guide rail (see illustration).

6.13 Remove the hydraulic tensioner

6.14a Lock the tensioner…

6.14b …unbolt and remove it

6.15 Remove the guide rail

6.16 Hang the chain from the camshaft journals

6.17a Remove the tensioner

6.17b Remove the balancer shaft guide rails

16 Lift the chain off the camshaft sprockets and rest it on the journals **(see illustration)**.

17 Remove the balancer shaft chain tensioner and then remove all three balancer shaft guide rails **(see illustrations)**.

18 At the crankshaft nose, slacken the crankshaft turning tool (T10531/2). Remove the sprocket and oil pump drive chain and then remove the camshaft chain and balancer shaft chain **(see illustrations)**.

Refitting

19 The crankshaft must be at TDC before starting. Check that the flat on the nose of the crankshaft is horizontal. Using the checking procedure as described in Section 2 if necessary. Mark the position of TDC on the engine block above the crankshaft and on the triple sprocket. Fit the sprocket and check the alighment **(see illustration)**.

20 Turn the idler and balancer shaft gear so that the markings on the gears are aligned. The markings are very difficult to see, so

6.18a Remove the turning tool...

6.18b ...lift off the chains...

6.18c ...and remove the triple sprocket

6.19 Use a permanent marker and mark the position of TDC on the engine block and triple sprocket

6.20 Align the front balancer shaft and idler gear

6.21 Note the position of the coloured links (A), the position of the double coloured links (B) and the lower link (C)

6.23 Refit the triple sprocket

highlight the markings with a permanent marker pen **(see illustration)**.

21 Temporarily remove the triple sprocket. Fit the balancer shaft drive chain and align the coloured links on the chain with the marks on the balancer shaft sprockets. Fit the upper balancer shaft guide rail **(see illustration)**.

22 Fit the timing chain to the camshaft sprocket journals so that the coloured links on the chain are on top of the journal. The coloured link for the exhaust camshaft will be at the 11 o'clock position and the coloured link for the inlet camshaft will be at the 1 o'clock position.

23 Fit the oil pump drive chain to the triple sprocket and slide it onto the nose of the crankshaft whilst engaging the balancer shaft chain and the camshaft chain **(see illustration)**. The balancer shaft chain coloured link must align with the mark on the sprocket and the sprocket must align with the mark on the engine block. Note that the camshaft chain will not be in contact with the sprocket at this point.

24 Fit the special clamping pin (T10531/2) and then install the crankshaft turning tool (T10531/3) and lock the crankshaft sprocket to the crankshaft. Tighten the clamping pin bolt.

25 Push the balancer shaft chain up to the

sprocket and install the tensioner guide rail and the fixed guide rail. Install the balancer shaft chain tensioner and then check that the coloured links on the chain align with the marks on all three sprockets **(see illustration)**.

26 Next fit the camshaft timing chain to the inlet camshaft and then the exhaust camshaft. The coloured links must align with the marks on the sprockets **(see illustration)**.

27 Install the fixed chain guide and the upper chain guide. Tighten the bolts to the specified torque.

28 Fit the special socket (T40266) to the exhaust camshaft, turn the tool (and sprocket) slightly clockwise and remove the sprocket locking tool.

29 Slowly release the exhaust camshaft sprocket until the chain is in contact with the upper guide rail. Hold the camshaft in this position and (with the aid of an assistant) install the tensioned guide rail. Tighten the guide rail bolt.

6.25 The coloured link on the balancer shaft chain must align with the mark on the sprocket behind the oil pump drive chain

6.26 The coloured links must align with the marks on the camshaft sprockets

6.32 Remove the inlet camshaft locking tool

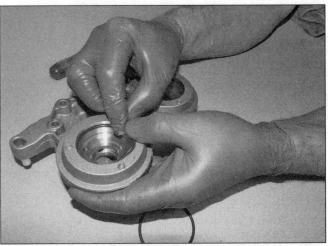

6.34a Fit new seals to the saddle

6.34b Refit the bearing saddle

6.35 Tighten the bolts in the order shown

30 Fit the tensioner with new bolts and tighten them to the specified torque.

31 Install the oil pump chain tensioner. Engage the spring in the recess and remove the locking pin.

32 Fit the special socket (T40266) to the inlet camshaft, turn the sprocket slightly anti-clockwise and remove the sprocket locking tool (see illustration).

33 Check that all the links on both chains are aligned with the respective marks on the sprockets.

34 Refit the centre bolts to the cylinder head. On models that have a roll pin at the centre install the pin to the saddle (it will be pulled into the cylinder head by the bolt). Fit new O-ring seals to the bearing saddles (see illustrations). Lubricate the seals with engine oil and refit the saddles. Tight the new bolts in sequence by hand. Do not tighten them to the specified torque at this stage.

35 Remove the locking pin from the chain tension and allow it to operate and then tighten the bearing saddle bolts in sequence to the specified torque (see illustration).

36 Refit the VVT valves and rotate the engine twice in the normal direction of rotation. Check that the sprocket timing marks all align. Note that the coloured links will not align.

37 Remove the turning tool from the crankshaft noise and refit the:
● The timing chain covers (Section 4).
● The crankshaft pulley (Section 5).
● The auxiliary drivebelt and tensioner (Chapter 1A Section 30).
● Replace the oil and filter (Chapter 1A Section 6).
● The engine mounting bracket (Section 17).

38 Refit the remaining components in the the reverse order to removal. If the engine has been removed, refit the engine.

39 The new timing chain may need adapting to the engine, using a diagnostic tool. Consult a Volkswagen dealer or suitably equipped garage.

7 Balancer shafts – removal and refitting

Note: *Volkswagen insist that the balancer shafts, needle roller bearings and the idler gear must all be replaced if removed.*

Removal

1 Remove the coolant pump drivebelt from the inlet camshaft as described in Chapter 3 Section 7.

2 With the belt removed, unbolt the drive sprocket from the inlet camshaft. Note that the bolt has a left-hand thread. Turn clockwise to slacken the bolt.

3 Remove the camshaft timing chain and the balancer shaft timing chain as described in Section 6.

4 With the timing marks aligned, remove the

7.4 Remove the idler gear bolt

8.7 Remove the EVAP control solenoid

8.9 Remove the oil separator/crankcase breather

idler shaft bolt **(see illustration)** and remove the idler gear. Remove the bush from the gear. Dispose of the idler gear – a new one must always be fitted.

5 Remove the bolts and pull out the balancer shafts.

Refitting

6 Where removed the refit the guide tube – the slots must be at the timing chain end.

7 Lubricate the needle bearing and bush on each shaft and fit the new shafts.

8 Fit the new bolts and tighten them to the specified torque.

9 Fit a new O-ring to the idler gear bush and fit the bush to the engine block, ensuring that the bush is correctly located.

10 A new idler gear is essential to set the backlash between the gears. Fit the new idler gear so that the timing marks align when refitted.

11 With the new idler fitted, tighten the new bolt to first stage torque setting, and then turn the idler gear. There must be no play between the gears, if necessary loosen the bolt and tighten it again.

12 Tighten the idler gear bolt to the second stage torque and the tighten it to the final angle torque.

13 Refit the remaining components in reverse order to removal.

8 Camshafts and camshaft cover – removal, inspection and refitting

Note: *The timing chain must be removed to remove the camshaft cover and the camshafts. Removal of the engine is recommended as described Section 6.*

Removal

1 Remove the engine top cover and then remove the air filter housing as described in Chapter 4A Section 3.

2 Drain the coolant as described in Chapter 1A Section 33.

3 Remove the ignition coils as described in Chapter 5B Section 3.

4 Remove the ignition coil wiring loom, releasing it from the retaining clips as required.

5 Unbolt the earth connector (where fitted) and then disconnect the wiring plugs from the camshaft control valves, camshaft timing units, high pressure pump, camshaft position sensor and the turbocharger cut off valve.

6 Disconnect the wiring plugs from the oil pressure switches, the fuel rail pressure sensor, the EVAP solenoid and the fuel injector plug. Unclip the loom from the support bracket and move it to the front of the engine.

7 Unbolt the EVAP solenoid from the valve cover and remove it **(see illustration)**.

8 Remove the coolant hoses from the top of the valve cover as required.

9 Unbolt and remove the crankcase breather from the valve cover **(see illustration)**.

10 Unbolt and remove the high pressure fuel pump (Chapter 4A Section 4) and then remove the vacuum pump (Chapter 9 Section 20).

11 Remove the camshaft switching solenoids **(see illustration)**.

12 Jack up and support the front of the vehicle (see *Jacking and vehicle support*). Remove the engine undershield and the lower section of the right-hand front wing liner.

13 At this point the engine and transmission should be removed as described in Chapter 2D Section 4. Alternatively the engine should now be supported and the engine mounting removed from the timing chain end of the engine.

14 Remove the timing chain upper cover (Section 4) the crankshaft pulley (Section 4) and then the lower timing chain cover (Section 4).

15 Remove the timing chain as described in Section 6.

16 Using the special socket (T40266) on the inlet camshaft turn the camshaft rearwards (anti-clockwise) slightly and remove the camshaft sprocket locking tool (T40271/2). Repeat the procedure for the exhaust camshaft, but turn the sprocket clockwise to remove the locking tool.

17 Unbolt the cylinder head cover bolts in the opposite sequence to that shown **(see illustration 8.28)**.

18 Remove the cover and lift out the camshafts **(see illustrations)**. Note that the

8.11 Remove the control solenoids from the camshaft cover

8.18a Remove the cover and...

8.18b ...lift out the camshafts

8.24 Fit the inlet camshaft to the cylinder head

8.25a Oil the bearing surfaces and...

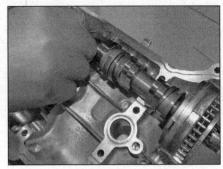

8.25b ...then install the exhaust camshaft to the camshaft cover

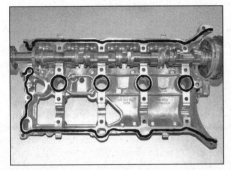

8.26 Apply a 2 -3 mm bead of sealant to the areas shown.

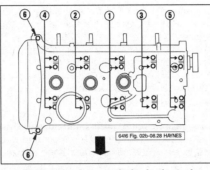

8.28 Tighten the new bolts in the order shown

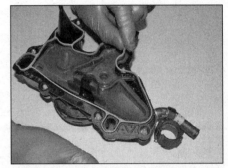

8.29 Fit a new gasket to the crankcase breather/oil separator

exhaust camshaft will be in the valve cover, so either hold it down onto the cylinder head or hold it in place in the camshaft cover as the cover is removed.

Inspection

19 Visually inspect each camshaft for evidence of wear on the surfaces of the lobes and journals. Normally their surfaces should be smooth and have a dull shine; look for scoring, erosion or pitting and areas that appear highly polished, indicating excessive wear. Accelerated wear will occur once the hardened exterior of the camshaft has been damaged, so always renew worn items. **Note:** *If these symptoms are visible on the tips of the camshaft lobes, check the corresponding tappet, as it will probably be worn as well.*

20 If the machined surfaces of the camshaft appear discoloured or blued, it is likely that it has been overheated at some point, probably due to inadequate lubrication. This may have distorted the shaft, so have it checked by a Volkswagen dealer or engine reconditioning specialist.

Refitting

21 Lower the pistons to the mid point in the cylinder bores.
22 Thoroughly clean the mounting surfaces of the cover and the cylinder head.
23 Check that the plungers on the camshaft actuators are fully retracted.
24 Lubricate the bearing journals and install

the inlet camshaft to the cylinder head **(see illustration)**. The lobes of the camshaft on cylinder number 4 should point straight up.
25 Install the exhaust camshaft to the cylinder head cover, so that the marks on the sprocket and the cover are aligned. It may be necessary to push the sliding cams along the shaft to fit the the camshaft to the cover **(see illustrations)**.
26 Apply a 2-3 mm bead of sealant to the surface of the camshaft cover as shown **(see illustration)**.
27 Hold the camshaft in position and refit the cover. Rock the camshaft sprockets slightly and settle the cover onto the cylinder head.
28 Fit new bolts to the cover and tighten them in the order shown **(see illustration)**.
29 Fit a new gasket to the crankcase

9.2 Work around the seal to remove it with and oil seal puller type tool

breather/oil separator and refit it **(see illustration)**.
30 Refit the camshaft locking tools (T40271/2 and T40721/1) and then turn the crankshaft to bring the number 1 piston to TDC.
31 Refit the timing chain as described in Section 6.
32 Refit the timing chain covers as described in Section 4.
33 Refit the crankshaft pulley as described in Section 5.
34 Refit the remaining components in reverse order to removal.

9 Crankshaft oil seals – renewal

Timing chain end oil seal

1 Remove the crankshaft pulley, with reference to Section 5.
2 The seal can be removed by drilling two small holes diagonally opposite each other, inserting self-tapping screws, and pulling on the heads of the screws with pliers. Alternatively an oil seal removal tool can be used **(see illustration)**. Note that if the lower timing chain cover is to be removed, new covers are supplied with an oil seal already fitted.
3 Position the new seal over the end of the crankshaft, ensuring the closed side of the seal faces outwards. Use a suitable socket

9.3 Using a large socket and the crankshaft turning tool to draw in the oil seal

9.7 Remove the end plate

9.9 Use a sharp blade to clean off the sealant

and the crankshaft turning tool to draw the new seal into position (see illustration).
4 Refit the crankshaft pulley, with reference to Section 5.

Flywheel end oil seal

5 Remove the transmission with reference to Chapter 7A Section 3 or Chapter 7B Section 2.
6 Remove the flywheel with reference to Section 12.
7 Pull the adapter plate from the locating

dowels on the rear of the cylinder block (see illustration) and remove it from the engine.
8 Unbolt and remove the housing. The seal is only available complete with the housing.
9 Carefully remove any sealant residue from the cylinder block and sump mating surfaces (see illustration).
10 Apply a 2-3 mm bead of sealant to the new seal housing (see illustration). The sealant should run inside the mounting bolt holes. Once the sealant has been applied

the new housing must be fitted within 5 minutes.
11 A guide sleeve (T20097) is available to aid installation of the new housing. This sleeve is essential.
12 The oil seal must be installed with the inner lip towards the crankshaft. Fit the new seal to the guide sleeve and push the sleeve (tapered side first) through the seal several times – this helps relax the seal. Lightly oil the nose of the crankshaft. Fit the sleeve from the front so that the inner lip is pointing towards the crankshaft and then position the seal and tool over the nose of the crankshaft. Push the seal off the sleeve and onto the nose of the crankshaft (see illustrations).
13 Fit the bolts hand tight and then tighten the bolts evenly in the sequence shown to the specified torque (see illustration). Remove the tool.
14 Refit the adapter plate, locating it over the oil seal housing, and onto the 2 dowels at the back of the cylinder head.
15 Refit the flywheel with reference to Section 12.
16 Refit the transmission as described in Chapter 7A Section 3 or Chapter 7B Section 2.

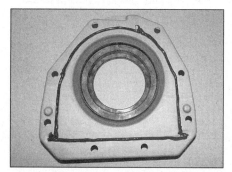

9.10 Apply a bead of sealant as shown

9.12a Fit the new seal with the guide sleeve

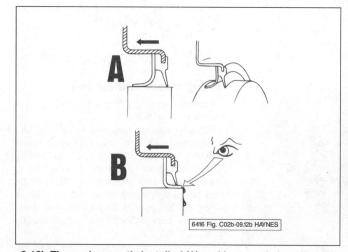

9.12b The seal correctly installed (A) and incorrectly installed (B)

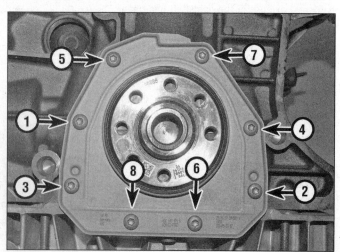

9.13 Tighten the bolts in the order shown

10 Cylinder head –
removal and refitting

Note: *Cylinder head dismantling and overhaul is covered in Chapter 2D Section 6.*
Note: *Removal of the engine and transmission is recommended. Though not essential, for the home mechanic it will be the safest and quickest way to to remove the cylinder head.*

Removal

1 Before starting work, switch off the ignition and all electrical consumers and remove the ignition key. Disconnect the battery as described in Chapter 5A Section 3.
2 Remove the engine top cover by pulling it upwards from its fasteners.
3 Remove the air filter housing **(see illustration)** and inlet ducts as described in Chapter 4A Section 3.
4 Apply the handbrake, then jack up the front of the vehicle and support it on axle stands (see *Jacking and vehicle support*).
5 Drain the cooling system as described in Chapter 1A Section 33.
6 If the engine and transmission are to be removed, at this point follow the procedure described in Chapter 2D Section 4 for engine removal.
7 Remove the timing chain (Section 6) and the camshafts as described in Section 8.
8 If the engine is still in the vehicle, refit the engine mounting (using the old bolts) and remove the trolley jack from sump.
9 Remove the front exhaust pipe and catalytic converter as described in Chapter 4C Section 6.
10 Remove the charge air hose from the intercooler **(see illustration)** and disconnect the charge air boost pressure sensor. Seal the openings with clean shop towels.
11 Remove the front coolant hose and then remove the smaller coolant hose from the cylinder head and turbocharger.
12 Disconnect the wiring plugs from the oil pressure switches and the piston cooling jet control valve.
13 Remove the inlet manifold as described in Chapter 4A Section 8.

10.3 Remove the air filter housing

14 At the rear of the engine, remove the heat shield then remove the turbocharger as described in Chapter 4C Section 4. Secure the turbocharger to the bulkhead – there is no need to remove it from the vehicle.
15 The rocker arms and hydraulic tappets can be removed now **(see illustration)** or left in position and removed with the cylinder head. If they are removed they must be stored in the correct order.
16 Slacken the cylinder head bolts in reverse order to that shown **(see illustration 10.23)**.
17 With the help of an assistant, lift the cylinder head from the block. If it is stuck, tap it free with a wooden mallet. Do not insert a lever into the gasket joint.
18 Remove the cylinder head gasket from the block.

Refitting

19 Thoroughly clean the contact faces of the cylinder head and block. Also clean any oil or coolant from the bolt holes in the block – if this precaution is not taken, not only will the tightening torque be incorrect but there is the possibility of damaging the block.
20 Locate a new gasket on the block, with the part number facing upwards, and readable from the intake side of the engine. Make sure that the location dowels are in position. Volkswagen recommend that the gasket is removed from its packaging just prior to fitting it. Handle the gasket with great care – damage to the silicone or indented areas will lead to leaks.

10.10 Remove the charge air hose

10.15 The rocker arms and tappets can be removed if required

21 In order to prevent any accidental piston-to-valve contact, rotate the crankshaft a quarter of a turn anti-clockwise if not already done so.
22 Carefully lower the head onto the block, making sure that it engages the location dowels correctly. Do not use any jointing compound on the cylinder head joint. Insert the new cylinder head bolts (the washers should still be in place on the cylinder head), and initially hand-tighten them.
23 Using the sequence shown **(see illustration)** tighten all the bolts to the Stage 1 torque given in the Specifications.
24 Angle-tighten the bolts in the same sequence to the Stage 2 and Stage 3 angles given in the Specifications **(see illustration)**.
25 Refit the camshafts and valve cover.
26 Rotate the crankshaft a quarter of a turn

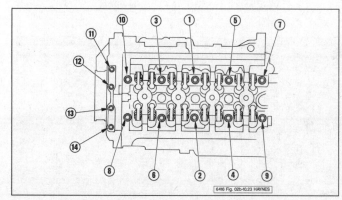

10.23 Tighten the bolts 1-10 in the order shown and then tighten bolts 11-14

10.24 Angle tighten the cylinder head bolts

clockwise, back to TDC on cylinders 1 and 4.

27 The remainder of refitting is a reversal of removal, noting the following points:

a) *Ensure all electrical connectors are securing reconnected, and the harnesses are correctly routed – refit any cable clips removed during dismantling.*

b) *Ensure all coolant hoses are reconnected, and all retaining clips are refitted in their original positions.*

c) *If any of the coolant hose clips appear weak or corroded – renew them.*

d) *On completion, refill the cooling system with new antifreeze mixture (see Chapter 1A Section 33).*

e) *If you suspect the engine oil has been contaminated with coolant, change the oil and filter as described in Chapter 1A Section 6.*

28 If any major components have been replaced (turbocharger or cylinder head for example) it is possible to set the oil pressure to the maximum (using a diagnostic tool) for the first 1000 miles. Consult a Volkswagen dealer or suitably equipped garage.

11 Hydraulic tappets – operational check

⚠️ *Warning: After fitting hydraulic tappets, wait a minimum of 30 minutes (or preferably, leave overnight) before starting the engine, to allow the tappets time to settle, otherwise the valve heads will strike the pistons.*

1 The hydraulic tappets are self-adjusting, and require no attention whilst in service.

2 Hydraulic tappet removal and refitting is described as part of the cylinder head overhaul sequence – see Chapter 2D Section 6 for details.

12 Flywheel – removal, inspection and refitting

Removal

1 On manual gearbox models, remove the transmission (see Chapter 7A Section 3) and clutch (Chapter 6A Section 5).

2 On semi-automatic (DSG) transmission models, remove the transmission as described in Chapter 7A Section 3.

3 All models are fitted with a dual-mass flywheel. Begin by making alignment marks between the flywheel and the crankshaft.

4 Rotate the outside of the dual-mass flywheel so that the bolts align with the holes **(see illustration)**.

5 Unscrew the bolts and remove the flywheel. Use a locking tool to counterhold the flywheel **(see illustration)**. Discard the bolts, new ones

must be fitted. **Note:** *In order not to damage the flywheel, do not use a pneumatic or impact driver to unscrew the bolts, only use hand tools.*

Inspection

6 Check the flywheel for wear and damage. Examine the starter ring gear for excessive wear to the teeth; if evident, the flywheel must be renewed complete as the ring gear is not supplied separately.

7 The following are guidelines only, but should indicate whether professional inspection is necessary. There should be no cracks in the drive surface of the flywheel. If cracks are evident, the flywheel may need renewing.The dual-mass flywheel should be checked as follows.

Warpage

8 Place a straight-edge across the face of the drive surface, and check by trying to insert a feeler gauge between the straight-edge and the drive surface **(see illustration)**. The flywheel will normally warp like a bowl – ie, higher on the outer edge. If the warpage is more than 0.40 mm, the flywheel may need renewing.

Free rotational movement

9 This is the distance the drive surface of the flywheel can be turned independently of the flywheel primary element, using finger effort alone. Move the drive surface in one direction and make a mark where the locating pin aligns

with the flywheel edge. Move the drive surface in the other direction (finger pressure only) and make another mark **(see illustration)**. The total of free movement should not exceed 10.0 mm. If it's more, the flywheel may need renewing.

Total rotational movement

10 This is the total distance the drive surface can be turned independently of the flywheel primary element. Insert two bolts into the clutch pressure plate/damper unit mounting holes, and with the crankshaft/flywheel held stationary, use a lever/pry bar between the bolts and use some effort to move the drive surface fully in one direction – make a mark where the locating pin aligns with the flywheel edge. Now force the drive surface fully in the opposite direction, and make another mark. The total rotational movement should not exceed 44.00 mm. If it does, have the flywheel professionally inspected.

Lateral movement

11 The lateral movement (up and down) of the drive surface in relation to the primary element of the flywheel, should not exceed 2.0 mm. If it does, the flywheel may need renewing. This can be checked by pressing the drive surface down on one side into the flywheel (flywheel horizontal) and making an alignment mark between the drive surface and the inner edge of the primary element. Now press down on the opposite side of the drive surface, and make another mark above the original one.

12.4 Align the bolts with the holes

12.5 Using a locking tool to hold the flywheel

12.8 Check the dual mass flywheel for warpage

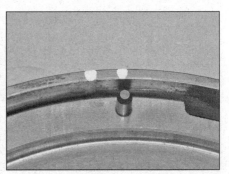

12.9 Check the free rotational movement of the dual mass flywheel

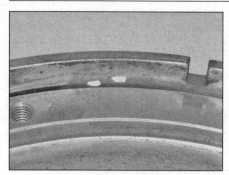

12.11 Check the lateral movement of the dual mass flywheel

13.6 Remove the sump

13.7a Remove the single bolt and...

The difference between the two marks is the lateral movement **(see illustration)**.

Refitting

12 Refitting is a reversal of removal, but use new bolts and tighten them to the specified torque.

13 Sump – removal and refitting

Lower sump

Note: *The vehicle may be fitted with a steel or plastic main sump. Removal and refitting is essentially the same, but note the different torque settings.*

Removal

1 Apply the handbrake, then jack up the front of the vehicle and support it on axle stands (see *Jacking and vehicle support*).
2 Release the fasteners and remove the engine undershield.
3 Position a container beneath the sump, then unscrew the drain plug and drain the engine oil as described in Chapter 1A Section 6.
4 Disconnect the oil temperature/level sensor wiring plug from the base of the sump.
5 Gradually unscrew and remove the sump bolts working clockwise around the sump.
6 Remove the sump **(see illustration)**. Plastic

sumps have a traditional gasket, steel sumps use sealant to form the gasket. If it is stuck, tap it gently with a mallet to free it.
7 If required unbolt and remove the baffle plate **(see illustrations)**. Note that if the upper sump is to be removed the baffle plate must be replaced.

Refitting

8 Where the baffle plate has been removed, fit new O-ring seals to the baffle plate.
9 Thoroughly clean the contact faces of the sump. It is recommended that a rotary wire brush is used to clean away the sealant on steel sumps.
10 On plastic sumps, fit a new gasket **(see illustration)**. On steel sumps apply a 2-3 mm bead of sealant to the sump. The sealant should pass inside the bolt holes and the sump must be installed within 5 minutes of applying the sealant.
11 Refit the sump and tighten the retaining bolts hand-tight initially. Progressively tighten the sump bolts in a diagonal pattern on models fitted with a steel sump, and clockwise on models fitted with a plastic sump. On models with a steel sump wait at least 30 minutes for the sealant to set before filling the engine with oil.
12 Refitting is a reversal of removal.

Upper sump

Note: *If the upper sump is removed the baffle plate must be replaced.*

Removal

13 Remove the transmission as described in Chapter 7A Section 3 or Chapter 7B Section 2. Support the engine with and engine crane or engine support bar.
14 Remove the lower sump as described in this Section.
15 Remove the baffle plate and then remove the oil pump as described in Section 14.
16 Remove the crankshaft oil seal housing (see Section 9).
17 Disconnect the wiring plug from the oil pressure control solenoid and then remove the 2 lower bolts from the lower timing chain cover (beneath the crankshaft pulley).
18 Remove the mounting bolts in reverse order to that shown **(see illustration 13.24)**.
19 Lever off the upper sump, starting at the transmission end. Avoid bending or damaging the timing chain lower cover.

Refitting

20 Clean all the old gasket material form the upper sump and engine block.
21 Clean and check the oil passages in the block and in the sump and then trial fit the upper sump. Check the alignment of the sump to the timing chain cover. If the timing chain cover was damaged during sump removal it must be replaced after the sump has been refitted.
22 Apply a 2-3 mm bead of sealant to the sump **(see illustration)** and then apply a bead of sealant to the joint between the timing

13.7b ...remove the baffle plate

13.10 On plastic sumps, fit a new gasket

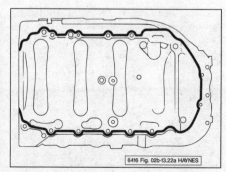

13.22a Apply a bead of sealant as shown

2B•20 2.0 litre direct injection petrol engine in-car repair procedures

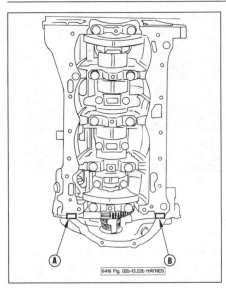

13.22b Apply a bead of sealant at point A and B

chain cover and the block **(see illustration)**. The sump must be installed within 5 minutes of applying the sealant.

23 Install the sump with the sump flush with the block at the transmission end. Use a straight edge to check if necessary.

24 Tighten the new bolts in the order shown **(see illustration)**.

25 Fit new bolts to the timing chain cover and fit the rear oil seal housing. Fit a new housing if there is any doubt about the condition of the seal.

14.2 Hold the chain tensioner back with a simple bracket

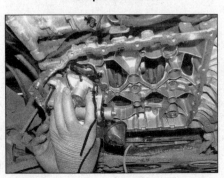

14.3b Unhook the pump from the chain...

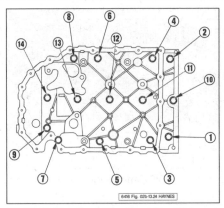

13.24 Tighten the bolts 1 to 14 to 8Nm and then tighten bolts 1 and 2 to 180°. Tighten bolts 3 to 9 a further 45°. Tighten bolt 10 to 180° and then tighten bolts 11 to 14 to 90°

26 Refit the oil pump and install a new baffle plate. Refit the lower sump.

27 Refit the remaining components in reverse order to removal and lower the vehicle to the ground. Fit a new oil filter and fill the engine with fresh oil.

14 Oil pump – removal, inspection and refitting

Removal

1 Remove the sump as described and baffle plate as described in Section 13.

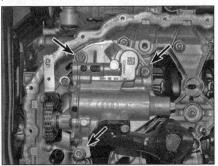

14.3a Remove the bolts

14.3c ...and remove it

2 The oil pump chain must be de-tensioned. Volkswagen list two special tools (T10118 and T40265). These are not essential as the spring loaded tensioner can be pushed back with a prybar and the tensioner locked with an easily fabricated bracket **(see illustration)**.

3 Remove the oil pump mounting bolts, unhook the pump from the chain and remove it **(see illustrations)**.

Inspection

4 Examine the drive chain for wear and damage. To remove the chain, the timing chain must be removed (see Section 4). Parts are not available for the pump. If is faulty then it must be replaced.

Refitting

5 On the bench prime the pump with oil by immersing the suction pipe in oil. Turn the sprocket by hand and draw oil into the pump.

6 Hook the chain over the pump sprocket and then bolt the pump to the upper sump.

7 Hold the tensioner in position and remove the bracket. Slowly release the tensioner and allow it to operate.

8 Fit new O-rings to the new baffle plate and using a new bolt, bolt the plate into position.

9 Refit the sump and after waiting a minimum of 30 minutes (models with a steel sump) refill the engine with fresh oil. Replacing the oil filter is recommended.

10 Refit the remaining components in reverse order to removal.

15 Oil pressure switches and oil control valves – general information, removal and refitting

General information

1 The 2.0 litre engine features variable oil pressure control, oil cooler control and piston cooling jet control. The system has three pressure oil pressure switches:

a) *An oil pressure switch mounted below the oil cooler (F22). This switch monitors the oil pump pressure in the in the high pressure stage (2.3 to 3 Bar).*

14.3d The fabricated bracket shown with the oil pump removed

15.2 Pressure switches and control valve mounted below the oil filter

A Piston cooling control valve
B Reduced oil pressure switch
C High pressure oil switch

15.9 The third stage oil pressure switch

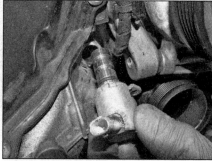

15.14 Remove the control valve

b) *An oil pressure switch (F378) mounted below the oil filter and above the first oil switch. This switch monitors the reduced oil pressure (0.5 to 0.8 Bar).*

c) *A third stage oil pressure switch (F447) mounted in the block below the inlet manifold. This switch monitors the oil pressure at the piston cooling jets (03. to 0.6 Bar).*

Note: *If an oil pressure switch is removed, Volkswagen insist it must be replaced.*

2 The control valves for oil pressure is mounted at the front of the block close to the crankshaft pulley. The control valve for piston jet cooling is fitted below the oil filter housing, close to the oil pressure switches **(see illustration)**.

Removal

Stage 1 and 2 switches

3 Both switches are mounted below the oil filter housing. Anticipating some oil spillage, place a clean shop towel below the switch.
4 Disconnect the wiring plug on the appropriate switch, unscrew the switch and remove it.

Stage 3 switch

5 Jack up and support the front of the vehicle (see *Jacking and vehicle support*). Remove the engine undershield.
6 Remove the air filter housing as described in Chapter 4A Section 3.
7 Unclip the wiring loom and remove the charge air pipe from above the starter motor.
8 Disconnect the wiring plug from the switch and then remove the cover from the coolant pump drive belt.
9 Anticipate some oil spillage and then unscrew the switch **(see illustration)**.

Refitting

10 Refitting is a reversal of removal. Always fit an new seal and switch. Check the oil level.

Oil control valves

Removal

Oil pressure control valve

11 Jack up and support the front of the vehicle (see *Jacking and vehicle support*). Remove the engine undershield.
12 Remove the auxiliary drivebelt as described in Chapter 1A Section 30.
13 Place a suitable container beneath the switch and then disconnect the switch wiring plug.
14 Remove the mounting bolt and pull off the control valve **(see illustration)**.

Piston cooling jet control valve

15 The control valve is fitted below the oil pressure switches. Disconnect the wiring plug.
16 Anticipating some oil spillage, remove the mounting bolt and pull the switch from the housing.

Refitting

17 Refitting is a reversal of removal. Use new seals and bolts.

16 Oil cooler – removal and refitting

Removal

1 Drain the coolant as described in Chapter 1A Section 33 and remove the coolant hose from the cooler.
2 Remove the auxiliary drivebelt (Chapter 1A Section 30) and then remove the alternator (Chapter 5A Section 5)
3 Remove the AC compressor as described in Chapter 3 Section 12 and secure the compressor to the side. Do not disconnect the refrigerant hoses.
4 Disconnect the wiring plugs from the oil pressure switches and the piston cooling control valve.
5 Remove the oil filter (Chapter 1A Section 6).
6 Remove the engine oil dipstick.
7 Remove the ancillary mounting bracket by

removing the bolts. Manoeuvre the bracket form the engine bay.
8 On the bench remove the cooler from the bracket. Recover the gasket.
9 Where require remove the switching valve from the bracket.

Refitting

10 Refitting is a reversal of removal. Use new O-ring seals and fit a new gasket.

17 Engine mountings – inspection and renewal

Inspection

1 If improved access is required, jack up the front of the vehicle, and support it securely on axle stands (see *Jacking and vehicle support*). Remove the engine undertray(s).
2 Check the mounting rubbers to see if they are cracked, hardened or separated from the metal at any point; renew the mounting if any such damage or deterioration is evident.
3 Check that all the mountings are securely tightened; use a torque wrench to check if possible.
4 Using a large screwdriver or a crowbar, check for wear in the mounting by carefully levering against it to check for free play. Where this is not possible, enlist the aid of an assistant to move the engine/transmission back-and-forth, or from side-to-side, whilst you observe the mounting. While some free play is to be expected, even from new components, excessive wear should be obvious. If excessive free play is found, check first that the fasteners are correctly secured, then renew any worn components as described in the following paragraphs.

Renewal

Right-hand mounting

5 Support the engine on a trolley jack under the sump. Use a block of wood between the sump and the head of the jack, to prevent any damage to the sump.
6 Unclip the fuel lines from the coolant reservoir.

17.7 Disconnect the level sensor wiring plug

17.8 Unclip the reservoir and move it to the side

17.9a Remove the bolts…

17.9b …and then lift out the mounting

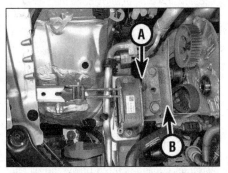

17.10a Align the mounting so that the gap (A) = 10 mm with the bracket (B) parallel to the lower bracket (C)

7 Disconnect the level sensor wiring plug **(see illustration)**.

8 Unclip the coolant reservoir and move it to one side **(see illustration)**.

9 Unscrew the bolts securing the mounting to the body and then unscrew the bolts securing it to the engine bracket. Withdraw the mounting from the engine compartment **(see illustrations)**.

10 Refitting is a reversal of removal, bearing in mind the following points.

a) *Use new securing bolts.*
b) *Align the mounting as shown* **(see illustration)**.
c) *Tighten all fixings to the specified torque.*

Left-hand mounting

Note: *New mounting bolts will be required on refitting.*

11 Support the transmission on a trolley jack with a block of wood placed between the head of the jack and the transmission to spread the load.

12 Remove the air filter (Chapter 1A Section 28) and the turbocharger inlet and outlet ducts.

13 Remove the battery and battery tray, as described in Chapter 5A Section 3.

14 On models fitted with a security cover remove the shear bolts and lift off the metal cover. Disconnect the wiring plugs from the ECU. Unclip the ECU from the bracket **(see illustrations)** and remove it from the vehicle.

15 Unbolt the ECU mounting bracket and

17.14a Disconnect the wiring plugs

17.14b Remove the ECU

17.14c Bag up the ECU wiring plugs to protect them from contamination

17.15 Lift up the loom to access the mounting bolts

17.16 Remove the bolts

17.17 Remove the bracket from the transmission

17.20 The rear torque arm

then unclip the wiring loom sufficiently to expose the transmission mounting bolts **(see illustration)**.

16 Remove the mounting to body bolts and then remove the bolts securing the mounting to the transmission bracket **(see illustration)**.

17 Lift out the mounting and then where required, unbolt and remove the bracket from the transmission **(see illustration)**. Removal

of the bracket is essential for transmission removal.

18 Refitting is a reversal of removal, bearing in mind the following points:

a) *Use new mounting bolts.*

b) *Tighten all fixings to the specified torque.*

Rear mounting (torque arm)

19 Apply the handbrake, then jack up the front of the vehicle and support securely on

axle stands (see *Jacking and vehicle support*).

20 Working under the vehicle, unscrew and remove the bolt securing the mounting to the subframe **(see illustration)**.

21 Unscrew the two bolts securing the mounting to the transmission, then withdraw the mounting from under the vehicle.

22 Refitting is a reversal of removal, but use new mounting securing bolts, and tighten all fixings to the specified torque.

Chapter 2 Part C
1.6 and 2.0 litre diesel engine in-car repair procedures

Contents

Section number

Camshaft and hydraulic tappets – removal, inspection and refitting 9
Camshaft cover – removal and refitting 4
Camshaft oil seals – renewal 10
Compression and leakdown tests – description and interpretation.. 2
Crankshaft oil seals – renewal 15
Crankshaft pulley – removal and refitting.................... 5
Cylinder head – removal, inspection and refitting 11
Engine assembly and valve timing marks – general information and usage... 3
Engine mountings – inspection and renewal 16

Section number

Engine oil cooler/filter housing – removal and refitting 17
Flywheel – removal, inspection and refitting 14
General Information 1
Oil level/temperature sender – removal and refitting 19
Oil pressure warning light switches and oil pressure regulating valve – removal and refitting.................................. 18
Oil pump and drivebelt – removal, inspection and refitting 13
Sump – removal and refitting 12
Timing belt – removal, inspection and refitting.................. 7
Timing belt covers – removal and refitting 6
Timing belt tensioner and sprockets – removal and refitting 8

Degrees of difficulty

Easy, suitable for novice with little experience	Fairly easy, suitable for beginner with some experience	Fairly difficult, suitable for competent DIY mechanic	Difficult, suitable for experienced DIY mechanic	Very difficult, suitable for expert DIY or professional

Specifications

General

Manufacturer's engine codes*:
1598 cc (1.6 litre), 16-valve, DOHC	CLHA, CLHB, CRKB, CXXA and DBKA
1968 cc (2.0 litre), 16 valve, DOHC	CKFC, CRBC, CRLB, CRMB and CUNA

Maximum outputs

	Power	Torque
Engine code (1.6 litre engines):		
CLHA	77 kW @ 3000 to 4400 rpm	250 Nm @ 1500 to 2750 rpm
CLHB	66 kW @ 3000 to 4000 rpm	230 Nm @ 1500 to 2750 rpm
CRKB	81 kW @ 3000 to 4000 rpm	250 Nm @ 1500 to 2750 rpm
CXXA.	63 kW @ 3000 to 4000 rpm	250 Nm @ 1500 to 3000 rpm
CXXB	81 kW @ 3000 to 4000 rpm	250 Nm @ 1500 to 3000 rpm
DBKA	81 kW @ 3250 to 4000 rpm	250 Nm @1500 to 3000 rpm
Engine code (2.0 litre engines):		
CKFC	110 kW @ 3500 to 4000 rpm	320 Nm @ 1750 to 3000 rpm
CRBC	110 kW @ 3500 to 4000 rpm	320 Nm @ 1750 to 3000 rpm
CRLB	110 kW @ 3500 to 4000 rpm	340 Nm @ 1750 to 3000 rpm
CRMB	110 kW @ 3000 to 4000 rpm	340 Nm @ 1750 to 3000 rpm
CUNA	135 kW @ 3500 to 4000 rpm	380 Nm @ 1750 to 3000 rpm

Bore:	
1.6 litre engines	79.5 mm
2.0 litre engines	81.0 mm
Stroke:	
1.6 litre engines	80.5 mm
2.0 litre engines	95.5 mm
Compression ratio	16.2 : 1 (except engine code CUNA = 15.8 : 1)
Compression pressure:	
New	25.0 – 30.0 bar
Wear limit	19.0 bar
Maximum difference between cylinders.	5.0 bar
Firing order	1 – 3 – 4 – 2
No.1 cylinder location.	Timing belt end

*See 'Vehicle identification' at the end of this manual for the location of the engine code markings

Lubrication system

Oil pump type. . . . . Gear type, belt-driven from crankshaft
Oil pressure switch (green). . . . . 0.3 to 0.6 bar
Oil pressure switch (brown) . . . . 2.5 to 3.2 bar

Torque wrench settings

	Nm	lbf ft
Ancillary (alternator, etc) bracket mounting bolts*:		
Stage 1 (all six bolts).	40	30
Stage 2 (for two upper bolts)	Angle-tighten a further 180°	
Stage 2 (for four lower bolts)	Angle-tighten a further 45°	
Auxiliary drivebelt tensioner securing bolt*:		
Stage 1	20	15
Stage 2	Angle-tighten a further 90°	
Big-end bearing caps bolts*:		
Stage 1	30	22
Stage 2	Angle-tighten a further 90°	
Camshaft housing bolts*:		
Stage 1	8	6
Stage 2	Angle-tighten a further 90°	
Camshaft cover bolts.	9	7
Camshaft adjuster cover bolts	8	6
Camshaft end cover bolts (engine without VVT)	8	6
Camshaft adjuster/control valve bolt (models with VVT)	50	37
Camshaft sprocket hub centre bolt	100	74
Camshaft sprocket adjuster bolt (in slot)	9	7
Common rail bolts	20	15
Coolant pump bolts*:		
Stage 1	20	15
Stage 2	Angle-tighten a further 45°	
Crankshaft oil seal housing bolts	13	10
Crankshaft pulley-to-sprocket bolts*:		
Stage 1	10	7
Stage 2	Angle-tighten a further 90°	
Crankshaft sprocket bolt*:		
Stage 1	180	133
Stage 2	Angle-tighten a further 135°	
Cylinder head bolts*:		
Stage 1	30	22
Stage 2	65	48
Stage 3	Angle-tighten a further 90°	
Stage 4	Angle-tighten a further 90°	
Engine mountings:		
RH engine mounting*:		
Mounting bracket to engine:		
Stage 1	7	5
Stage 2	40	30
Stage 3	Angle-tighten a further 180°	
Mounting to body:		
Stage 1	40	30
Stage 2	Angle-tighten a further 90°	
Mounting to bracket (front bolt):		
Stage 1	40	30
Stage 2	Angle-tighten a further 90°	
Mounting to bracket (rear bolt)		
Stage 1	60	44
Stage 2	Angle-tighten a further 90°	
LH engine/transmission mounting*:		
Mounting to body:		
Stage 1	50	37
Stage 2	Angle-tighten a further 90°	
Mounting to bracket on transmission:		
Stage 1	60	44
Stage 2	Angle-tighten a further 90°	
Pendulum (rear) link*:		
Link-to-transmission:		
Front bolt:		
Stage 1	50	37
Stage 2	Angle-tighten a further 90°	

Rear bolt:		
Stage 1	50	37
Stage 2	Angle-tighten a further 90°	
Link-to-subframe:		
Stage 1	130	96
Stage 2	Angle-tighten a further 90°	
Flywheel*:		
Stage 1	60	44
Stage 2	Angle-tighten a further 90°	
Fuel pump hub nut	95	70
Fuel pump sprocket bolts*		
Short bolt		
Stage 1	20	15
Stage 2	Angle-tighten a further 45°	
Long bolt		
Stage 1	20	15
Stage 2	Angle-tighten a further 180°	
Main bearing cap bolts*:		
Stage 1	65	48
Stage 2	Angle-tighten a further 90°	
Oil drain plug*	30	22
Oil filter housing-to-cylinder block bolts*:		
Stage 1	20	15
Stage 2	Angle-tighten a further 90°	
Oil filter cover	25	18
Oil level/temperature sensor-to-sump bolts.	9	7
Oil pick-up pipe securing bolts	9	7
Oil pressure warning light switch	22	16
Oil/Vacuum pump bolts*:		
Torx head bolt	16	11
Stage 1	12	9
Stage 2	Angle-tighten a further 180°	
Hex head bolt		
Stage 1	10	7
Stage 2	Angle-tighten a further 180°	
Piston oil spray jet bolt	27	19
Sump:		
Sump to block bolts		
Stage 1	5	4
Stage 2	13	10
Sump to transmission bolts	40	30
Thermostat housing	16	12
Timing belt outer cover bolts	12	9
Timing belt tensioner roller securing nut*:		
Stage 1	20	15
Stage 2	Angle-tighten a further 45°	
Timing belt idler pulleys (nut and bolt)	20	15

*Do not re-use fasteners

1 General Information

How to use this Chapter

1 This Part of Chapter 2 describes those repair procedures that can reasonably be carried out on the engine while it remains in the vehicle. If the engine has been removed from the vehicle and is being dismantled as described in Part D, any preliminary dismantling procedures can be ignored.

2 Note that while it may be possible physically to overhaul certain items while the engine is in the vehicle, such tasks are not usually carried out as separate operations, and usually require the execution of several additional procedures (not to mention the cleaning of components and of oilways); for this reason, all such tasks are classed as major overhaul procedures, and are described in Part D of this Chapter.

Engine description

3 Throughout this Chapter, engines are referred to by type, and are identified and referred to by the manufacturer's code letters. A listing of all engines covered, together with their code letters, is given in the Specifications at the start of this Chapter.

4 The engines are from the EA288 family of 'modular' diesel engines, developed from the previous generation of common rail engines (EA189 family) and designed to meet current (and future) emission requirements.

5 The engines are water-cooled, double overhead camshafts (DOHC), in-line four-cylinder units, with gray cast iron cylinder blocks. This is an alloy of cast iron and flake graphite. The cylinder head is manufactured from an aluminium alloy. All are mounted transversely at the front of the vehicle, with the transmission bolted to the left-hand end of the engine.

6 The crankshaft is of five-bearing type, and thrustwashers are fitted to the centre main bearing (No.3) to control crankshaft endfloat.

7 The camshafts are mounted in a single

piece camshaft carrier. They can not be removed and in the event of failure the complete carrier assembly (including the camshafts) must be replaced. Drive for the exhaust camshaft is by a toothed timing belt from the crankshaft, with the intake camshaft driven by interlocking gears at the left-hand end of both camshafts. The gears incorporate a toothed backlash compensator element. Some versions have variable valve timing on the inlet camshaft.

8 The valves are closed by coil springs, and run in guides pressed into the cylinder head. The valves are operated by roller rocker arms incorporating hydraulic tappets.

9 The variable output vane type oil pump is driven by a belt from the right-hand (timing belt) end of the crankshaft. The oil pump also incorporates the vacuum pump. Oil is drawn from the sump through a strainer, and then forced through an externally mounted, renewable filter. From there, it is distributed to the cylinder head, where it lubricates the camshaft journals and hydraulic tappets, and also to the crankcase, where it lubricates the main bearings, connecting rod big-ends, gudgeon pins and cylinder bores. A coolant-fed oil cooler is fitted to the oil filter housing on all engines. Oil jets are fitted to the base of each cylinder – these spray oil onto the underside of the pistons, to improve cooling.

10 Oil pressure is controlled by the engine control unit via a control solenoid. At low engine speeds (up to 3000 rpm) the oil pump delivers pressurised oil at between 1.8 to 2.0 bar. At speeds above 3000 rpm the pressure increases to between 3.8 to 4.2 bar.

11 On all engines, engine coolant is circulated by a switchable coolant pump, driven by the timing belt. For details of the cooling system, refer to Chapter 3.

Operations with engine in car

12 The following operations can be performed without removing the engine:
a) *Compression pressure – testing.*
b) *Camshaft cover – removal and refitting.*
c) *Crankshaft pulley – removal and refitting.*
d) *Timing belt covers – removal and refitting.*
e) *Timing belt – removal, refitting and adjustment.*
f) *Timing belt tensioner and sprockets – removal and refitting.*
g) *Camshaft oil seals – renewal.*
h) *Camshafts and hydraulic tappets – removal, inspection and refitting.*
i) *Cylinder head – removal and refitting.*
j) *Cylinder head and pistons – decarbonising.*
k) *Sump – removal and refitting.*
l) *Oil pump – removal, overhaul and refitting.*
m) *Crankshaft oil seals – renewal.*
n) *Engine/transmission mountings – inspection and renewal.*
o) *Flywheel/driveplate – removal, inspection and refitting.*

Note: It is possible to remove the pistons and connecting rods (after removing the cylinder head and sump) without removing the engine. However, this is not recommended. Work of this nature is more easily and thoroughly completed with the engine on the bench, as described in Chapter 2D Section 3.

2 Compression and leakdown tests – description and interpretation

Compression test

Note: A compression tester suitable for use with diesel engines will be required for this test.

1 When engine performance is down, or if misfiring occurs which cannot be attributed to the ignition or fuel systems, a compression test can provide diagnostic clues as to the engine's condition. If the test is performed regularly, it can give warning of trouble before any other symptoms become apparent.

2 The engine must be fully warmed-up to normal operating temperature, the battery must be fully charged, and you will require the aid of an assistant.

3 Remove the glow plugs as described in Chapter 5C Section 2, and then fit a diesel engine compression tester to the No.1 cylinder glow plug hole **(see illustration)**. *Note: Part of the glow plug removal procedure is to disconnect the fuel injector wiring plugs. As a result of the plugs being disconnected and the engine cranked, faults may be stored in the ECU memory. These must be erased after the compression test.*

4 Have your assistant crank the engine for several seconds on the starter motor. After one or two revolutions, the compression pressure should build-up to a maximum figure and then stabilise. Record the highest reading obtained.

5 Repeat the test on the remaining cylinders, recording the pressure in each.

6 The cause of poor compression is less easy to establish on a diesel engine than on a petrol engine. The effect of introducing oil into the cylinders (wet testing) is not conclusive, because there is a risk that the oil will sit in the recess on the piston crown, instead of passing to the rings. However, the following can be used as a rough guide to diagnosis.

7 All cylinders should produce very similar pressures. Any difference greater than that specified indicates the existence of a fault. Note that the compression should build-up quickly in a healthy engine. Low compression on the first stroke, followed by gradually increasing pressure on successive strokes, indicates worn piston rings. A low compression reading on the first stroke, which does not build-up during successive strokes, indicates leaking valves or a blown head gasket (a cracked head could also be the cause).

8 A low reading from two adjacent cylinders is almost certainly due to the head gasket having blown between them and the presence of coolant in the engine oil will confirm this.

9 On completion, remove the compression tester, and refit the glow plugs, with reference to Chapter 5C Section 2.

10 Reconnect the wiring to the injector solenoids. Finally, have a Volkswagen dealer or suitably equipped specialist erase any fault codes from the ECU memory.

Leakdown test

11 A leakdown test measures the rate at which compressed air fed into the cylinder is lost. It is an alternative to a compression test, and in many ways it is better, since the escaping air provides easy identification of where pressure loss is occurring (piston rings, valves or head gasket) **(see illustration)**.

12 The equipment required for leakdown testing is unlikely to be available to the home mechanic. If poor compression is suspected, have the test performed by a suitably equipped garage.

3 Engine assembly and valve timing marks – general information and usage

General information

1 TDC is the highest point in the cylinder that each piston reaches as it travels up-and-down

2.3 A specific diesel engine compression tester must be used

2.11 Checking the cylinder leakage rate

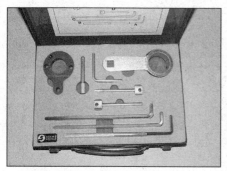

3.3 A suitable set of aftermarket timing tools

3.8 Fit the tool. The slot on the camshaft sprocket will be close to the 4 o'clock position

3.9 Fit the tool to the hole in the oil seal housing…

3.11 Check the correct position of the high pressure pump

when the crankshaft turns. Each piston reaches TDC at the end of the compression stroke and again at the end of the exhaust stroke, but TDC generally refers to piston position on the compression stroke. No 1 piston is at the timing belt end of the engine.

2 Positioning No 1 piston at TDC is an essential part of many procedures, such as timing belt removal and camshaft removal.

3 The design of the engines covered in this Chapter is such that piston-to-valve contact may occur if the camshaft or crankshaft is turned with the timing belt removed. For this reason, it is important to ensure that the camshaft and crankshaft do not move in relation to each other once the timing belt has been removed from the engine.

Setting TDC on No 1 cylinder

Note: *VAG special tools 3359, T10265, T10492 and T10490 (or their aftermarket equivalents) will be required to lock the crankshaft sprocket in the TDC position (see illustration).*

4 Raise the front of the vehicle and support it securely on axle stands (see *Jacking and vehicle support*). Remove the front right-hand road wheel, then release the fasteners and remove the lower section of the wheelarch liner.

5 Remove the auxiliary drivebelt as described in Chapter 1B Section 30

6 Remove the crankshaft pulley/vibration damper as described in Section 5.

7 Remove the timing belt outer covers as described in Section 6.

8 Using a spanner or socket on the crankshaft sprocket bolt, turn the crankshaft in the normal direction of rotation (clockwise) until the locking pin can be inserted into the camshaft. The elongated slot in the camshaft sprocket will be in the 4 o'clock position and the arrow mark on the camshaft sprocket will be vertical **(see illustration)**.

9 While in this position it should be possible to insert the VAG tool T10490 to lock the crankshaft **(see illustration)**.

10 The engine is now set to TDC on No.1 cylinder.

11 If required the position of the high pressure pump can now be checked by inserting tool T10492 into the slot at the side of the sprocket – this is in the 10 o'clock position **(see illustration)**.

4 Camshaft cover – removal and refitting

Removal

1 Remove the engine cover (where fitted) and then remove the fuel injectors as described in (Chapter 4B Section 5).

2 Remove the timing belt upper cover as described in Section 6.

3 Where fitted disconnect the vacuum hoses from the camshaft cover **(see illustration)**.

4 Squeeze together the sides of the collar, and disconnect the breather hose from the

camshaft cover **(see illustration)**. On some versions the hose must be disconnected at the connector on the turbo/air hose – the breather hose will stay on the valve cover.

5 Release the hose clips, remove the single fixing and free the inlet hose from the airflow sensor and turbocharger. Remove the hose.

6 Release the wiring from the clips/bracket at the rear of the cover, then unscrew the camshaft cover retaining bolts in the REVERSE order to that shown **(see illustration 4.9)**. Lift the cover away. If the cover sticks, do not attempt to lever it off – instead free it by working around the cover and tapping it lightly with a soft-faced mallet **(see illustration)**.

7 Recover the camshaft cover gasket. Inspect the gasket carefully, and renew it if damage or deterioration is evident – note that

4.3 Remove the vacuum hoses

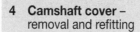

4.4 Squeeze together the sides of the collar to disconnect the breather hose

4.6 Undo the bolts and lift away the camshaft cover

4.7a Renew the cover seal if necessary

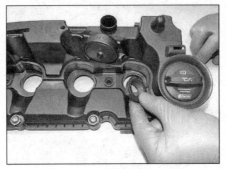

4.7b Recover the injector seals

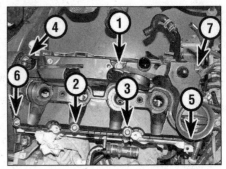

4.9 Tighten the bolts in the order shown

the retaining bolts and seals must be pushed fully through the cover **(see illustrations)**.

8 Clean the mating surfaces of the cylinder head and camshaft cover thoroughly, removing all traces of oil – take care to avoid damaging the surfaces as you do this.

Refitting

9 Refit the camshaft cover by following the removal procedure in reverse, tightening the cover retaining bolts to the specified torque, in the order shown **(see illustration)**. The gasket can be reused if in good condition, but the injector seals should always be replaced.

5 Crankshaft pulley – removal and refitting

Removal

1 Switch off the ignition and all electrical consumers and remove the ignition key.

2 Raise the front right-hand side of the vehicle, and support securely on axle stands (see *Jacking and vehicle support*). Remove the roadwheel.

3 Remove the securing fasteners and withdraw the lower section of the front wheel arch liner.

4 Slacken the bolts securing the crankshaft pulley to the sprocket **(see illustration)**. If necessary, the pulley can be prevented from turning by counterholding with a spanner or socket on the crankshaft sprocket bolt.

5.4 Undo the pulley bolts, counter holding the pulley with a socket on the centre sprocket bolt

5 Remove the auxiliary drivebelt, as described in Chapter 1B Section 30.

6 Unscrew the bolts securing the pulley to the sprocket, and remove the pulley **(see illustration)**. Discard the bolts – new ones must be fitted.

Refitting

7 Refit the pulley over the locating peg on the crankshaft sprocket, then fit the new pulley securing bolts.

8 Refit the auxiliary drivebelt as described in Chapter 1B Section 30.

9 Prevent the crankshaft from turning as during removal, then fit the pulley securing bolts, and tighten to the specified torque.

10 Refit the wheel arch liner.

11 Refit the roadwheel and lower the vehicle to the ground.

5.6 Remove the pulley

6 Timing belt covers – removal and refitting

Upper outer cover

1 Pull the engine top cover upwards to release it from the mountings.

2 Release the fuel and coolant hoses from the retaining clips on the right-hand side of the cylinder head and move them to one side.

3 Disconnect the wiring plug from the coolant reservoir and then unclip the reservoir and move it to the side **(see illustrations)**.

4 Anticipating some fuel spillage, disconnect the fuel lines at the quick release connectors. Plug and seal the fuel lines immediately and clean up any spilt fuel **(see illustration)**.

6.3a Disconnect the wiring connector ...

6.3b ... and release the clip

6.4 Disconnect the fuel lines

6.5a Unbolt the filter...

6.5b ... and move it to the side

6.6 Disconnect and remove the temperature sensor

5 Undo the fixings and then remove the fuel filter from the inner wing. Move it to one side and secure it with a cable tie or similar if required **(see illustrations)**. The fuel hoses do not need to be disconnected from the filter.
6 Unscrew the exhaust gas temperature sensor **(see illustration)**.
7 Unclip the wiring plug, remove the hose and/or unscrew the bracket from the cover as necessary and move the pressure sensors out of the way **(see illustrations)**.
8 Release the clips and remove the timing belt upper cover **(see illustration)**. Note that on certain models the heat shield at the rear of the cover hinders removal.
9 Refitting is a reversal of removal, noting that

the lower edge of the upper cover engages with the lower cover.

Lower cover

10 Remove the upper cover as described previously.
11 If not already done, remove the crankshaft pulley as described in Section 5.
12 There are two versions of the lower cover fitted, and earlier one and a later one. Both have a locking tab that is part of the cover. In both cases this must be removed.

Early style lower cover

13 On early versions the locking tab can only be broken off, after an access hole has been drilled in the cover.

Caution: Take care with the drilling. There is a possibility of damage to the timing belt.
14 From the base of the small slot (in the bottom of the cover) measure up 10 mm. Make a mark at this point centrally above the slot in the cover. Drill an 8 mm hole at this point and then insert a screwdriver through the hole and break off the tab.

Later style cover

15 Insert a screwdriver into the slot and rotate it to break off the tab **(see illustration)**.

All versions

16 With the tab broken off the lower cover, remove the fixings (2 per side), lift off and

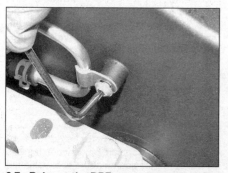

6.7a Release the DPF sensor pressure pipe

6.7b Disconnect...

6.7c ...unbolt...

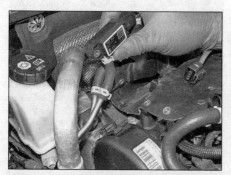

6.7d ...and move the sensors to the side as required

6.8 Manoeuvre the upper cover from place

6.15 Break off the tab

6.16a Undo the lower cover retaining bolts

6.16b ...and manoeuvre the lower cover from place

7.5 Slacken the bolt

lower the cover from the vehicle (see illustrations). Recover the locking tab if it has broken off completely.

17 Refitting is a reversal of removal. If a new lower cover is to be fitted, the locking tab must be removed first.

Rear cover

18 Remove the timing belt, tensioner and sprockets as described in Section 7 and Section 8.

19 Remove the coolant pump as described in Chapter 3 Section 7.

20 Unbolt and remove the rear cover.

21 Refitting is a reversal of removal, but clean and then apply thread locking compound to the bolt.

7 Timing belt – removal, inspection and refitting

Note: It is consider best practise to always replace the tensioner, idler and coolant pump whenever the timing belt is replaced. Any mounting studs should also be replaced at the same time. Most of the components (apart from the coolant pump) will be supplied with a timing belt kit. Note also that most manufactures will not guarantee a belt against premature failure if the idler(s) and tensioner are not replaced with the belt.

Removal

1 The primary function of the toothed timing belt is to drive the camshaft, but it also drives the coolant pump and high-pressure fuel pump. Should the belt slip or break in service, the valve timing will be disturbed and piston-to-valve contact may occur, resulting in serious engine damage. For this reason, it is important that the timing belt is tensioned correctly and renewed at the correct interval.

2 Switch off the ignition and all electrical consumers and remove the ignition key.

3 Remove the timing belt covers (Section 6) and then remove the right-hand engine mounting.

4 Set the engine to TDC on No. 1 cylinder as described in Section 3. If not already done so, insert the locking tool into the slot on the high pressure pump.

Caution: The timing tools are designed to lock the camshaft, crankshaft and high pressure pump in position. They are not designed to hold the sprockets whilst they are slackened. Always use a counterhold tool for this purpose.

5 Remove the locking pin from the camshaft pulley. Using the counterhold tool, slacken the main sprocket bolt (see illustration) Slacken the smaller bolt. Refit the locking pin.

6 Remove the locking pin from the high pressure pump and then using a counterhold tool (T10492) slacken the pump sprocket (see illustration). Note that due to the high

torque value of the pump sprocket nut, the counterhold tool is essential. Refit the locking pin.

7 Insert a suitable Allen key into the tensioner, then slacken the retaining nut and rotate the tensioner hub anti-clockwise until it can be locked in place using the VAG tool T10265 or a 2.0 mm pin/drill bit (see illustration). Note that one version of the tensioner does not have the pin slot for tool T10265. On this type of tensioner, the tensioner is held in the slack position with the hex key and the nut tightened.

8 Leaving the pin in place, now rotate the tensioner hub clockwise to the stop, and hand-tighten the retaining nut.

9 If the original timing belt is to be refitted, mark the running direction of the belt, to ensure correct refitting (see illustration).

Caution: If the belt appears to be in good condition and can be re-used, it is essential that it is refitted the same way around, otherwise accelerated wear will result, leading to premature failure.

10 Slide the belt from the sprockets, taking care not to twist or kink the belt excessively if it is to be re-used.

Inspection

11 Examine the belt for evidence of contamination by coolant or lubricant. If this is the case, find the source of the contamination before progressing any further. Check the

7.6 Slacken the high-pressure fuel pump sprocket

7.7 Insert an Allen key, slacken the nut, and rotate the hub anti-clockwise until a 2 mm rod/drill bit can be inserted to lock the hub to the pulley

7.9 Mark the direction of rotation

belt for signs of wear or damage, particularly around the leading edges of the belt teeth. Renew the belt if its condition is in doubt; the cost of belt renewal is negligible compared with potential cost of the engine repairs, should the belt fail in service. The belt must be renewed if it has covered the mileage given in Chapter 1B Section 2, however, if it has covered less, it is prudent to renew it regardless of condition, as a precautionary measure.

12 If the timing belt is not going to be refitted for some time, it is a wise precaution to hang a warning label on the steering wheel, to remind yourself (and others) not to attempt to start the engine. Have the battery disconnected to prevent any engine damage.

Refitting

13 Fit the new tensioner (and locking nut) and idler pulleys – see Section 8.

14 Ensure that the crankshaft and camshaft are still set to TDC on No 1 cylinder, as described in Section 3.

15 The camshaft sprocket should be free to turn and the bolt should be in the centre of the elongated slot.

16 The locking tool must be fitted to the high pressure pump sprocket and the sprocket must be free to turn.

17 Turn both the camshaft sprocket and the high pressure pump clockwise against the stops.

18 Fit the timing belt in the following order:
● Crankshaft pulley
● Tensioner
● Camshaft sproket
● High pressure pump sprocket
● Coolant pump

19 Slacken the tensioner locking nut and (if fitted) remove the pin tool. Allow the tensioner to operate and take up the slack in the belt.

20 Check that the camshaft sprocket locking bolt is in the centre of the elongated slot. If this is not the case, the belt must be removed and moved over one tooth on the sprocket.

21 Install the hex key into the tensioner and turn clockwise until the indicator arrow is in the centre of the gap in the base plate. Hold the tensioner and tighten the nut **(see illustration)**.

22 Fit the counterhold tool to the camshaft sprocket and tighten the adjusting bolt of the camshaft sprocket and the high pressure pump to 20 Nm.

23 Check that the upper mark on the high pressure pump is not in line with the pump locking tool (T10492). If the mark is in line with the tool the belt must be removed and high pressure pump sprocket moved one tooth. Refit the belt and repeat the procedure **(see illustration)**.

24 Remove the locking tools and rotate the crankshaft (by the crankshaft bolt) two revolutions clockwise, until just before the TDC (Top Dead Centre) position. Fit the crankshaft locking tool (T10490) and rotate the crankshaft until the tool is in position and the crankshaft is locked.

25 Fit the locking pin to the camshaft sprocket and the locking pin to the pump sprocket. Note that it may be difficult to fit the locking tool into the pump slot. A slight deviation is acceptable.

26 Check that the tensioner pointer is in the centre of the backplate cutout. A slight deviation (up to 5 mm) is acceptable.

27 Tighten the smaller camshaft sprocket bolt (in the centre of the elongated slot) to the specified torque.

28 If the timing is correct, remove the locking pins and tighten the camshaft adjuster bolt, the tensioner nut and the high pressure pump sprocket to the specified torque settings. If the timing is not correct minor adjustment can be carried out, as detailed below.

29 Using a spanner or wrench and socket on the crankshaft pulley centre bolt, rotate the crankshaft clockwise through two complete revolutions. Check that the timing tools can be fitted.

Correcting valve timing

30 If the camshaft sprocket can not be locked, slide back the crankshaft locking tool until the pin is just clear of the hole in the engine block and turn the crankshaft back slightly (anticlockwise).

31 Next turn the crankshaft in the normal direction (clockwise) until the camshaft locking tool can be fitted. Slacken the camshaft locking bolt.

32 If the locking pin of the crankshaft locking tool is to the left of the locating hole, then turn the crankshaft clockwise until the pin engages in the hole. Tighten the camshaft sprocket bolt to 20 Nm.

33 If the locking pin of the crankshaft locking tool is to the right of the locating hole, then turn the crankshaft anticlockwise slightly past the tool locating hole and then turn the crank clockwise (the normal rotation) until the pin engages in the hole. Tighten the camshaft sprocket bolt to 20 Nm.

34 Turn the crankshaft twice in the normal direction of rotation and fit the locking pins. If the timing is now correct, remove the locking pins and tighten the camshaft adjuster bolt, the tensioner nut and the high pressure pump sprocket to the specified torque settings.

35 Using a spanner or wrench and socket on the crankshaft pulley centre bolt, rotate the crankshaft clockwise through two complete revolutions. Check that the timing tools can be fitted.

36 The remainder of refitting is a reversal of removal.

8 Timing belt tensioner and sprockets – removal and refitting

1 Removal of any of the timing belt sprockets, idlers or tensioner requires the removal of the timing belt (Section 7) and the engine mounting. Either support the engine from above using a crossbeam or an engine hoist or support if from underneath with a trolley jack and block of wood.

Timing belt tensioner

Removal

2 Unscrew the timing belt tensioner nut, and remove the tensioner from the engine.

Refitting

3 When refitting the tensioner to the engine, ensure that the lug on the tensioner backplate engages with the corresponding cut-out in the rear timing belt cover, then refit the tensioner nut **(see illustration)**.

7.21 The pointer correctly aligned

7.23 The locking pin should align with the centre mark on the sprocket

8.3 Ensure the lug on the backplate engages with the cut-out in the timing belt cover

8.10a Remove the bolt

8.10b Note the flat on the crankshaft nose

8.11 Align the flat on the sprocket with the flat on the crankshaft

4 The remainder of refitting is a reversal of removal.

Idler pulleys

Removal

5 Unscrew the relevant idler pulley/roller securing bolt/nut, and then withdraw the pulley.

Refitting

6 Refit the pulley and tighten the securing bolt or nut to the specified torque. **Note:** *Renew the large roller/pulley retaining bolt (where applicable).*
7 Refit and tension the timing belt as described in Section 7.

Crankshaft sprocket

Note: *A new crankshaft sprocket securing bolt must be used on refitting.*

Removal

8 The crankshaft must be prevented from turning to remove the sprocket bolt. To hold the sprocket, make up a suitable tool, and screw it to the sprocket using a two bolts screwed into two of the crankshaft pulley bolt holes.
9 Hold the sprocket using the tool, then slacken the sprocket securing bolt. Take care, as the bolt is very tight. Do not allow the crankshaft to turn as the bolt is slackened.
10 Unscrew the bolt **(see illustrations)** and slide the sprocket from the end of the crankshaft, noting which way round the sprocket's raised boss is fitted. If required, use a puller to withdraw the sprocket from the end of the crankshaft.

Refitting

11 Commence refitting by positioning the sprocket on the end of the crankshaft **(see illustration)**.
12 Fit a new sprocket securing bolt, then counterhold the sprocket using the method employed on removal, and tighten the bolt to the specified torque in the two stages given in the Specifications.
13 Refit the timing belt as described in Section 7.

Camshaft sprocket

Removal

14 Rotate the crankshaft 90° anti-clockwise to prevent any accidental piston-to-valve contact.
15 Unscrew and remove the smaller adjusting bolt and then using a counterhold undo the main sprocket bolt **(see illustration 7.5)**. Remove the camshaft sprocket from the camshaft.

Refitting

16 Refit the sprocket ensuring that it is fitted the correct way round and tighten by hand only at this stage.
17 If the crankshaft has been turned, turn the crankshaft clockwise 90° back to TDC.
18 Refit and tension the timing belt as described in Section 7.

Coolant pump sprocket

19 The coolant pump sprocket is integral with the coolant pump. Refer to Chapter 3 Section 7 for details of coolant pump removal.

---

9 Camshaft and hydraulic tappets – removal, inspection and refitting

---

Note: *The camshafts and carrier are a complete assembly. If the camshafts or bearing surfaces are worn the complete unit must be replaced.*

9.5 Check the tappets

Checking

1 If the concern is noise from the top end of the engine, some preliminary checks can be made before completely dismantling the camshaft and valve train assembly.
2 Start the engine and run it up to normal operating temperature. The engine cooling fan should cut in. Have an assistant hold the engine at 2,500 rpm whilst listening for any undue noise. Road test the vehicle if necessary. Note that some noise (from cold) is normal as the hydraulic tappets come up to pressure. If the noise occurs with a warm engine and at every start, then it is likely that oil is draining from the tappets due to a faulty check valve in the oil filter housing.
3 If there is an irregular noise from the top end of the engine one (or more) of the hydraulic tappets may be faulty. Remove the camshaft cover as described in Section 4.
4 Raise the front of the vehicle (see Jacking and support 13) and gain access to the crankshaft pulley.
5 Working in turn rotate the engine via the crankshaft pulley bolt, so that the lobe of each cam is pointing away from the rocker arm. Press down on the tappet end of the rocker arm and attempt to slide a 0.20 mm feeler blade under the camshaft lobe **(see illustration)**. If the blade can be inserted, then the tappet should be considered faulty. Repeat the procedure for each tappet. If one or more faulty tappet is found, remove the camshaft carrier (as described below) and replace the tappet.
6 If no further work is required, refit the camshaft cover as described in Section 4.

Removal

7 Remove the timing belt as described in Section 7 and then remove the camshaft cover as described in Section 4.
8 At the left-hand end of the cylinder head, unbolt the coolant pipes and move them away from the cylinder head.
9 Unbolt the support bracket from the catalytic converter/DPF module.
10 Unbolt the fuel line and move it away from the cylinder head and then disconnect the wiring plug from the camshaft position sensor.
11 Disconnect and unclip the coolant pump wiring plug and then remove the single bolt

and lift out (with difficulty) the cover from the rear of the coolant pump (see illustration).

12 On models fitted with variable valve timing, disconnect the wiring plug from the actuator and then (with the engine still set at TDC) install the camshaft locking pin (T10492) to the inlet camshaft. Remove the housing and then unbolt adjuster. Recover the special friction washer.

13 At the rear of the engine remove the screw type bracket that secure the catalytic converter/particulate filter to the turbocharger. Reach down the back of the engine and (with difficulty) remove the converter/particulate filter mounting bolts.

14 Push the converter rearwards and secure it out of harms way with cable ties or similar.

15 Remove the camshaft sprocket as described in Section 8.

16 Slacken the bolts in two stages in reverse order to that shown (see illustration 9.28).

17 Remove the bolts and carefully lift the carrier from the cylinder head (see illustration). Note that the carrier is held in position with liquid gasket (there is no conventional gasket) and considerable care should be taken when releasing the carrier from the cylinder head. Avoid the temptation to force metal tools in between the cylinder head and the camshaft carrier to break the seal.

18 Discard the bolts – they must be replaced.

19 Remove the rocker arms and store them in the correct order.

20 Remove the hydraulic tappets, store them in order, keeping them vertical at all times. Alternatively store them individual submerged in clean engine oil.

Inspection

21 Visually inspect the camshafts for evidence of wear on the surfaces of the lobes and journals. Normally their surfaces should be smooth and have a dull shine; look for scoring, erosion or pitting and areas that appear highly polished, indicating excessive wear. Accelerated wear will occur once the hardened exterior of the camshaft has been damaged.
Note: *If these symptoms are visible on the tips of the camshaft lobes, check the corresponding rocker arm, as it will probably be worn as well.*
22 If the machined surfaces of the camshaft

9.11 Remove the cover

appear discoloured or blued, it is likely that it has been overheated at some point, probably due to inadequate lubrication. This may have distorted the shaft – the camshafts must turn freely in the carrier. If there is any doubt, have an automotive machine shop inspect the camshafts and carrier. Note that the camshafts and carrier are a single item. Individual parts are are not available
23 Inspect the hydraulic tappets and followers (rocker arms) for obvious signs of wear or damage (see illustration), and renew if necessary. Check that the oil holes in the tappets are free from obstructions.

Refitting

24 Oil the rocker arms and hydraulic tappets, and then refit them to their original positions.

⚠ *Warning: After fitting hydraulic tappets, wait a minimum of 30*

9.17 Lift off the camshaft module

minutes (or preferably, leave overnight) before starting the engine; to allow the tappets time to settle, otherwise the valve heads will strike the pistons.
25 Clean the gasket material from the carrier and cylinder head. Avoid blocking any oilways or bearing surfaces with the debris from cleaning.
26 Degrease the cylinder head and camshaft carrier and then apply a 2 mm wide bead of sealant to the camshaft carrier as shown (see illustrations).
27 The housing must be installed within 5 minutes of applying the sealant. After installing the housing wait 30 minutes for the sealant to dry.
28 Install the camshaft carrier and tighten the bolts to the specified torque in the sequence show (see illustration).
29 Generously lubricate the camshaft lobes,

9.23 Check the tappets for wear

9.26a Using fresh sealant…

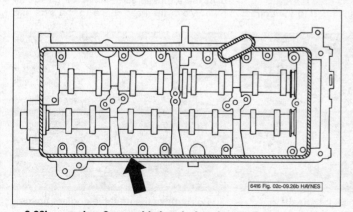
9.26b …apply a 2 mm wide bead of sealant to the area shown

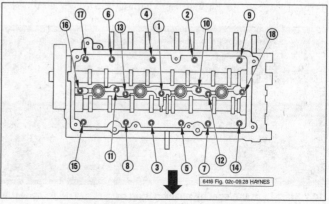
9.28 Tighten the bolts in the order shown

9.29 Lubricate the tappets and camshaft lobes

10.4 Remove the seal

rocker arm and tappets with new engine oil **(see illustration)** and then refit the camshaft cover.

30 Refitting of the remaining components is a reversal of removal, but note the following:
● If the cmashaft end cover was removed, refit it with a new gasket.
● On models with VVT on the inlet manifold, if the camshaft adjuster was removed refit it with a new gasket.
● Change the oil and filter if the camshaft carrier, rocker arms or tappets have been replaced.
● Disable the ignition (or use a remote starter) and crank the engine until the oil warning lights have extinguished.

10 Camshaft oil seals – renewal

Note: *Only the right-hand end of the camshaft has an oil seal.*
1 Remove the timing belt as described in Section 7.
2 Remove the camshaft sprocket as described in Section 8.
3 Measure the depth of the oil seal in the camshaft carrier. Note down the depth.
4 The seal can be hooked out, without

damage to the nose of the camshaft **(see illustration)**.
5 Alternatively, drill two small holes into the existing oil seal, diagonally opposite each other. Take great care to avoid drilling through into the seal housing or camshaft sealing surface. Thread two self-tapping screws into the holes, and using a pair of pliers, pull on the heads of the screws to extract the oil seal.
6 Clean out the seal housing and the sealing surface of the camshaft by wiping it with a lint-free cloth. Remove any swarf or burrs that may cause the seal to leak.
7 Do not lubricate the lip and outer edge of the new oil seal, push it over the camshaft until it is positioned in place above its housing. To prevent damage to the sealing lips, wrap some adhesive tape around the end of the camshaft **(see illustration)**.
8 Using a hammer and a socket of suitable diameter, drive the seal squarely into its housing. Where available a bolt can be used with the socket to draw the seal into position **(see illustration)**. Make sure the seal is fitted the correct way around, some have 'OUTSIDE' stamped on the seal. **Note:** *Select a socket that bears only on the hard outer surface of the seal, not the inner lip that can easily be damaged.*
9 Check that the seal is fitted to the correct

depth by checking the depth, against the measurement noted in in paragraph 3.
10 Refit the camshaft sprocket and timing belt as described in Section 8 and Section 7.

11 Cylinder head – removal, inspection and refitting

Note: *The cylinder head must be removed with the engine cold. New cylinder head bolts and a new cylinder head gasket will be required on refitting.*

Removal

1 Disconnect and then remove the battery as described in Chapter 5A Section 3.
2 Drain the cooling system (Chapter 1B Section 33) and engine oil (Chapter 1B Section 6).
3 Remove the engine cover by pulling it upwards to release it from its mountings.
4 Remove the air filter housing as described in Chapter 4B Section 3.
5 Remove the coolant pipes and hoses from the front, rear and side of the cylinder head **(see illustration)**.
6 At the turbocharger remove the charge air pipe. Move the heat shield to the side and

10.7 Start to fit the seal by pushing it on by hand

10.8 Draw the seal into position

11.5 Remove the multiple coolant hoses (left-hand ones shown)

11.6 Remove the charge air pipe

11.7 Disconnect the exhaust from the DPF/ catalytic converter

11.8a The upper DPF/converter mounting bolt

11.8b The lower mounting bracket (DPF/ converter removed). This bracket also secures the turbocharger

disconnect the wiring plug. Remove the bolts from the mounting bracket and then slacken the turbocharger to catalytic converter/ particulate filter hose clip **(see illustration)**.

7 Disconnect the exhaust pipe from the catalytic converter/particulate filter **(see illustration)**. Recover the gasket.

8 Unbolt the pressure sensor pipe from the timing belt upper cover, slacken the lower coolant pipe mounting (at the bottom right-hand side of the engine block, close to the sump) and then unbolt the catalytic converter/particulate filter from the engine **(see illustrations)**. Secure the assembly to the bulkhead – or remove it completely.

9 Disconnect the wiring plugs and remove the hoses from the sensors mounted on the plenum chamber front panel.

10 Remove the timing belt (Section 7) and the camshaft cover (Section 4).

11 If not already done so, unbolt and remove the inlet elbow from the turbocharger (on the left-hand end of the cylinder head).

12 Anticipate some oil spillage and then unbolt the turbocharger oil feed and return pipe.

13 Unbolt and remove the turbocharger support bracket and then unbolt the turbocharger. Secure the turbocharger to the bulkhead or remove it completely.

14 On models with variable valve timing (VVT) disconnect the wiring plug.

15 Disconnect the wiring plugs from the intercooler temperature sensors (before and after the intercooler), the charge pressure sensor and the throttle body.

16 On models fitted with VVT, remove the throttle body.

17 Unbolt the dipstick guide tube and then remove the inlet manifold as described in Chapter 4B Section 6.

18 Remove the camshaft housing as described in Section 9.

19 Disconnect the wiring plug from the coolant pump and then remove the cover.

20 Disconnect the vacuum hose from the front of the engine.

21 At the left-hand end of the cylinder head, disconnect the coolant temperature sensor and the vacuum hose.

22 If not already done so, disconnect the wiring plugs from the glow plugs **(see illustration)**. Unclip the wiring loom and move it to the side.

23 Remove the rocker arms and recover the hydraulic tappets. Keep the arms and tappets in order. Store the tappets upright, or immersed in clean engine oil.

24 Slacken the cylinder head bolts in reverse order to that shown **(see illustration 11.42a)**. Crack each bolt a half turn to start (in order) and then fully slacken each bolt the second time around.

25 Prepare a suitable surface and have a couple of lengths of timber available to support the cylinder head when it is removed. Note that the glow plugs protrude above the surface, so the head can not be laid flat.

26 Make a final check that everything has been disconnected and (with the aid of an assistant) lift off the cylinder head **(see**

illustration) and support it with blocks of wood on the prepared work surface.

27 Remove the gasket from the top of the block, noting the locating dowels. If the dowels are a loose fit, remove them and store them with the head for safekeeping. Do not discard the gasket yet – it will be needed for identification purposes.

Inspection

28 Dismantling and inspection of the cylinder head is covered in Chapter 2D Section 6.

Cylinder head gasket selection

Note: *A dial test indicator (DTI) will be required for this operation.*

29 Examine the old cylinder head gasket for manufacturer's identification markings **(see illustration)**. These will be in the form of

11.22 Disconnect the glow plugs

11.26 Remove the cylinder head

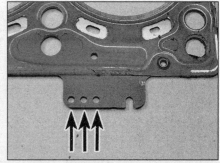

11.29 The holes identify the thickness of the cylinder head gasket

11.32 Measure the piston protrusion using a DTI gauge

11.43a Ensure the dowels are in place...

11.43b and then fit the new gasket with the part number uppermost

holes, and a part number on the edge of the gasket. Unless new pistons have been fitted, the new cylinder head gasket must be of the same type as the old one.

30 If new piston assemblies have been fitted as part of an engine overhaul, or if a new short engine is to be fitted, the projection of the piston crowns above the cylinder head mating face of the cylinder block at TDC must be measured. This measurement is used to determine the thickness of the new cylinder head gasket required.

31 Anchor a dial test indicator (DTI) to the top face (cylinder head gasket mating face) of the cylinder block, and zero the gauge on the gasket mating face.

32 Rest the gauge probe on No 1 piston crown, and turn the crankshaft slowly by hand until the piston reaches TDC. Measure and record the maximum piston projection at TDC **(see illustration)**.

33 Repeat the measurement for the remaining pistons, and record the results.

34 If the measurements differ from piston-to-piston, take the highest figure, and use this to determine the thickness of the head gasket required as follows.

Piston projection	Gasket identification (number of holes)
0.91 to 1.00 mm	1
1.01 to 1.10 mm	2
1.11 to 1.20 mm	3

35 Purchase a new gasket according to the results of the measurements.

Refitting

36 The mating faces of the cylinder head and block must be perfectly clean before refitting the head. Use a scraper to remove all traces of gasket and carbon, also clean the tops of the pistons. Take particular care with the aluminium surfaces, as the soft metal is easily damaged.

37 Make sure that debris is not allowed to enter the oil and water passages – this is particularly important for the oil circuit, as carbon could block the oil supply to the camshaft and crankshaft bearings. Using adhesive tape and paper, seal the water, oil and bolt holes in the cylinder block.

38 To prevent carbon entering the gap between the pistons and bores, smear a little grease in the gap. After cleaning a piston, rotate the crankshaft so that the piston moves down the bore, and then wipe out the grease and carbon with a cloth rag. Clean the other piston crowns in the same way.

39 Check the head and block for nicks, deep scratches and other damage. If slight, they may be removed carefully with a file. More serious damage may be repaired by machining, but this is a specialist job.

40 If warpage of the cylinder head is suspected, use a straight-edge to check it for distortion, as described in Chapter 2D Section 7.

41 Ensure that the cylinder head bolt holes in the crankcase are clean and free of oil. Syringe or soak up any oil left in the bolt holes. This is most important in order that the correct bolt tightening torque can be applied,

and to prevent the possibility of the block being cracked by hydraulic pressure when the bolts are tightened.

42 Turn the crankshaft anti-clockwise until all the pistons at an equal height, approximately half-way down their bores from the TDC position (see Section 3). This will eliminate any risk of piston-to-valve contact as the cylinder head is refitted.

43 Ensure that the cylinder head locating dowels are in place in the cylinder block, and then fit the new cylinder head gasket over the dowels, ensuring that the part number is uppermost **(see illustrations)**. Note that Volkswagen recommend that the gasket is only removed from its packaging immediately prior to fitting.

44 Lower the cylinder head into position on the gasket, ensuring that it engages correctly over the dowels **(see illustration)**. Refit the timing belt tensioner as the cylinder head is refitted.

45 Fit the new cylinder head bolts to the locations, and screw them in as far as possible by hand. Do not oil the bolt threads.

46 Working progressively, in sequence, tighten all the cylinder head bolts to the specified Stage 1 torque **(see illustration)**.

47 Again working progressively, in sequence, tighten all the cylinder head bolts to the specified Stage 2 torque.

48 Tighten all the cylinder head bolts, in sequence, through the specified Stage 3 angle **(see illustration)**.

49 Finally, tighten all the cylinder head bolts, in sequence, through the specified Stage 4 angle.

11.44 Lower the head into position

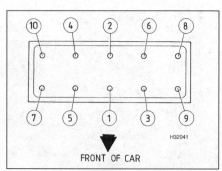

11.46 Cylinder head bolt tightening sequence

11.48 Use an angle-tightening gauge

12.5a Release the clips at the rear of the sump

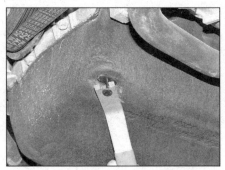

12.5b At the front, prise down the centre pin and pull the clip downwards

12.5c Remove the insulation cover from the around the sump

50 The remainder of the refitting procedure is a reversal of the removal procedure, noting the following points:
a) *Tighten all fasteners to their specified torque where given.*
b) *Renew all seals and gaskets.*
c) *Refill the cooling system as described, in Chapter 1BSection 33.*
d) *Refill the engine oil, as described in Chapter 1B Section 6.*
e) *Ensure all wiring is correctly routed.*
f) *Run the vehicle and make sure the cooling fans operate when the engine gets up to temperature.*
g) *Where new components have been installed (cylinder head, short engine, camshaft housing or turbocharger) then the engine oil pressure should be set to maximum (using a diagnostic tool) for run in period of 6000 miles.*

12 Sump – removal and refitting

Removal

1 Apply the handbrake, then jack up the front of the vehicle and support securely on axle stands (see *Jacking and vehicle support*).
2 Remove the securing screws and remove the engine undershield(s).
3 Disconnect the wiring plug from the level sensor.
4 Drain the engine oil as described in Chapter 1B Section 6.

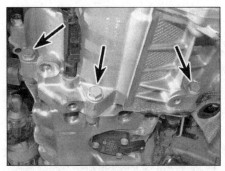

12.6a Undo the three transmission to sump bolts...

12.6b Lower the sump from the cylinder block

5 Release the retaining clips and remove the sump insulation cover from the sump **(see illustrations)**.
6 Unscrew and remove the bolts securing the sump to the transmission. Remove the sump to block bolts and then withdraw the sump **(see illustrations)**. If necessary, release the sump by tapping with a soft-faced hammer. due to the adhesive nature of the sealant, prising the sump from the block may be required. Avoid damaging the mating surfaces.

Refitting

7 Begin refitting by thoroughly cleaning the mating faces of the sump and cylinder block. Ensure that all traces of old sealant are removed.
8 Ensure that the cylinder block mating face of the sump is free from all traces of old sealant, oil and grease, and then apply a 2.0

to 3.0 mm thick bead of silicone sealant (VW D 176 404 A2 or equivalent) to the sump. On versions where there is a slight mismatch between the oil seal housing (timing belt end) and the block the diameter of the sealant applied should be increased to 3.0 to 4.0 mm **(see illustrations)**. Note that the sealant should be run around the inside of the bolt holes in the sump. The sump must be fitted within 5 minutes of applying the sealant.
9 Offer the sump up to the cylinder block, then refit the sump-to-cylinder block bolts, and lightly tighten them by hand, working progressively in a diagonal sequence in two stages. Note that the sump to transmission bolts have a higher torque setting. **Note:** *If the sump is being refitted with the engine and transmission separated, make sure that the sump is flush with the flywheel end of the cylinder block* **(see illustration)**.

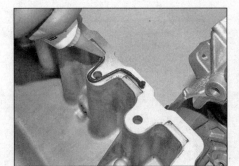

12.8a The sealant must run inside the bolt holds

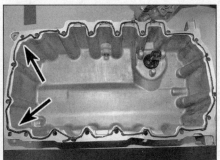

12.8b Increase the diameter of the sealant (see text) between the points (A)

12.9 Check that the sump is flush with the block

10 Refit the sump to transmission casing bolts, and tighten them lightly, using a socket.
11 Again working in a diagonal sequence, lightly tighten the sump-to-cylinder block bolts, using a socket.
12 Tighten the sump to transmission casing bolts to the specified torque.
13 Working in a diagonal sequence, progressively tighten the sump-to-cylinder block bolts to the specified torque.
14 The remainder of refitting is a reversal of removal, noting to allow at least 30 minutes from the time of refitting the sump for the sealant to dry, then refill the engine with oil, with reference to Chapter 1B Section 6.

13.2a Remove the oil pick-up pipe/filter...

13.2b ...and recover the O-ring seal

13 Oil pump and drivebelt – removal, inspection and refitting

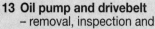

Note: *The oil pump is a variable pressure pump and also the vacuum pump. Individual parts are not available.*

Oil pump removal

1 Remove the sump as described in Section 12.
2 Unscrew the flange bolts and remove the oil pick-up pipe/filter from the oil pump **(see illustrations)**. Recover the O-ring seal and discard, as a new one will be required for refitting.
3 Unscrew and remove the mounting bolts, and release the oil pump from the dowels in the crankcase. Unhook the oil pump drive sprocket from the belt and withdraw the oil pump and oil pick-up pipe from the engine (see illustrations).

Drivebelt removal

4 If the drivebelt requires replacement, remove the timing belt (Section 7) and the timing belt crankshaft sprocket (Section 8).
5 Protect the nose of the crankshaft by taping it up (or by fitting a protective sleeve – special tool T1005/3) and then remove the bolts. Release the oil seal housing and slide it off the crankshaft nose, taking care not to damage the oil seal **(see illustrations)**. Note that the seal is part of the housing and not available separately.
6 Unhook the oil pump drivebelt from the sprocket and remove it **(see illustration)**.

Oil pump and drivebelt inspection

7 Clean the pump thoroughly, and inspect for signs of damage or wear. If evident, renew the oil pump. At the time of writing no parts were available.
8 If the drivebelt has been removed, replace it regardless of the condition.

Drivebelt refitting

9 Fit the new drivebelt over the crankshaft sprocket.
10 Clean the face of the sump (if still in place) of all the old sealant and then apply a 2-3 mm wide bead of sealant (D 176 404 A2 or equivalent) to the housing on the inside of the bolts. Note that sealant is only applied to the sump interface as the housing has a built in seal. If the sump is in position, because the oil seal housing has be removed to cure a leaking oil seal for example, apply sealant to the base of the housing (where it meets the sump). Install the housing within 5 minutes of applying the sealant.

13.3a Oil pump mounting bolts

13.3b Note the different length bolts

13.3c Recover the pump to block seal

13.5a Remove the bolts and...

13.5b ...slide off the housing

13.6 Remove the belt

13.11 Installing the housing over the protective sleeve

13.16 Fit a new seal to the end of the oil pick-up pipe

14.3 Flywheel bolts are offset and can only be fitted in one position – DSG transmission shown

11 Slide the housing over the nose of the crankshaft and install the bolts. Remove the tape (or sleeve) from the nose of the crankshaft **(see illustration)**.

12 Fully tighten the bolts to the specified torque in a diagonal sequence. Remove any surplus sealant from the bottom of the block.

13 Refit the crankshaft sprocket (Section 8) and timing belt as described in Section 7.

Oil pump refitting

14 Prime the pump with oil by pouring oil into the pick-up pipe aperture while turning the driveshaft.

15 Engage the oil pump sprocket with the drive belt, and then locate the oil pump on the dowels. Refit and tighten the mounting bolts to the specified torque.

16 Refit the pick-up pipe to the oil pump, using a new O-ring seal, and tighten the securing bolts **(see illustration)**.

17 Refit the sump as described in Section 12.

18 Replace the engine oil and filter as described in Chapter 1B Section 6. Do not fill the engine to the maximum mark at this point, just ensure the level is above minimum, as the level will rise when the vehicle is lowered to the ground.

19 Disable the engine and then crank the engine over until the oil pressure warning light(s) has gone out. Check the oil level (topping up if required) and then start the engine. Check for oil leaks from around the sump and crankshaft (if the crankshaft oil seal/flange has been removed or replaced).

20 Fit the engine undershield and lower the vehicle to the ground. Make a final check of the oil level, top up the level up if required.

14 Flywheel – removal, inspection and refitting

Removal

1 On manual gearbox models, remove the gearbox (see Chapter 7A Section 3) and clutch (see Chapter 6A Section 5).

2 On semi-automatic (DSG) transmission models, remove the transmission as described in Chapter 7B Section 2.

3 The flywheel can only be fitted in one position due to the offset of the flywheel mounting holes in the end of the crankshaft **(see illustration)**.

4 Rotate the outside of the dual-mass flywheel so that the bolts align with the holes (if necessary).

5 Unscrew the bolts and remove the flywheel. Using a locking tool, counter-hold the flywheel to prevent it from turning **(see illustration)**. Discard the bolts, as new ones must be fitted. **Note:** *In order not to damage the flywheel, do not allow the bolt heads to make contact with the flywheel during the unscrewing procedure.*

Inspection

6 Check the dual-mass flywheel for wear and damage. Examine the starter ring gear for excessive wear to the teeth. If the driveplate or its ring gear are damaged, the complete driveplate must be renewed. The flywheel ring gear, however, may be renewed separately from the flywheel, but the work should be entrusted to a dealer. If the clutch friction face is discoloured or scored excessively, it may be possible to regrind it, but this work should also be entrusted to a dealer.

7 The following are guidelines only, but should indicate whether professional inspection is necessary. The dual-mass flywheel should be checked as follows:

Warpage

8 Place a straight edge across the face of the drive surface, and check by trying to insert a feeler gauge between the straight edge and the drive surface **(see illustration)**. The flywheel will normally warp like a bowl – ie. Higher on the outer edge. If the warpage is more than 0.40 mm, the flywheel may need replacing.

Free rotational movement

9 This is the distance the drive surface of the flywheel can be turned independently of the flywheel primary element, using finger effort alone. Move the drive surface in one direction and make a mark where the locating pin aligns with the flywheel edge. Move the drive surface in the other direction (finger pressure only) and make another mark **(see illustration)**. The total of free movement should not exceed 20.0 mm. If it's more, the flywheel may need replacing.

14.5 Use a locking tool to counterhold the flywheel

14.8 Flywheel warpage check – see text

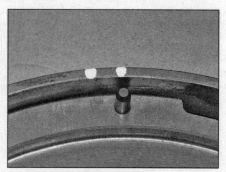

14.9 Flywheel free rotational movement check alignment marks – see text

Total rotational movement

10 This is the total distance the drive surface can be turned independently of the flywheel primary element. Insert two bolts into the clutch pressure plate/damper unit mounting holes, and with the crankshaft/flywheel held stationary, use a lever/pry bar between the bolts and use some effort to move the drive surface fully in one direction – make a mark where the locating pin aligns with the flywheel edge. Now force the drive surface fully in the opposite direction, and make another mark. The total rotational movement should not exceed 44.00 mm. If it does, have the flywheel professionally inspected.

Lateral movement

11 The lateral movement (up and down) of the drive surface in relation to the primary element of the flywheel, should not exceed 2.0 mm. If it does, the flywheel may need replacing. This can be checked by pressing the drive surface down on one side into the flywheel (flywheel horizontal) and making an alignment mark between the drive surface and the inner edge of the primary element. Now press down on the opposite side of the drive surface, and make another mark above the original one. The difference between the two marks is the lateral movement **(see illustration)**.

12 There should be no cracks in the drive surface of the flywheel. If cracks are evident, the flywheel may need replacing.

Refitting

13 Refitting is a reversal of removal. Use new bolts when refitting the flywheel or driveplate **(see illustration)**, and coat the threads of

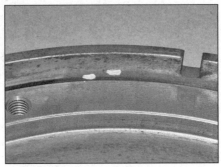

14.11 Flywheel lateral movement check marks – see text

the bolts (if not already coated with locking compound) with locking fluid before inserting them. Tighten them to the specified torque.

15 Crankshaft oil seals – renewal

Note: *The oil seals are a PTFE (Teflon) type and are fitted dry, without using any grease or oil. These have a wider sealing lip and have been introduced instead of the coil spring type oil seal.*

Timing belt end oil seal

1 The oil seal and housing are a single item. Removal and refitting of the seal is described in Section 13 (oil pump drivebelt).

Flywheel end oil seal

Note: *In these engines, the seal, sealing flange and sender wheel are a complete unit. Special*

14.13 Use new bolts when refitting

tools are required to refit the sealing flange, and press the sender wheel onto the end of the crankshaft. It is not possible to accurately fit these parts without the special Volkswagen group tools (T10134). They are also available from aftermarket automotive tool specialists. E.g. Draper tools, AST. Laser etc).

2 Remove the flywheel as described in Section 14, then prise the intermediate plate from the locating dowels on the cylinder block and unhook it from behind the top of the seal housing **(see illustrations)**.

3 Undo the bolt securing the crankshaft speed sensor and remove it from the seal housing, then undo the bolts securing the sealing flange to the cylinder block **(see illustrations)**.

4 Insert three 6 x 35 mm bolts into the threaded holes in the sealing flange. Tighten the bolts gradually and evenly, and press the sealing flange, and sender wheel from the crankshaft/cylinder block **(see illustrations)**.

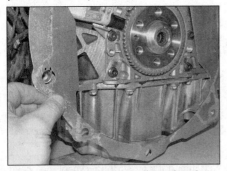

15.2a Remove the intermediate plate from the dowels …

15.2b … and from behind the top of the crankshaft seal housing

15.3a Undo the crankshaft speed sensor retaining bolt

15.3b Sealing flange bolts

15.4a Screw in three 6 x 35 mm bolts …

15.4b …and draw the sealing flange and sender wheel from place

15.6a Rotate the nut until its level with the end of the flat clamping surface…

15.6b …then clamp it in a vice

15.7a Rotate the nut until the inner part of the tool …

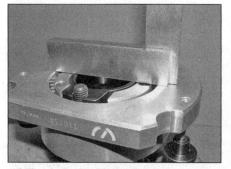

15.7b …is flush with the flat surface of the housing

15.8a Remove the securing clip …

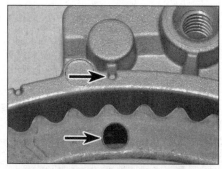

15.8b …the hole in the sender wheel should align with the marking on the flange

The seal, sender wheel and sealing flange are supplied as a complete unit.

5 Ensure the mating face of the cylinder block is clean and free from debris. The new sealing flange/seal/sender wheel assembly is supplied with a sealing lip support ring, which serves as a fitting sleeve, and must not be removed prior to installation. Equally, the sender wheel must not be separated from the assembly.

6 If using the VW tool, proceed as follows. If using an aftermarket tool specialist's product, follow the instructions supplied with the tool. Rotate the large spindle nut until it's level with the end of the clamping surface of the spindle, then clamp the spindle in a vice (see illustrations).

7 Press the tool housing downwards until it rests on the nut and washer. Rotate the nut until the inner part of the tool is at the same height as the housing (see illustrations).

8 Remove the seal securing clip. The hole on the sender wheel must align with the marking on the sealing flange (see illustrations).

9 Place the flange outer side down on a clean, flat surface, then press the seal guide fitting sleeve (supplied ready fitted), housing, and sender wheel downwards until all the components are flat on the surface. In this position the upper edge of the sender wheel should be level with the edge of the sealing flange (see illustrations).

10 Place the sealing flange on the assembly tool, so the pin locates in the hole in the sender wheel (see illustration).

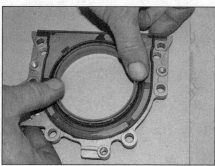

15.9a Press the assembly downwards on a clean, flat surface…

11 Push the sealing flange and guide fitting sleeve against the tool whilst tightening the 3 knurled screws. Ensure the pin is still located in the sender wheel (see illustration).

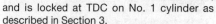

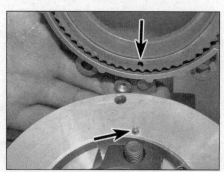

15.10 Fit the flange to the tool, ensuring the pin locates in the hole

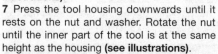

15.9b …so the upper edge of the sender wheel is level with the edge of the flange

12 Ensure the end of the crankshaft is clean, and is locked at TDC on No. 1 cylinder as described in Section 3.

13 Unscrew the large nut to the end of

15.11 With the pin engaged in the hole, tighten the 3 knurled screws to secure the flange to the tool

15.13a Unscrew the nut to the end of the thread …

15.13b …and push the spindle in as far as possible

15.14 Hand-tighten the hex bolts to secure the tool to the crankshaft

the spindle threads, then press the spindle inwards as far as possible **(see illustrations)**.

14 Align the flat side of the assembly with the sump flange, then secure the tool to the crankshaft using the integral Allen bolts **(see illustration)**. Only hand tighten the bolts.

15 Insert two M7x 35 mm bolts to guide the sealing flange to the cylinder block **(see illustration)**.

16 Using hand pressure alone, push the tool assembly onto the crankshaft until the seal guide fitting sleeve contacts the crankshaft flange, then push the guide pin (black knob) into the hole in the crankshaft. This is to ensure the sender wheel reaches its correct installation position **(see illustration)**.

17 Rotate the large nut until it makes contact with the tool housing, then tighten it to 35 Nm. After tightening this nut, a small air gap must

still be present between the sealing flange and cylinder block **(see illustrations)**.

18 Unscrew the large nut; the two M7 x 35 Nm screws, the three knurled screws and the Allen bolts securing the tool to the crankshaft. Remove the tool, and pull the seal guide fitting sleeve from place (if it didn't come out with the tool) **(see illustration)**.

19 Use a vernier caliper or feeler gauge to measure the fitted depth of the sender wheel in relation to the crankshaft flange **(see illustration)**. The correct depth is 0.5 mm.

20 If the gap is correct, fit the sealing flange bolts and tighten them to the specified torque.

21 If the gap is too small, re-attach the tool to the sealing flange and crankshaft, then refit the two M7 x 35 mm guide bolts to the flange. Tighten the large spindle nut to 40 Nm, remove the tool and re-measure the air gap. If

the gap is still too small, re-attach the tool and tighten the spindle nut to 45 Nm. Re-measure the gap. When the gap is correct, refit the flange retaining bolts, and tighten them to the specified torque.

22 The remainder of refitting is a reversal of removal.

16 Engine mountings – inspection and renewal

Inspection

1 If improved access is required, jack up the front of the vehicle, and support it securely on axle stands (see *Jacking and vehicle support*). Remove the engine undertray(s).

15.15 Use two M7 x 35 mm bolts to guide the sealing flange

15.16 Push the black knob into the hole in the crankshaft

15.17a After tightening the spindle nut to 35 Nm …

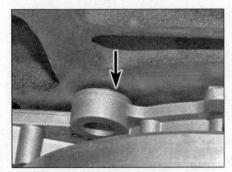

15.17b …there should be an air gap between the sealing flange and the cylinder block

15.18 Remove the tool and seal fitting guide sleeve

15.19 Measure the fitted depth of the sender wheel in relation to the end of the crankshaft

16.7 Disconnect the level sensor wiring plug

16.8 Unclip the reservoir and move it to the side

16.9a Remove the bolts...

2 Check the mounting rubbers to see if they are cracked, hardened or separated from the metal at any point; renew the mounting if any such damage or deterioration is evident.

3 Check that all the mountings are securely tightened; use a torque wrench to check if possible.

4 Using a large screwdriver or a crowbar, check for wear in the mounting by carefully levering against it to check for free play. Where this is not possible, enlist the aid of an assistant to move the engine/transmission back-and-forth, or from side-to-side, whilst you observe the mounting. While some free play is to be expected, even from new components, excessive wear should be obvious. If excessive free play is found, check first that the fasteners are correctly secured, then renew any worn components as described in the following paragraphs.

Renewal

Right-hand mounting

5 Support the engine on a trolley jack under the sump. Use a block of wood between the sump and the head of the jack, to prevent any damage to the sump.

6 Unclip the fuel lines from the coolant reservoir.

7 Disconnect the level sensor wiring plug (see illustration).

8 Unclip the coolant reservoir and move it to one side (see illustration).

16.9b ...and then lift out the mounting

9 Unscrew the bolts securing the mounting to the body and then unscrew the bolts securing it to the engine bracket. Withdraw the mounting from the engine compartment (see illustrations).

10 Refitting is a reversal of removal, bearing in mind the following points.
a) Use new securing bolts.
b) Align the mounting as shown (see illustration).
c) Tighten all fixings to the specified torque.

Left-hand mounting

Note: New mounting bolts will be required on refitting.

11 Support the transmission on a trolley

16.10 Align the mounting so that the gap (A) = 10 mm with the bracket (B) parallel to the lower bracket (C)

jack with a block of wood placed between the head of the jack and the transmission to spread the load.

12 Remove the air filter (Chapter 1A Section 28) and the turbocharger inlet and outlet ducts.

13 Remove the battery and battery tray, as described in Chapter 5A Section 3.

14 On models fitted with a security cover remove the shear bolts and lift off the metal cover. Disconnect the wiring plugs from the ECU. Unclip the ECU from the bracket (see illustrations) and remove it from the vehicle.

15 Unbolt the ECU mounting bracket and then unclip the wiring loom sufficiently to

16.14a Disconnect the wiring plugs

16.14b Remove the ECU

16.14c Bag up the ECU wiring plugs to protect them from contamination

16.15 Lift up the loom to access the mounting bolts

16.16 Remove the bolts

expose the transmission mounting bolts **(see illustration)**.

16 Remove the mounting to body bolts and then remove the bolts securing the mounting to the transmission bracket **(see illustration)**.

17 Lift out the mounting and then where required, unbolt and remove the bracket from the transmission **(see illustration)**. Removal of the bracket is essential for transmission removal.

18 Refitting is a reversal of removal, bearing in mind the following points:
a) Use new mounting bolts.
b) Tighten all fixings to the specified torque.

Rear mounting (torque arm)

19 Apply the handbrake, then jack up the front of the vehicle and support securely on axle stands (see *Jacking and vehicle support*).

20 Working under the vehicle, unscrew and remove the bolt securing the mounting to the subframe **(see illustration)**.

21 Unscrew the two bolts securing the mounting to the transmission, then withdraw the mounting from under the vehicle.

22 Refitting is a reversal of removal, but use new mounting securing bolts, and tighten all fixings to the specified torque.

17 Engine oil cooler/filter housing – removal and refitting

Removal

Note: *The oil cooler is part of the oil filter housing and is removed with the housing. DO NOT separate the cooler from filter the housing. In the event of a fault or coolant/oil leak, the complete assembly must be replaced.*

1 Remove the air filter housing as described in Chapter 4B Section 3.

2 Remove the radiator cowl/fan housing as described in Chapter 3 Section 5.

3 Position a container beneath the oil filter housing to catch escaping oil and coolant.

4 Clamp the oil cooler coolant hoses to minimise coolant spillage, or drain the cooling system as described in Chapter 1B Section 33.

5 Disconnect the coolant pipes and then unbolt the intercooler coolant pump. Move the pump to the side.

6 Disconnect the wiring plugs from the oil pressure control valve and the oil pressure switches.

7 Unscrew the oil cooler/filter housing fixings (in a diagonal sequence) and remove the housing from the engine block. Discard the bolts and recover the gasket.

Refitting

8 Refitting is a reversal of removal, bearing in mind the following points:
a) Use a new gasket.
b) Fit new bolts and tighten them to the correct torque in a diagonal sequence.
c) On completion, check and if necessary top-up the oil and coolant levels.

16.17 Remove the bracket from the transmission

16.20 The rear torque arm

18 Oil pressure warning light switches and oil pressure regulating valve – removal and refitting

Note: *There are two oil pressure warning switches: A high pressure switch (brown) mounted to the front of the oil filter housing and a low pressure switch (green) mounted on the side of the housing. An oil pressure control valve is also fitted behind the AC compressor/ accessory mounting bracket.*

Oil pressure switches

Removal

1 Remove the engine cover. For access to the high pressure switch remove the radiator cowl as described in Chapter 3 Section 5. For access to the low pressure switch remove the air filter housing as described in Chapter 4B Section 3.
2 Disconnect the wiring plug of the appropriate switch **(see illustration)**.
3 Place a shop towel beneath the switch and then remove the switch. If the switch is to be left removed from the engine for any length of time, plug the aperture in the cylinder head.

Refitting

Note: *Volkswagen recommend replacement of the switch if it is removed*
4 Refitting is a reversal of removal. Check the engine oil level, run the engine and check for oil leaks on completion.

Oil pressure control valve

Removal

5 Remove the auxiliary drivebelt as described in Chapter 1B Section 30.
6 Unbolt the AC compressor and secure it to the side with cable ties or similar. DO NOT disconnect the refrigerant lines.
7 Disconnect the wiring plug and then place shop towels below the valve.
8 Unbolt the valve and remove it **(see illustration)**.

18.2 Disconnect the wiring plug (high pressure switch)

19.1 Oil level/temperature sensor location

Refitting

9 Refitting is a reversal of removal, bit fit a new O-ring seal to the valve.

19 Oil level/temperature sender – removal and refitting

Removal

1 The oil level/temperature sender is fitted to bottom of the sump **(see illustration)**.
2 Drain the engine oil as described in Chapter 1B Section 6.
3 Disconnect the wiring connector from the sender.

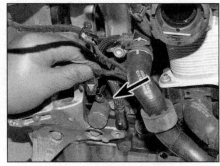

18.8 The oil pressure control valve

19.4 Remove the insulation cover to access the bolts

4 Release the retaining clips and remove the insulation cover from the sump **(see illustration)**.
5 Wipe clean the area around the sender, then undo the three retaining bolts and remove the sender.

Refitting

6 Examine the sealing washer for signs of damage or deterioration and if necessary renew.
7 Refit the switch and tighten the retaining bolts to the specified torque.
8 Refit the insulation cover, then reconnect the wiring connector and refill the engine with oil (refer to Chapter 1B Section 6).

Notes

Chapter 2 Part D
Engine removal and overhaul procedures

Contents

Section number

Crankshaft – checking endfloat and inspection 13
Crankshaft – refitting 17
Crankshaft – removal 10
Cylinder block/crankcase – cleaning and inspection 11
Cylinder head – dismantling 6
Cylinder head – reassembly 8
Cylinder head and valves – cleaning and inspection 7
Engine – initial start-up after overhaul and reassembly 19
Engine and transmission – removal and refitting 4
Engine overhaul – general information 2

Section number

Engine overhaul – preliminary information 5
Engine overhaul – reassembly sequence 15
Engine/transmission removal – preparation and precautions 3
General Information 1
Main and big-end bearings – inspection and selection 14
Piston rings – refitting 16
Piston/connecting rod assemblies – cleaning and inspection 12
Piston/connecting rod assemblies – refitting 18
Piston/connecting rod assemblies – removal 9

Degrees of difficulty

Easy, suitable for novice with little experience	**Fairly easy,** suitable for beginner with some experience	**Fairly difficult,** suitable for competent DIY mechanic	**Difficult,** suitable for experienced DIY mechanic	**Very difficult,** suitable for expert DIY or professional

Specifications

Engine codes*

1.2 litre petrol engine	CJZA, CJZB, and CYVA
1.4 litre petrol engine:	CPTA, CHPA, CMBA, CXSA, CPVA, CZEA and CZDA
2.0 litre petrol	CHHA, CHHB, CJXE and CXDA
1.6 litre diesel engine	CLHA, CLHB, CRKA, CRKB, CXXA, CXXB and DBKA
2.0 litre diesel engine	CKFC, CRBA, CRBC, CRLB, CRMB and CUNA

See 'Vehicle identification' at the end of this manual for the location of the engine code markings

Piston rings

	New	Wear limit
End gaps:		
1.2 and 1.4 petrol engines:		
Compression ring	0.20 to 0.35 mm	1.00 mm
Oil scraper ring (2 part)	0.20 to 0.40 mm	3.00 mm
Oilscarper ring (3 part)	0.50 to 0.75 mm	3.00 mm
2.0 litre:		
1st compression ring	0.30 to 0.40 mm	0.80 mm
2nd compression ring	0.40 to 0.50 mm	0.80 mm
Oil scraper ring	0.20 to 0.40 mm	0.80 mm
1.6 and 2.0 diesel engines:		
1st compression ring	0.30 to 0.40 mm	0.55 mm
2nd compression ring	0.20 mm to 0.45 mm	0.95 mm
Oil scraper ring	0.25 to 0.50 mm	0.75 mm
Ring-to-groove clearance:		
Petrol engines:		
1.2 and 1.4 litre:		
1st compression ring (Federal Mogul)	0.050 to 0.090 mm	0.15 mm
1st compression ring (Mahle)	0.035 to 0.085 mm	0.15 mm
2nd compression ring	0.030 to 0.070	0.15 mm
Oil scraper ring (3 parts)	Not measurable	
Oil scraper ring (2 parts)	0.04 to 0.80 mm	
2.0 litre:		
1st compression ring	0.06 to 0.09 mm	0.20 mm
2nd compression ring	0.03 to 0.06 mm	0.15 mm
Oil scraper ring	Not measurable	
1.6 and 2.0 diesel engines		
1st compression ring	0.06 to 0.09 mm	0.08 mm
2nd compression ring	0.05 to 0.08 mm	0.08 mm
Oil scraper ring	0.03 to 0.06 mm	0.08 mm

Crankshaft endfloat

	New	Wear limit
Petrol engines:		
1.2 and 1.4 litre*	0.066 to 0.233 mm	N/A
2.0 litre	0.07 to 0.23 mm	0.30 mm
1.6 and 2.0 diesel engines	0.07 to 0.17 mm	0.37 mm

Crankshaft must not be removed

Cylinder head

Maximum cylinder head gasket face distortion:
All engines	0.05 mm	

Valves

	Inlet valves	Exhaust valves
Valve stem diameter:		
Petrol engines:		
1.2 and 1.4 litre..	4.973 mm	4.963 mm
2.0 litre	5.98 mm	5.96 mm
Diesel engines:		
All engines	5.975 mm	5.965 mm
Valve seat angle (all engines)	45°	45°

Torque wrench settings

Refer to Chapter 2A, Chapter 2B or Chapter 2C specifications as applicable.

1 General Information

How to use this Chapter

1 Included in this Part of Chapter 2 are details of removing the engine from the car and general overhaul procedures for the cylinder head, cylinder block and all other engine internal components.

2 The information given ranges from advice concerning preparation for an overhaul and the purchase of new parts, to detailed step-by-step procedures covering removal, inspection, renovation and refitting of engine internal components.

3 After Section 6, all instructions are based on the assumption that the engine has been removed from the car. For information concerning in-car engine repair, as well as the removal and refitting of those external components necessary for full overhaul, refer to the relevant in-car repair procedure section and to Section 5 of this Chapter. Ignore any preliminary dismantling operations described in the relevant in-car repair sections that are no longer relevant once the engine has been removed from the car.

4 Apart from torque wrench settings, which are given at the beginning of the relevant in-car repair procedure in Chapter 2A Section 0, Chapter 2B Section 0 or Chapter 2C Section 0 (as applicable) all specifications relating to engine overhaul are given at the beginning of this Part of Chapter 2.

2 Engine overhaul – general information

1 It is not always easy to determine when, or if, an engine should be completely overhauled, as a number of factors must be considered.

2 High mileage is not necessarily an indication that an overhaul is needed, while low mileage does not preclude the need for an overhaul. Frequency of servicing is probably the most important consideration. An engine which has had regular and frequent oil and filter changes, as well as other required maintenance, should give many thousands of miles of reliable service. Conversely, a neglected engine may require an overhaul very early in its life.

3 Excessive oil consumption is an indication that piston rings, valve seals and/or valve guides are in need of attention. Make sure that oil leaks are not responsible before deciding that the rings and/or guides are worn. Perform a compression (or leakdown) test, as described in Chapter 2A Section 3 (1.2 and 1.4 litre petrol engines) Chapter 2B Section 3 (2.0 litre petrol engines) Chapter 2C Section 2 (diesel engines), as applicable to determine the likely cause of the problem.

4 Check the oil pressure with a gauge fitted in place of the oil pressure switch, and compare it with that specified (see Specifications in Chapter 2A Section 0, Chapter 2B Section 0 or Chapter 2C Section 0). If it is extremely low, the main and big-end bearings, and/or the oil pump, are probably worn.

5 Loss of power, rough running, knocking or metallic engine noises, excessive valve gear noise, and high fuel consumption may also point to the need for an overhaul, especially if they are all present at the same time. If a complete service does not remedy the situation, major mechanical work is the only solution.

6 An engine overhaul involves restoring all internal parts to the specification of a new engine. During an overhaul, the pistons and the piston rings are renewed. New main and big-end bearings are generally fitted (where possible); if necessary, the crankshaft may be renewed to restore the journals. The valves are also serviced as well, since they are usually in less-than-perfect condition at this point. While the engine is being overhauled, other components, such as the starter and alternator, can be overhauled as well. The end result should be an as-new engine that will give many trouble-free miles. **Note:** *Critical cooling system components such as the hoses, thermostat and coolant pump should be renewed when an engine is overhauled. The radiator should be checked carefully, to ensure that it is not clogged or leaking. Also, it is a good idea to renew the oil pump whenever the engine is overhauled.*

7 Before beginning the engine overhaul, read through the entire procedure, to familiarise yourself with the scope and requirements of the job. Overhauling an engine is not difficult if you follow carefully all of the instructions, have the necessary tools and equipment, and pay close attention to all specifications. It can, however, be time-consuming. Plan on the

car being off the road for a minimum of two weeks, especially if parts must be taken to an engineering works for repair or reconditioning. Check on the availability of parts and make sure that any necessary special tools and equipment are obtained in advance. Most work can be done with typical hand tools, although a number of precision measuring tools are required for inspecting parts to determine if they must be renewed. Often the engineering works will handle the inspection of parts and offer advice concerning reconditioning and renewal. **Note:** *Always wait until the engine has been completely dismantled, and until all components (especially the cylinder block and the crankshaft) have been inspected, before deciding what service and repair operations must be performed by an engineering works. The condition of these components will be the major factor to consider when determining whether to overhaul the original engine, or to buy a reconditioned unit. Do not, therefore, purchase parts or have overhaul work done on other components until they have been thoroughly inspected. As a general rule, time is the primary cost of an overhaul, so it does not pay to fit worn or sub-standard parts.*

8 As a final note, to ensure maximum life and minimum trouble from a reconditioned engine, everything must be assembled with care, in a spotlessly-clean environment.

3 Engine/transmission removal – preparation and precautions

1 If you have decided that the engine must be removed for overhaul or major repair work, several preliminary steps should be taken.
2 Locating a suitable place to work is extremely important. Adequate work space, along with storage space for the vehicle, will be needed. If a workshop or garage is not available, at the very least a solid, level, clean work surface is required.
3 If possible, clear some shelving close to the work area and use it to store the engine components and ancillaries as they are removed and dismantled. In this manner, the components stand a better chance of staying clean and undamaged during the overhaul. Laying out

components in groups together with their fixings bolts, screws, etc, will save time and avoid confusion when the engine is refitted.
4 Clean the engine compartment and engine before beginning the removal procedure; this will help visibility and help to keep tools clean.
5 The help of an assistant is essential; there are certain instances when one person cannot safely perform all of the operations required to remove the engine from the vehicle. Safety is of primary importance, considering the potential hazards involved in this kind of operation. A second person should always be in attendance to offer help in an emergency. If this is the first time you have removed an engine, advice and aid from someone more experienced would also be beneficial.
6 Plan the operation ahead of time. Before starting work, obtain (or arrange for the hire of) all of the tools and equipment you will need. Access to the following items will allow the task of removing and refitting the engine to be completed safely and with relative ease: a hoist and lifting tackle – rated in excess of the weight of the engine, complete sets of spanners and sockets as described at the rear of this manual, wooden blocks, and plenty of rags and cleaning solvent for mopping-up spilled oil, coolant and fuel. A selection of different-sized plastic storage bins will also prove useful for keeping dismantled components grouped together. If any of the equipment must be hired, make sure that you arrange for it in advance, and perform all of the operations possible without it beforehand; this may save you time and money.
7 Plan on the vehicle being out of use for quite a while, especially if you intend to carry out an engine overhaul. Read through the whole of this Section and work out a strategy based on your own experience, and the tools, time and workspace available to you. Some of the overhaul processes may have to be carried out by a Volkswagen dealer or an automotive machine shop – these establishments often have busy schedules, so it would be prudent to consult them before removing or dismantling the engine, to get an idea of the amount of time required to carry out the work.
8 When removing the engine from the vehicle, be methodical about the disconnection of

external components. Labelling cables and hoses as they are removed will greatly assist the refitting process.
9 Always be extremely careful when lifting the engine from the engine compartment. Serious injury can result from careless actions. If help is required, it is better to wait until it is available rather than risk personal injury and/ or damage components by continuing alone. By planning ahead and taking your time, a job of this nature, although major, can be accomplished successfully and without incident.

4 Engine and transmission – removal and refitting

Removal

1 For the home mechanic the easiest way to remove the engine and transmission assembly is by completely removing the front lock carrier panel and dragging the assembly out of the front of the engine bay. On models with air conditioning the AC system must be de-gassed (by an air conditioning specialist) before removing the panel. Alternatively the engine and transmission can be removed by lowering it from the engine bay. However this approach still requires the lock carrier moving to the service position (as described in this section), so it may as well be removed completely.
2 Switch off the ignition and all electrical consumers, and remove the ignition key.
3 Where fitted, remove the engine top cover and air filter, as described in Chapter 4A Section 3 (petrol engines) or Chapter 4B Section 3 (diesel engines) and all associated air ducting (see illustration).
4 Remove the battery as described in Chapter 5A Section 3, then remove the battery tray (see illustrations).
5 Apply the handbrake, then jack up the front of the vehicle and support it on axle stands (see *Jacking and vehicle support*). Remove both front roadwheels.
6 Drain the cooling system as described in Chapter 1A Section 33 (petrol engines) or Chapter 1B Section 33 (diesel engines).

4.3 Remove the air filter housing

4.4a Remove the battery...

4.4b ...and tray

4.8 Mark the position of the lock carrier in relation to the chaasi legs

4.9a Support the lock carrier with the factory tool…

4.9b …or a length of threaded bar

7 Move the lock carrier to the service position by:
a) *Removing the bumper cover (Chapter 11 Section 6).*
b) *Removing both headlights (Chapter 12 Section 8).*
c) *Disconnecting the bonnet release cable at the junction on the right-hand side (Chapter 11 Section 9).*
d) *Unplug the ambient air temperature sensor.*
e) *On models with ACC (Active Cruise Control) disconnect the wiring plug from the sensor.*
f) *Unclipping the windscreen washer neck from the slam panel.*

8 Mark the position of the panel before removal **(see illustration)**.
9 Remove a single bolt from each end of the lock carrier and insert either the correct

special tool (T10093) or lengths of threaded bar (approximately 300 mm long) **(see illustrations)**.
10 Remove the remaining bolts from the front panel and pull the panel forward enough to access the coolant hoses, intercooler hoses and the AC refrigerant lines.

 Warning: The AC system must be evacuated using specialist equipment. It is a criminal offence to knowingly discharge the refrigerant to atmosphere.

11 Disconnect the coolant hoses from the radiator and intercooler and then disconnect the refrigerant lines at the condenser **(see illustration)**.
12 Disconnect the wiring plugs from the bonnet lock switch, the crash sensor and the radiator fans.
13 Check that everything is disconnected

and then with the aid of an assistant remove the lock carrier panel complete with the fans, radiator and intercooler.
14 Noting their locations, disconnect all wiring, coolant hoses, vacuum hoses and fuel lines from the engine/transmission, with reference to the relevant Chapters of this Manual. Alternatively, the engine wiring loom may remain on the engine by disconnecting it from engine management ECU as described in Chapter 4A Section 4 (petrol engines) or Chapter 4B Section 4 (diesel engines). Tape over or plug fuel lines to prevent entry of dust and dirt **(see illustrations)**.
15 Remove the front exhaust pipe/catalytic converter **(see illustrations)**as described in Chapter 4C Section 6 (petrol engines) or Chapter 4D Section 9 (diesel engines).
16 Unbolt the rear engine support/torque arm from the transmission **(see illustration)**.

4.11 Disconnect the refrigerant lines

4.14a Unplug the connectors from the ECU

4.14b Disconnect and seal the fuel lines

4.15a Disconnect the exhaust system from the catalytic converter/DPF on the diesel engine…

4.15b …and on the petrol engines (2.0 litre shown)

4.16 Remove the rear engine torque arm

4.17 Disconnect the gearchange cables and unbolt the bracket

4.20 Unbolt the driveshafts

4.22 Preparing to lift the engine/transmission with an engine crane

4.23 Remove the mountings with the engine supported

17 Disconnect the gearchange mechanism **(see illustration)** with reference to Chapter 7A Section 2 (manual transmission) or Chapter 7B Section 4 (DSG transmission)

18 On manual transmission models, remove the clutch slave cylinder or disconnect the clutch hose (models with a concentric slave cylinder). **Note:** *Do not depress the clutch pedal once the slave cylinder has been removed.*

19 Whilst access is easy (assuming the lock carrier has been removed), refer to Chapter 3 Section 12 and unbolt the air conditioning compressor from the front of the engine. If the AC system has been de-gassed remove the compressor completely. If the AC system is still charged (because the lock carrier is only in the service position) suspend the compressor to one side of the engine compartment and do not remove the refrigerant lines.

20 Disconnect the driveshafts from the transmission drive flanges as described in Chapter Section. Suspend them from the underbody or remove them completely **(see illustration)**.

21 Unclip the coolant expansion tank and place to one side.

22 Connect a hoist and lifting tackle to the engine lifting brackets on the cylinder head, and raise the hoist to just take the weight of the engine/transmission **(see illustration)**.

23 Unbolt the right and left-hand engine mountings **(see illustration)**.

24 Make a final check to ensure that all relevant wiring, hoses and pipes have been disconnected, then carefully withdraw the engine and transmission the engine compartment, lifting and lowering as required.

Separation

Engine and transmission

25 Remove the starter motor as described in Chapter 5A Section 8.

26 Ensure that both engine and transmission are adequately supported, then unscrew the engine to transmission bolts, noting the location of each bolt, and the locations of any brackets secured by the bolts.

27 Carefully withdraw the transmission from the engine, ensuring that the weight of the transmission is not allowed to hang on the input shaft while it is engaged with the clutch friction disc. Recover the engine-to-transmission plate **(see illustrations)**.

4.27a The transmission separated from the engine

4.27b Remove the end plate

Reconnection and refitting

Engine and transmission

28 Reconnection and refitting are a reversal of removal, bearing in mind the following points:

a) *Ensure that any brackets noted before removal are in place on the engine-to-transmission bolts.*

b) *Tighten all fixings to the specified torque, where given.*

c) *Where applicable, have the air conditioning system recharged with refrigerant by a suitably-qualified professional.*

d) *Ensure that all wiring, hoses and pipes are correctly reconnected and routed as noted before removal.*

e) *Ensure that the fuel lines are correctly reconnected.*

f) *On completion, refill the cooling system as described in Chapter 1A Section 33 (petrol engines) or Chapter 1B Section 33 (diesel engines).*

5 Engine overhaul – preliminary information

1 It is much easier to dismantle and work on the engine if it is mounted on a portable engine stand. These stands can often be hired from a tool hire shop. Before the engine is mounted on a stand, the flywheel should be removed, so that the stand bolts can be tightened into the end of the cylinder block/crankcase. **Note:** *Do not measure cylinder bore dimensions with the engine mounted on this type of stand.*

2 If a stand is not available, it is possible to dismantle the engine with it blocked up on a sturdy workbench, or on the floor. Be very careful not to tip or drop the engine when working without a stand.

3 If you intend to obtain a reconditioned engine, all ancillaries must be removed first, to be transferred to the new engine (just as they will if you are doing a complete engine overhaul yourself). These components include the following (it may be necessary to transfer additional components, such as the oil level dipstick/tube assembly, oil filter housing, etc, depending on which components are supplied with the reconditioned engine:

Petrol engines

a) *Alternator (including mounting brackets) and starter motor (Chapter 5A Section 5).*

b) *The ignition system components including all sensors and spark plugs (Chapter 1A Section 29 and Chapter 5B Section 3).*

c) *The fuel injection system components (Chapter 4A Section 4).*

d) *All electrical switches, actuators and sensors, and the engine wiring harness.*

e) *Inlet and manifolds and the turbocharger (Chapter 4A Section 8, Chapter 4C*

Section 6 and Chapter 4C Section 4).

f) *Engine mountings (Chapter 2A Section 17 or Chapter 2B Section 17).*

g) *Clutch components (Chapter 6A Section 5 or Chapter 6B Section 2 or Chapter 6B Section 3).*

h) *Oil separator (where applicable).*

i) *Vacuum pump (Chapter 9 Section 20 – 2.0 litre engines only).*

Diesel engines

a) *Alternator (including mounting brackets) and starter motor (Chapter 5A Section 5).*

b) *The glow plug/preheating system components (Chapter 5C Section 2).*

c) *All fuel system components, including fuel injectors, all sensors and actuators (Chapter 4B Section 4).*

d) *The brake vacuum pump (Chapter 2C Section 13).*

e) *All electrical switches, actuators and sensors, and the engine wiring harness.*

f) *Inlet manifolds and turbocharger (Chapter 4B Section 6 and Chapter 4D Section 5).*

g) *Engine mountings (see Chapter 2C Section 16).*

h) *Clutch components (Chapter 6A Section 5, Chapter 6B Section 2 or Chapter 6B Section 3).*

All engines

Note: *When removing the external components from the engine, pay close attention to details that may be helpful or important during refitting. Note the fitted position of gaskets, seals, spacers, pins, washers, bolts, and other small components.*

4 If you are obtaining a short engine (the engine cylinder block/crankcase, crankshaft, pistons and connecting rods, all fully assembled), then the cylinder head, sump, oil pump, timing belt(s) and chain (as applicable – together with tensioner(s) and covers), auxiliary drivebelt (together with its tensioner), coolant pump, thermostat housing, coolant outlet elbows, oil filter housing and where applicable oil cooler will also have to be removed.

5 If you are planning a full overhaul, the engine can be dismantled in the order given below:

a) *Inlet manifolds and turbocharger.*

b) *Timing belt (or chain), sprockets and tensioner.*

c) *Cylinder head.*

d) *Flywheel.*

e) *Sump.*

f) *Oil pump.*

g) *Piston/connecting rod assemblies.*

h) *Crankshaft.*

6 Cylinder head – dismantling

Note: *A valve spring compressor tool will be required for this operation.*

1 With the cylinder head removed (as described in Chapter 2A Section 12, Chapter 2B Section 10 or Chapter 2C Section 11) proceed as follows.

2 Remove the camshaft and hydraulic tappets/roller rocker fingers, as described in Chapter 2A Section 10, Chapter 2B Section 11 or Chapter 2C Section 9.

3 On 2.0 litre petrol engines and all diesel engines remove the coolant hose outlets.

4 On diesel engine, if not already done so, remove the glow plugs, with reference to Chapter 5C Section 2.

5 On diesel engines, unscrew the nut and remove the timing belt tensioner pulley from the stud on the timing belt end of the cylinder head and then remove the stud.

6 Unbolt any remaining auxiliary brackets and/or engine lifting brackets from the cylinder head as necessary, noting their locations to aid refitting.

7 Turn the cylinder head over, and rest it on one side.

8 Using a valve spring compressor, compress each valve spring in turn until the split collets can be removed. Release the compressor, and lift off the spring cap and spring. If, when the valve spring compressor is screwed down, the spring cap refuses to free and expose the split collets, gently tap the top of the tool, directly over the spring cap, with a light hammer. This will free the retainer **(see illustrations)**.

6.8a Compress a valve spring with a compressor tool

6.8b Remove the collets and release the spring compressor

6.8c Remove the spring cap...

6.8d ...and valve spring

6.9a The valve guide oil seals are removed...

9 Using a pair of pliers, or a removal tool, carefully extract the valve stem oil seal from the top of the valve guide **(see illustrations)**.
10 Withdraw the valve from the gasket side of the cylinder head **(see illustration)**.
11 It is essential that each valve is stored together with its collets, cap, spring and spring seat. The valves should be kept in their correct sequences, unless they are so badly worn that they are to be renewed.

6.9b ...with special pliers

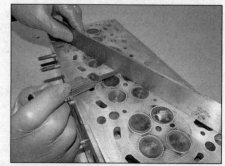

6.10 Removing a valve

7 Cylinder head and valves – cleaning and inspection

1 Thorough cleaning of the cylinder head and valve components, followed by a detailed inspection, will enable you to decide how much valve service work must be carried out during engine overhaul. **Note:** *If the engine has been severely overheated, it is best to assume that the cylinder head is warped, check carefully for signs of this.*

Cleaning

2 Using a suitable degreasing agent, remove all traces of oil deposits from the cylinder head, paying particular attention to the camshaft bearing surfaces, hydraulic tappet bores, valve guides and oilways. Scrape off any traces of old gasket from the mating surfaces, taking care not to score or gouge them. If using emery paper, do not use a grade of less than 100. Turn the head over and, using a blunt blade, scrape any carbon deposits from the combustion chambers and ports. Finally, wash the entire head casting with a suitable solvent to remove the remaining debris.
3 Clean the valve heads and stems using a fine wire brush (or a power-operated wire brush). If the valve is covered with heavy carbon deposits, scrape off the majority of the deposits with a blunt blade first, then use the wire brush.
4 Thoroughly clean the remainder of the components using solvent and allow them to dry completely. Discard the oil seals, as new ones must be fitted when the cylinder head is reassembled.

Inspection

Cylinder head

Note: *The vehicle manufacturer may define what constitutes a repairable fault with the cylinder head. In many cases the manufacturer's solution will be to replace the cylinder head. However specialist automotive machine shops may be able to suggest a repair, that whilst not strictly approved by the manufacturer will be a permanent and cost effective solution. Always consult a automotive machine shop before replacing the cylinder head.*
5 Examine the head casting closely to identify any damage or cracks that may have developed. Cracks can often be identified from evidence of coolant or oil leakage. Pay particular attention to the areas around the valve seats and spark plug/fuel injector holes. If cracking is discovered in this area, then an automotive machine shop will be able to advise. If the a repair is not possible the cylinder head will have to be replaced.
6 Moderately pitted and scorched valve seats can be repaired by lapping the valves in during reassembly, as described later in this Chapter. Badly worn or damaged valve seats may be restored by recutting. An automotive machine shop should be consulted if the valves and valve seats need reworking.
7 Measure any distortion of the gasket surfaces using a straight-edge and a set of feeler blades. Take one measurement

longitudinally on the manifold mating surface(s). Take several measurements across the head gasket surface, to assess the level of distortion in all planes **(see illustration)**. Compare the measurements with the figures in the Specifications.

Camshaft

8 Inspection of the camshaft is covered in Chapter 2A Section 9 (1.2 and 1.4 petrol engines), Chapter 2B Section 8 (2.0 litre petrol engines) or Chapter 2C Section 9 (diesel engines) as applicable.

Valves and associated components

9 Examine each valve closely for signs of wear. Inspect the valve stems for wear ridges, scoring or variations in diameter; measure their diameters at several points along their

7.7 Measure the distortion of the cylinder head gasket surface

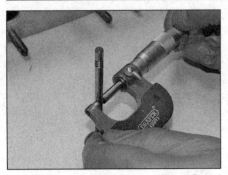

7.9 Measure the diameter of the valve stems using a micrometer

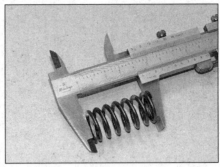

7.12 Measure the free length of each valve spring

7.13 Check the squareness of a valve spring

lengths with a micrometer, and compare with the figures given in the Specifications **(see illustration)**.

10 The valve heads should not be cracked, badly pitted or charred. Note that light pitting of the valve head can be rectified by lapping-in the valves during reassembly, as described in Section 8.

11 Check that the valve stem end face is free from excessive pitting or indentation; this could be caused by defective hydraulic tappets.

12 Using vernier calipers, measure the free length of each of the valve springs. As a manufacturer's figure is not quoted, the only way to check the length of the springs is by comparison with a new component. Note that valve springs are usually renewed during a major engine overhaul **(see illustration)**.

13 Stand each spring on its end on a flat surface, against an engineer's square **(see illustration)**. Check the squareness of the spring visually, and renew it if it appears distorted.

14 Renew the valve stem oil seals regardless of their apparent condition.

8 Cylinder head – reassembly

Note: *A valve spring compressor tool will be required for this operation.*

1 To achieve a gas-tight seal between the valves and their seats, it will be necessary to lap-in (or grind-in) the valves. To complete this process you will need a quantity of fine/coarse grinding paste and a grinding tool – this can either be of the rubber sucker type, or the automatic type which is driven by a rotary power tool.

2 Smear a small quantity of fine grinding

paste on the sealing face of the valve head. Turn the cylinder head over so that the combustion chambers are facing upwards and insert the valve into the correct guide. Attach the grinding tool to the valve head and using a backward/forward rotary action, grind the valve head into its seat. Periodically lift the valve and rotate it to redistribute the grinding paste **(see illustration)**.

3 Continue this process until the contact between valve and seat produces an unbroken, matt grey ring of uniform width, on both faces. Repeat the operation on the remaining valves.

4 If the valves and seats are so badly pitted that coarse grinding paste must be used, then a automotive machine shop should be able to cut the valve seats and reface the valves. Note that on some engines the valve seats may need replacing as cutting the seats may raise the height of the valve in the head so much that the hydraulic tappets can not operate properly. If there is any doubt about the condition of the valves, valve seats and cylinder head always consult a machine shop who will be able to advise on the best course of action.

5 Assuming the repair is feasible, work as described previously, but use coarse grinding paste initially, to achieve a dull finish on the valve face and seat. Wash off the coarse paste with solvent and repeat the process using fine grinding paste to obtain the correct finish.

6 When all the valves have been ground in, remove all traces of grinding paste from the cylinder head and valves using solvent, and allow the head and valves to dry completely.

7 Turn the cylinder head on its side.

8 Working on one valve at a time, lubricate the valve stem with clean engine oil, and insert the valve into its guide. Fit one of the protective plastic sleeves supplied with the new valve stem oil seals over the end of the valve stem – this will protect the oil seal as it is being fitted **(see illustrations)**.

9 Dip a new valve stem seal in clean engine oil, and carefully push it over the valve stem and onto the top of the valve guide – take care not to damage the stem seal as it is fitted. Use a suitable long-reach socket or a valve stem seal fitting tool to press the seal firmly into position **(see illustration)**. Remove the protective sleeve from the valve stem.

8.2 Lapping in a valve

8.8a Lubricate the valve stem with clean engine oil

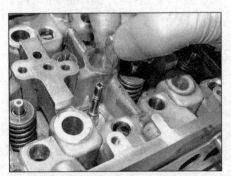

8.8b Fit a protective sleeve over the valve stem before fitting the stem seal

8.9 Using a socket to install the valve stem oil seal

8.10 Fit a valve spring

8.11a Fit the upper spring seat

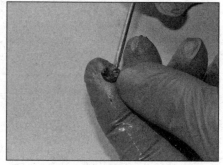

8.11b Use grease to hold the split collets in the groove

10 Locate the valve spring over the valve stem, ensuring that the lower end of the spring seats correctly on the cylinder head **(see illustration)**.

11 Fit the upper spring seat over the top of the spring, then using a valve spring compressor, compress the spring until the upper seat is pushed beyond the collet grooves in the valve stem. Refit the split collets. Gradually release the spring compressor, checking that the collets remain correctly seated as the spring extends. When correctly seated, the upper spring seat should force the collets securely into the grooves in the end of the valve stem **(see illustrations)**.

12 Repeat this process for the remaining sets of valve components, ensuring that all components are refitted to their original locations. The traditional method of settling the the collets by striking the head of the valve with a block of wood and a hammer after installation is not recommended. Instead slightly compress and release the valves several times with the spring compressor. Check before progressing any further that the split collets remain firmly seated in the grooves in the end of the valve stem.

13 Refit any auxiliary brackets and/or engine lifting brackets to their original locations, as noted before removal.

14 Where applicable, refit the camshaft position sensor.

15 Where applicable, refit the coolant housing/dirtibution block to the cylinder head, using a new seal.

16 Follow the procedure in Chapter 2A

Section 12 (1.2 and 1.4 litre engines) or Chapter 2B Section 10 (2.0 litre engines) and refit the cylinder head.

Diesel engines

17 Proceed as described in paragraphs 1 to 13.

18 Refit the timing belt tensioner pulley to the stud on the cylinder head, and refit the securing nut.

19 Refit the cylinder head as described in Chapter 2C Section 11.

9 Piston/connecting rod assemblies – removal

1 Proceed as follows according to engine type:

a) On 1.2 and 1.4 litre petrol engines, remove the cylinder head, sump, oil pump and upper sump as described in Chapter 2A.

b) On 2.0 litre engines, remove the cylinder head, sump, baffle plate, oil pump and upper sump as described in Chapter 2B.

c) On diesel engines, remove the cylinder head, sump and oil baffle plate, and oil pump and pick-up pipe, as described in Chapter 2C.

2 Inspect the tops of the cylinder bores for ridges at the point where the pistons reach top dead centre. These must be removed otherwise the pistons may be damaged when they are pushed out of their bores. Use a scraper or ridge reamer to remove the ridges.

Such a ridge indicates excessive wear of the cylinder bore.

3 Check the connecting rods and big-end caps for identification markings. Both connecting rods and caps should be marked with the cylinder number on one side of each assembly. Note that No 1 cylinder is at the timing belt end of the engine. If no marks are present, using a hammer and centre-punch, paint or similar, mark each connecting rod and big-end bearing cap with its respective cylinder number – note on which side of the connecting rods and caps the marks are made **(see illustration)**.

4 Similarly, check the piston crowns for direction markings. An arrow on each piston crown should point towards the timing belt end of the engine. On some engines, this mark may be obscured by carbon build-up, in which case the piston crown should be cleaned to check for a mark. In some cases, the direction arrow may have worn off, in which case a suitable mark should be made on the piston crown using a scriber – do not deeply score the piston crown, but ensure that the mark is easily visible.

5 Turn the crankshaft to bring Nos 1 and 4 pistons to bottom dead centre.

6 Unscrew the bolts or nuts, as applicable, from No 1 piston big-end bearing cap. Lift off the cap, and recover the bottom half bearing shell. If the bearing shells are to be re-used, tape the cap and bearing shell together. Note that if the bearing shells are to be re-used, they must be fitted to the original connecting rod and cap **(see illustrations)**.

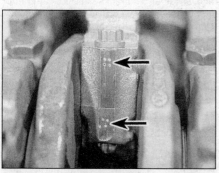

9.3 Mark the big-end caps and connecting rods with their cylinder numbers

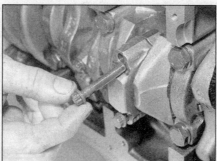

9.6a Unscrew the big-end bearing cap bolts...

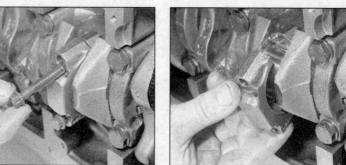

9.6b ...and remove the cap

9.7 Wrap the threaded ends of the bolts with tape

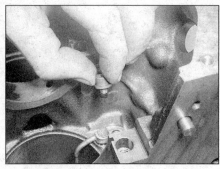

9.12a Remove the securing bolts...

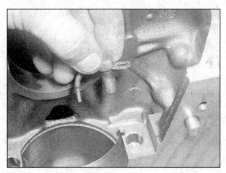

9.12b ...and withdraw the piston cooling oil spray jets

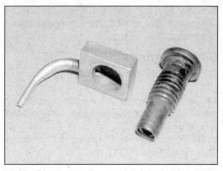

9.12c Piston cooling spray jet and retainer

7 Where the bearing caps are secured with nuts, wrap the threaded ends of the bolts with insulating tape to prevent them scratching the crankpins and bores when the pistons are removed **(see illustration)**.

8 Using a hammer handle, push the piston up through the bore, and remove it from the top of the cylinder block. Where applicable, take care not to damage the piston cooling oil spray jets in the cylinder block as the piston/connecting rod assembly is removed. Recover the upper bearing shell, and tape it to the connecting rod for safe-keeping.

9 Loosely refit the big-end cap to the connecting rod, and secure with the bolts or nuts, as applicable – this will help to keep the components in their correct order.

10 Remove No 4 piston assembly in the same way.

11 Turn the crankshaft as necessary to bring Nos 2 and 3 pistons to bottom dead centre, and remove them in the same way.

12 Where applicable, remove the securing bolts, and withdraw the piston cooling oil spray jets from the bottom of the cylinder block **(see illustrations)**.

10 Crankshaft – removal

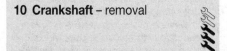

Note: *If no work is to be done on the pistons and connecting rods, there is no need to push the pistons out of the cylinder bores. The pistons should just be pushed far enough up the bores so that they are positioned clear of the crankshaft journals.*

Caution: *On 1.2 and 1.4 litre engines the crankshaft must not be removed, as the main bearing pedestals will deform and the bearings will be damaged. Consult an automotive machine shop for advice or fit a replacement 'short' engine from the vehicle manufacturer.*

1 Proceed as follows according to engine type:

a) On 2.0 petrol engines, remove the timing chain, sump, oil pump, transmission, flywheel, oil seal housing and upper sump as described in Chapter 2B and Chapter 7A Section 3 or Chapter 7B Section 2.

b) On diesel engines, remove the timing belt and crankshaft sprocket, sump, baffle plate, oil pump, transmission, flywheel and the crankshaft oil seal housings, as described in Chapter 2C and Chapter 7A Section 3 or Chapter 7B Section 2.

2 Remove the pistons and connecting rods, or disconnect them from the crankshaft, as described in Section 9.

3 Check the crankshaft endfloat as described in Section 13, then proceed as follows.

4 The main bearing caps should be numbered 1 to 5 from the timing belt end of the engine. If the bearing caps are not marked, mark them accordingly using a centre-punch. Note the orientation of the markings to ensure correct refitting.

5 Slacken and remove the main bearing cap bolts, and lift off each cap. On 2.0 litre engine the side bolts must also be removed. If the caps appear to be stuck, tap them with a soft-faced mallet to free them from the cylinder block **(see illustration)**. Recover the lower bearing shells, and tape them to their caps for safe-keeping.

6 Recover the lower crankshaft endfloat control thrustwasher halves from either side of the No 3 main bearing cap, noting their orientation.

7 Lift the crankshaft from the cylinder block **(see illustration)**. Take care, as the crankshaft is heavy. On engines with a crankshaft speed/position sensor fitted, lay the crankshaft on wooden blocks – do not rest the crankshaft on the sensor wheel.

8 Recover the upper bearing shells from the cylinder block, and tape them to their respective caps for safe-keeping. Similarly, recover the upper crankshaft endfloat control thrustwasher halves, noting their orientation.

9 On engines with a crankshaft speed/position sensor wheel, unscrew the securing bolts, and remove the sensor wheel, noting which way round it is fitted.

11 Cylinder block/crankcase – cleaning and inspection

Cleaning

1 Remove all external components and electrical switches/sensors from the block, including mounting brackets, the coolant

10.5 Slacken and remove the main bearing cap bolts

10.7 Lift the crankshaft from the cylinder block

11.1 Typical oil cooler located on the front of the engine

11.7 To clean the cylinder block threads, run a correct-size tap into the holes

12.4 Old feeler blades can be used to prevent piston rings from dropping into empty grooves

pump, the oil filter, and oil cooler **(see illustration)**, etc. For complete cleaning, the core plugs should ideally be removed. Drill a small hole in the plugs, then insert a self-tapping screw into the hole. Extract the plugs by pulling on the screw with a pair of grips, or by using a slide hammer.

2 Scrape all traces of gasket and sealant from the cylinder block/crankcase, taking care not to damage the sealing surfaces.

3 Remove all oil gallery plugs (where fitted). The plugs are usually very tight – they may have to be drilled out, and the holes retapped. Use new plugs when the engine is reassembled.

4 If the casting is extremely dirty, it should be steam-cleaned. After this, clean all oil holes and galleries one more time. Flush all internal passages with warm water until the water runs clear. Dry thoroughly, and apply a light film of oil to all mating surfaces and cylinder bores, to prevent rusting. If you have access to compressed air, use it to speed up the drying process, and to blow out all the oil holes and galleries.

Warning: Wear eye protection when using compressed air.

5 If the castings are not very dirty, you can do an adequate cleaning job with hot, soapy water and a stiff brush. Take plenty of time, and do a thorough job. Regardless of the cleaning method used, be sure to clean all oil holes and galleries very thoroughly, and to dry all components well. Protect the cylinder bores as described above, to prevent rusting.

6 Where applicable, check the piston cooling oil spray jets for damage, and renew if necessary. Check the oil spray hole and the oil passages for blockage.

7 All threaded holes must be clean, to ensure accurate torque readings during reassembly. To clean the threads, run the correct-size tap into each of the holes to remove rust, corrosion, thread sealant or sludge, and to restore damaged threads **(see illustration)**. If possible, use compressed air to clear the holes free of debris produced by this operation. **Note:** *Take extra care to exclude all cleaning liquid from blind tapped holes, as the casting may be cracked by hydraulic action if a bolt is threaded into a hole containing liquid.*

8 After coating the mating surfaces of the new core plugs with suitable sealant, fit them to the cylinder block. Make sure that they are driven in straight and seated correctly, or leakage could result.

9 Apply suitable sealant to the new oil gallery plugs, and insert them into the holes in the block. Tighten them securely.

10 If the engine is not going to be reassembled immediately, cover it with a large plastic bag to keep it clean; protect all mating surfaces and the cylinder bores, to prevent rusting.

Inspection

11 Visually check the castings for cracks and corrosion. Look for stripped threads in the threaded holes. If there has been any history of internal coolant leakage, it may be worthwhile having an engine overhaul specialist check the cylinder block/crankcase for cracks with special equipment. If defects are found, have them repaired, if possible, or renew the assembly.

12 Check each cylinder bore for scuffing and scoring.

13 If in any doubt as to the condition of the cylinder block have the block/bores inspected and measured by an engine reconditioning specialist. They will be able to advise on whether the block is serviceable, whether a rebore is necessary, and supply the appropriate pistons and rings.

14 If the bores are in reasonably good condition and not excessively worn, then it may only be necessary to renew the piston rings.

15 If this is the case, the bores should be honed, to allow the new rings to bed-in correctly and provide the best possible seal. Consult an engine reconditioning specialist

16 On diesel engines, if the oil/water pump housing was removed, it can be refitted at this stage if wished. Use a new gasket, and before fully tightening the bolts, align the housing faces with those of the engine block.

17 The cylinder block/crankcase should now be completely clean and dry, with all components checked for wear or damage, and repaired or overhauled as necessary.

18 Apply a light coating of engine oil to the

mating surfaces and cylinder bores to prevent rust forming.

19 Refit as many ancillary components as possible, for safe-keeping. If reassembly is not to start immediately, cover the block with a large plastic bag to keep it clean, and protect the machined surfaces as described above to prevent rusting.

12 Piston/connecting rod assemblies – cleaning and inspection

Cleaning

1 Before the inspection process can begin, the piston/connecting rod assemblies must be cleaned, and the original piston rings removed from the pistons.

2 The rings should have smooth, polished working surfaces, with no dull or carbon-coated sections (showing that the ring is not sealing correctly against the bore wall, so allowing combustion gases to blow by) and no traces of wear on their top and bottom surfaces. The end gaps should be clear of carbon, but not polished (indicating a too-small end gap), and all the rings (including the elements of the oil control ring) should be free to rotate in their grooves, but without excessive up-and-down movement. If the rings appear to be in good condition, they are probably fit for further use; check the end gaps (in an unworn part of the bore) as described in Section 12.

3 If any of the rings appears to be worn or damaged, or has an end gap significantly different from the specified value, the usual course of action is to renew all of them as a set. **Note:** *While it is usual to renew piston rings when an engine is overhauled, they may be re-used if in acceptable condition. If re-using the rings, make sure that each ring is marked during removal to ensure that it is refitted correctly.*

4 Carefully expand the old rings over the top of the pistons. The use of two or three old feeler blades will be helpful in preventing the rings dropping into empty grooves **(see illustration)**. Be careful not to scratch the

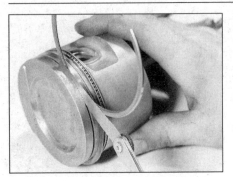

12.17 Measure the piston ring-to-groove clearance using a feeler blade

piston with the ends of the ring. The rings are brittle, and will snap if they are spread too far. They are also very sharp – protect your hands and fingers. Note that the third ring incorporates an expander. Keep each set of rings with its piston if the old rings are to be re-used. Note which way up each ring is fitted to ensure correct refitting.

5 Scrape away all traces of carbon from the top of the piston. A hand-held wire brush (or a piece of fine emery cloth) can be used, once the majority of the deposits have been scraped away.

6 Remove the carbon from the ring grooves in the piston, using an old ring. Break the ring in half to do this (be careful not to cut your fingers – piston rings are sharp). Be careful to remove only the carbon deposits – do not remove any metal, and do not nick or scratch the sides of the ring grooves.

7 Once the deposits have been removed, clean the piston/connecting rod assembly with paraffin or a suitable solvent, and dry thoroughly. Make sure that the oil return holes in the ring grooves are clear.

Inspection

8 If the pistons and cylinder bores are not damaged or worn excessively, and if the cylinder block does not need to be rebored, the original pistons can be refitted.

9 Have the pistons and cylinder bore measure by an engine reconditioning specialist. They will be able to advise on possible repairs, and supply the correct replacement parts. **Note:** *If the cylinder block was rebored during a previous overhaul, oversize pistons may already have been fitted.*

10 Normal piston wear shows up as even vertical wear on the piston thrust surfaces, and slight looseness of the top ring in its groove. New piston rings should always be used when the engine is reassembled.

11 Carefully inspect each piston for cracks around the skirt, around the gudgeon pin holes, and at the piston ring 'lands' (between the ring grooves).

12 Look for scoring and scuffing on the piston skirt, holes in the piston crown, and burned areas at the edge of the crown. If the skirt is scored or scuffed, the engine may have been suffering from overheating, and/or abnormal combustion which caused excessively high operating temperatures. The cooling and lubrication systems should be checked thoroughly.

13 Scorch marks on the sides of the pistons show that blow-by has occurred.

14 A hole in the piston crown, or burned areas at the edge of the piston crown, indicates that abnormal combustion (pre-ignition, knocking, or detonation) has been occurring.

15 If any of the above problems exist, the causes must be investigated and corrected, or the damage will occur again. The causes may include incorrect ignition/injection pump timing, inlet air leaks or incorrect air/fuel mixture (petrol engines), or a faulty fuel injector (diesel engines).

16 Corrosion of the piston, in the form of pitting, indicates that coolant has been leaking into the combustion chamber and/or the crankcase. Again, the cause must be corrected, or the problem may persist in the rebuilt engine.

17 Locate a new piston ring in the appropriate groove and measure the ring-to-groove clearance using a feeler blade **(see illustration)**. Note that the rings are of different widths, so use the correct ring for the groove. Compare the measurements with those listed; if the clearances are outside of the tolerance band, then the piston must be renewed. Confirm this by checking the width of the piston ring with a micrometer.

18 Examine each connecting rod carefully for signs of damage, such as cracks around the big-end and small-end bearings. Check that the rod is not bent or distorted. Damage is highly unlikely, unless the engine has been seized or badly overheated. Detailed checking of the connecting rod assembly can only be carried out by a Volkswagen dealer or engine repair specialist with the necessary equipment.

19 The gudgeon pins are of the floating type, secured in position by two circlips. The pistons and connecting rods can be separated as follows.

20 Using a small flat-bladed screwdriver, prise out the circlips, and push out the gudgeon pin **(see illustrations)**. Hand pressure should be sufficient to remove the pin. Identify the piston and rod to ensure correct reassembly. Discard the circlips – new ones must be used on refitting. If the gudgeon pin proves difficult to remove, heat the piston to 60°C with hot water – the resulting expansion will then allow the two components to be separated.

21 Examine the gudgeon pin and connecting rod small-end bearing for signs of wear or damage. It should be possible to push the gudgeon pin through the connecting rod bush by hand, without noticeable play. Wear can be cured by renewing both the pin and bush. Bush renewal, however, is a specialist job – press facilities are required, and the new bush must be reamed accurately.

22 Examine all components, and obtain any new parts from your Volkswagen dealer or engine reconditioning specialist. If new pistons are purchased, they will be

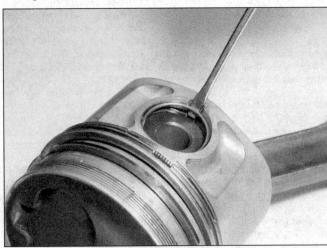

12.20a Use a small flat-bladed screwdriver to prise out the circlip...

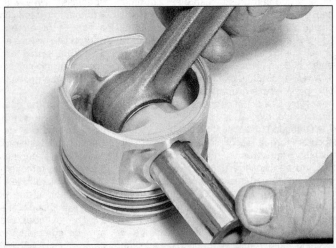

12.20b ...then push out the gudgeon pin and separate the piston and connecting rod

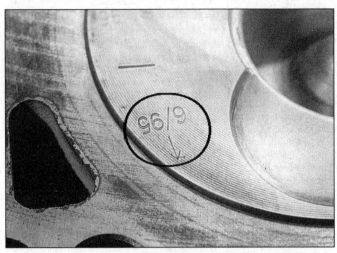

12.23a The piston crown is marked with an arrow which must point towards the timing belt/chain end of the engine

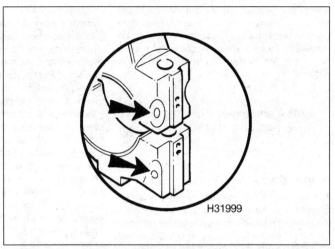

12.23b The recesses (where present) in the connecting rod and bearing cap must face the timing belt/chain end of the engine

supplied complete with gudgeon pins and circlips. Circlips can also be purchased individually.

23 The orientation of the piston with respect to the connecting rod must be correct when the two are reassembled. The piston crown is marked with an arrow (which may be obscured by carbon deposits); this must point towards the timing belt/chain end of the engine when the piston is installed. The connecting rod and its bearing cap both have recesses machined into them on one side, close to their mating surfaces – these recesses must both face the same way as the arrow on the piston crown (ie, towards the timing belt/chain end of the engine) when correctly installed. Reassemble the two components to satisfy this requirement **(see illustrations)**.

24 Apply a smear of clean engine oil to the gudgeon pin. Slide it into the piston and through the connecting rod small-end. Check that the piston pivots freely on the rod, then secure the gudgeon pin in position with two new circlips. Ensure that each circlip is correctly located in its groove in the piston.

25 Repeat the cleaning and inspection process for the remaining pistons and connecting rods.

13 Crankshaft – checking endfloat and inspection

Checking endfloat

1 If the crankshaft endfloat is to be checked, this must be done when the crankshaft is still installed in the cylinder block/crankcase, but is free to move.

2 Check the endfloat using a dial gauge in contact with the end of the crankshaft. Push the crankshaft fully one way, and then zero the gauge. Push the crankshaft fully the other way, and check the endfloat. The result can be compared with the specified amount,

and will give an indication as to whether new thrustwasher halves are required **(see illustration)**. Note that all thrustwashers must be of the same thickness.

3 If a dial gauge is not available, feeler blades can be used. First push the crankshaft fully towards the flywheel end of the engine, then use feeler blades to measure the gap between the web of No 3 crankpin and the thrustwasher halves **(see illustration)**.

Inspection

4 Clean the crankshaft using paraffin or a suitable solvent, and dry it, preferably with compressed air if available. Be sure to clean the oil holes with a pipe cleaner or similar probe, to ensure that they are not obstructed.

⚠ **Warning: Wear eye protection when using compressed air.**

5 Check the main and big-end bearing journals for uneven wear, scoring, pitting and cracking.

6 Big-end bearing wear is accompanied by distinct metallic knocking when the engine is running (particularly noticeable when the engine is pulling from low speed) and some loss of oil pressure.

7 Main bearing wear is accompanied by severe engine vibration and rumble – getting

progressively worse as engine speed increases – and again by loss of oil pressure.

8 Check the bearing journal for roughness by running a finger lightly over the bearing surface. Any roughness (which will be accompanied by obvious bearing wear) indicates that the crankshaft requires regrinding (where possible) or renewal.

9 If the crankshaft has been reground, check for burrs around the crankshaft oil holes (the holes are usually chamfered, so burrs should not be a problem unless regrinding has been carried out carelessly). Remove any burrs with a fine file or scraper, and thoroughly clean the oil holes as described previously.

10 Have the crankshaft measured and inspected by an engine reconditioning specialist. They will be able to advise any possible repairs and supply the correct parts.

11 Check the oil seal contact surfaces at each end of the crankshaft for wear and damage. If the seal has worn a deep groove in the surface of the crankshaft, consult an engine overhaul specialist; repair may be possible, but otherwise a new crankshaft will be required.

12 If the crankshaft journals have not already been reground, it may be possible to have the crankshaft reconditioned, and to fit undersize

13.2 Measure crankshaft endfloat using a dial gauge

13.3 Measure crankshaft endfloat using feeler blades

shells (see Section 14). If no undersize shells are available and the crankshaft has worn beyond the specified limits, it will have to be renewed. Consult your VW dealer or engine specialist for further information on parts availability.

14 Main and big-end bearings – inspection and selection

Inspection

1 Even though the main and big-end bearings should be renewed during the engine overhaul, the old bearings should be retained for close examination, as they may reveal valuable information about the condition of the engine **(see illustration)**.

2 Bearing failure can occur due to lack of lubrication, the presence of dirt or other foreign particles, overloading the engine, or corrosion. Regardless of the cause of bearing failure, the cause must be corrected before the engine is reassembled, to prevent it from happening again.

3 When examining the bearing shells, remove them from the cylinder block/crankcase, the main bearing caps, the connecting rods and the connecting rod big-end bearing caps. Lay them out on a clean surface in the same general position as their location in the engine. This will enable you to match any bearing problems with the corresponding crankshaft journal. Do not touch any shell's internal bearing surface with your fingers while checking it, or the delicate surface may be scratched.

4 Dirt and other foreign matter gets into the engine in a variety of ways. It may be left in the engine during assembly, or it may pass

through filters or the crankcase ventilation system. It may get into the oil, and from there into the bearings. Metal chips from machining operations and normal engine wear are often present. Abrasives are sometimes left in engine components after reconditioning, especially when parts are not thoroughly cleaned using the proper cleaning methods. Whatever the source, these foreign objects often end up embedded in the soft bearing material, and are easily recognised. Large particles will not embed in the bearing, but will score or gouge the bearing and journal. The best prevention for this cause of bearing failure is to clean all parts thoroughly, and keep everything spotlessly-clean during engine assembly. Frequent and regular engine oil and filter changes are also recommended.

5 Lack of lubrication (or lubrication breakdown) has a number of interrelated causes. Excessive heat (which thins the oil), overloading (which squeezes the oil from the bearing face) and oil leakage (from excessive bearing clearances, worn oil pump or high engine speeds) all contribute to lubrication breakdown. Blocked oil passages, which usually are the result of misaligned oil holes in a bearing shell, will also oil-starve a bearing, and destroy it. When lack of lubrication is the cause of bearing failure, the bearing material is wiped or extruded from the steel backing of the bearing. Temperatures may increase to the point where the steel backing turns blue from overheating.

6 Driving habits can have a definite effect on bearing life. Full-throttle, low-speed operation (labouring the engine) puts very high loads on bearings, tending to squeeze out the oil film. These loads cause the bearings to flex, which produces fine cracks in the bearing face (fatigue failure). Eventually, the bearing material will loosen in pieces, and tear away from the steel backing.

7 Short-distance driving leads to corrosion of bearings, because insufficient engine heat is produced to drive off the condensed water and corrosive gases. These products collect in the engine oil, forming acid and sludge. As the oil is carried to the engine bearings, the acid attacks and corrodes the bearing material.

8 Incorrect bearing installation during engine assembly will lead to bearing failure as well. Tight-fitting bearings leave insufficient bearing running clearance, and will result in oil starvation. Dirt or foreign particles trapped behind a bearing shell result in high spots on the bearing, which lead to failure.

9 Do not touch any shell's internal bearing surface with your fingers during reassembly as there is a risk of scratching the delicate surface, or of depositing particles of dirt on it.

10 As mentioned at the beginning of this Section, the bearing shells should be renewed as a matter of course during engine overhaul. To do otherwise is false economy.

Selection

11 Main and big-end bearings for the engines described in this Chapter are available in standard sizes and a range of undersizes to suit reground crankshafts.

12 Have the crankshaft measured by an engine reconditioning specialist. They will be able to supply the correctly sized bearings.

15 Engine overhaul – reassembly sequence

1 Before reassembly begins, ensure that all new parts have been obtained, and that all necessary tools are available. Read through the entire procedure to familiarise yourself with the work involved, and to ensure that all items necessary for reassembly of the engine are at hand. In addition to all normal tools and materials, thread-locking compound will be needed. A suitable tube of liquid sealant will also be required for the joint faces that are fitted without gaskets.

2 In order to save time and avoid problems, engine reassembly can be carried out in the following order, referring to Part A, B, C or D of this Chapter unless otherwise stated. Where applicable, use new gaskets and seals when refitting the various components.

a) *Crankshaft (Section 17).*
b) *Piston/connecting rod assemblies (Section 18).*
c) *Oil pump.*
d) *Sump.*
e) *Flywheel/driveplate.*
f) *Cylinder head.*
g) *Timing belt/chain, tensioner and sprockets.*
h) *Engine external components.*

3 At this stage, all engine components should be absolutely clean and dry, with all faults repaired. The components should be laid out (or in individual containers) on a completely clean work surface.

16 Piston rings – refitting

1 Before fitting new piston rings, the ring end gaps must be checked as follows.

2 Lay out the piston/connecting rod assemblies and the new piston ring sets, so that the ring sets will be matched with the same piston and cylinder during the end gap measurement and subsequent engine reassembly.

3 Insert the top ring into the first cylinder, and push it down the bore using the top of the piston. This will ensure that the ring remains square with the cylinder walls. Position the ring approximately 15.0 mm the bottom of the cylinder bore, at the lower limit of ring travel.

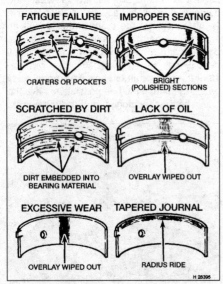

14.1 Typical bearing failures

FATIGUE FAILURE — CRATERS OR POCKETS

IMPROPER SEATING — BRIGHT (POLISHED) SECTIONS

SCRATCHED BY DIRT — DIRT EMBEDDED INTO BEARING MATERIAL

LACK OF OIL — OVERLAY WIPED OUT

EXCESSIVE WEAR — OVERLAY WIPED OUT

TAPERED JOURNAL — RADIUS RIDE

H 28395

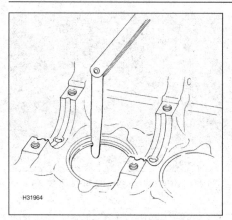

16.4 Check a piston ring end gap using a feeler blade

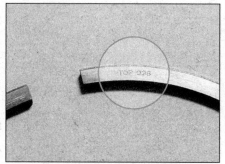

16.9 Piston ring TOP marking

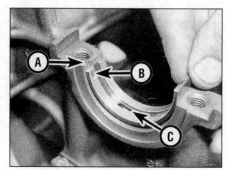

17.2 Bearing shell correctly refitted

A Recess in cylinder block
B Lug on bearing shell
C Oil hole

Note that the top and second compression rings are different.

4 Measure the end gap using feeler blades, and compare the measurements with the figures given in the Specifications **(see illustration)**.

5 If the gap is too small (unlikely if genuine Volkswagen parts are used), it must be enlarged, or the ring ends may contact each other during engine operation, causing serious damage. Ideally, new piston rings providing the correct end gap should be fitted. As a last resort, the end gap can be increased by filing the ring ends very carefully with a fine file. Mount the file in a vice equipped with soft jaws, slip the ring over the file with the ends contacting the file face, and slowly move the ring to remove material from the ends. Take care, as piston rings are sharp, and are easily broken.

6 With new piston rings, it is unlikely that the end gap will be too large. If the gaps are too large, check that you have the correct rings for your engine and for the particular cylinder bore size.

7 Repeat the checking procedure for each ring in the first cylinder, and then for the rings in the remaining cylinders. Remember to keep rings, pistons and cylinders matched up.

8 Once the ring end gaps have been checked

and if necessary corrected, the rings can be fitted to the pistons.

9 Fit the piston rings using the same technique as for removal. Fit the bottom (oil control) ring first, and work up. Note that a two- or three-section oil control ring may be fitted; where a two-section ring is fitted, first insert the wire expander, then fit the ring. Ensure that the rings are fitted the correct way up – the top surface of the rings is normally marked TOP **(see illustration)**. Offset the piston ring gaps by 120° from each other. **Note:** *Always follow any instructions supplied with the new piston ring sets – different manufacturers may specify different procedures. Do not mix up the top and second compression rings, as they have different cross-sections.*

17 Crankshaft – refitting

1 Wipe off the surfaces of the bearing shells in the crankcase and bearing caps.

2 Press the bearing shells into their locations, ensuring that the tab on each shell engages In the notch in the cylinder block or bearing cap, and that the oil holes In the cylinder block and bearing shell are aligned **(see illustration)**. Take care not to touch any shells bearing surface with your fingers.

A Recess in cylinder block
B Lug on bearing shell
C Oil hole

3 Where applicable, refit the crankshaft speed/position sensor wheel, and tighten the securing bolts to the specified torque. Make sure that the sensor wheel is correctly orientated as noted before removal.

4 Liberally coat the bearing shells in the crankcase with clean engine oil of the appropriate grade **(see illustration)**. Make sure that the bearing shells are still correctly seated in their locations.

5 Lower the crankshaft into position so that No 1 cylinder crankpin is at BDC, ready for fitting No 1 piston. Ensure that the crankshaft endfloat control thrustwasher halves, either side of the No 3 main bearing location, remain in position. Where applicable, take care not to damage the crankshaft speed/position sensor wheel as the crankshaft is lowered into position.

6 Lubricate the lower bearing shells in the main bearing caps with clean engine oil. Make sure that the crankshaft endfloat control thrustwasher halves are still correctly seated either side of No 3 bearing cap **(see illustrations)**.

7 Fit the main bearing caps in the correct order and orientation – No 1 bearing cap must be at the timing belt end of the engine and the bearing shell tab locating recesses in the crankcase and bearing caps must be adjacent

17.4 Lubricate the upper bearing shells

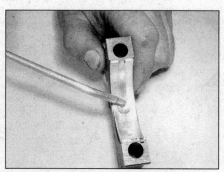

17.6a Lubricate the lower bearing shells...

17.6b ...and make sure that the thrustwashers are correctly seated

17.7 Fitting No 1 main bearing cap

17.8a Tighten the main bearing cap bolts to the specified torque…

17.8b …then through the specified angle

to each other **(see illustration)**. Insert the bearing cap bolts (using new bolts where necessary), and hand-tighten them only.

8 Working from the centre bearing cap outwards, tighten the bearing cap bolts to their specified torque. On engines where two Stages are given for the torque, tighten all bolts to the Stage 1 torque, then go round again, and tighten all bolts through the Stage 2 angle **(see illustrations)**. On 2.0 litre petrol engines tighten the cap side bolts after tightening the main bearing cap bolts.

9 Check that the crankshaft rotates freely by turning it by hand. If resistance is felt, recheck the bearing running clearances, as described previously.

10 Check the crankshaft endfloat as described at the beginning of Section 13. If the thrust surfaces of the crankshaft have been checked and new thrustwashers have been fitted, then the endfloat should be within specification.

11 Refit the pistons and connecting rods or reconnect them to the crankshaft as described in Section 18.

12 Proceed as follows according to engine type:
a) *On 2.0 petrol engines, refit the upper sump crankshaft oil seal housing, flywheel oil pump and pick-up pipe and sump as described in Chapter 2B.*
b) *On diesel engines, refit the crankshaft oil seal housings, flywheel, oil pump, baffle, sump and crankshaft sprocket as described in Chapter 2C.*

18 Piston/connecting rod assemblies – refitting

Note: *A piston ring compressor tool will be required for this operation.*

1 Note that the following procedure assumes that the crankshaft main bearing caps are in place.

2 Where applicable, refit the piston cooling oil spray jets to the bottom of the cylinder block, and tighten the securing bolts to the specified torque.

3 On engines where the big-end bearing caps are secured by nuts, fit new bolts to the connecting rods. Tap the old bolts out of the connecting rods using a soft-faced mallet, and tap the new bolts into position.

4 Ensure that the bearing shells are correctly fitted, as described at the beginning of this Section. If new shells are being fitted, ensure that all traces of the protective grease are cleaned off using paraffin. Wipe dry the shells and connecting rods with a lint-free cloth.

5 Lubricate the cylinder bores, the pistons, piston rings and upper bearing shells with clean engine oil **(see illustrations)**. Lay out each piston/connecting rod assembly in order on a clean work surface. Where the bearing caps are secured with nuts, pad the threaded ends of the bolts with insulating tape to prevent them scratching the crankpins and bores when the pistons are refitted.

6 Start with piston/connecting rod assembly No 1. Make sure that the piston rings are

still spaced as described in Section 16, then clamp them in position with a piston ring compressor tool.

7 Insert the piston/connecting rod assembly into the top of cylinder No 1. Lower the big-end in first, guiding it to protect the cylinder bores. Where oil jets are located at the bottoms of the bores, take particular care not to damage them when guiding the connecting rods onto the crankpins.

8 Ensure that the orientation of the piston in its cylinder is correct – the piston crown, connecting rod and big-end bearing cap have markings, which must point towards the timing belt end of the engine when the piston is installed in the bore – refer to Section 18 for details.

9 Using a block of wood or hammer handle against the piston crown, tap the assembly into the cylinder until the piston crown is flush with the top of the cylinder **(see illustration)**.

10 Ensure that the bearing shell is still correctly installed in the connecting rod, then liberally lubricate the crankpin and both bearing shells with clean engine oil.

11 Taking care not to mark the cylinder bores, tap the piston/connecting rod assembly down the bore and onto the crankpin. On engines where the big-end caps are secured by nuts, remove the insulating tape from the threaded ends of the connecting rod bolts. Oil the bolt threads, and on engines where the big-end caps are secured by bolts, oil the undersides of the bolt heads.

12 Fit the big-end bearing cap, tightening its retaining nuts or bolts (as applicable) finger-tight at first. The connecting rod and

18.5a Lubricate the pistons…

18.5b …and big-end upper bearing shells with clean engine oil

18.9 Using a hammer handle to tap the piston into its bore

its bearing cap both have recesses machined into them on one side, close to their mating surfaces – these recesses must both face the same way as the arrow on the piston crown (ie, towards the timing end of the engine) when correctly installed. Reassemble the two components to satisfy this requirement.

13 Tighten the retaining bolts or nuts (as applicable) to the specified torque and angle, in the two stages given in the Specifications **(see illustrations)**.

14 Refit the remaining three piston/connecting rod assemblies in the same way.

15 Rotate the crankshaft by hand. Check that it turns freely; some stiffness is to be expected if new parts have been fitted, but there should be no binding or tight spots.

16 On diesel engines, if new pistons have been fitted, or if a new short engine has been fitted, the projection of the piston crowns above the cylinder head mating face of the cylinder block at TDC must be measured. This measurement is used to determine the thickness of the new cylinder head gasket required. This procedure is described as part of the Cylinder head – removal, inspection and refitting procedure in Chapter 2C Section 11.

17 With the crankshaft, pistons and connecting rods installed, refit the upper sump (petrol engines only), oil pump, baffle, sump, crankshaft oil seals etc as required.

19 Engine – initial start-up after overhaul and reassembly

1 Refit the remainder of the engine components in the order listed in Section 3 of this Chapter. Refit the engine to the vehicle as described in the relevant Section of this Chapter. Double-check the engine oil and coolant levels, and make a final check that everything has been reconnected. Make sure that there are no tools or rags left in the engine compartment.

2 Reconnect the battery leads with as described in Chapter 5A Section 3.

Petrol models

3 Remove the spark plugs, referring to Chapter 1A Section 29 for details.

18.13a Tighten the big-end bearing cap bolts/nuts to the specified torque…

4 The engine must be immobilised such that it can be turned over using the starter motor without starting – disable the fuel pump by unplugging the fuel pump relay from the relay board with reference to Chapter 14, and also disable the ignition system by disconnecting the wiring from the coils.

Caution: To prevent damage to the catalytic converter, it is important to disable the fuel system.

5 Turn the engine using the starter motor until the oil pressure warning lamp goes out. If the lamp fails to extinguish after several seconds of cranking, check the engine oil level and oil filter security. Assuming these are correct, check the security of the oil pressure switch wiring – do not progress any further until you are satisfied that oil is being pumped around the engine at sufficient pressure.

6 Refit the spark plugs, and reconnect the wiring to the fuel pump relay and coils.

Diesel models

7 Disconnect the wiring plugs from the fuel injectors as described in Chapter 4B Section 5.

8 Turn the engine using the starter motor until the oil pressure warning lamp goes out.

9 If the lamp fails to extinguish after several seconds of cranking, check the engine oil level and oil filter security. Assuming these are correct, check the security of the oil pressure switch cabling – do not progress any further until you are satisfied that oil is being pumped around the engine at sufficient pressure.

18.13b …then through the specified angle

10 Reconnect the injector wiring plug.

All models

11 Start the engine, but be aware that as fuel system components have been disturbed, the cranking time may be a little longer than usual.

12 While the engine is idling, check for fuel, water and oil leaks. Don't be alarmed if there are some odd smells and the occasional plume of smoke as components heat up and burn off oil deposits.

13 Assuming all is well, keep the engine idling until hot water is felt circulating through the top hose.

14 After a few minutes, recheck the oil and coolant levels, and top-up as necessary.

15 There is no need to retighten the cylinder head bolts once the engine has been run following reassembly.

16 On engines that have variable oil pressure it is possible to have the oil pressure set to maximum during the run-in period. A professional level diagnostic tool will be required to do this. Consult your local dealer or suitably equipped garage.

17 If new pistons, rings or crankshaft bearings have been fitted, the engine must be treated as new, and run-in for the first 600 miles. Do not operate the engine at full-throttle, or allow it to labour at low engine speeds in any gear. It is recommended that the engine oil and filter are changed at the end of this period.

Notes

Chapter 3
Cooling, heating and air conditioning systems

Contents

Section number

Air conditioning system – general information and precautions 11
Air conditioning system components – removal and refitting 12
Coolant pump – removal and refitting 7
Cooling system electrical sensors – testing, removal and refitting .. 6
Cooling system hoses – disconnection and renewal 2
Electric cooling fans – testing, removal and refitting 5

Section number

General information and precautions......................... 1
Heating and ventilation system – general information 8
Heating and ventilation system components – removal and refitting 9
Heating/ventilation system vents – removal and refitting......... 10
Radiators – removal, inspection and refitting.................. 3
Thermostat – removal, testing and refitting 4

Degrees of difficulty

Easy, suitable for novice with little experience	**Fairly easy,** suitable for beginner with some experience	**Fairly difficult,** suitable for competent DIY mechanic	**Difficult,** suitable for experienced DIY mechanic	**Very difficult,** suitable for expert DIY or professional

Specifications

Engine codes*
Petrol engines:
1.2 litre	CJZA, CJZB and CYVB
1.4 litre	CPTA, CHPA, CMBA, CXSA, CPVA, CZEA and CZDA
2.0 litre	CHHA, CHHB, CJXE and CXDA

Diesel engines:
1.6 litre	CLHA, CLHB, CRKB, CXXA, CXXB and DBKA
2.0 litre	CKFC, CRBA, CRBC, CRLB, CRMB and CUNA

*See 'Vehicle identification' at the end of this manual for the location of the engine code markings

Cooling system pressure cap
Opening pressure....................................	1.6 to 1.8 bar

Thermostat

Petrol engines:	Begins to open	Fully open
1.2 and 1.4 litre engines. Large cooling circuit (up to 11/12)	80°C	N/A
1.2 and 1.4 litre engines. Large cooling circuit (after 11/12)........	87°C	N/A
1.2 and 1.4 litre engines. Small cooling circuit...................	105°C	N/A
2.0 litre engines (mapped thermal management)................	113°C (emergency opening only)	N/A
Diesel engines	87°C	102°C

Torque wrench settings

	Nm	lbf ft
1.2 and 1.4 litre petrol engines		
Coolant pump belt cover bolts	8	6
Coolant temperature sensor bolt	8	6
Coolant sprocket bolt (on camshaft)*		
Stage 1	20	15
Stage 2	Angle-tighten a further 90°	
Thermostat housing to coolant pump bolts	8	6
Thermostat cover bolts	8	6
2.0 litre petrol engines:		
Coolant pump bolts	9	7
Coolant pump belt cover bolts	9	7
Coolant regulator mounting bolts	9	7
Coolant regulator outlet elbow bolts	9	7
Coolant pump sprocket bolt (on balancer shaft)* CAUTION: LEFT-HAND THREAD		
Stage 1	10	7
Stage 2	Angle-tighten a further 90°	
Coolant temperature sensor bolt: *		
Stage 1	4	2
Stage 2	Angle-tighten a further 45°	
1.6 and 2.0 litre diesel engines		
Coolant pipe mounting (at front of engine) bolt	20	15
Coolant pump bolts: *		
Stage 1	20	15
Stage 2	Angle-tighten a further 45°	
Thermostat housing bolts	20	15
AC compressor bolts (all engines)	25	18
Cooling fan mounting bolts (all engines)	5	3
Electric coolant pump mounting bolts (all engines)	20	15

*Use new fixings

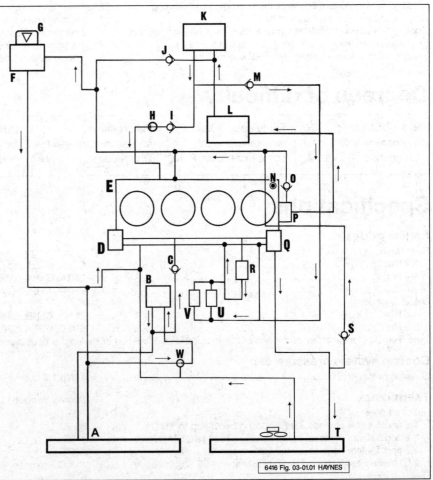

1.1 Schematic of the cooling system (typical)

A Intercooler radiator
B Charge air cooler (in inlet manifold)
C Check valve
D Coolant pump
E Engine
F Coolant reservoir
G Reservoir cap
H Electric coolant pump (for cabin heating)
I Check valve
J Check valve (some vehicles)
K Heater matrix (cabin heating)
L EGR cooler
M Check valve
N Coolant temperature sensor
O Check valve
P Coolant distribution housing
Q Thermostat
R Oil cooler
S Check valve
T Radiator
U Throttle body
V EGR control motor
W Charge air cooling pump

6416 Fig. 03-01.01 HAYNES

1 General information and precautions

1 All engines covered by this manual have a sophisticated engine cooling and cabin heating system fitted (see illustration). Most models also feature manual air conditioning, with high end model also having climate control fitted. All the cooling systems are designed to minimise engine warm up time and to keep the engine temperature at optimum levels, so that fuel economy is maximised and emissions minimised.

2 On all models a pressurised cooling system is used, with a coolant pump, a crossflow radiator and one (or two) electric cooling fans. All models have a thermostat and a heater matrix, as well as the interconnecting hoses. 1.2 and 1.4 litre petrol engines have dual thermostats. Note however that on 2.0 litre models the thermostat is only an emergency bypass thermostat in case the rotary valve of the mapped cooling system fails.

3 The system functions as follows. Coolant is circulated through the cylinder block and head passages by the coolant pump. On diesel engines the pump is driven by the timing belt. On 1.2 and 1.4 petrol engines the pump is driven by an auxiliary belt attached to the exhaust camshaft. 2.0 litre petrol engines also have a pump driven by an auxiliary belt, but on these engines the belt is driven by the balancer shaft. On most models an electrically operated coolant pump is also fitted to provide heating to to the cabin.

1.2 and 1.4 petrol engine cooling system

4 The thermostats and coolant pump are integrated into a single unit. The larger thermostat (closest to the cylinder head) opens at 87°C or 80°C depending on the year of production. This thermostat controls the flow coolant from the radiator to the cylinder head. The second smaller thermostat controls the flow of coolant between the radiator and the engine block and opens at 105°C. Both thermostats are available as parts.

5 A separate cooling circuit, with it's own electric coolant pump controls the flow of coolant between the charge air cooler (part of the inlet manifold) and the charge air cooler radiator (intercooler). Turbocharger cooling is integrated into this circuit. The charge air cooler and the engine cooling circuit share the same coolant expansion tank with coolant for the charge air cooler being tapped off via a Tee junction and one way check valve. In the event of an unexplained coolant loss both coolant circuits should be checked for leaks.

2.0 litre petrol engine cooling system

6 The 2.0 litre engine uses two rotary valves

to precisely regulate the coolant temperature. An actuator controls the position of the valves (and consequently the flow of coolant). Feedback is proved by a hall effect sensor fitted to the rotary shaft, this enables the engine management system to monitor the position of the valve.

7 The rotary valve operates in three phases: A static phase where no coolant flows. Cabin heating is provided by a separate electric coolant pump. The second phase sees the rotary valves open and allows coolant to flow around the engine and the turbocharger. There is no flow through the radiator. The third stage allows coolant to flow through the radiator. In the event of failure of the rotary valve an emergency bypass thermostat is fitted that operates as soon as the coolant temperature exceeds 113°C. A fault code will be logged and a warning message will be displayed on the instrument panel.

8 On models fitted with a semi-automatic DSG transmission a transmission gear cooler is added with a shut off valve and separate auxiliary radiator.

1.6 and 2.0 litre diesel engine cooling system

9 The coolant pump in the diesel engines is shut off at start up – there is no coolant flow around the engine block. Cabin heating and EGR cooling is provided by a separate electric cooling pump directly connected to the cylinder head. As soon as the engine warms up the coolant pump engages and coolant flows through the engine block, oil cooler and throttle body. When the engine temperature increases further the thermostat opens and coolant flows through the radiator.

10 The charge air cooler is a separate circuit with it's own electric coolant pump. Cooling is controlled by the engine management ECU independently of the main cooling circuit. Both circuits share the same coolant reservoir.

Air conditioning

11 Refer to Section 11 for information on the air conditioning system.

Precautions

 Warning: Do not attempt to remove the expansion tank filler cap or disturb any part of the cooling system while the engine is hot, as there is a high risk of scalding. If the expansion tank filler cap must be removed before the engine and radiator have fully cooled (even though this is not recommended) the pressure in the cooling system must first be relieved. Cover the cap with a thick layer of cloth, to avoid scalding, and slowly unscrew the filler cap until a hissing sound can be heard. When the hissing has stopped, indicating that the pressure has reduced, slowly unscrew the

filler cap until it can be removed; if more hissing sounds are heard, wait until they have stopped before unscrewing the cap completely. At all times keep well away from the filler cap opening.

 Warning: Do not allow antifreeze to come into contact with skin or painted surfaces of the vehicle. Rinse off spills immediately with plenty of water. Never leave antifreeze lying around in an open container or in a puddle in the driveway or on the garage floor. Children and pets are attracted by its sweet smell. Antifreeze can be fatal if ingested.

 Warning: If the engine is hot, the electric cooling fan may start rotating even if the engine is not running, so be careful to keep hands, hair and loose clothing well clear when working in the engine compartment.

 Warning: Refer to Section 11 for additional precautions to be observed when working on models with air conditioning.

2 Cooling system hoses – disconnection and renewal

Note: Refer to the warnings given in Section 1 of this Chapter before proceeding.

1 If the checks described in the relevant part of Chapter 1A Section 10 or Chapter 1B Section 10 reveal a faulty hose, it must be renewed as follows.

2 First drain the cooling system as described in Chapter 1A Section 33 or Chapter 1B Section 33. If the coolant is not due for renewal, it may be re-used if it is collected in a clean container.

3 To disconnect a hose, release its retaining clips, then move them along the hose, clear of the relevant inlet/outlet union. Carefully work the hose free (see illustration).

4 In order to disconnect the radiator inlet and outlet hoses, apply pressure to hold the hose on to the relevant union, pull out the spring

2.3 The hoses removed from the intercooler. Note that spring type clips are used extensively

2.4 Pull out the retaining clip. The thermostat housing on some models also uses a horseshoe type clip

clip and pull the hose from the union **(see illustration)**. Note that the radiator inlet and outlet unions are fragile; do not use excessive force when attempting to remove the hoses. If a hose proves to be difficult to remove, try to release it by rotating the hose ends before attempting to free it.

5 When fitting a hose, first slide the clips onto the hose, then work the hose into position. If clamp type clips were originally fitted, it is a good idea to use screw type clips when refitting the hose. If the hose is stiff, use a little soapy water as a lubricant, or soften the hose by soaking it in hot water.

6 Work the hose into position, checking that it is correctly routed, then slide each clip along the hose until it passes over the flared end of the relevant union, before securing it in position with the retaining clip.

7 Prior to refitting a radiator inlet or outlet

3.7 Remove the air deflectors

hose, renew the connection O-ring regardless of condition. The connections are a push-fit over the radiator unions.

8 Refill the cooling system as described in Chapter 1A Section 33 or Chapter 1B Section 33.

9 Check thoroughly for leaks as soon as possible after disturbing any part of the cooling system.

3 Radiators – removal, inspection and refitting

Note: *This section covers the removal of both the engine cooling radiator and the charge air cooling radiator. The radiators are either removed together, or the engine cooling radiator is removed first followed by the charge air radiator. Removal and refitting is very similar for all models covered by this manual.*

3.10a Remove the radiators by pulling them up

3.10b Unclip the the radiators from each other

3.15a Remove the coolant hoses...

3.15b ...and the intercooler hoses

Note: *Some models fitted with the semi-automatic DSG transmission may have an additional auxiliary radiator fitted.*

1.2 and 1.4 litre petrol engines

Removal

1 Switch off the ignition and all electrical consumers.

2 Jack up and support the front of the vehicle (see *Jacking and vehicle support*) remove the undershield and then drain the cooling system as described in Chapter 1A Section 33.

3 Remove the cooling fans and cowling,as described in Section 5.

4 Remove the front bumper cover as described in Chapter 11 Section 6.

5 If not already done so, disconnect the coolant hoses from both the radiator and the intercooler (charge air radiator). Anticipate some coolant spillage

6 Remove the central support panel from the front of the radiator **(see illustration 3.30a and 3.30b)**.

7 At both ends of the condenser unclip the brackets and air deflectors **(see illustration)**.

8 Unhook the AC condenser from the charge air radiator (intercooler) and secure the condenser to the bumper reinforcement.

9 Release the catches at each end of the radiator. These are hard to release and can be cut off if required. Provision is made for a self-tapping screw to be fitted when the radiator is refitted if necessary **(see illustrations 3.31a and 3.31b)**.

10 Push both radiators back slightly, so that they clear the bonnet slam panel. Both radiators can now be lifted out of the engine bay together **(see illustrations)**, or the engine cooling radiator can be unclipped from the charge air radiator (intercooler) and removed separately.

11 Check and inspect the radiator(s) as described below in this section.

Refitting

12 Refitting is a reversal of removal, but note that the O-ring seals at the quick release connectors should be replaced. Refill the cooling system as described in Chapter 1A Section 33.

2.0 litre petrol engines

Removal

13 Switch off the ignition and all electrical consumers.

14 Jack up and support the front of the vehicle (see *Jacking and vehicle support*) remove the undershield and then drain the cooling system as described in Chapter 1A Section 33.

15 If not already done so disconnect the radiator hoses. To improve access remove the intercooler hoses **(see illustrations)** – anticipate some coolant spillage as the radiator hoses are removed.

16 Remove the cooling fans and cowling,as described in Section 5.

17 Remove the radiator grille from the bumper cover as described in Chapter 11 Section 6. There is no need to remove the bumper cover.
18 Unclip the air deflectors from the front of the condenser/charge air radiator **(see illustration)**.
19 Working through the hole in the lock carrier, release the the radiator holding catches **(see illustration)**.
20 Push the radiator away from the charger air radiator (intercooler) and lift it from the mountings on the charge air radiator. Lower the radiator from the engine bay and remove it downwards. If required the charge air cooler can now be released **(see illustrations 3.31a and 3.31b)**, unclipped from the condenser and removed.
21 Check and inspect the radiator(s) as described below in this section.

Refitting

22 Refitting is a reversal of removal, but note that the O-ring seals at the quick release connectors should be replaced. Refill the cooling system as described in Chapter 1A Section 33.

1.6 and 2.0 litre diesel engines

Removal

23 Switch off the ignition and all electrical consumers.
24 Jack up and support the front of the vehicle (see *Jacking and vehicle support*) remove the undershield and then drain the cooling system as described in Chapter 1A Section 33 or Chapter 1B Section 33.

3.18 Remove the air deflectors

25 Remove the cooling fans and cowling,as described in Section 5.
Note: *Check how the radiator (for engine cooling) is connected to the charge air radiator (intercooler). On some diesel engines the radiator can be removed without removing the bumper cover.*
26 Remove the front bumper cover as described in Chapter 11 Section 6.
27 Release the refrigerant lines from their retaining clips on the right-hand chassi leg. Do not open the refrigerant circuit.
28 On all models disconnect the radiator hoses – anticipate some coolant spillage as the hoses are removed.
29 On some diesel models the radiator can now be unclipped from the charge air radiator (intercooler). On these models the radiator is lifted up (after releasing the clips) to free it

3.19 Release the catches at both ends

from the lower mountings and then lowered from the engine bay.
30 Where fitted, unscrew and remove the central rail from the lock carrier **(see illustrations)**.
31 Unclip the air deflectors and then release the catches at each end of the radiator. These are hard to release and can be cut off if required. Provision is made for a self-tapping screw to be fitted when the radiator is refitted if necessary **(see illustrations)**.
32 Remove the inner air deflectors and then release the AC condenser **(see illustration)**from the radiator (or charge air cooler on models with a full height charge air radiator) by lifting it out of the catches. Secure the AC condenser by tying it to the bumper.
33 Til the radiator and charge air cooler inwards and lift the from the locating pegs in the lock carrier panel. Fully lift up and remove both radiators **(see illustration)**.

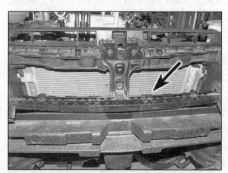
3.30a Unbolt and...

3.30b ...remove the central support panel

3.31a Release the catches. The central hole can be used to fit a screw if required

3.31b Two large screwdrivers will be needed to release the catches

3.32 Unclip the AC condenser

3.33 Remove the radiator

3.34a Some versions have the charge air cooler (radiator) fitted below the main radiator. Unclip and...

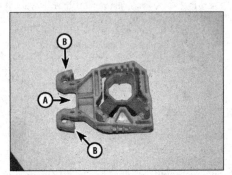

3.49b Note the provision for the fitting of a screw (A) if the locking tabs (B) have to be removed to release the intercooler or radiator

34 On the bench separate the radiators **(see illustrations)**.
35 Check and inspect the radiator(s) as described below in this section.

Refitting

36 Refitting is a reversal of removal, but note that the O-ring seals at the quick release connectors should be replaced. Refill the cooling system as described in Chapter 1B Section 33.

Auxiliary radiator

Removal

37 Switch off the ignition and all electrical consumers.
38 Jack up and support the front of the vehicle (see *Jacking and vehicle support*).

4.4a Remove the coolant hoses

3.34b ...separate the two radiators

39 Remove the left or right wheel, depending on the location of the radiator and then remove the wing liner on the appropriate side.
40 Remove the engine undershield and then remove the front bumper cover as described in Chapter 11 Section 6.
41 Unclip the air duct from the front of the auxiliary radiator.
42 Anticipate some coolant loss and where available install hose clamps to the coolant hoses. Release the spring clamps from the flow and return hoses. If the hoses have not been clamped a large container will be required to collect the coolant.
43 If working on a vehicle with the radiator mounted on the right, remove the mounting bolts and then lift the radiator up from the mountings. Lower the radiator from the bracket and remove it. If working on a radiator mounted on the left, remove the radiator complet with the mounting bracket and then remove the radiator from the bracket on the bench.

Refitting

44 Refitting is a reversal of removal. Refill the cooling system as described in Chapter 1A Section 33 or Chapter 1B Section 33.

Inspection

45 If the radiator has been removed due to suspected blockage, reverse flush it as described in the relevant part of Chapter 1A Section 33 or Chapter 1B Section 33.
46 Clean dirt and debris from the radiator fins, using an airline (in which case, wear eye protection) or a soft brush. Be careful, as the fins are sharp and easily damaged.

4.4b Remove the cover

3.49a Remove the flexible mountings to inspect them

47 If necessary, a radiator specialist can perform a 'flow test' on the radiator, to establish whether an internal blockage exists.
48 A leaking radiator must be referred to a specialist for permanent repair. Do not attempt to weld or solder a leaking radiator, as damage may result.
49 Check the radiator mounting rubbers, and renew if necessary **(see illustrations)**.

4 Thermostat –
removal, testing and refitting

1 Jack up and support the front of the vehicle (see *Jacking and vehicle support*) and then remove the engine undershield.
2 Drain the coolant as described in Chapter 1A Section 33 or Chapter 1B Section 33. There is no need to remove all the coolant. Drain the coolant below the level of the thermostat.

1.2 and 1.4 petrol engines

Large cooling circuit thermostat

Removal

3 Remove the air filter housing and the charge air pipe.
4 The the thermostat for the large cooling circuit is fitted behind the top cover of the coolant pump/thermostat housing. Remove the coolant hose (or hoses) from the cover. Remove the screws and then remove the cover to expose the thermostat **(see illustrations)**.
5 Volkswagen list a special socket (T10508) to

4.4c The large cooling circuit thermostat

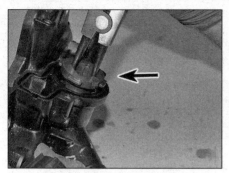

4.5 Remove the thermostat

4.8a Remove the bolts in the order shown

4.8b Lift the coolant pump from the thermostat housing

4.9 Remove the thermostat

4.10 Fit a new gasket

4.14 Remove the coolant hoses

aid removal of the large circuit thermostat, but this tool is not essential. The thermostat can be removed with long nose pliers or circlips pliers. Hold the termostat with the pliers, push down slightly and rotate the thermostat to remove it **(see illustration)**.

Refitting

6 Refitting is a reversal of removal. Use a new gasket and tighten the bolts to the specified torque. Refit the coolant hose(s) and refill the system with coolant as described in Chapter 1A Section 33. Refit the undershield and lower the vehicle to the ground.

Small cooling circuit thermostat

Removal

7 Remove the coolant pump as described in Section 7.

8 Remove the coolant pump from the thermostat housing **(see illustrations)**.
9 Lift out the thermostat noting the orientation **(see illustration)**.

Refitting

10 Refitting is a reversal of removal, noting the following:
a) *Use a new gasket* **(see illustration)**.
b) *Lubricate the new gasket with coolant.*
c) *Tighten the bolts in the reverse order to that shown* **(see illustration 4.8a)**.
d) *Refit the coolant pump with reference to Section 7.*
e) *Refill the cooling system as described in Chapter 1A Section 33.*
f) *Refit the undershield and lower the vehicle to the ground.*

2.0 litre petrol engines

11 The 2.0 litre engine does not use a traditional thermostat – see the introduction to this Section 1.

Removal

12 Remove the coolant pump as described in Section 7.
13 Remove the throttle body as described in Chapter 4A Section 4 and then remove the coolant pipe from the inlet manifold.
14 Remove the coolant hoses from the regulator **(see illustration)**.
15 Disconnect the wiring plug and then remove the regulator and actuator **(see illustrations)**.

Refitting

16 Refitting is a reversal of removal, but use

4.15a Disconnect the wiring plug

4.15b Unbolt and remove the regulator

4.15c Recover the small connector

4.16a Fit new seals to the connector...

4.16b ...and a new gasket to the regulator

4.18 Remove the charge air pipe

4.20a Rotate the cover (note the bayonet fitting)...

4.20b ...and remove it (shown with inlet manifold removed for clarity)

Testing – all models

23 On model fitted with a removable thermostat the traditional testing method is to place the thermostat in a pan of water with a thermometer. Heat the water and check the opening temperature of the thermostat. However, given the low cost of a new thermostat, if the thermostat is suspect then simply replace it.

5 Electric cooling fans –
testing, removal and refitting

new gaskets **(see illustrations)** and O-rings. Refill the coolant as described in Chapter 1A Section 33. Refit the engine undershield and lower the vehicle to the ground.

1.6 and 2.0 litre diesel engines

Removal

17 Remove the air filter housing as described in Chapter 4B Section 3.
18 Unbolt and remove the charge air pipe from the left-hand end of the engine **(see illustration)**.

19 Remove the radiator fan(s) and cowl as described in Section 5.
20 Remove the coolant hose from the thermostat housing and then remove the housing by rotating it to remove it **(see illustrations)**.
21 Remove the thermostat and recover the O-ring **(see illustration)**.

Refitting

22 Refitting is a reversal of removal, but use a new seal **(see illustration)**. Refill the cooling system as described in Chapter 1B Section 33. Refit the engine undershield and lower the vehicle to the ground.

Testing

1 One or Two electric cooling fans are fitted to all models. Activationof the cooling fans is fully controlled by the engine management ECU (Electronic Control Unit). Testing of the cooling fan circuit is as follows.
2 If a fan does not appear to work, first check the fuses and fusible links. If they are good, run the engine until normal operating temperature is reached, then allow it to idle. If the fan does not cut-in within a few minutes, the cause may be the temperature sensor(s) (where applicable) which can be checked by

4.21 Remove the thermostat

4.22 Fit a new seal

5.7a Remove the complete air inlet duct (on some models)…

5.7b …or remove the top cover and then the lower section

5.10a Locate and then…

a Volkswagen dealer or suitably equipped garage using specialist diagnostic equipment.
3 The motors can be checked by disconnecting the motor wiring connector and connecting a 12 volt supply directly to the motor terminals. If the motor is faulty, it must be renewed, as no spares are available.
4 If the fan still fails to operate, check the cooling fan circuit wiring (Chapter 14). Check each wire for continuity and ensure that all connections are clean and free of corrosion.
5 On models with a cooling fan control unit, if no fault can be found, then it is likely that the cooling fan control unit is faulty. Testing of the unit should be entrusted to a Volkswagen dealer or specialist; if the unit is faulty it must be renewed.

Removal

6 Switch off the ignition and all electrical consumers. Where fitted remove the engine top cover.
7 Remove the air intake duct from the slam panel **(see illustrations)**. On 2.0 litre petrol models remove the complete air filter assembly as described in Chapter 4A Section 3.
8 On all models except 1.2 and 1.4 petrol models, jack up and support the front of the vehicle (See *Jacking and vehicle support*). Remove the engine undershield.
9 On 2.0 litre petrol models drain the coolant as described in Chapter 1A Section 33 and remove the lower charge air coolant hose.
10 Disconnect the fan wiring plug at the base of the cowl **(see illustrations)**.

11 Release the cowl from the mounting clips and then lift out the fan and cowl. Lift the complete assembly up and out of the engine bay, or where it is easier lower the assembly down and out **(see illustrations)**.
12 To remove the fans and motors from the shroud, first disconnect and release the wiring plugs, then unscrew the nuts and remove the units.

Refitting

13 Refitting is a reversal of removal.

---

6 Cooling system electrical sensors – testing, removal and refitting

Note: *All vehicles covered by this manual have a cylinder head mounted temperature sensor. Petrol models have an additional sensor fitted to the engine coolant radiator outlet hose. The sensors provide information to the engine management control unit for the efficient running of the engine and control of the cooling fan(s).*

Cooling fan temperature sensor

Testing

1 Where fitted, the sensor is located in the coolant hose outlet elbow at the bottom left-hand side of the radiator.
2 The sensor contains a thermistor, which consists of an electronic component whose electrical resistance decreases at a predetermined rate as its temperature

5.10b …disconnect the wiring plug

rises. When the coolant is cold, the sensor resistance is high, current flow through the sensor is reduced. No resistance-to-temperature values are available, however a simple check can be made by checking that the resistance changes (with a multimeter) according to temperature – in a similar manner to checking a thermostat. The only method of accurately checking the sensor is with dedicated diagnostic equipment, but as the sensor is a low cost item, if the sensor is suspect it should be replaced.

Removal and refitting

3 The engine and radiator should be cold before removing the sensor. Switch off the ignition and all electrical consumers.
4 Jack up and support the front of the vehicle (see *Jacking and vehicle support*). Remove the engine undershield.

5.11a Release the cowl from the clips at both sides

5.11b Lift out the fan and cowling (1.4 petrol shown)…

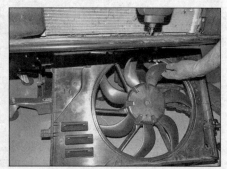

5.11c …or lower the fan and cowling (1.6 litre diesel shown)

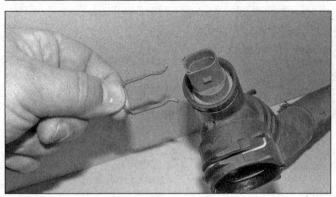

6.8a Pull out the clip...

6.8b ...and remove the sensor

5 Open the filler cap on the coolant reservoir (this will release any residual pressure in the system) and then close it.

6 Have the replacement sensor ready or a suitable plug which can be used to plug the sensor aperture whilst it is removed. If the reservoir cap has been replaced the vacuum should help keep most of the coolant in the system

7 Disconnect the wiring plug from the sensor.

8 Pull out the clip and remove the sensor from the elbow (see illustrations). Recover the O-ring seals from the elbow and sensor.

9 Refitting is a reversal of removal. On completion, top up the cooling system with the correct type and quantity of coolant as described in *Weekly checks*.

10 Start the engine and run it until it reaches normal operating temperature, then continue to run the engine and check that the cooling fan cuts in and functions correctly.

Coolant temperature sensor

Testing

11 The sensor is located at the rear left-hand end of the cylinder head on 1.2 and 1.4 petrol engines or on the left-hand end of the cylinder head on 2.0 litre petrol and diesel engines

(see illustrations).

12 The sensor contains a thermistor, which consists of an electronic component whose electrical resistance decreases at a predetermined rate as its temperature rises. When the coolant is cold, the sensor resistance is high, current flow through the sensor is reduced. The change in resistance and the voltage returned to the Engine Control Unit (ECU) is critical to the efficient operation of the engine. A faulty sensor may cause poor or inefficient running (as well as a temperature gauge that reads incorrectly). Diagnostic equipment can identify a faulty sensor, but given the low cost of a replacement, if the sensor is suspect it should be replaced.

Removal and refitting

13 The engine and radiator should be cold before removing the sensor. Switch off the ignition and all electrical consumers.

14 Where fitted, remove the engine top cover.

15 Open the filler cap on the coolant reservoir (this will release any residual pressure in the system) and then close it.

16 Remove the air filter housing and the charge air pipe as required.

17 Disconnect the wiring plug from the sensor.

18 Remove the bolt and withdraw the sensor from the housing. Recover the O-ring. Note that on some engines a support ring is fitted behind the O-ring seal. Use a small pick to recover the ring if required.

19 Refitting is a reversal of removal. Bearing in mind the following points.

a) *Refit the sensor with a new O-ring.*

b) *Top-up the cooling system as described in 'Weekly checks'.*

c) *Start the engine and run it until it reaches normal operating temperature. Check the operation of the coolant temperature gauge and check that the cooling fan cuts in and functions correctly.*

---

7 Coolant pump – removal and refitting

1.2 and 1.4 petrol engines

Removal

1 Drain the cooling system as described in Chapter 1A Section 33.

2 Remove the air filter housing and charge air hose as described in Chapter 4A Section 3.

6.11a The engine coolant temperature sensor on the 1.6 diesel engine...

6.11b ...and on the 2.0 litre petrol engine

7.4 Remove the breather hose

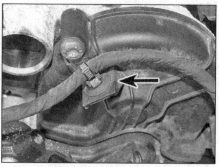

7.5a Unclip the wiring loom…

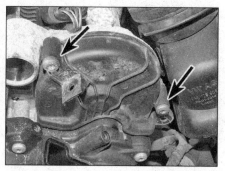

7.5b …remove the bolts…

7.5c …and lift off the cover

7.7a Always fit a new gasket

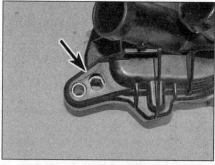

7.7b The hex hole in the pump for belt tensioning

3 Remove the battery and battery tray as described in Chapter 5A Section 3.

4 Remove the EVAP hose from the top of the valve cover **(see illustration)**.

5 Release the wiring loom clip from the coolant pump drivebelt cover and then remove the cover **(see illustrations)**.

6 Remove the coolant hoses from the pump. Working in the sequence shown **(see illustration 7.7d)** unbolt the pump and remove it with complete with the drivebelt.

Refitting

7 Refitting is a reversal of removal, noting the following:

a) Fit a new gasket **(see illustration)**.

b) The drivebelt must be replaced.

c) Set piston number one to TDC (Top Dead Centre) as described in Chapter 2A Section 3.

d) Install the pump and hand tighten the bolts in order **(see illustration)**.

e) Tighten the bolts in order to the second stage torque and then slocken the bolts by one full turn.

f) An assistant will be required to complete the next stage.

g) Using the hex hole provided **(see illustration)** on the pump fit a torque wrench, set at 30 Nm and turn the pump with the wrench so that the belt is tensioned to 30 Nm.

h) With the aid of an assistant (and whilst

still holding the torque wrench at 30 Nm) tighten the bolts 2, 1 and 5 to the third stage torque.

i) Remove the torque wrench and tighten the bolts to the fourth stage torque.

j) The remainder of refitting is a reversal of removal.

2.0 litre petrol engines

Removal

8 Drain the coolant as described in Chapter 1A Section 33.

9 Remove the air filter housing as described in Chapter 4A Section 3.

10 Remove the air inlet duct from the top of the radiator **(see illustration)**.

7.7c Tension the pump with a torque wrench

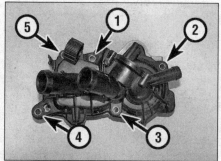

7.7d Tighten the bolts in the order shown

7.10 Remove both sections of the air intake

7.13 Remove the coolant hoses

7.14a Disconnect the wiring plugs...

7.14b ...and remove the bracket

11 Unclip the wiring loom and then remove the charge air pipe from the left-hand end of the engine.

12 Remove the throttle body as described in Chapter 4A Section 4.

13 Remove the coolant hoses from the rotary valve **(see illustration)**.

14 Disconnect the wiring plugs, unbolt the mounting bracket and move it to the side **(see illustrations)**. Note that access to the bracket screws is difficult.

15 Disconnect the wiring plug from the oil pressure switch and then remove the coolant pump drivebelt cover **(see illustration)**.

16 At this point it is possible to remove the drivebelt without removing the coolant pump by removing the bolt from the balancer shaft sprocket and removing the belt with the sprocket. Note that the belt can only be removed if the drivebelt sprocket is slackened (or removed) as there is insufficient clearance between the sprocket and the engine block **(see illustrations)**.

Caution: The balancer shaft sprocket bolt has a LEFT-HAND thread and must be replaced if removed.

17 Remove the bolts and lift off the coolant pump **(see illustrations)**.

18 Recover or remove the gasket.

Refitting

19 Refitting is a reversal of removal, noting the following:

a) *Fit a new gasket* **(see illustration)**.

b) *Tighten the bolts in the order show* **(see illustration 7.17a)**.

1.6 and 2.0 litre diesel engines

Removal

20 Remove the timing belt as described in Chapter 2C Section 7. If the timing belt is not being replaced (recommended) then the belt can be left on the crankshaft pulley.

21 Disconnect the wiring plug from the control valve, remove the bolt and pull the valve from the coolant pump (see

7.15 Remove the drivebelt cover

7.16a Slacken (or remove) the sprocket bolt...

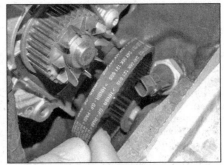

7.16b ...and remove the belt

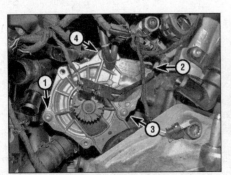

7.17a Remove the bolts...

7.17b ...and lift off the coolant pump

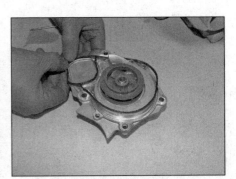

7.19 Fit a new gasket

7.21a Disconnect the wiring plug...

7.21b ...unbolt and...

7.21c ...remove the control valve

illustrations). Note that the control valve can be removed after removing the coolant pump.
22 Remove the bolts and withdraw the coolant pump from the engine block (see illustrations). Recover the O-ring seal from the groove in the pump. If the pump is faulty, it must be renewed.

Refitting

23 Refitting is a reversal of removal, bearing in mind the following points.
a) Fit the coolant pump with a new O-ring.
b) Lubricate the O-ring with coolant.
c) Refit the timing belt. Replacing the belt and tensioner is recommended.
d) Refill the cooling system as described in Chapter 1B Section 33.

Electric cooling pump

24 All models feature one or two electric cooling pumps. They are fitted to circulate coolant around the air to liquid intercooler and inlet manifold. On some engines a pump is fitted to circulate coolant to the cabin heater matrix. Removal and refitting is essentially the same regardless of the engine type or position of the pump (see illustrations).

Removal

25 Jack up and support the front of the vehicle (see *Jacking and vehicle support*). Remove the engine undershield.
26 Drain the coolant as described in Chapter 1A Section 33 or Chapter 1B Section 33. Alternatively (and where possible) clamp the coolant hoses with hose clamp pliers.
27 Disconnect the wiring plug.

7.22a Unbolt and...

7.22b ...remove the coolant pump

28 Anticipate some coolant spillage and remove the hose clips. Work the coolant hoses free from the pump.
29 Unbolt the pump and remove it.

Refitting

30 Refitting is a reversal of removal.

8 Heating and ventilation system – general information

1 The heating/ventilation system consists of a four-speed blower motor (housed in the passenger compartment), face-level vents in the centre and at each end of the facia, and air ducts to the front and rear footwells.
2 The control unit is located in the facia, and the controls operate flap valves to deflect and mix the air flowing through the various parts of the heating/ventilation system. The flap valves are contained in the air distribution housing, which acts as a central distribution unit, passing air to the various ducts and vents.
3 Cold air enters the system through the grille at the rear of the engine compartment. A pollen filter is fitted to filter out dust, soot, pollen and spores from the air entering the vehicle.
4 The airflow, which can be boosted by the blower, flows through the various ducts, according to the settings of the controls. Stale air is expelled through ducts beneath the rear bumper. If warm air is required, the cold air is passed through the heater matrix, which is heated by the engine coolant.
5 If necessary, the outside air supply can be closed off, allowing the air inside the vehicle to be recirculated. This can be useful to prevent unpleasant odours entering from outside the vehicle, but should only be used briefly, as the recirculated air quality inside the vehicle will soon deteriorate.

9 Heating and ventilation system components – removal and refitting

Heater/ventilation control unit

1 Switch off the ignition and all electrical consumers.

7.24a Typical rear mounted electric coolant pump for cabin heating

7.24b Typical location of the electric cooling pump for charge air cooling

9.3 Unclip the trim panel

9.4a Remove the scrivet type clips

9.4b Pull the control unit forward...

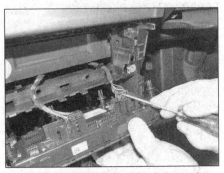

9.4c ...release the locking tabs and disconnect the wiring plugs

9.7a Clamp the coolant hoses

9.7b Remove the coolant hoses

2 On models fitted with stop/start, turn the engine off with the stop/start button. Alternatively disconnect the battery as described in Chapter 5A Section 3.

3 Using a plastic trim too, work around the surround and remove the trim panel from the control panel **(see illustration)**.

4 Prise out the spreader pegs from the 'scrivet' type clips. Pull the control unit forward and disconnect the wiring plugs **(see illustrations)**.

5 Refitting is a reversal of removal. A replacement unit must be adapted to the vehicle using diagnostic equipment. Consult a Volkswagen dealer or suitably equipped specialist.

Heater matrix

6 On diesel engines remove the crankcase breather from the top of thew engine and then remove the short extension section of the charge air pipe. This will improve access to the heater hoses.

7 Using hose clamps, clamp the heater matrix inlet and return hoses located on the bulkhead at the rear of the engine compartment. Place a container beneath the hoses, then remove them either at the quick release connectors or at the spring clips **(see illustrations)**. Note the location of the hoses for correct refitting. If hose clamps are not available partially drain the coolant as described in Chapter 1A Section 33 or Chapter 1B Section 33.

8 With the hoses disconnected, remove the coolant from the matrix by blowing air into the upper tube, preferably using an airline.

9 Working inside the vehicle, remove the glovebox as described in Chapter 11 Section 25.

10 Remove the air distribution duct **(see illustration)**.

11 Remove the centre console front side panel **(see illustration)**.

12 On models fitted with an auxiliary electric heater, disconnect the wiring plugs and remove the heater **(see illustration)**.

13 One of two versions of the heater matrix may be fitted, both are very similar, but the Valeo unit uses a sliding horseshoe type clip to hold the upper coolant hose in position. The Denso version uses screw type clamps and has longer outlet pipes on the matrix.

14 Place cloth rags or similar on the floor beneath the heater matrix, then release the pipe clamps and/or slide off the horseshoe

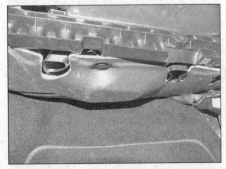

9.10 Remove the panel and air distribution duct

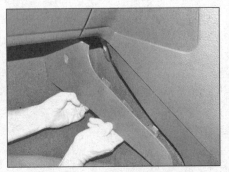

9.11 Remove the side panel

9.12 Where fitted remove the auxiliary heater

9.14a Release the pipe clamps...

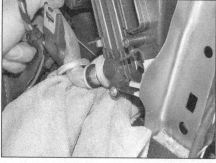

9.14b ...and pull the coolant pipes from the matrix

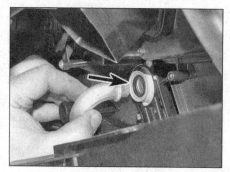

9.14c Recover the seals

9.15a Where fitted, remove the cover

9.15b Pull out the matrix

9.18 Remove the insulation

type clip. Pull the coolant pipes from the matrix **(see illustrations)**. Note that the seals may come out with the pipes or remain in the matrix.

15 With difficulty, remove the heater matrix from the heater unit **(see illustrations)**.

16 Refitting is a reversal of removal, noting the following.

a) *Make sure the seal is fitted correctly around the perimeter of the matrix.*

b) *Always fit new seals and clamps.*

c) *When reconnecting the coolant pipes, moisten the seals with coolant and make sure the conical ends locate in the matrix. After reconnecting the pipes, the clamps*

must turn easily before tightening them securely.

d) *Top-up the coolant level with reference to 'Weekly checks' at the beginning of this Manual.*

Heater unit

Note: *Removal of the complete heater box is a long and involved task. The main reason to remove it completely will be to replace the AC evaporator or some of the internal air distribution flaps. Most of the control motors and cables are accessible once the facia panel is removed (Chapter 11 Section 27). Note that some of the control motors are also accessible with the glovebox or steering column removed.*

17 Disconnect the battery (Chapter 5A Section 3) and on models fitted with AC have the system degassed by a suitably equipped garage or air conditioning specialist.

18 Where fitted remove the heat shield (or insulation) from the front of the plenum chamber to access the coolant and refrigerant lines **(see illustration)**.

19 Disconnect the heater matrix coolant hoses **(see illustrations 9.7a and 9.7b)** and where available blow compressed air through the matrix to clear the coolant out.

20 Disconnect the refrigerant lines at the plenum chamber **(see illustrations)**. Seal the open lines and the expansion valve.

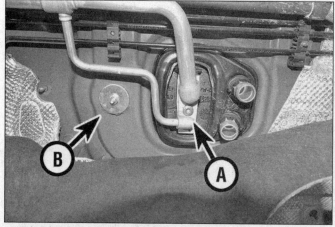

9.20a Unbolt the refrigerant lines (A) and note the nut (B)

9.20b Seal the AC lines and the expansion valve as soon as they are disconnected

9.23a Remove the carpet and...

9.23b ...then remove the air distribution ducts

9.26 The heater unit ready for removal

21 Partially release the grommet from around the pipes and AC expansion valve (where AC is fitted).
22 Remove the facia panel as described in Chapter 11 Section 27 and then remove the crossmember (Chapter 11 Section 28).
23 Remove the air distribution ducts (at both sides) for the rear footwells (see illustrations).
24 Disconnect the wiring plugs from the airbag control unit (at the front of the transmission tunnel) and the blower motor.
25 On models with AC disconnect the evaporator drain tube from the housing.
26 Work around the housing and disconnect the wiring plugs as required (see illustration). Release the wiring loom from the housing – again as required. Make a final check and then remove the nut from the front of the plenum chamber (see illustration 9.20a).
27 Carefully pull the heater unit from the bulkhead, taking care not to damage or bend the matrix tubes on the bulkhead (see

illustration). The help of an assistant may be required. Be prepared for coolant spillage as the assembly is removed from inside the car.
28 If necessary, the heater may be further dismantled on the bench.
29 Refitting is a reversal of removal, but top-up the coolant with reference to *Weekly checks* at the beginning of this Manual. Have the AC system regassed by the company that removed the refrigerant.

Heater blower motor

30 Switch off the ignition and all electrical consumers.
31 Remove the passenger side glovebox as described in Chapter 11 Section 27, the lower cover and air distribution duct.
32 Disconnect the wiring plug from the blower motor (see illustration 9.36a).
33 Remove the three screws, release the catch and lower the motor from the heater housing (see illustration).

34 Refitting is a reversal of removal.

Heater blower motor series resistor

35 Remove the blower motor as described above.
36 Disconnect the wiring plug, remove the screws and pull out the resistor pack (see illustrations).
Caution: The resistor may be very hot if the heater has recently been in use.
37 Refitting is the reverse of removal.

Fresh/recirculating air flap and positioning motor

Note: *All the various control motors for the heating and (where fitted) AC have a diagnostic capability and can output fault codes that can be read by a suitable code reader (scan tool). Consult a Volkswagen dealer or suitably equipped garage before replacing any component part of the system.*
38 The facia and crossmember must be removed as described in Chapter 11 Section 27 and Chapter 11 Section 28.
39 Remove the control motor and then lever off the actuator.
40 Remove the lever arm from the defrost flap, remove the bolts and lift the mechanism upwards to remove it.
41 Refitting is a reversal of removal. Note that if the motor is renewed, its basic settings must be reprogrammed by a Volkswagen dealer or suitably equipped garage using specialist equipment.

Temperature flap control motor

42 Remove the trim panel from below the glovebox and then remove the centre console as described in Chapter 11 Section 26.
43 Reach up and unhook the actuating lever and then remove the mounting bolts. Note that the upper fixing is difficult to access. Disconnect the wiring plug as the motor is lowered.
44 Refitting is a reversal of removal. Ensure that the gears align correctly before fully tightening the fixings.

Auxiliary heater

45 Some diesel models are equipped with an auxiliary electrically powered heating element within the heating unit.

9.27 Remove the heater unit

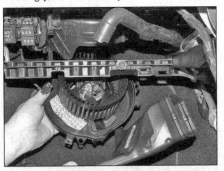

9.33 Remove the motor

9.36a Disconnect the wiring plug and remove the screws

9.36b Lift out the resistor pack

46 Remove the glovebox as described Chapter 11 Section 27.
47 Unbolt the earth connection, release the locking tab and remove the main wiring plug.
48 Remove the upper and lower mounting bolts. Slide the heater out of the housing. Note that it will contact the facia as it is removed, but with care it is just possible to manoeuvre the element past the facia. If this proves impossible then remove the centre console (Chapter 11 Section 26) and then remove all the fascia screws from the left-hand end of the facia (Chapter 11 Section 27). This will allow the fascia to be lifted slightly to allow the passage of the heater.
49 Refitting is a reversal of removal.

10 Heating/ventilation system vents – removal and refitting

1 Removal and fitting of the vents is covered in Chapter 12 Section 19 (central vents) and Chapter 12 Section 11 (right-hand vent. Left-hand vent is removed in the same manner).

11 Air conditioning system – general information and precautions

General information

1 Air Conditioning (AC) is fitted as standard to most models, and is available as manually-operated system or automatically-operated climate control system (climatronic). The Climatronic system works in conjunction with the heating and air conditioning systems to maintain a selected vehicle interior temperature fully automatically.
2 The air conditioning system enables the temperature of incoming air to be lowered, and dehumidifies the air, which makes for rapid demisting and increased comfort. The cooling side of the system works in the same way as a domestic refrigerator. Refrigerant gas is drawn into a belt-driven compressor and passes into a condenser mounted in front of the radiator, where it loses heat and

becomes liquid. The liquid passes through an expansion valve to an evaporator, where it changes from liquid under high pressure to gas under low pressure. This change is accompanied by a drop in temperature, which cools the evaporator. The refrigerant returns to the compressor and the cycle begins again.
3 Air blown through the evaporator passes to the air distribution unit, where it is mixed with hot air blown through the heater matrix to achieve the desired temperature in the passenger compartment.
4 The heating side of the system works in the same way as on models without air conditioning.
5 The operation of the system is controlled electronically by coolant temperature switches, and pressure switches which are screwed into the compressor high-pressure line. Any problems with the system should be referred to a Volkswagen dealer or an air conditioning specialist.
6 The only operation which can be carried out easily without discharging the refrigerant is the renewal of the compressor drivebelt, which is covered in the relevant part of Chapter 1A Section 30 (petrol models) or Chapter 1B Section 30 (diesel models). Removal of the evaporator and condenser requires the evacuation of the refrigerant. If necessary the compressor can be unbolted and moved aside, without disconnecting its flexible hoses, after removing the drivebelt **(see illustration)**.

Precautions

When an air conditioning system is fitted, it is necessary to observe special precautions whenever dealing with any part of the system, its associated components and any items which require disconnection of the system. If for any reason the system must be disconnected, entrust this task to your Volkswagen dealer or an air conditioning specialist.

⚠️ *Warning: The refrigeration circuit contains a refrigerant and it is therefore dangerous to disconnect any part of the system without specialised knowledge and equipment. The refrigerant is potentially dangerous and should only be handled*

by qualified persons. If it is splashed onto the skin it can cause frostbite. It is not itself poisonous, but in the presence of a naked flame (including a cigarette) it forms a poisonous gas. Uncontrolled discharging of the refrigerant is dangerous and potentially damaging to the environment. Do not operate the air conditioning system if it is known to be short of refrigerant, as this may damage the compressor.

12 Air conditioning system components – removal and refitting

Sunlight sensor

Note: *Only fitted to models with full climate control (climatronic).*
1 Switch off the ignition and all electrical consumers.
2 Using a plastic trim tool, gently prise out the sensor.
3 Disconnect the wiring plug and remove the sensor.
4 Refitting is a reversal of removal.

Footwell temperature sensor

Note: *Only fitted to models with full climate control (climatronic).*
5 Switch off the ignition and all electrical consumers.
6 Remove the lower trim panel from the drivers side as described in Chapter 11 Section 27 and then remove the knee airbag as described in Chapter 12 Section 24.
7 The sensor is located in the air duct. Disconnect the wiring plug, lift the sensor slightly to access the retaining tabs. Compress the tabs and remove the sensor.
8 Refitting is a reversal of removal.

Side vent temperature sensors

Note: *Only fitted to models with full climate control (climatronic).*
Note: *Sensors are fitted behind both fascia side vents. The removal and refitting procedure is the same for both sides.*
9 Switch off the ignition and all electrical consumers.
10 Remove the fascia end panel as described in Chapter 11 Section 27.
11 Disconnect the wiring plug from the sensor.
12 Turn the sender through 90°, and withdraw it from the housing.
13 Refitting is a reversal of removal.

Evaporator temperature sensor

14 The sensor is located to the right-hand side of the heater housing, close to the evaporator, to the left of the clutch pedal **(see illustration)**.
15 Working in the driver's side footwell, reach up to the left of the clutch pedal (where fitted) to access the sensor.
16 Disconnect the wiring plug connector and pull the sensor from the housing.

11.6 Air conditioning compressor bolted to the front of the cylinder block

12.14 Evaporator temperature sensor (shown with heater housing removed)

12.19 Ambient temperature sensor location below the bumper reinforcement

12.22 Remove the rubber/foam grommet from the pipes

12.23a Remove the heater pipes from the matrix

12.23b Remove the horseshoe style clip...

12.23c ...and recover the seal

17 Refitting is a reversal of the removal procedure.

Ambient temperature sensor

Note: *Several versions of the sensor are fitted.*
18 On some models remove unclip the centre grille to access the sensor. On other models remove the front bumper cover as described in Chapter 11 Section 6.
19 Unclip the sensor from its retainer and disconnect the wiring plug **(see illustration)**.
20 Refitting is a reversal of removal. Make sure the wiring is fully connected to prevent entry of water.

Evaporator

21 Remove the heater matrix and heater housing, as described earlier in Section 9.
22 Remove the rubber gaiter and foam cushion from around the coolant and refrigerant pipes **(see illustration)**.
23 Release any retaining clips and remove the coolant pipes from the housing **(see illustrations)**.
24 Working your way around the housing, undo the retaining bolts and split the housing into two parts **(see illustrations)**.
25 To remove the evaporator, undo the retaining bolts and split the upper and lower halves of the housing, then withdraw the evaporator from the housing together with the refrigerant lines and rubber grommet **(see illustrations)**.

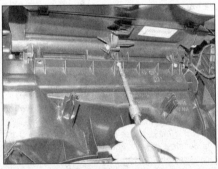

12.24a Unscrew the bolts securing the two sections of the heater housing...

12.24b ...and separate them

12.25a Unscrew and unclip the evaporator housing...

12.25b remove the top section...

12.25c ...then remove the evaporator

12.29 Remove the air deflectors

12.30a Unbolt and...

12.30b ...remove the refrigerant lines

26 Refitting is a reversal of removal, fit new seals and have the system recharged by a Volkswagen dealer or refrigeration specialist.

Condenser

Note: *It is possible to remove the cooling fans, radiator, intercooler and condenser as a single unit. If this approach is adopted the aid of an assistant is essential.*

 Warning: It is a criminal offence to knowingly discharge refrigerant to the atmosphere.

27 Have the refrigerant evacuated from the air conditioning system by a Volkswagen dealer or automotive refrigeration specialist. Many garages will have the equipment and mobile services are available at a reasonable cost.

28 Remove the front bumper cover as described in Chapter 11 Section 6.

29 At each end of the condenser remove the air deflectors by unclipping them **(see illustration)**.

30 Undo the screws and disconnect the refrigerant lines from the condenser **(see illustrations)**. Recover the seals and plug the lines and condenser openings to prevent entry of foreign matter and water vapour.

31 Unclip the condenser from the radiator and then lower the condenser to remove it **(see illustration)**.

32 Refitting is a reversal of removal, but fit new seals, and have the system recharged by a Volkswagen dealer or refrigeration specialist.

12.30c Seal the lines and the condenser

12.31 Unclip the condenser

Compressor

Note: *Several versions of the compressor are fitted to the Golf range. Removal and refitting is essentially the same for all versions.*

33 Have the refrigerant evacuated from the air conditioning system by a Volkswagen dealer or refrigeration specialist. Note that the compressor can be moved forward and secured to the front panel if removal is only required for access to other components. There is no need to have the system evacuated if this is the case.

34 Jack up and support the front of the vehicle (see *Jacking and vehicle support*). Remove the engine undershield and the right-hand lower section of the wing liner.

35 Remove the auxiliary drivebelt as described in Chapter 1A Section 30 or Chapter 1B Section 30.

36 Where required remove the air filter housing and air intake duct as described in Chapter 4A Section 3 or Chapter 4B Section 3.

37 On some engine versions, drain the coolant (as described in Chapter 1A Section 33 or Chapter 1B Section 33) and remove the charge air hoses from the intercooler (charge air radiator).

38 Unscrew the retaining bolts and disconnect the refrigerant lines from the compressor **(see illustration)**. Recover the O-ring seals. Plug the open pipes and ports to prevent the ingress of moisture.

39 Disconnect the wiring plug connector from the rear of the compressor **(see illustration)**.

40 Undo the retaining bolts **(see illustration)** and withdraw the compressor from the mounting bracket.

41 Refitting is a reversal of the removal procedure, ensure that all the fixings are

12.38 Unbolt the refrigerant lines from the compressor

12.39 Disconnect the wiring connector

12.40 Remove the bolts

12.46 Remove the cap to access the drier

12.53a Disconnect the wiring plug…

12.53b …and unscrew the sensor

tightened to the specified torque settings, where given. Lubricate the new O-rings seals with compressor oil and fit them to the refrigerant lines. Have the system recharged by a Volkswagen dealer or refrigeration specialist.

Receiver/drier

Note: *Check for the availability of parts before removal, there are different makes of receiver/drier and some cannot be renewed separately from the condenser.*

42 Have the refrigerant evacuated from the air conditioning system by a Volkswagen dealer or refrigeration specialist.

43 The receiver/drier is attached to the left-hand side of the condenser.

44 Complete removal of the condenser is not required. Remove the bumper cover and then lift the condenser out of the mounting brackets.

45 Tip the top of the condenser away from the bonnet slam panel to access the receiver/drier.

Keihin and Modine types

46 Unscrew the cap (with a T50 torx socket) from the top of the receiver/drier **(see illustration)**. Peel back the warning label, where fitted.

Caution: DO NOT remove this cap if the system has not been evacuated, as it will be under high pressure.

47 Insert a bolt into the receiver/drier sealing cover, push downwards slightly and extract the retaining circlip.

48 A length of welding rod or similar will be required to fabricate a simple hooked tool to remove the desiccant. The rod should be at least 400 mm long with a small turned up hook at the end. Insert the rod and hook out the desiccant cartridge.

Denso type

49 The Denso version is removed in exactly the same manner as the Keihin and Modine types, except that the drier is attached to the sealing plug (there is no circlip).

50 Unscrew the hex head sealing cap and

lift out the receiver drier. Unclip the desiccant from the sealing plug.

51 Refitting is a reversal of the removal procedure, ensure that all the fixings are tightened to the specified torque settings, where given. On completion, fit new O-rings and then have the system recharged by a Volkswagen dealer or refrigeration specialist.

Refrigerant pressure sensor

52 The sensor is mounted in the refrigerant line behind the right-hand headlight.

53 Disconnect the wiring plug and whilst counterholding the refrigerant line with a spanner, unscrew the sensor **(see illustrations)** – note there is a schrader valve below the sensor and this will seal as the sensor is removed. However caution will be required, because if the valve is faulty refrigerant will escape. If there is any sound of escaping refrigerant, immediately refit the sensor and have the system professionally evacuated before removing the sensor.

54 Refitting is a reversal of removal.

Chapter 4 Part A
Petrol engine fuel systems

Contents

Section number

Air filter housing and inlet system – removal and refitting 3
Fuel injection system – depressurisation 7
Fuel injection system – testing and adjustment 9
Fuel lift pump and gauge sender unit – removal and refitting 5
Fuel pipes and connections 2

Section number

Fuel system components – removal and refitting 4
Fuel tank – removal and refitting 6
General information and precautions 1
Inlet manifold and associated components – removal and refitting . . 8

Degrees of difficulty

Easy, suitable for novice with little experience	**Fairly easy,** suitable for beginner with some experience	**Fairly difficult,** suitable for competent DIY mechanic	**Difficult,** suitable for experienced DIY mechanic	**Very difficult,** suitable for expert DIY or professional

Specifications

Engine codes*

1.2 litre	CJZA, CJZB and CYVA
1.4 litre	CPTA, CHPA, CMBA, CXSA, CPVA, CZEA and CZDA
2.0 litre	CHHA, CHHB, CJXE and CXDA

*See 'Vehicle identification' at the end of this manual for the location of the engine code markings

System type

1.2 litre engines	Bosch motronic ME17.5.21
1.4 litre engines:	
Engine codes CHPA, CHPB, CMBA,CPTA, CXSA, CZDA, CZDD and CZEA. Bosch motronic ME17	
Engine codes CZCA.	Bosch motronic ME17.5.21
2.0 litre engines:	
Engine code CHHA and CHHB	Bosch Motronic MED 17.5
Engine code CJXE and CXDA	N/A

Fuel system data

Regulated fuel pressure (all engines)	4.0 to 7.0 bar
Engine idle speed.	non-adjustable, electronically controlled
Idle CO content (non-adjustable, electronically-controlled)	0.5% max

Torque wrench settings

	Nm	lbf ft
All models		
Accelerator pedal to bulkhead	10	7
Fuel tank strap retaining bolt	25	18
Oxygen sensor(s)	50	37
1.2 and 1.4 litre engines		
Fuel rail bolts	9	7
Fuel rail pressure sensor	22	16
High pressure fuel pump bolt: *		
M8 bolts		
Stage 1	Screw in by hand	
Stage 2	Screw alternatively until in contact with camshaft housing	
Stage 3	20	15
Stage 4	Angle-tighten a further 90°	
M6 bolts		
Stage 1	Screw in by hand	
Stage 2	Screw in alternatively until pump makes contact with camshaft housing	
Stage 3	8	6
Stage 4	Angle-tighten a further 90°	
Inlet manifold	8	6
Knock sensor	20	15

Use new nuts/bolts

	Nm	lbf ft
2.0 litre engines		
Fuel pressure sensor (high pressure rail)	27	20
Fuel pressure sensor (low pressure rail)	15	11
Fuel rail mounting bolts	9	7
High-pressure fuel line to fuel rail:	27	20
High pressure fuel pump		
M6 bolts*		
Stage 1	8	6
Stage 2	Angle-tighten a further 90°	
M8 bolts	20	15
Inlet manifold to cylinder head bolts	9	7
Inlet manifold support bracket (to cylinder head).	20	15
Knock sensor*:		
Stage 1	8	6
Stage 2	Angle-tighten a further 90°	
Throttle body mounting bolts.	7	5

Use new nuts/bolts

1 General information and precautions

General information

1 The systems described in this Chapter are all self-contained engine management systems, which control both the fuel injection and ignition. This Chapter deals with the fuel system components only – see Chapter 4C for information on the turbocharger, exhaust and emission control systems, and to Chapter 5B for details of the ignition system.

2 The fuel injection system consists of a fuel tank, an electric fuel lift pump/level sender unit, fuel supply and return lines, a throttle housing/module, four electronic fuel injectors, and an Electronic Control Unit (ECU) together with its associated sensors, actuators and wiring. All models have a direct (high pressure) injection system where the injectors inject fuel directly into the combustion chambers.

Additionally 2.0 litre engines also have low pressure manifold injectors fitted, making a total of eight fuel injectors on these engines.

3 The direct injection system uses a high-pressure fuel pump mounted on top of the camshaft housing, actuated by a plunger in contact with the inlet camshaft. Fuel under high pressure is fed into a fuel rail fitted below the inlet manifold. The injectors are located between the fuel rail and cylinder head, and inject fuel directly into the combustion chambers.

4 The low pressure fuel injectors on 2.0 litre engines are fitted to the inlet manifold and inject fuel into the manifold.

5 The fuel lift pump is immersed in the fuel inside the tank, and delivers a constant supply of fuel to the high-pressure fuel pump. The fuel pump mounted pressure regulator maintains a constant fuel pressure to the fuel injectors. A low pressure fuel line delivers fuel to the low pressure (manifold) injectors on 2.0 litre engines.

6 The fuel injectors are opened and closed by an Electronic Control Unit (ECU), which calculates the injection timing and duration according to engine speed, crankshaft/camshaft position, throttle position and rate of opening, inlet manifold depression, inlet air temperature, coolant temperature, roadspeed and exhaust gas oxygen content information, received from sensors mounted on and around the engine.

7 The temperature and pressure of the air entering the throttle housing is measured by a sensor mounted on the charge air pipe. This information is used by the ECU to fine-tune the fuelling requirements for different operating conditions. All engines are turbocharged and have an air to liquid charge air cooler (intercooler), except for 2.0 litre engines that use a standard air to air intercooler. Details of the turbocharger and charge air system are given in Chapter 4C.

8 Idle speed control is achieved partly by an electronic throttle valve positioning module, which is part of the throttle housing, and partly by the ignition system, which gives fine control of the idle speed by altering the ignition timing. As a result, manual adjustment of the engine idle speed is not necessary or possible.

9 The exhaust gas oxygen content is constantly monitored by the ECU by oxygen sensors (also known as lambda sensors), one before the catalytic converter, and one after - this improves sensor response time and accuracy, and the ECU compares the signals from each sensor to confirm that the converter is working correctly. The ECU uses the information from the sensors to modify the injection timing and duration to maintain the optimum air/fuel ratio.

10 The ECU also controls the operation of the activated charcoal filter evaporative loss system - refer to Chapter 4C Section 2 for further details.

11 It should be noted that fault diagnosis of all the engine management systems described in this Chapter is only possible with dedicated electronic test equipment. Problems with the systems operation should therefore be referred to a Volkswagen dealer or suitably equipped garage for assessment. Note however that low cost diagnostic equipment is now available to the home mechanic and whilst it will not offer the depth of coverage of professional equipment it may help to guide the home mechanic in the right direction. Once the fault has been identified, the removal/refitting sequences detailed in the following Sections will then allow the appropriate component(s) to be renewed as required.

Precautions

 Warning: Petrol is extremely flammable – great care must be taken when working on any part of the fuel system.

● Do not smoke, or allow any naked flames or uncovered light bulbs near the work area. Note that gas-powered domestic appliances with pilot flames, such as heaters boilers and tumble-dryers, also present a fire hazard – bear this in mind if you are working in an area where such appliances are present. Always keep a suitable fire extinguisher close to the work area, and familiarise yourself with its operation before starting work. Wear eye protection when working on fuel systems, and wash off any fuel spilt on bare skin immediately with soap and water. Note that fuel vapour is just as dangerous as liquid fuel – possibly more so; a vessel that has been emptied of liquid fuel will still contain vapour, and can be potentially explosive.

● Many of the operations described in this Chapter involve the disconnection of fuel lines, which may cause an amount of fuel spillage. Before commencing work, refer to the above 'Warning' and the information in 'Safety first!' at the beginning of this manual.

● Residual fuel pressure always remains in the fuel system, long after the engine has been switched off. This pressure must be relieved in a controlled manner before work can commence on any component in the fuel system – refer to Section 7 for details.

● When working with fuel system components, pay particular attention to cleanliness – dirt entering the fuel system may cause blockages, which will lead to poor running.

● In the interests of personal safety and equipment protection, many of the procedures in this Chapter suggest that the negative lead be removed from the battery terminal. This firstly eliminates the possibility of accidental short-circuits being caused as the vehicle is being worked upon, and secondly prevents damage to electronic components (eg,

sensors, actuators, ECUs) which are particularly sensitive to the power surges caused by disconnection or reconnection of the wiring harness whilst they are still 'live'. Refer to Chapter 5A Section 3.

2 Fuel pipes and connections

1 Disconnect the battery as described in Chapter 5A Section 3.

2 The fuel supply pipe connects the fuel pump in the fuel tank to the high pressure fuel pump on the engine.

3 Whenever you're working under the vehicle, be sure to inspect all fuel and evaporative emission pipes for leaks, kinks, dents and other damage. Always replace a damaged fuel pipe immediately.

4 If you find signs of dirt in the pipes during disassembly, disconnect all pipes and blow them out with compressed air. Inspect the fuel strainer on the fuel pump pick-up unit for damage and deterioration.

Steel tubing

5 It is critical that the fuel pipes be replaced with pipes of equivalent type and specification.

6 Some steel fuel pipes have threaded fittings. When loosening these fittings, hold the stationary fitting with a spanner while turning the union nut.

Plastic tubing

 Warning: When removing or installing plastic fuel tubing, be careful not to bend or twist it too much, which can damage it. Also, plastic fuel tubing is NOT heat resistant, so keep it away from excessive heat.

7 When replacing fuel system plastic tubing, use only original equipment replacement plastic tubing.

Flexible hoses

8 When replacing fuel system flexible hoses, use original equipment replacements, or hose to the same specification.

9 Don't route fuel hoses (or metal pipes) within 100 mm of the exhaust system or within 280 mm of the catalytic converter. Make sure that no rubber hoses are installed directly against the vehicle, particularly in places where there is any vibration. If allowed to touch some vibrating part of the vehicle, a hose can easily become chafed and it might start leaking. A good rule of thumb is to maintain a minimum of 8.0 mm clearance around a hose (or metal pipe) to prevent contact with the vehicle underbody.

Disconnecting Fuel pipe Fittings

10 Typical fuel pipe fittings:

2.10a Two-tab type fitting; depress both tabs with your fingers, then pull the fuel pipe and the fitting apart

2.10b On this type of fitting, depress the two buttons on opposite sides of the fitting, then pull it off the fuel pipe

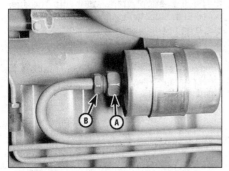

2.10c Threaded fuel pipe fitting; hold the stationary portion of the pipe or component (A) while loosening the union nut (B) with a flare-nut spanner

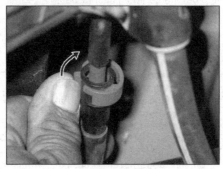

2.10d Plastic collar-type fitting; rotate the outer part of the fitting

2.10e Metal collar quick-connect fitting; pull the end of the retainer off the fuel pipe and disengage the other end from the female side of the fitting…

2.10f …insert a fuel pipe separator tool into the female side of the fitting, push it into the fitting and pull the fuel pipe off the pipe

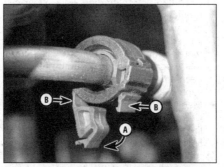

2.10g Some fittings are secured by lock tabs. Release the lock tab (A) and rotate it to the fully-opened position, squeeze the two smaller lock tabs (B)…

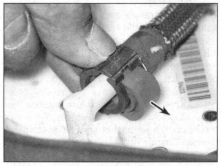

2.10h …then push the retainer out and pull the fuel pipe off the pipe

2.10i Spring-lock coupling; remove the safety cover, install a coupling release tool and close the tool around the coupling…

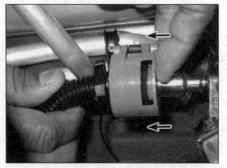

2.10j …push the tool into the fitting, then pull the two pipes apart

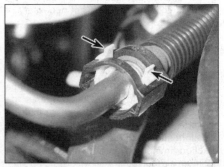

2.10k Hairpin clip type fitting: push the legs of the retainer clip together, then push the clip down all the way until it stops and pull the fuel pipe off the pipe

3 Air filter housing and inlet system – removal and refitting

Removal

1.2 and 1.4 engines

1 Release the spring type hose clip from the inlet air duct (see illustrations).
2 Pull off the breather hose and then release the outlet duct at the air filter or the turbocharger (see illustrations).
3 Remove the housing by pulling it straight up off the mounting rubbers (see illustration).
4 If required the charge air pipe (turbocharger to throttle body) can now be removed.
5 Disconnect the wiring plug from the

3.1a Release the spring type clamps. Note the special tool

3.1b Remove the inlet duct

airflow sensor and then release the spring clips from the throttle body and the inlet manifold (see illustrations). Remove the duct.

6 The air filter inlet duct can also be removed. Remove the screws at both ends and then unclip the duct from the bonnet slam panel (see illustrations).

3.2a Remove the breather hose

3.2b Release the duct at the turbocharger…

3.2c …or the air filter housing

3.3 Remove the air filter housing

3.5a Disconnect the wiring plug…

3.5b …and release the spring clips at the throttle

3.5c Release the duct at the turbocharger

3.6a Remove the screws and…

3.6b …and remove the inlet duct

3.8a Remove the screws...

3.8b ...and lift off the cover

3.8c Unclip the coolant hose...

3.8d ...and remove the lower section

3.9a Remove the vent hose, release the hose clip...

3.9b ...and remove the housing

2.0 litre engines

7 The air filter housing is located in front of the battery on the left-hand side of the engine compartment.

8 Remove the screws at each end of the air inlet duct, lift off the cover, unclip the coolant hose and then unclip the lower section (see illustrations).

9 Remove the vent hose from the filter housing, release the hose lip and then pull the complet air filter housing off the rubber mountings (see illustrations).

Refitting

10 Refitting is a reversal of removal.

4   Fuel system components – removal and refitting

Note: *Observe the precautions in Section 1 before working on any component in the fuel system. Information on the engine management system sensors which are more directly related to the ignition system will be found in Chapter 5B.*

Throttle body

1.2 and 1.4 litre engines

1 Remove the short section of hose on the air filter housing and the charge air pipe ducting as described in Section 3.

2 Disconnect the wiring from the throttle body (see illustration).

3 Unscrew and remove the bolts, then lift the throttle body away from the inlet manifold. Recover the O-ring seal.

4 Refitting is a reversal of removal, but always fit a new seal.

2.0 litre engines

5 Remove the engine cover and air filter housing as described in Section 3.

6 Jack up and supprt the front of the vehicle – see 'Jacking and support ' and then remove the engine undershield.

7 Unbolt the coolant pipe and move it to the side. If the coolant has already been removed, then remove the pipe completely. Release the hose clip and remove the upper charge air pipe from the intercooler (see illustrations).

8 Working from below, disconnect the wiring plug from the boost pressure sensor and unclip the coolant hose from the bracket.

9 Disconnect the wiring plug from the throttle

4.2 Disconnect the wiring plug

4.7a Remove the coolant pipe and...

4.7b ...charge air pipe

4.9a Disconnect the wiring plug

4.9b Remove the throttle body

4.12 Disconnect the wiring plug

body, remove the screws and remove the throttle body **(see illustrations)**. Recover the seal if necessary.

10 Refitting is a reversal of removal, but always fit a new seal.

Fuel injectors (and fuel rail where applicable)

Note: *Observe the precautions in Section 1 before working on any component in the fuel system. If a faulty injector is suspected, before removing the injectors, it is worth trying the effect of one of the proprietary injector-cleaning treatments. These can be added to the petrol in the tank, and are intended to clean the injectors as you drive. Note that*

Volkswagen technicians use tool T10133C to remove the injectors and fit the new injector seals – although the tool may not be required to remove the injectors, tools T10133/5 and T10133/6 (part of the kit) it will be required to fit the new seals.

High pressure injectors (all engines)

⚠️ *Warning: The fuel injection system operates at high pressure and must be depressurised before starting work as described in Section 7.*

11 Remove the inlet manifold as described in Section 8.

12 Disconnect the wiring plug from the pressure sensor **(see illustration)**.

13 Place shop towels below the fuel rail to absorb any escaping fuel. Unbolt the high pressure fuel supply pipe from the rail. Seal the rail **(see illustration)**.

14 Remove the mounting bolts from the fuel rail and pull the rail of the injectors **(see illustrations)**. The injectors may come out with the fuel rail, if this is the case disconnect the wiring plug from the injector(s) as the fuel rail is removed.

15 Disconnect the wiring plugs from the fuel injectors **(see illustration)**.

16 Remove the injector support ring and seal from the cylinder head **(see illustrations)**.

17 Where the special tool is available, install the impact sleeve over the injector

4.13 Seal the fuel rail

4.14a Remove the bolts and...

4.14b ...lift off the fuel rail

4.15 Disconnect the wiring plugs from the injectors

4.16a Remove the support rings...

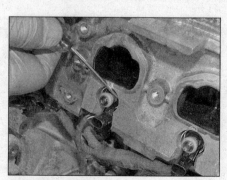

4.16b ...and seals from each injector

4.17 Gently tap the injector

4.18a Always try to pull out the injectors by hand first

4.18b Using the slide hammer to remove the injector

4.19 Provide a fulcrum and lever out the injector

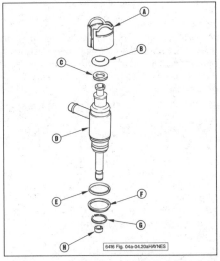

4.20a 1.2 and 1.4 litre engine fuel injector details

A Support ring	E Upper seal
B O-ring seal	F Lower seal
C Spacer	G Circlip
D Injector	H Teflon seal

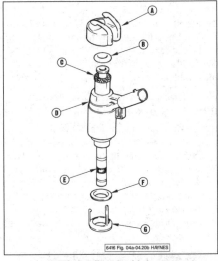

4.20b 2.0 litre fuel injector details

A Support ring	E Teflon seal
B O-ring seal	F Lower seal
C Spacer	G Lower seal
D Injector	support

and gently tap each injector in turn to break the seal. Where the tool is not available use a suitable drift or bolt **(see illustration)**. Do not uses excessive force or the injector will be damaged.

18 At this stage Volkswagen technicians use the puller tool from the tool kit to extract the injector. Note that earlier version of the special tool have a slide hammer as part of the tool kit. Where available this can also be used **(see illustrations)**.

19 Where the correct tool is not available is also possible to remove the injectors by carefully prising them from the cylinder head. Use a block of wood or similar soft material as the fulcrum to avoid damage to the cylinder head **(see illustration)**. Where this is not possible the fuel injectors must be removed with the correct tool.

Injector seals

20 The injectors fitted to the 1.2 and 1.4 litre engines are slightly different to those fitted to the 2.0 litre engine **(see illustrations)**, however removal and refitting of the seals is essentially the same.

21 Refitting is a reversal of removal, but thoroughly clean the cylinder head seatings,

and fit new injector seals **(see illustrations)**. On all engine codes the seals are made of Teflon, and the special VAG tool will be required to compress the seals before fitting the injectors to the cylinder head. Do not grease or oil the seals.

22 With the new seal in position the tool can be used to compress the seal fully into the groove. Leaving the injector for a reasonable

4.21a Thoroughly clean the injector seatings in the cylinder head

4.21b Cut off the old seal with a sharp knife

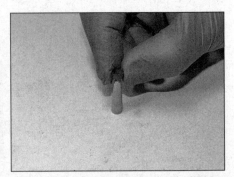

4.21c Fit the new seal onto the assembly taper

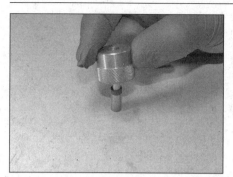

4.21d Push the seal down on the taper with the sleeve tool

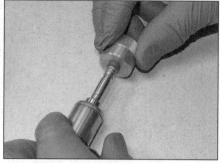

4.21e Fit the taper to the injector, invert the sleeve and push the seal onto the injector

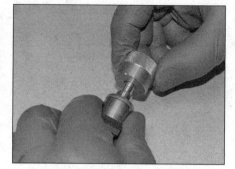

4.21f Rotate the sleeve as the seal is pushed into the groove

4.23 Fit a new seal and support ring. Note the orientation of the support ring

4.24 Oil the O-rings before fitting the fuel rail

4.29 Disconnect the wiring plugs. The main connector shown connects all four injectors

time period will also help the seal contract around the groove in the injector.

23 Fit a new support ring and then fit a new O-ring seal to the top of the injector **(see illustration)**. Fit new lower lower seals and a new circlip on 1.2 and 1.4 litre engines. On 2.0 litre engines fit a new lower seal.

24 Fit a new upper collar and then install the injector in the cylinder head, taking care to align them correctly. Oil the O-ring seals and refit the fuel rail **(see illustration)**.

25 Refitting the remaining components is a reversal of removal.

26 Start the vehicle and check carefully for any fuel leaks.

Low pressure injectors (2.0 litre engines only)

 Warning: The fuel injection system operates at pressure and must be depressurised before starting work as described in Section 7.

27 Remove the engine cover.

28 Remove the clamps and release the wiring loom. Unbolt the coolant hose and move it to the side.

29 Disconnect the wiring plugs from the fuel pressure sensor, the manifold sensor and the main injector wiring plug **(see illustration)**.

30 Anticipate the loss of fuel and place shop towels below the fuel inlet. Remove the spring clip and remove the fuel supply line. Seal the fuel line and fuel rail.

31 Remove the fuel rail mounting bolts and pull up the fuel rail complete with the injectors **(see illustrations)**.

32 Place shop towels beneath the injectors, disconnect the wiring plugs, remove the retaining clips and pull the injectors from the fuel rail.

33 Remove the O-ring seals from the injectors

and fit new ones. Oil the seals and refit the injectors to the fuel rail **(see illustrations)**.

34 Clean the bores in the cylinder head and then refit the fuel rail.

4.31a Remove the bolts and...

4.31b ...pull off the fuel rail

4.33a Fit new injector seals (the brown seal fits to the manifold side of the injector)...

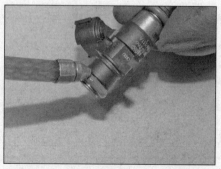

4.33b ...and oil both the upper and lower seal

4.37 Remove the footrest panel

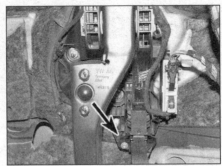

4.38 Remove the bolt

4.41 Disconnect the wiring plug

4.46a Release the locking tabs...

4.46b ...and remove the sensor

35 Refit the remaining components in reverse order to removal.
36 Start the vehicle and check carefully for any fuel leaks.

Throttle pedal/position sensor

37 All models are fitted with a 'fly-by-wire' throttle where the position sensor is integral with the accelerator pedal. Working inside the car, remove the footrest panel from below the accelerator and brake pedals **(see illustration)**.
38 Fold back the floor covering and disconnect the wiring plug. Remove the bolt **(see illustration)** and remove the throttle sensor.
39 Refitting is a reversal of removal.

Inlet air temperature/ pressure sensor

1.2 and 1.4 litre engines

40 The combined air temperature and manifold pressure sensor is located on the top of the inlet manifold.
41 Remove the air filter and then, disconnect the wiring plug **(see illustration)**.
42 Release the locking tabs and remove the sensor from the manifold. Recover the seal and discard, as a new one must be used on refitting.
43 Refitting is a reversal of removal, but fit a new seal.

2.0 litre engines

44 The sensor is located on the top of the inlet manifold. Remove the engine cover.
45 Disconnect the wiring plug and remove the single bolt.
46 Open the locking tabs and remove the sensor **(see illustrations)**. Recover the seal and discard, as a new one must be used on refitting.
47 Refitting is a reversal of removal, but fit a new seal.

Boost pressure sensor

48 The sensor is fitted to the charge air pipe.

1.2 and 1.4 litre engines

49 The sensor is fitted close to the air filter housing. Disconnect the wiring plug **(see illustration)** and unclip the sensor from the charge air pipe.
50 Refitting is a reversal of removal, but fit a new seal.

2.0 litre engine

51 Jack up and support the front of the vehicle – see *Jacking and vehicle support*. Remove the engine undershield.
52 Disconnect the wiring plug, remove the bolts and pull the sensor out of the charge air pipe.
53 Refitting is a reversal of removal, but fit a new seal.

Camshaft position sensors

1.2 and 1.4 litre engines

54 Both sensors are fitted to the left-hand end of the valve cover. Remove the air inlet duct from the turbocharger. This is best removed with the air filter housing as described in Section 3.
55 Disconnect the wiring plug, remove the bolt and pull out the sensor **(see illustration)**. Repeat the procedure for the other sensor.
56 Refitting is a reversal of removal, but fit a new O-ring seal.

2.0 litre engines

57 Remove the engine cover.
58 To remove the inlet camshaft sensor, remove the inlet manifold as described in Section 8. The exhaust camshaft sensor is

4.49 Disconnect the wiring plug

4.55 Disconnect the wiring plug (inlet camshaft sensor shown)

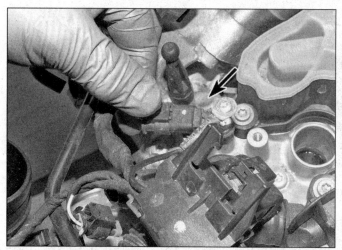

4.58a The exhaust camshaft position sensor

4.58b The inlet camshaft position sensor

accessible after the engine cover has been removed **(see illustrations)**.

59 Disconnect the wiring plug, remove the bolt and lift out the sensor.

60 Refitting is a reversal of removal, but fit a new O-ring seal.

Crankshaft position sensor

1.2 and 1.4 litre engines

61 Jack up and support the front of the vehicle – see *Jacking and vehicle support*. Remove the engine undershield.

62 The sensor is fitted at the front left-hand end of the engine, close to the transmission bell housing.

63 Unbolt the charge air coolant pump and move it to the side. There is no need to drain the coolant.

64 Disconnect the wiring plug and remove the hex head bolt. Note that access is difficult and a ball end hex key makes the task slightly easier. Remove the sensor.

65 Refitting is a reversal of removal.

2.0 litre engines

66 Jack up and support the front of the vehicle – see *Jacking and vehicle support*. Remove the engine undershield.

67 The sensor is fitted at the front left-hand end of the engine, close to the transmission bell housing.

68 Unclip the coolant hoses from the bracket and secure it to the side.

69 Disconnect the wiring plug, remove the bolt and pull out the sensor.

70 Refitting is a reversal of removal, but fit a new seal to the sensor.

Knock sensor

1.2 and 1.4 litre engines

71 The sensor is fitted below the fuel rail, close to the oil cooler **(see illustration)**.

72 Remove the auxiliary drivebelt as described in Chapter 1A Section 30 and then unbolt the AC compressor and secure it to

the side (see Chapter 3 Section 12). DO NOT disconnect the refrigerant lines.

73 Disconnect the wiring plug, remove the bolt and remove the sensor.

74 Refitting is a reversal of removal.

2.0 litre engines

75 The sensor is located close to the rotary valve behind the coolant pump **(see illustration)**. Access is restricted.

76 Disconnect the sensor wiring plug and the rotary valve/coolant temperature sensor wiring plug(s).

77 Unbolt the sensor and remove it.

78 Refitting is a reversal of removal.

Coolant temperature sensor

79 Refer to Chapter 3 Section 6.

Oxygen (lambda) sensors

⚠ *Warning: Working on the sensors is only advisable with the engine (and therefore the exhaust system) completely cold. The catalytic converter in particular will be very hot for some time after the engine has been switched off.*

80 All models have one sensor fitted before the catalytic converter, and a second sensor mounted downstream of the converter. Refer to Chapter 4C Section 6 for more details.

4.71 The knock sensor

81 On all models the sensor wiring plugs are mounted on the front wall of the plenum chamber. Typically, the wiring plug is coloured black for the upstream sensor, and brown for the downstream sensor – do not confuse exhaust gas temperature sensors fitted to the exhaust system – mark them for identification prior to disconnection.

82 Unscrew and remove the sensor, taking care to avoid damaging the sensor probe as it is removed. **Note:** *As a flying lead remains connected to the sensor after it has been disconnected, if the correct-size spanner is not available, a slotted socket will be required to remove the sensor.*

83 Apply a little high-temperature anti-seize grease to the sensor threads – avoid contaminating the probe tip.

84 Refit the sensor, tightening it to the correct torque. Reconnect the wiring.

Electronic control unit (ECU)

Caution: Always wait at least 30 seconds after switching off the ignition before disconnecting the wiring from the ECU. When the wiring is disconnected, all the learned values are erased. Note also that if the ECU is renewed, the identification of the new ECU must be transferred to the immobiliser control unit by a Volkswagen dealer.

4.75 The knock sensor (shown with the rotary valve removed)

4.87a A rotary tool can be used to cut a slot in the shear bolts

4.87b Remove the shear bolts with a screwdriver in the cut slot

4.87c Remove the security cover

4.88a Unclip the ECU...

4.88b ...slide up the locking clamps...

4.88c ...disconnect the wiring plug and remove the ECU

85 The ECU is fitted next the the under bonnet fusebox.

86 Disconnect, and remove the battery as described in Chapter 5A Section 3.

87 Some models have a security bracket covering the ECU. This must be removed before the ECU can be removed **(see illustrations)**.

Warning: Cover the engine with a fire blanket and have a fire extinguisher to hand. DO NOT use a rotary tool if any fuel line is open or leaking.

88 Unclip the ECU from the bracket, slide up the locking clamp (or clamps) and remove the wiring plug **(see illustrations)**.

89 Refitting is a reversal of removal. Bear in mind the comments made in the Caution above.

High-pressure fuel pump

Caution: The system must be depressurised before the pump is removed – see Section 7.

1.2 and 1.4 litre engines

90 Remove the air filter housing as described in Section 3.

91 Remove the throttle body as described in in this section. This will allow easy access to the high pressure fuel line at the fuel rail.

92 Place shop towels beneath the pump and then remove the fuel supply hose and the high pressure fuel line **(see illustration)**.

93 Disconnect the wiring plug and unbolt the pump.

94 Extract the bucket tappet/push rod from the housing.

95 Refitting is a reversal of removal, noting the following:

a) *Clean the mating faces of the pump and camshaft housing.*

b) *Lubricate the bucket tappet/push rod with clean engine oil, then insert it in the camshaft housing.*

c) *Smear clean engine oil on the new O-ring seal, then refit the fuel pump together with the O-ring seal. Insert the mounting bolts and tighten to the specified torque.*

d) *Reconnect the wiring, then reconnect the fuel lines and tighten the union nut(s) to the specified torque. To ensure correct seating, the pump bolts must be progressively tightened to their specified torque.*

e) *Refit the air filter housing as described in Section 3.*

2.0 litre engines

96 Remove the engine cover and the air filter housing as described in Section 3.

97 Unclip the wiring loom and then remove the charge air pipe from the left-hand end of the engine.

98 Remove the bolts that secure the coolant hose at the top of the engine and then unbolt the high pressure fuel line support bracket **(see illustration)**.

99 Slacken the high pressure fuel line at the fuel rail and then whilst counterholding the union nut at the pump unbolt the high pressure fuel line. Note that if the union nut is slackened it must be replaced.

4.92 Remove the fuel lines

4.98 The high pressure pipe support bracket

4.100 Remove the low pressure fuel lines

4.101a Remove the pump and...

4.101b ...recover the tappet

100 Disconnect the wiring plug and then remove the low pressure injector fuel supply hose and the fuel supply hose **(see illustration)**.

101 Remove the mounting bolts evenly and withdraw the pump. Recover the follower tappet **(see illustrations)**.

102 Refitting is a reversal of removal, noting the following:

a) *Clean the mating faces of the pump and camshaft housing.*

b) *The camshaft lobe must be at bottom dead centre before refitting the pump. Rotate the crankshaft as required.*

c) *Lubricate the follower with clean engine oil and refit it.*

d) *Fit a new seal to the pump*

e) *Install the pump and tighten the bolts evenly and progressively to the specified torque.*

f) *Lubricate the ball ends of the high pressure pipe before installing the pipe.*

g) *Refit the remaining components in reverse order to removal.*

Fuel pressure regulator

103 On all engines the fuel pressure regulator is mounted on the high pressure fuel pump.

104 Gain access to the fuel pump as described above.

105 Depressurise the fuel injection system as described in Section 7.

106 Disconnect the wiring plug and unbolt the sensor.

107 Refitting is a reversal of removal.

4.120 The location of the fuel pressure sensor (shown with inlet manifold removed)

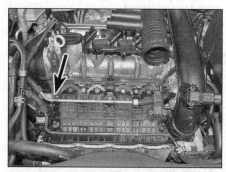

4.110 The fuel pressure sensor (1.4 litre engine shown)

Fuel pressure sensors

108 A fuel pressure sensor is fitted to the high pressure fuel rail on all engines. 2.0 litre engines also have a low pressure sensor fitted to the low pressure fuel rail.

109 Depressurise the fuel injection system as described in Section 7.

1.2 and 1.4 litre engines

110 On 1.2 and 1.4 litre engines the sensor is easily accessible at the end of the fuel rail **(see illustration)**.

111 Disconnect the wiring from the sensor, then unscrew and remove it. Be prepared for some loss of fuel by positioning a suitable container beneath the sensor.

112 Refitting is a reversal of removal, but tighten the sensor to the specified torque.

4.121 The low pressure fuel rail pressure sensor

4.118 Remove the manifold support strut

2.0 litre engines

113 Remove the engine cover and air filter housing as described in Section 3.

114 Unbolt the coolant pipe from the front of the engine/inlet manifold.

115 If not already done so, remove the inlet duct from the top of the radiator.

116 Jack up and support the front of the vehicle (see *Jacking and vehicle support*), remove the engine undershield.

117 Unclip the coolant hose (next to the charge air pipe), disconnect the boost pressure sensor and then remove the charge air pipe.

118 Remove the support strut from the bottom of the inlet manifold **(see illustration)**.

119 Disconnect the wiring plug from the alternator and the fuel pressure sensor.

120 Anticipate some petrol spillage and unbolt the pressure sensor **(see illustration)**.

121 The low pressure fuel rail pressure sensor can easily be removed after removing the engine cover **(see illustration)**.

122 Disconnect the wiring plug, pull out the horseshoe type clip and remove the sensor.

123 Refitting of all the sensors is a reversal of removal.

5	Fuel lift pump and gauge sender unit – removal and refitting	

Note: *Observe the precautions in Section 4B Section 1 before working on any component in the fuel system.*

5.3a Remove the seat squab

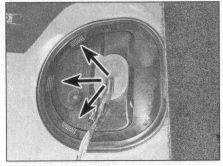

5.3b Leverage points are provide on the cover

5.3c Lever up the cover with a trim tool

⚠ *Warning: Avoid direct skin contact with fuel – wear protective clothing and gloves when handling fuel system components. Ensure that the work area is well ventilated to prevent the build-up of fuel vapour.*

General information

1 The fuel lift pump and gauge sender unit are combined in one assembly, which is mounted in the top of the fuel tank. The unit protrudes into the fuel tank, and its removal involves exposing the contents of the tank to the atmosphere.

Removal

2 Ensure that the vehicle is parked on a level surface, then disconnect the battery as described in Chapter 5A Section 3.
3 Remove the rear seat squab as described in Chapter 11 Section 22 and then prise off the

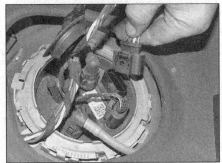

5.3d Disconnect the wiring plugs

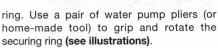

5.4 Disconnect the fuel lines

cover. Release the locking tab and disconnect the wiring plugs **(see illustrations)**.
4 Disconnect the fuel lines and seal them. Note the position of the flow and return lines **(see illustration)**.
5 Note the position of the alignment marks, then unscrew and remove the securing

ring. Use a pair of water pump pliers (or home-made tool) to grip and rotate the securing ring **(see illustrations)**.
6 Lift out the lift pump/gauge sender unit, holding it above the level of the fuel in the tank until the excess fuel has drained out. Recover the flange and seal **(see illustration)**.
7 With the pump/sender unit removed from the car, lay it on an absorbent card or rag. Inspect the float at the end of the sender unit swinging arm for punctures and fuel ingress – renew the unit if it appears damaged.
8 The fuel pick-up incorporated in the assembly is spring-loaded to ensure that it always draws fuel from the lowest part of the tank. Check that the pick-up is free to move under spring tension with respect to the sender unit body.
9 Inspect the rubber seal from the fuel tank aperture for signs of fatigue – renew it if necessary **(see illustration)**.

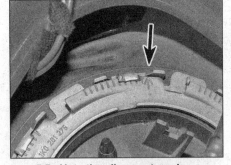

5.5a Note the alignment marks...

5.5b ...then use a suitable tool to unscrew...

5.5c ...and remove the securing ring

5.6 Removing the lift pump/gauge sender unit from the fuel tank

5.9 If not removed with the unit, recover the rubber seal and check its condition

10 Inspect the sender unit wiper and track; clean off any dirt and debris that may have accumulated, and look for breaks in the track.
11 If required, the sender unit can be separated from the pump assembly.
12 Disconnect the wiring from the top of the unit and then unclip the float and potentiometer **(see illustration)**.
13 If required simple resistance checks can be mode on the fuel gauge sender with a multimeter set to ohms **(see illustration)**.

Refitting

14 Refit the lift pump/sender unit by following the removal procedure in reverse, noting the following points:
a) *Take care not to bend the float arm as the unit is refitted.*
b) *Smear the outside of tank aperture rubber seal with clean fuel or lubricating spray, to ease fitting. Locate the seal in the tank aperture before fitting the lift pump/sender unit.*
c) *Tighten the securing ring to the specified torque setting.*
d) *Reconnect the fuel hoses to the correct ports – observe the direction-of-flow arrow markings, and refer to paragraph 6. Ensure that the fuel hose fittings click fully into place.*
e) *On completion, check that all associated pipes are securely clipped to the tank, then run the engine and check for fuel leaks.*

6 Fuel tank – removal and refitting

Note: *Observe the precautions in Section 4B Section 1 before working on any component in the fuel system.*

Removal

1 Before the tank can be removed, it must be drained of as much fuel as possible. As no drain plug is provided, it is preferable to carry out this operation with the tank almost empty.
2 Disconnect the battery as described in Chapter 5A Section 3 and then using a hand pump or syphon, remove any remaining fuel from the tank.

5.12 Disconnect the small wires...

3 Lift up the rear seat squab and disconnect the wiring plug from the pump/sender unit – as described in Section 4B Section 8.
4 Open the fuel filler flap, and unscrew the fuel filler cap – leave the cap loosely in place.
5 Loosen the right-hand rear wheel bolts, then jack up the rear of the car (see *Jacking and vehicle support*). Remove the right-hand rear wheel.
6 Undo the retaining screws, release the retaining clips and remove the left-hand rear wheel arch liner.
7 Open the fuel filler flap, and unscrew the fuel cap from the top of the filler neck.
8 Unscrew the screw at the filler neck **(see illustrations)**.
9 Working inside the wheel arch remove the filler neck support bracket **(see illustration)**.
10 With reference to Chapter 4D Section 9, remove the rear section of the exhaust system.

6.8a Remove the screw...

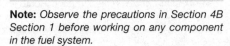

6.9 Remove the bracket

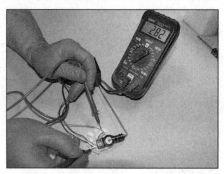
5.13 Checking that the resistance varies with the position of the float

11 Disconnect the fuel lines from the connections at the front of the fuel tank **(see illustration)**.
12 On models fitted with the multi-link rear suspension, mark the relationship between the rear hub and the trailing arm on the right-hand side and then unbolt the trailing arm and lower it.
13 On models fitted with a torsion beam rear suspension remove the rear axle beam as described in Chapter 10 Section 17.
14 Position a trolley jack under the centre of the tank. Insert a block of wood between the jack head and the tank to prevent damage to the tank surface. Raise the jack until it just takes the weight of the tank.
15 Unscrew the mounting bolts and detach the tank straps **(see illustration)**.
16 Lower the jack and tank away from the underside of the vehicle.
17 Continue to lower the tank, whilst guiding

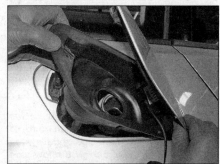
6.8b ...and lift out the surround and filler flap

6.11 Disconnect the fuel lines

6.15 Remove the tank straps

the filler neck past the suspension arm. Remove the tank from the vehicle.

18 If the tank is contaminated with sediment or water, remove the fuel pump/sender unit (see Section 4B Section 8) and swill the tank out with clean fuel. The tank is injection-moulded from a synthetic material, and if damaged, it should be renewed. However, in certain cases it may be possible to have small leaks or minor damage repaired. Seek the advice of a suitable specialist before attempting to repair the fuel tank.

Refitting

19 Refitting is the reverse of the removal procedure, noting the following points:
a) When lifting the tank back into position, make sure the mounting rubbers are correctly positioned, and take care to ensure none of the hoses get trapped between the tank and vehicle body.
b) Ensure that all pipes and hoses are correctly routed, are not kinked, and are securely held in position with their retaining clips.
c) Tighten the tank strap retaining bolts to the specified torque.
d) On completion, refill the tank with fuel, and exhaustively check for signs of leakage prior to taking the vehicle out on the road.

7 Fuel injection system – depressurisation

Note: *Observe the precautions in Section 1 before working on any component in the fuel system.*

⚠ **Warning: The following procedure will merely relieve the pressure in the fuel system – remember that fuel will still be present in the system components and take precautions accordingly before disconnecting any of them.**

⚠ **Warning: The high pressure fuel injection system can run up to 120 bar on the high side of the system and up to 7 bar on the low side. Exercise extreme caution when working with these systems.**

8.6 Remove the coolant hoses

8.4 Disconnect the fuel lines

⚠ **Warning: Do not work on any aspect of the fuel system with a hot engine.**

1 The fuel system referred to in this Section is defined as the tank mounted fuel lift pump, the high pressure fuel pump, the fuel injectors, the fuel pressure regulator, the fuel pressure sensor and the metal pipes and flexible hoses of the fuel lines between these components. All these contain fuel, which will be under pressure while the engine is running and/or while the ignition is switched on. The pressure will remain for some time after the ignition has been switched off, and must be relieved before any of these components are disturbed for servicing work. Ideally, the engine should be allowed to cool completely before work commences.

2 The fuel pump will run and prime the system as soon as a door is opened. To prevent this, on all engines, identify and remove the fuel pump fuse (or relay). Refer to Chapter 12 Section 3.

3 Disconnect the battery negative lead and position it away from the terminal as described in Chapter 5A Section 3.

4 Place a suitable container beneath the relevant connection/union to be disconnected, and have a large rag ready to soak up any escaping fuel not being caught by the container.

5 Slowly open the connection to avoid a sudden release of pressure, and position the rag around the connection to catch any

8.8 Remove the fuel line

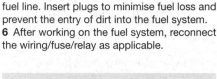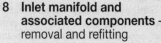
8.5 Disconnect the vacuum line close to the throttle body

fuel spray which may be expelled. Once the pressure has been released, disconnect the fuel line. Insert plugs to minimise fuel loss and prevent the entry of dirt into the fuel system.

6 After working on the fuel system, reconnect the wiring/fuse/relay as applicable.

8 Inlet manifold and associated components – removal and refitting

Note: *Observe the precautions in Section 1 before working on any component in the fuel system.*

1.2 and 1.4 litre engines

Removal

1 Jack up and support the front of the vehicle – see *Jacking and vehicle support*. Remove the engine undershield.

2 Drain the coolant as described in Chapter 1A Section 33.

3 Remove the air filter housing as described in Section 3.

4 Release the fuel pressure as described in Section 7 and then disconnect the fuel lines at the connectors close to the right-hand strut tower (see illustration).

5 If not already done so remove the charge air pipe from the turbocharger and then disconnect the vacuum line (see illustration).

6 Have a container ready and then remove the coolant hoses from the inlet manifold (see illustration).

7 Disconnect the wiring plugs from the EVAP solenoid, the throttle body and the inlet manifold sensor.

8 Release the EVAP and fuel lines from the manifold (see illustration).

9 Disconnect the wiring plugs from the fuel pressure sensor and the oil pressure switch.

10 Remove the bolts and lift off the inlet manifold (see illustrations).

Refiting

11 Refitting is a reversal of removal, but fit new seals (see illustration) and tighten the bolts to the specified torque.

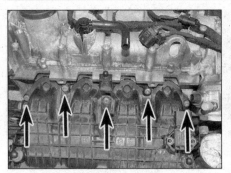

8.10a Remove the bolts…

8.10b …and lift off the manifold

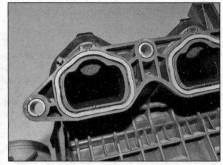

8.11 Fit new seals to the manifold

2.0 litre engines

Removal

12 Remove the engine cover and then disconnect the battery as described in Chapter 5A Section 3.

13 Remove the air filter housing and inlet duct from the top of the radiator as described in Section 3.

14 Unbolt the rigid coolant line from the from the front inlet manifold **(see illustration)**.

15 Jack up and support the front of the vehicle (see *Jacking and vehicle support*)

16 Remove the engine undershield and then unclip the coolant hose at the front of the engine (close to the charge air pipe).

17 Disconnect the wiring plug from the boost pressure sensor and then remove charge air pipe **(see illustration)**.

18 At the left-hand end of the engine (above the starter motor) remove the charge air hose from the turbocharger and unclip the wiring loom. Secure the wiring loom to the side.

19 Remove the charge air hose from the intercooler and then remove the manifold support bracket.

20 Work around the manifold and disconnect the wiring plugs **(see illustration)** from the:

● Manifold flap sensor.
● Low pressure fuel rail pressure sensor.
● Central fuel injector connector.
● Inlet manifold pressure sensor.
● Camshaft position sensor.
● Throttle body.
● Rotary valve.

21 Remove the vacuum line from the inlet manifold flap control solenoid.

22 Release the wiring loom from the manifold

and then unbolt the coolant line and lift it clear.

23 Unclip the fuel line from the manifold. On vehicles with an auxiliary radiator (some DSG transmissions only) unclip the coolant hose that supplies the radiator.

24 Release the pressure from the fuel lines (see Section 7) and then remove the high pressure fuel line from the high pressure pump.

25 Remove the manifold bolts, pull the manifold forward and unbolt the wiring plug connector bracket **(see illustrations)**. Fully remove the inlet manifold.

Refitting

26 Refitting is a reversal of removal, but fit a new gasket **(see illustration)**.

8.14 Unbolt the coolant line

8.17 Remove the charge air pipe

8.20 Disconnect the two wiring plugs from the left-hand end of the manifold

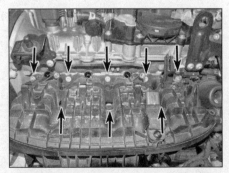

8.25a Remove the two nuts and six bolts

8.25b Lift up the manifold and remove the support bracket before fully removing the manifold

8.26 Fit a new gasket

9.2 The diagnostic socket (DLC – Data Link Connector)

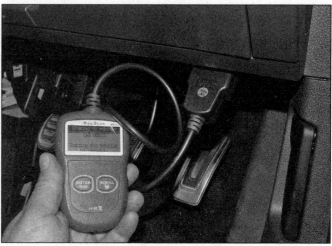

9.3 A low cost fault code reader capable of displaying the mandatory emissions related fault codes

9 Fuel injection system – testing and adjustment

1 If a fault appears in the fuel injection system, first ensure that all the system wiring connectors are securely connected and free of corrosion. Then ensure that the fault is not due to poor maintenance; ie, check that the air cleaner filter element is clean, the spark plugs are in good condition and correctly gapped, the cylinder compression pressures are correct, the ignition system wiring is in good condition and securely connected, and the engine breather hoses are clear and undamaged, referring to Chapter 1A, Chapter 2A, Chapter 2B and Chapter 5B.

2 If these checks fail to reveal the cause of the problem, the vehicle should be taken to a Volkswagen dealer or suitably equipped garage for testing. A diagnostic connector is incorporated in the engine management system wiring harness, into which dedicated electronic test equipment can be plugged (see illustration). The test equipment is capable of 'interrogating' the engine management system ECU electronically and accessing its internal fault log (reading fault codes).

3 Fault codes can only be extracted from the ECU using a dedicated fault code reader. A Volkswagen dealer will obviously have the VAG approved tester, but many independent garages will have invested in the equipment (or at least near dealer level test equipment). Low cost diagnostic testers are also available in the aftermarket and whilst these will not have the depth of coverage of the factory tester (or other professional equipment) they will at least display the mandatory EOBD (European On Board Diagnostic) emissions related fault codes (see illustration). Some aftermarket equipment may also be capable of interrogating other on board systems, such as the ABS for example.

4 Using this equipment, faults can be isolated. However just because a fault code for a misfire (for example) has been logged, some basic system testing will still be required to isolate the reason for the misfire.

Chapter 4 Part B
Diesel engine fuel systems

Contents

Section number

Air filter assembly – removal and refitting 3
Diesel engine management system – component removal
  and refitting. 4
Fuel filter – renewal. 7
Fuel lift pump and gauge sender unit – removal and refitting 8
Fuel pipe and connectors. 2
Fuel rail – removal and refitting 12

Section number

Fuel system bleeding. 11
Fuel tank – removal and refitting 9
General information and precautions. 1
High pressure fuel pump – removal and refitting 10
Injectors – general information, checking, removal and refitting 5
Inlet manifold – removal and refitting. 6

Degrees of difficulty

Easy, suitable for novice with little experience

Fairly easy, suitable for beginner with some experience

Fairly difficult, suitable for competent DIY mechanic

Difficult, suitable for experienced DIY mechanic

Very difficult, suitable for expert DIY or professional

Specifications

Engine codes*
1.6 litre	CLHA, CLHB, CRKB, CXXA, CXXB and DBKA
2.0 litre	CKFC, CRBC, CRLB, CRLD, CRMB and CUNA

*See 'Vehicle identification' at the end of the manual for the location of the engine code markings

General
Fuel injection system	Electronic, common rail injection with solenoid valve fuel injectors
Firing order	1-3-4-2
Maximum engine speed	N/A (ECU controlled)
Engine fast idle speed	N/A (ECU controlled)

Turbocharger
Type	Variable Vane Turbocharger (VVT) with air to liquid intercooler

Torque wrench settings
	Nm	lbf ft
Camshaft position sensor	9	7
Common fuel rail	20	15
Charge air temperature sensor	22	16
EGR pipe flange bolts	25	18
EGR valve mounting bolt:	20	15
Engine speed/TDC sender	5	4
Flap motor housing	10	7
Fuel hip pressure pipe	28	21
Fuel pressure sensor (on rail)	100	70
Fuel pressure regulating valve (on rail)*	80	59
Fuel tank straps*:		
Stage 1	20	15
Stage 2	Angle-tighten a further 90°	
High pressure pump mounting bolts*:		
Short bolt		
Stage 1	20	15
Stage 2	Angle-tighten a further 45°	
Long bolt		
Stage 1	20	15
Stage 2	Angle-tighten a further 180°	
High pressure pump sprocket nut	95	70

Torque wrench settings (continued)

	Nm	lbf ft
Injector clamp bolt*:		
Stage 1	8	6
Stage 2	Angle-tighten a further 270°	
Inlet manifold to cylinder head*:		
Stage 1	20	15
Stage 2	Angle-tighten a further 90°	

* Use new fixings

1 General information and precautions

General information

1 All engines covered by this Manual are fitted with a common rail direct-injection fuelling system, incorporating a fuel tank, an engine-bay mounted fuel filter with an integral water separator, fuel supply and return lines and four fuel injectors.

2 All versions use the familiar Common Rail (CR) system, where fuel is supplied from a timing belt-driven high-pressure pump to a common fuel rail (or reservoir). The four injectors are fitted into the cylinder head and are connected to the fuel rail by rigid metal pipes. The precise timing of the pre-, main, and post-injections are controlled by the engine management ECM and (unlike earlier versions) an electrically operated solenoid valve incorporated into the injector design. All engines are fitted with a turbocharger.

3 The common rail fuelling system is controlled electronically by a diesel engine management system, comprising an Electronic Control Module (ECM) and its associated sensors, actuators and wiring. In addition, the ECM manages the operation of the Exhaust Gas Recirculation (EGR) emission control system (Chapter 4D Section 3), the turbocharger boost pressure control system and the glow plug control system (Chapter 5C Section 1).

4 A flap valve/throttle valve module fitted to the intake manifold. It controls engine 'judder as the engine is switched and it also regulates air pressure (and quantity) in the inlet manifold.

5 It should be noted that fault diagnosis of the diesel engine management system is only possible with dedicated electronic test equipment. Problems with the system's

1.6 The EOBD diagnostic connector is located under the drivers side of the facia

operation should therefore be referred to a Volkswagen dealer or suitably equipped specialist for assessment. Note however that low cost diagnostic tools are available in the aftermarket for the keen home mechanic. These tools will not have the full range of features as the factory tool or professional aftermarket tools, but they will all display the mandatory emissions related fault codes. Once the fault has been identified, the removal/ refitting sequences detailed in the following Sections will then allow the appropriate component(s) to be renewed as required.

6 The EOBD diagnostic connector is located under the drivers side of the facia **(see illustration)**.

Precautions

7 Many of the operations described in this Chapter involve the disconnection of fuel lines, which may cause an amount of fuel spillage. Before commencing work, refer to the warnings below and the information in *'Safety first!'* at the beginning of this manual.

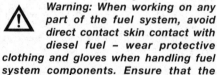 *Warning: When working on any part of the fuel system, avoid direct contact skin contact with diesel fuel – wear protective clothing and gloves when handling fuel system components. Ensure that the work area is well-ventilated to prevent the build-up of diesel fuel vapour.*

● Fuel injectors operate at extremely high pressures and the jet of fuel produced at the nozzle is capable of piercing skin, with potentially fatal results. When working with pressurised injectors, take care to avoid exposing any part of the body to the fuel spray. It is recommended that a diesel fuel systems specialist should carry out any pressure testing of the fuel system components.

● Under no circumstances should diesel fuel be allowed to come into contact with coolant hoses – wipe off accidental spillage immediately. Hoses that have been contaminated with fuel for an extended period should be renewed.

● Diesel fuel systems are particularly sensitive to contamination from dirt, air and water. Pay particular attention to cleanliness when working on any part of the fuel system, to prevent the ingress of dirt. Thoroughly clean the area around fuel unions before disconnecting them. Only use lint-free cloths and clean fuel for component cleansing.

● Store dismantled components in sealed containers to prevent contamination and the formation of condensation.

2 Fuel pipe and connectors

1 Disconnect the battery (see Chapter 5A Section 3) before proceeding.

2 The fuel supply pipe connects the fuel pump in the fuel tank to the fuel filter on the engine.

3 Whenever you're working under the vehicle, be sure to inspect all fuel and evaporative emission pipes for leaks, kinks, dents and other damage. Always replace a damaged fuel pipe immediately.

4 If you find signs of dirt in the pipes during disassembly, disconnect all pipes and blow them out with compressed air. Inspect the fuel strainer on the fuel pump pick-up unit for damage and deterioration.

Steel tubing

5 It is critical that the fuel pipes be replaced with pipes of equivalent type and specification.

6 Some steel fuel pipes have threaded fittings. When loosening these fittings, hold the stationary fitting with a spanner while turning the union nut.

Plastic tubing

 Warning: When removing or installing plastic fuel tubing, be careful not to bend or twist it too much, which can damage it. Also, plastic fuel tubing is NOT heat resistant, so keep it away from excessive heat.

7 When replacing fuel system plastic tubing, use only original equipment replacement plastic tubing.

Flexible hoses

8 When replacing fuel system flexible hoses, use original equipment replacements, or hose to the same specification.

9 Don't route fuel hoses (or metal pipes) within 100 mm of the exhaust system or within 280 mm of the catalytic converter. Make sure that no rubber hoses are installed directly against the vehicle, particularly in places where there is any vibration. If allowed to touch some vibrating part of the vehicle, a hose can easily become chafed and it might start leaking. A good rule of thumb is to maintain a minimum of 8.0 mm clearance around a hose (or metal pipe) to prevent contact with the vehicle underbody.

Disconnecting Fuel pipe Fittings

10 Typical fuel pipe fittings:

2.10a Two-tab type fitting; depress both tabs with your fingers, then pull the fuel pipe and the fitting apart

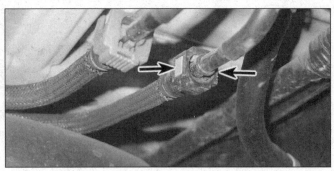

2.10b On this type of fitting, depress the two buttons on opposite sides of the fitting, then pull it off the fuel pipe

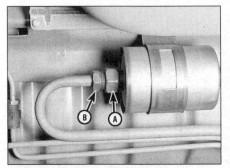

2.10c Threaded fuel pipe fitting; hold the stationary portion of the pipe or component (A) while loosening the union nut (B) with a flare-nut spanner

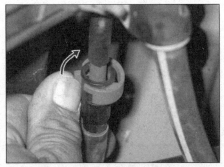

2.10d Plastic collar-type fitting; rotate the outer part of the fitting

2.10e Metal collar quick-connect fitting; pull the end of the retainer off the fuel pipe and disengage the other end from the female side of the fitting…

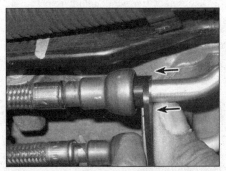

2.10f …insert a fuel pipe separator tool into the female side of the fitting, push it into the fitting and pull the fuel pipe off the pipe

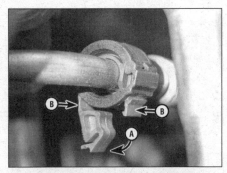

2.10g Some fittings are secured by lock tabs. Release the lock tab (A) and rotate it to the fully-opened position, squeeze the two smaller lock tabs (B)…

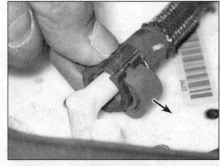

2.10h …then push the retainer out and pull the fuel pipe off the pipe

2.10i Spring-lock coupling; remove the safety cover, install a coupling release tool and close the tool around the coupling…

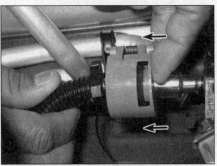

2.10j …push the tool into the fitting, then pull the two pipes apart

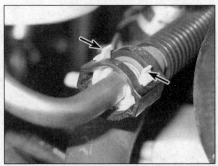

2.10k Hairpin clip type fitting: push the legs of the retainer clip together, then push the clip down all the way until it stops and pull the fuel pipe off the pipe

3.1a Unclip the coolant hose

3.1b Remove the screws and lift off the top cover

3.1c Unclip and then...

3.1d ...remove the inner section

3.2 Disconnect the MAF (Mass Airflow) sensor wiring plug

3.3 Disconnect the vacuum hose

3.4 Compress the spring clip and disconnect the air intake hose

3 Air filter assembly – removal and refitting

Note: *There are variations in the procedure for removing the air filter assembly, however the removal procedure is essentially the same for all models.*

Removal

1 Unclip the coolant hose and then unscrew and unclip the top cover from the inlet duct. Release and remove the short inlet duct **(see illustrations)**.
2 Disconnect the wiring plug from the air mass meter **(see illustration)**.
3 Disconnect the vacuum pipe from the air intake hose **(see illustration)**.
4 Loosen the clip and disconnect the air duct from the air mass meter **(see illustration)**.
5 Lift the air cleaner assembly upwards to release it from the locating pegs **(see illustration)**. As the air cleaner is removed, withdraw the water drain hose, under the air filter assembly out from the inner wing panel.
6 With the housing removed the inlet pipe and outlet charge air pipes can be removed **(see illustrations)**.

Refitting

7 Refit the air filter assembly by following the

3.5 Pull the complete housing up to remove it

3.6a Remove the bolts, release the hose clips...

3.6b ...and lift out the charge air pipe

3.7 Make sure the assembly is located correctly on the mounting pegs

4.2 Remove the wiring plug and undo the pedal retaining bolt

4.4 Remove the engine cover

removal procedure in reverse. Make sure the assembly is located correctly on the lower mounting pegs **(see illustration)**.

4 Diesel engine management system – component removal and refitting

Throttle pedal/position sensor

1 Remove the footrest panel and then fold back the carpet in front of the pedal.
2 Disconnect the wiring plug, remove the bolt and unhook the throttle pedal from the bulkhead **(see illustration)**.
3 Refitting is a reversal of removal.

Throttle valve housing/module

4 Remove the engine cover **(see illustration)**.

5 Remove the air filter housing and charge air pipes as described in Section 3.
6 Clamp the coolant hoses with hose clamps (or partially drain the coolant), release the hose clips and then unbolt the coolant pipes from the valve body and inlet manifold **(see illustration)**. Note that the number of hoses varies according to the model.
7 Remove the bolt from the inlet manifold support strut **(see illustration)**.
8 Disconnect the wiring plug connector, from the throttle housing/module and the charge air temperature sensor **(see illustrations)**.
9 Unscrew and remove the retaining bolts, then lift the throttle body away from the inlet manifold **(see illustration)**. Recover the gasket and dispose of it. A new one will be required for refitting.
10 Refitting is a reversal of removal, noting the following:

a) Use a new throttle housing-to-inlet manifold gasket.
b) Tighten the throttle housing bolts evenly to the specified torque.
c) Ensure that all hoses and electrical connectors are refitted securely.

Coolant temperature sensors
11 Refer to Chapter 3 Section 6.

Fuel temperature sensor

Removal

12 The fuel temperature sensor is located in the fuel supply line at the top of the high-pressure fuel pump. Remove the engine cover (where fitted) and then disconnect the wiring plug.
13 Wrap a cloth around the sensor and slowly unscrew the sensor **(see illustration)**. Anticipate some fuel spillage as the sensor is removed.

4.6 Remove the bolts

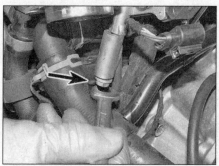

4.7 Remove the support strut bolt

4.8a Disconnect the wiring plug from the air temperature sensor...

4.8b ...and the throttle body

4.9 Remove the throttle body

4.13 Fuel temperature sensor

4.17a The charge air temperature sensor (before cooler)

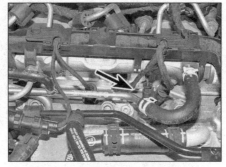

4.17b The charge air temperature sensor (after cooler)

4.20 The boost pressure sensor

Refitting

14 Refit the fuel temperature sensor by reversing the removal procedure, using a new O-ring seal.

Inlet air temperature sensor

15 The ambient air temperature sensor is built into the Mass Air flow Meter (MAF) – this sensor is an integral part of the air mass meter, and cannot be renewed separately.

Charge air temperature sensors

Note: *All models have a temperature sensor fitted before the intercooler and one fitted after the intercooler.*

Removal

16 Remove the engine cover. The pre-intercooler sensor is fitted to the elbow before the inlet manifold and the post-intercooler sensor is mounted at the front of the inlet manifold.

17 Disconnect the wiring then undo the screw and unscrew the sensor from its location **(see illustrations)**.

Refitting

18 Refit the sensor by reversing the removal procedure, using a new O-ring seal.

Charge air boost pressure sensor

19 Remove the engine cover. The sensor is located at the front left-hand side of the inlet manifold.

20 Disconnect the wiring plug **(see illustration)**and unbolt the sensor. Inspect the condition of the O-ring seal.

21 Refitting is a reversal of removal.

Engine speed/TDC sensor

Note: *Access to the sensor is limited. Removing the oil cooler hoses and coolant hoses improves access. Note that the illustrations show the sensor position with the transmission removed for clarity.*

22 The engine speed/TDC sensor is mounted on the front cylinder block, adjacent to the mating surface of the block and transmission bellhousing **(see illustration)**.

23 Access is from beneath the engine compartment. Apply the handbrake, and then jack up the front of the vehicle and support it on axle stands (see *Jacking and vehicle support*). Remove the engine undertray.

24 Remove the retaining screw and withdraw the sensor from the cylinder block **(see illustrations)**.

25 Refit the sensor by reversing the removal procedure.

Mass airflow sensor

Removal

26 On all models the Mass Airflow (MAF) sensor is located in the outlet from the air cleaner assembly on the left-hand side of the engine compartment. It is integral with the housing and can not be removed.

27 Disconnect the wiring plug, loosen the clips and disconnect the air ducting from the sensor **(see illustration)**.

28 Release the spring clip and remove the outlet duct.

29 Remove the screws and remove the duct from the air filter.

Caution: Handle the sensor carefully – its internal components are easily damaged.

Refitting

30 Refitting is a reversal of removal.

Absolute pressure (altitude) sensor

31 The absolute pressure sensor is an integral part of the ECU, and hence cannot be renewed separately.

Clutch pedal switch

Removal

32 The clutch pedal switch is clipped to the clutch master cylinder. Reach up from the footwell and disconnect the wiring plug.

4.22 Crankshaft position speed sensor

4.24a Undo the retaining bolt ...

4.24b ... and withdraw the sensor

4.27 Disconnect the wiring plug

4.36a Disconnect the wiring plugs by levering up the catch

4.36b Lift up the bracket to release the ECU

4.36c If the ECU is removed, protect the wiring plugs from debris and liquids by sealing them in plastic bags

33 Unclip the locking catch and pull out the pedal switch.

Refitting

34 Refitting is a reversal of removal, but note that the switch should engage with an audible click.

Electronic control unit (ECU)

Caution: Always wait at least 30 seconds after switching off the ignition before disconnecting the wiring from the ECU. When the wiring is disconnected, all the learned values are erased, however any Specifications of the fault memory are retained. Note that if the ECU is to be renewed, the adaption (learned) values of the ECU must be downloaded to the diagnostic machine and then uploaded to the new ECU.

Removal

35 The ECU is located between the battery and the under bonnet fusebox. Disconnect the battery (as described in Chapter 5A Section 3) and isolate the positive terminal of the battery. If the body of the ECU is shorted between ground (negative) and the positive terminal of the battery it will be destroyed.

36 Disconnect the wiring plugs and remove the ECU **(see illustrations)**.

Refitting

37 Refitting is a reversal of removal.

Fuel pressure regulating valve

38 The fuel pressure regulating valve is

fitted to the left-hand end of the fuel rail **(see illustration)**. If the valve is removed from the fuel rail, then it will need to be renewed, as it has a deformable sealing lip as part of the valve.

39 To check the operation of the regulating valve, first disconnect the fuel return hose from the fuel rail and plug the end **(see illustration)**. Then fit a piece of hose to the fuel rail and the other end into a container. There are three checks that can be made, the first two with the engine running and the third if the vehicle will not start:

a) *Start the engine and run at idle for 30 seconds, there should be approx. 75ml of fuel (1.6 litre engines) or 100ml of fuel (2.0 litre engines) in the container.*

b) *Start engine and increase engine speed to 2000rpm, there should be 0ml of fuel in the container (allow for a few droplets of fuel).*

c) *On vehicles that will not run, turn the ignition key and crank the engine, there should be 0ml of fuel in the container (allow for a few droplets of fuel).*

40 If any of these readings are not attained, renew the regulating valve.

41 To renew the valve, remove the fuel rail as described in Section 12.

42 Clean around the valve, then slacken the valve from the end of the fuel rail **(see illustration)**. Counterhold the fuel rail using the flats on the housing. Plug the end of the rail to prevent dirt from entering.

43 Fit the new valve by reversing the removal procedure, making sure that the threads are

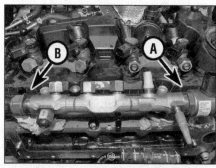

4.38 The fuel pressure regulator valve (A) and the fuel pressure sensor (B)

all clean before fitting. Check the deformable seal on the new valve, before fitting, to check it is not damaged. Apply a small amount of Molybdenum grease to seal and threads.

Fuel pressure sensor

44 The fuel pressure sensor is fitted to the right-hand end of the fuel rail **(see illustration 4.38)**. If the engine will not start, disconnect the fuel pressure sensor wiring connector and see if the engine will start. If the engine starts, the fuel pressure sensor is faulty. With the connector removed a value is taken from the control unit, so that the engine will start, in this mode the maximum engine speed is limited to 3000rpm.

45 To renew the sensor, first disconnect the wiring plug connector **(see illustration)**.

46 Clean around the sensor, then slacken it

4.39 Disconnect the fuel hose

4.42 Pressure regulator valve fitted to the left-hand end of the fuel rail

4.45 Disconnect the wiring connector from the fuel pressure sensor

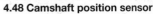

4.48 Camshaft position sensor

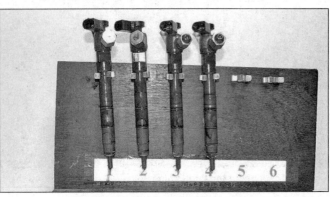

5.1 A storage rack is simple to construct

from the end of the fuel rail. Plug the end of the rail to prevent dirt from entering.

47 Refit the pressure sensor by reversing the removal procedure, making sure that the threads are all clean before refitting. The sensor has a deformable seal, check for damage. Keep the threads free of oil and grease.

Camshaft position sensor

48 The camshaft position sensor is located at the front of the cylinder head **(see illustration)**.

49 Remove the fuel line bracket bolts and move the fuel line to the side.

50 Disconnect the sensor wiring plug connector and remove the sensor retaining bolt. Remove the sensor.

51 Refitting is a reversal of removal.

Boost pressure control valve

52 The control valve is mounted on the front of the plenum chamber, at the left-hand side behind the battery.

53 Disconnect the wiring plug, remove the vacuum hoses and unbolt the sensor.

54 Refitting is a reversal of removal.

Boost pressure position sensor

55 The sensor is part of the vacuum control unit for the turbocharger. Removal and refitting are as described in Chapter 4D Section 6.

---

5 Injectors – general information, checking, removal and refitting

---

⚠ *Warning: Exercise extreme caution when working on the fuel injectors. Never expose the hands or any part of the body to injector spray, as the high pressure can cause the fuel to penetrate the skin, with possibly fatal results. You are strongly advised to have any work which involves testing the injectors under pressure carried out by a dealer or fuel injection specialist. Refer to the precautions given in Section 1 of this Chapter before proceeding.*

General information

1 Injectors do deteriorate with prolonged use,

and it is reasonable to expect them to need reconditioning or renewal after 60 000 miles (100 000 km) or so. Accurate testing, overhaul and calibration of the injectors must be left to a specialist.

Note: *Take care not to allow dirt into the injectors or fuel pipes during this procedure. Do not drop the injectors or allow the needles at their tips to become damaged. The injectors are precision-made to fine limits, and must not be handled roughly. Keep the injectors identified for position to ensure correct refitting. Always keep the injectors upright at all times where possible. Store them securely* **(see illustration)**

Checking

2 Remove the engine cover and (anticipating some fuel spillage), disconnect the fuel return line.

3 Seal the opening on the return connection and then connect an extension hose to the return line. Place the hose in a graduated container with a capacity of at least 500 ml.

4 Start the engine and run it at idle for 2 minutes. Stop the engine and check the level in the container – it should be between 0 ml to 50 ml.

5 If the above specification is met, run the engine at between 2,000 to 2,500 rpm for 2 minutes. Check the level in the container – it should be less than 250 ml.

6 If either test shows a greater flow rate than that specified, then each individual injector should be checked. A specialist test rig is available either from VW (VAG tool VAS6684)

or the aftermarket (Draper CRDIFK-2B or AST 6070 for example). It is also possible to fabricate a home made kit.

7 Install the correct adaptors and hoses to each injector and then (using a hose clamp), clamp off the fuel return line.

8 Start the engine and run it at idle speed whilst monitoring the levels in the graduated containers. The levels should be (more or less) equal in each container. A significant difference in one (or more) injectors indicates a faulty injector.

9 Remove the test rig and refit the fuel return lines. Where the return line has been clamped, remove the clamp (or reconnect the fuel line). Start the engine and check for fuel leaks and then refit the engine cover.

Removal

Note: *Take care not to allow dirt into the injectors or fuel pipes during this procedure. Do not drop the injectors or allow the needles at their tips to become damaged. The injectors are precision-made to fine limits, and must not be handled roughly. Keep the injectors identified for position to ensure correct refitting.*

10 Pull the engine cover and remove it.

11 Ensure the area around the injectors and the pipes/return hoses is clean and free from debris. The use of a vacuum cleaner is recommended. Plug all fuel lines when they have been disconnected to prevent any dirt ingress **(see illustration)**.

12 Disconnect the injector wiring plug connectors **(see illustration)**.

![photo]

5.11 Sealing cap made from an old high pressure pipe nut

5.12 Disconnect the wiring plugs from the injectors

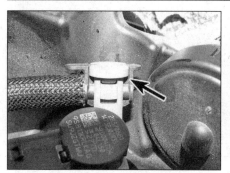

5.13a Pull up the top cap…

5.13b … and disconnect the fuel return pipes

5.13c Remove the return hose from the engine top

5.14a Mark the position of each high pressure pipe

5.14b …and note the position of the pipe dampers

5.15 Remove the injector clamp retaining bolts

13 There are two different type of fuel return lines used on these engines. The first type (fitted to engine codes CXXA and CXXB) requires the centre section of the fitting to be pulled up to release the fuel return line. A special tool is available (VAG 3370), but the centre can also be released with a simple hook type tool. On all other engine codes the fuel return line can be removed by pulling up the release tabs on the fitting. Discard the o-ring seals, as new ones will be required for refitting (see illustrations).

14 Counterhold the injector with an open-ended spanner when releasing the pipe union. Undo the unions and remove the high-pressure pipes from between the fuel rail and the injectors (see illustrations). Plug the openings to prevent contamination.

15 Undo the bolt securing the injector clamp (see illustration), Each clamp secures two

injectors in place. Note that there are also two versions of the clamp, but both are removed in a similar manner.

16 VW technicians use a slide hammer (tool T10055) and adapter (T10415 or T10537) to pull the injector from the cylinder head. Versions of this tool are available in the aftermarket.

17 Two injectors will need to be removed together, as the clamping piece is slotted into both injectors. Remove them in the sequence: 2, 1, 4 and then 3. Recover the copper seal and O-rings and discard. New ones must be used for refitting (see illustration). Note: *The injectors can only be refitted to their original positions. Mark the injectors to avoid confusion if refitting the original injectors.*

Refitting

18 Ensure the area around the injector

locations in the cylinder head are clean and free from debris. Use a vacuum cleaner if available. Clean any carbon deposits from the injector and sealing surfaces with a cloth soaked in clean engine oil or rust-releasing spray.

19 To remove the copper sealing washer, spray rust-releasing spray around the injector nozzle, then clamp the seal in a vice, and use a twisting motion to pull the injector from the seal. Do not touch the very end of the injector, or you could block up the nozzle. Unpick and then remove the O-ring seal.

20 To renew the main injector O-ring seal, VW specify the use of tool VAG special tool T10377. This tool allows the O-ring to slide over the end of the injector without twisting. With care, the seals can be fitted without the tool (see illustrations). Where required fit new O-ring seals to the injector bleed off port.

5.17 Remove two injectors at a time with retaining clamp

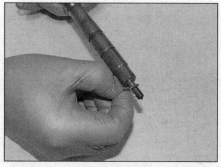

5.20a Fit a new main O-ring seal without twisting it…

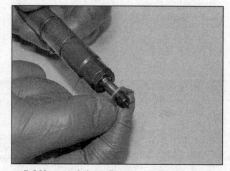

5.20b …and then fit a new copper seal

5.21 Slide the injectors down into the cylinder head

6.3 Remove and disconnect the coolant hoses

6.4 Remove the coolant pipes

21 Fit new seals to the valve cover. Apply a smear of clean engine oil to the main O-ring seal, and insert the injector into place in the cylinder head **(see illustration)**. Note that if the original injectors are being refitted, they must go into their original positions. Tighten the new injector clamping bolt/nut to the specified torque.

Note: *There are different length bolts available. Check that the replacement injector hold down bolts are the same as those removed.*

22 Refit the high-pressure fuel pipes and tighten the unions to the specified torque. Note that the pipes may be re-used providing the tapered seats are undamaged and the pipes are not deformed, constricted or corroded. Counterhold the injector with an open-ended spanner when tightening the pipe union.

23 The remainder of refitting is a reversal of removal, noting the following:
a) If one or more injectors have been renewed, the 'injector delivery calibration values' and 'injector voltage calibration values' must be entered into the ECM using VAG group diagnostic equipment. Entrust this task to a VW dealer or suitably equipped specialist.
b) After completion of the work, the fuel system must be bled as described in Section 11.

6 Inlet manifold – removal and refitting

Note: *The inlet manifold and the intercooler (charge air cooler) are combined into a single unit.*

Removal

1 Remove the engine cover by pulling it upwards.
2 Drain the coolant as described in Chapter 1B Section 33. The coolant only needs to be drained below the level of the manifold.
3 Release the hose clips and remove the intercooler supply and return coolant hoses **(see illustration)**.

4 Unbolt and remove the coolant pipes as required **(see illustration)**.
5 Remove the pump to rail high pressure fuel line as described in Section 12.
6 Remove the air filter housing as described in Section 3.
7 At the left-hand end of the engine remove the fixings from the throttle body. Remove the charge air pipe mounting bolts, slacken the hose clip and remove the charge air pipe **(see illustration)**.
8 At the front of the engine, disconnect the wiring plug from the fuel temperature sensor and then release the fuel line hoses. Unbolt the fuel line from the cylinder head and either remove it completely or secure it to the back of the cylinder head **(see illustration)**. Seal the openings in the fuel line.

9 At the left-hand end of the engine remove the vacuum hose and unbolt the connector **(see illustrations)**.
10 Disconnect the wiring plug from the throttle valve and (where fitted the) the VVT control solenoid.
11 Disconnect the wiring plugs from the charge air temperature sensors (before and after the intercooler) and the boost pressure sensor (see Section 4).
12 Remove the radiator cowl as described in Chapter 3 Section 3 and then unbolt and remove the coolant hoses attached to the manifold.
13 Remove the throttle body as described in Section 4.
14 Unbolt and remove the dipstick guide

6.7 Remove the charge air pipe

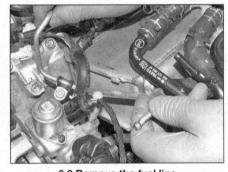

6.8 Remove the fuel line

6.9a Disconnect the vacuum lines for the brakes servo...

6.9b ...and turbocharger from the distribution block

6.14a Unbolt the dipstick guide tube

6.14b Remove the right-hand support bracket bolt...

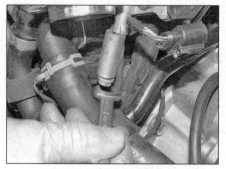

6.14c ...and the left-hand

tube and then remove both manifold support brackets (see illustrations).

15 Slacken the main mounting bolts in the reverse order to that shown. Remove the manifold and recover the gasket (see illustration).

Refitting

16 Refitting is a reversal of removal, using new seals and gaskets (see illustration). Remember to renew any self-locking nuts. Tighten the manifold retaining bolts to the specified torque setting, starting at the bottom left (looking at the manifold) and working around anti-clockwise in order.

7 Fuel filter – renewal

1 Refer to Chapter 1B Section 29.

8 Fuel lift pump and gauge sender unit – removal and refitting

Note: Observe the precautions in Section 1 before working on any component in the fuel system.

⚠ **Warning: Avoid direct skin contact with fuel – wear protective clothing and gloves when handling fuel system components. Ensure that the work area is well ventilated to prevent the build-up of fuel vapour.**

General information

1 The fuel lift pump and gauge sender unit are combined in one assembly, which is mounted in the top of the fuel tank. The unit protrudes into the fuel tank, and its removal involves exposing the contents of the tank to the atmosphere.

Removal

2 Ensure that the vehicle is parked on a level surface, then disconnect the battery as described in Chapter 5A Section 3.

3 Remove the rear seat squab as described in Chapter 11 Section 22 and then prise off the cover. Release the locking tab and disconnect the wiring plugs (see illustrations).

6.15 Remove the inlet manifold

6.16 Fit a new gasket

8.3a Remove the seat squab

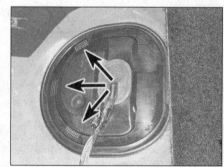

8.3b Leverage points are provide on the cover

8.3c Lever up the cover with a trim tool

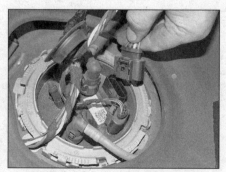

8.3d Disconnect the wiring plugs

8.4 Disconnect the fuel lines

8.5a Note the alignment marks…

8.5b …then use a suitable tool to unscrew…

8.5c …and remove the securing ring

8.6 Removing the lift pump/gauge sender unit from the fuel tank

8.9 If not removed with the unit, recover the rubber seal and check its condition

4 Disconnect the fuel lines and seal them. Note the position of the flow and return lines **(see illustration)**.

5 Note the position of the alignment marks, then unscrew and remove the securing ring. Use a pair of water pump pliers (or home-made tool) to grip and rotate the securing ring **(see illustrations)**.

6 Lift out the lift pump/gauge sender unit, holding it above the level of the fuel in the tank until the excess fuel has drained out. Recover the flange and seal **(see illustration)**.

7 With the pump/sender unit removed from the car, lay it on an absorbent card or rag. Inspect the float at the end of the sender unit swinging arm for punctures and fuel ingress – renew the unit if it appears damaged.

8 The fuel pick-up incorporated in the assembly is spring-loaded to ensure that it always draws fuel from the lowest part of the

tank. Check that the pick-up is free to move under spring tension with respect to the sender unit body.

9 Inspect the rubber seal from the fuel tank aperture for signs of fatigue – renew it if necessary **(see illustration)**.

10 Inspect the sender unit wiper and track; clean off any dirt and debris that may have accumulated, and look for breaks in the track.

11 If required, the sender unit can be separated from the pump assembly.

12 Disconnect the wiring from the top of the unit and then unclip the float and potentiometer **(see illustration)**.

13 If required simple resistance checks can be mode on the fuel gauge sender with a multimeter set to ohms **(see illustration)**.

Refitting

14 Refit the lift pump/sender unit by following

the removal procedure in reverse, noting the following points:

a) *Take care not to bend the float arm as the unit is refitted.*

b) *Smear the outside of tank aperture rubber seal with clean fuel or lubricating spray, to ease fitting. Locate the seal in the tank aperture before fitting the lift pump/sender unit.*

c) *Tighten the securing ring to the specified torque setting.*

d) *Reconnect the fuel hoses to the correct ports – observe the direction-of-flow arrow markings, and refer to paragraph 6. Ensure that the fuel hose fittings click fully into place.*

e) *On completion, check that all associated pipes are securely clipped to the tank, then run the engine and check for fuel leaks.*

9 Fuel tank – removal and refitting

Note: *Observe the precautions in Section 1 before working on any component in the fuel system.*

Removal

1 Before the tank can be removed, it must be drained of as much fuel as possible. As no drain plug is provided, it is preferable to carry out this operation with the tank almost empty.

2 Disconnect the battery as described in Chapter 5A Section 3 and then using a hand pump or syphon, remove any remaining fuel from the tank.

8.12 Disconnect the small wires…

8.13 Checking that the resistance varies with the position of the float

9.8a Remove the screw...

9.8b ...and lift out the surround and filler flap

9.9 Remove the bracket

9.11 Disconnect the fuel lines

9.15 Remove the tank straps

3 Lift up the rear seat squab and disconnect the wiring plug from the pump/sender unit – as described in Section 8.

4 Open the fuel filler flap, and unscrew the fuel filler cap – leave the cap loosely in place.

5 Loosen the right-hand rear wheel bolts, then jack up the rear of the car (see *Jacking and vehicle support*). Remove the right-hand rear wheel.

6 Undo the retaining screws, release the retaining clips and remove the left-hand rear wheel arch liner.

7 Open the fuel filler flap, and unscrew the fuel cap from the top of the filler neck.

8 Unscrew the screw at the filler neck (**see illustrations**).

9 Working inside the wheel arch remove the filler neck support bracket (**see illustration**).

10 With reference to Chapter 4D Section 9, remove the rear section of the exhaust system.

11 Disconnect the fuel lines from the connections at the front of the fuel tank (**see illustration**).

12 On models fitted with the multi-link rear suspension, mark the relationship between the rear hub and the trailing arm on the right-hand side and then unbolt the trailing arm and lower it.

13 On models fitted with a torsion beam rear suspension remove the rear axle beam as described in Chapter 10 Section 17.

14 Position a trolley jack under the centre of the tank. Insert a block of wood between the jack head and the tank to prevent damage to the tank surface. Raise the jack until it just takes the weight of the tank.

15 Unscrew the mounting bolts and detach the tank straps (**see illustration**).

16 Lower the jack and tank away from the underside of the vehicle.

17 Continue to lower the tank, whilst guiding the filler neck past the suspension arm. Remove the tank from the vehicle.

18 If the tank is contaminated with sediment or water, remove the fuel pump/sender unit (see Section 8) and swill the tank out with clean fuel. The tank is injection-moulded from a synthetic material, and if damaged, it should be renewed. However, in certain cases it may be possible to have small leaks or minor damage repaired. Seek the advice of a

suitable specialist before attempting to repair the fuel tank.

Refitting

19 Refitting is the reverse of the removal procedure, noting the following points:

a) *When lifting the tank back into position, make sure the mounting rubbers are correctly positioned, and take care to ensure none of the hoses get trapped between the tank and vehicle body.*

b) *Ensure that all pipes and hoses are correctly routed, are not kinked, and are securely held in position with their retaining clips.*

c) *Tighten the tank strap retaining bolts to the specified torque.*

d) *On completion, refill the tank with fuel, and exhaustively check for signs of leakage prior to taking the vehicle out on the road.*

10.2a A small three legged puller can be used to remove the hub

10 High pressure fuel pump – removal and refitting

Removal

1 Remove the timing belt and pump sprocket as described in Chapter 2C Section 7 and Chapter 2C Section 8.

2 A suitable puller (or VAG special tool T10489) will be required to remove the high pressure pump hub. Engage the puller and remove the hub (**see illustrations**). Note that the hub is a tight fit on the shaft and the puller used must be narrow enough to avoid damage to the mounting bracket.

3 Disconnect the wiring connector from the

10.2b The hub removed from the pump

10.3 Disconnect the pump wiring connector

10.4 Remove the low pressure return hose

10.5 The pump openings sealed

10.6 Fuel pump mounting bolts

fuel metering valve on top of the fuel pump **(see illustration)**.

4 Remove the fuel return pipe **(see illustration)** and seal both the pipe and the opening at the pump.

5 Slacken the fuel pipe unions and remove the high-pressure pipe from the pump to the fuel rail **(see illustration)**. Seal the pump outlet and the injector.

6 Undo the 3 retaining bolts and remove the pump **(see illustration)**.

Refitting

7 Refitting is a reversal of removal, noting the following points:

a) *Ensure all fuel pipes/hose connections are clean and free from debris.*

b) *The high-pressure fuel pipe from the pump to the common rail maybe re-used providing it's not been damaged.*

c) *Tighten all fasteners to their specified torque where given.*

d) *Fill the pump with clean fuel through the*

fuel supply pipe aperture prior to starting.

e) *Bleed the fuel system as described in Section 11.*

11 Fuel system bleeding

1 Prime the high pressure fuel pump by filling it with clean diesel through the fuel supply aperture **(see illustration 10.5)**, then operate the starter for shorts bursts (no more than 10 seconds at a time) until the engine starts. Operate the engine at a fast idle (approx 2000 rpm) for several minutes before allowing it to return to its normal idle speed.

2 If the engine fails to start, it must be filled/bled using VW diagnostic equipment (VAS5051 etc.). Using this equipment operates the electric fuel pumps for 3 minutes. Alternatively remove the access cover from

the in tank fuel pump, identify the pump supply wiring and supply the pump directly with 12 volts (see the wiring diagrams at the end of this manual for details).

3 Once the engine has been started, test drive the vehicle over a distance of at least 15 miles with at least one period of full acceleration. If there is any air left in the fuel system, the engine management ECM may switch to 'limp home' mode, and store a fault code. Have the fault code cleared and road test the vehicle again.

12 Fuel rail – removal and refitting

Note: *Observe the precautions in Section 1 before working on any component in the fuel system.*

Removal

1 Remove the engine cover by pulling it upwards. Ensure the area around the fuel rail

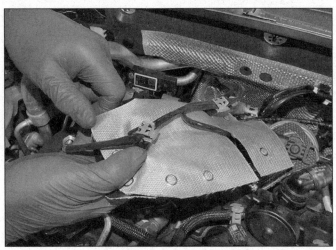

12.5a Open the heat shields...

12.5b ...and disconnect the wiring plugs

and pipes is clean and free from debris. If available, use a vacuum cleaner.

2 Disconnect the wiring connectors from the fuel injectors, the fuel pump, the fuel temperature sensor and the charge air pressure sensor.

3 At the fuel rail disconnect the wiring plugs from the fuel pressure regulator and the fuel pressure sensor.

4 Disconnect the wiring plug from the charge air temperature sensor and the coolant pump.

5 Open the heat shield and disconnect the wiring plugs from the pressure sensors (see illustrations).

6 Unbolt the low pressure fuel line and move it to the side. Disconnect the camshaft position sensor.

7 Disconnect the wiring plugs from the glow plugs and then unclip the wiring loom bracket.

8 Counterhold the injector with an open-ended spanner when releasing the pipe union. Undo the unions and remove the high-pressure pipes from between the fuel rail and the injectors (see illustration). Plug the openings to prevent contamination.

9 Release the retaining clips and disconnect the fuel return hose from the fuel rail.

10 Slacken the fuel pipe unions and remove the high-pressure pipe from the pump to the fuel rail.

11 Undo the multi-spline retaining bolts and remove the fuel rail (see illustrations).

12 If required, note their fitted positions, then unscrew the fuel pressure sensor and pressure regulating valve from the fuel rail, as described in Section 4. Note: VW insist that once removed, the pressure regulating valve cannot be re-used.

Refitting

13 Where applicable, refit the fuel pressure sensor and the new regulating valve to the fuel rail, and tighten them to the specified torque. Note that the threads of the sensors must be clean and free from oil and grease.

14 The remainder of refitting is a reversal of removal, noting the following points:

a) Refit the high-pressure fuel pipes and tighten the unions to the specified torque. Note that the high-pressure fuel pipes may be re-used providing the tapered seats are undamaged and the pipes are not deformed, constricted or corroded.

b) After completion of the work, the fuel system must be bled as described in Section 11.

12.8 Remove the high pressure pipes from the rail and injectors

12.11a Undo the fuel rail mounting bolts...

12.11b ...and lift out the fuel rail

Chapter 4 Part C
Emission control and exhaust systems – petrol engines

Contents

Section number

Catalytic converter – general information and precautions 7
Crankcase emission system – general information 3
Evaporative loss emission control system – information and
    component renewal 2

Section number

Exhaust system – component renewal. 6
General Information 1
Intercooler – general information 5
Turbocharger – general information, precautions, removal and refitting. . 4

Degrees of difficulty

Easy, suitable for novice with little experience	Fairly easy, suitable for beginner with some experience	Fairly difficult, suitable for competent DIY mechanic	Difficult, suitable for experienced DIY mechanic	Very difficult, suitable for expert DIY or professional

Specifications

Engine codes*

1.2 litre	CJZA, CJZB and CYVA
1.4 litre	CPTA, CHPA, CMBA, CXSA, CPVA, CZEA and CZDA
2.0 litre	CHHA, CHHB, CJXE and CXDA

*See 'Vehicle identification' at the end of this manual for the location of the engine code markings

Emission control standards

1.2 litre engine codes CJZA and CJZB	Euro 5
1.2 litre engine code CYVA.	Euro 6
1.4 litre engine codes CHPA, CMBA, CXSA and CPVA	Euro 5
1.4 litre engine codes CPTA, CZEA and CZDA	Euro 6
2.0 litre engine (all engines)	Euro 6

Torque wrench settings

	Nm	lbf ft
1.2 and 1.4 litre engines		
Crankcase breather hose (at turbocharger)*	5	3
Crancase breather oil separator bolt*	9	7
Catalytic converter to bracket and bracket to engine nuts/bolts.	20	15
Catalytic converter to turbocharger clamp.	15	11
Exhaust clamp nut	30	22
Intercooler bolts (at inlet manifold)	15	11
Turbocharger mounting nuts*	14	10
Turbocharger heat shield bolts (to turbocharger)	25	18
Turbocharger boost controller*	9	7
Turbocharger oil supply bolts	9	7
Turbocharger coolant line bolt	8	6
2.0 litre engines		
Catalytic converter to bracket and bracket to engine nuts/bolts.	20	15
Catalytic converter to turbocharger clamp.	5	11
Crankcase breather bolt.	9	7
Exhaust clamp nut	30	22
Turbocharger mounting nuts*	25	18
Turbocharger heat shield bolts.	9	7
Turbocharger coolant line supply bolt	9	7
Turbocharger oil supply bolt.	9	7
Turbocharger bracket bolt (to engine)	30	22
Turbocharger bracket bolt (to engine)	30	22

*Do not re-use
**Use thread-locking compound

1 General Information

Emission control systems

1 All petrol models are designed to use unleaded petrol, and are controlled by engine management systems that are programmed to give the best compromise between driveability, fuel consumption and exhaust emission production. In addition, a number of systems are fitted that help to minimise other harmful emissions. A crankcase emission control system is fitted, which reduces the release of pollutants from the engine's lubrication system, and a catalytic converter is fitted which reduces exhaust gas pollutant. An evaporative loss emission control system is fitted which reduces the release of gaseous hydrocarbons from the fuel tank.

Crankcase emission control

2 To reduce the emission of unburned hydrocarbons from the crankcase into the atmosphere, the engine is sealed and the blow-by gases and oil vapour are drawn from inside the crankcase, through a wire-mesh oil separator, into the inlet tract to be burned by the engine during normal combustion.

3 Under conditions of high manifold depression, the gases will be sucked positively out of the crankcase. Under conditions of low manifold depression, the gases are forced out of the crankcase by the (relatively) higher crankcase pressure. If the engine is worn, the raised crankcase pressure (due to increased blow-by) will cause some of the flow to return under all manifold conditions.

Exhaust emission control

4 To minimise the amount of pollutants which escape into the atmosphere, all petrol models are fitted with a catalytic converter in the exhaust system. The fuelling system is of the closed-loop type, in which an oxygen (lambda) sensor in the exhaust system provides the engine management system ECU with constant feedback, enabling the ECU to adjust the air/fuel mixture to optimise combustion.

5 The oxygen sensor has a built-in heating element, controlled by the ECU through the oxygen sensor relay, to quickly bring the sensor's tip to its optimum operating temperature. The sensor's tip is sensitive to oxygen, and sends a voltage signal to the ECU that varies according to the amount of oxygen in the exhaust gas. If the inlet air/fuel mixture is too rich, the exhaust gases are low in oxygen so the sensor sends a low-voltage signal, the voltage rising as the mixture weakens and the amount of oxygen rises in the exhaust gases. Peak conversion efficiency of all major pollutants occurs if the inlet air/fuel mixture is maintained at the chemically-correct ratio for the complete combustion of petrol of 14.7 parts (by weight) of air to 1 part of fuel (the stoichiometric ratio). The sensor output voltage alters in a large step at this point, the ECU using the signal change as a reference point and correcting the inlet air/fuel mixture accordingly by altering the fuel injector pulse width.

6 Note that some models have a broadband oxygen sensor fitted before the catalytic converter. These are five wire sensors and output a linear signal (not the rich/lean signal of a traditional sensor). The output signal is proportional to the oxygen content of the exhaust and allows fine tuning of the engine emissions.

7 To bring the converter up to operating temperature quickly the exhaust manifold has been integrated into the cylinder head. None of the engines covered in this manual have a traditional exhaust manifold. The turbocharger is bolted directly to the cylinder head.

8 All models have two sensors, one before and one after the main catalytic converter. This enables the efficiency of the converter to be checked.

Evaporative emission control

9 To minimise the escape of unburned hydrocarbons into the atmosphere, an evaporative loss emission control system is fitted to all petrol models. The fuel tank filler cap is sealed and a charcoal canister is mounted underneath the right-hand rear wing to collect the petrol vapours released from the fuel contained in the fuel tank. It stores them until they can be drawn from the canister (under the control of the fuel injection/ignition system ECU) via the purge valve into the inlet tract, where they are then burned by the engine during normal combustion.

10 To ensure that the engine runs correctly when it is cold and/or idling and to protect the catalytic converter from the effects of an over-rich mixture, the purge control valve(s) are not opened by the ECU until the engine has warmed-up, and the engine is under load; the valve solenoid is then modulated on and off to allow the stored vapour to pass into the inlet tract.

Exhaust systems

11 On all models, the exhaust system consists of the front pipe (permanently attached to the converter), the intermediate pipe and silencer, and tailpipe and silencer. The systems fitted differ in mostly in regard to the type of rear suspension fitted and engine size.

12 The system is supported by various metal brackets screwed to the vehicle floor, with rubber vibration dampers fitted to suppress noise **(see illustration)**.

2 Evaporative loss emission control system – information and component renewal

1 The evaporative loss emission control system consists of the purge valve, the activated charcoal filter canister and a series of connecting vacuum hoses.

2 The canister is located in the right-hand rear wheel arch.

3 Jack up and support the rear of the vehicle (see *Jacking and vehicle support*). Remove the wheel and wing liner **(see illustration)**.

4 Disconnect the vapour lines from the canister **(see illustration)**.

1.12 Typical exhaust pipe mounting

2.3 Remove the wing liner

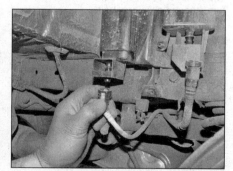
2.4 Disconnect the vapour lines

2.5a Remove the bolt...

2.5b ...release the tab and remove the canister

5 Remove the single bolt, depress the locking tab and remove the canister **(see illustrations)**.
6 The control (purge) valve is mounted away from the canister (the exact location depends on the engine fitted). Disconnect the wiring plug and remove the hoses **(see illustration)**.
7 Refitting is a reversal of removal.

3 Crankcase emission system – general information

1 The crankcase emission control system consists of hoses connecting the crankcase to the air cleaner or inlet manifold. Oil separator units are fitted to all petrol engines. On 1.2 and 1.4 engines the separator is fitted below the oil cooler at the left-hand end of the engine block. On 2.0 litre engines the separator is fitted on the valve cover.

2 The system requires no attention other than to check at regular intervals that the hoses, valve and oil separator are free of blockages and in good condition. If required the oil separators can be removed.

1.2 and 1.4 litre engines

Removal

3 Jack up and support the front of the vehicle (see *Jacking and vehicle support*)
4 Remove the engine undershield and then unbolt the intercooler coolant pump. Secure the pump to the side. Note that there is no need to drain the coolant
5 Remove the breather hose and then release the cover from the separator.
6 Remove the bolts in reverse order to that shown **(see illustration 3.11)**.
7 Carefully remove the separator from the engine block. The separator is held in place with sealant.

Refitting

8 Clean the mounting surface of the block and separator of all the old sealant.
9 To ensure correct alignment fit two studs (M6 X 20 mm) diagonally opposite each other into the engine block.
10 Apply a 2 mm bead of sealant to the face of the separator. The bead must pass inside the bolt holds and the separator must be fitted within 5 minutes of applying the sealant.
11 Slide the separator over the studs and fit the bolts hand tight. Remove the studs and fit the remaining two bolts. Tighten the bolts in the order shown to the specified torque **(see illustration)**.
12 Fit the remaining components in reverse order to removal.

2.0 litre engines

Removal

13 Remove the engine cover and disconnect

2.6 The purge valve (2.0 litre engine shown)

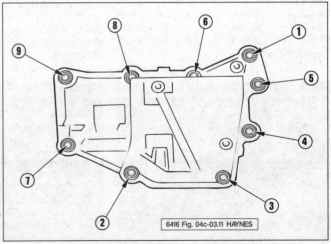

3.11 Tighten the bolts in the order shown

3.14a Remove the ignition coils (shown removed)...

3.14b ...and the breather

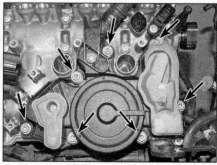

3.15 Remove the bolts

the wiring plugs from the ignition coils.

14 Remove the coils from cylinders 3 and 4, remove the hose from the EVAP solenoid and then remove the breather hose from the turbocharger **(see illustrations)**.

15 Remove the bolts and lift off the oil separator **(see illustration)**.

Refitting

16 Refitting is a reversal of removal, but new gaskets **(see illustration)** and seals must be used.

4	**Turbocharger** – general information, precautions, removal and refitting

General information

1 The turbocharger is bolted directly to the cylinder head. Lubrication is provided by an oil supply pipe that is feed from an oil gallery at the rear of the engine block. Oil is returned to the sump through a return pipe that also connects to the block. The turbocharger wastegate is controlled electrical and incorporates a position sensor.

2 The turbocharger's internal components rotate at a very high speed, and as such are sensitive to contamination; a great deal of damage can be caused by small particles of dirt, particularly if they strike the delicate turbine blades.

Precautions

3 The turbocharger operates at extremely high speeds and temperatures. Certain precautions must be observed to avoid premature failure of the turbo, or injury to the operator.

● Do not operate the turbo with any parts exposed. Foreign objects falling onto the rotating vanes could cause excessive damage and (if ejected) personal injury.

● Cover the turbocharger air inlet ducts to prevent debris entering, and clean using lint-free cloths only.

● Do not race the engine immediately after start-up, especially if it is cold. Give the oil a few seconds to circulate.

● Observe the recommended intervals for oil and filter changing, and use a reputable oil of the specified quality. Neglect of oil changing, or use of inferior oil, can cause carbon formation on the turbo shaft and subsequent failure. Thoroughly clean the area around all oil pipe unions before disconnecting them, to prevent the ingress of dirt. Store dismantled components in a sealed container to prevent contamination.

Caution: Thoroughly clean the area around all oil pipe unions before disconnecting them, to prevent the ingress of dirt. Store dismantled components in a sealed container to prevent contamination. Cover the turbocharger air inlet ducts to prevent debris entering, and clean using lint-free cloths only.

1.2 and 1.4 litre petrol engines

Removal

4 Apply the handbrake, then jack up the front of the vehicle and support it on axle stands (see *Jacking and vehicle support*). Remove engine undershield.

5 Drain the cooling system as described in Chapter 1A Section 33.

6 Remove the heat shield from above the right-hand driveshaft.

7 Disconnect the wiring plug from the oil pressure switch. Have shop towels close to hand and unbolt the oil supply and oil return lines.

8 Remove the screw type clamp from the catalytic converter/turbocharger and then unbolt the converter. Ether remove it completely as described in Section 6, or secure it to the side.

9 Remove the air filter housing and charge air pipe as described in Chapter 4A Section 3.

10 Disconnect the EVAP hose from the breather hose and remove the breather from the turbocharger.

11 Disconnect the wiring plug from the wastegate controller and then remove the short charge air pipe from the turbocharger **(see illustration)**.

12 Remove the coolant hose from the turbocharger, release the hose from the retaining brackets and move it to the side **(see illustration)**.

3.16 Fit a new gasket

4.11 Remove the short elbow from the turbocharger

4.12 Remove the coolant hose

4.13 Remove the heatshield

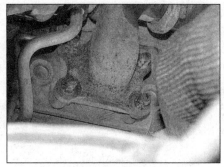

4.14 Remove the bolts

4.20 Remove the charge air pipe

13 Remove the upper heatshield **(see illustration)**.

14 Remove the mounting bolts and lift out the turbocharger **(see illustration)**. Recover the metal gasket form the turbocharger.

Refitting

15 Refit the turbocharger by following the removal procedure in reverse, noting the following points:

a) *Renew all gaskets, sealing washers and O-rings.*

b) *Before reconnecting the oil supply pipe, fill the turbocharger with fresh oil using an oil can.*

c) *Tighten all nuts and bolts to the specified torque, where given.*

d) *Ensure that the air hose clips are securely tightened, to prevent air leaks.*

e) *Disable the ignition system and crank the engine over until the oil pressure warning light extinguishes.*

f) *When the engine is started after refitting, allow it to idle for approximately one minute to give the oil time to circulate around the turbine shaft bearings. Check for signs of oil or coolant leakage from the relevant unions.*

2.0 litre engines

Removal

16 Apply the handbrake, then jack up the front of the vehicle and support it on axle

4.22a Remove the heat shield...

4.22b ...and O2 sensor

stands (see *Jacking and vehicle support*). Remove engine undershield.

17 Drain the coolant as described in Chapter 1A Section 33.

18 Remove the catalytic converter as as described in Section 6.

19 Remove the air filter housing as described in Chapter 4A Section 3.

20 At the left-hand end of the engine, remove the charge air pipe from the turbocharger **(see illustration)**.

21 Where fitted remove the earth wires from the ignition coils and then remove the coolant hoses and wiring loom from the cylinder head.

22 Remove the heatshield and then remove the pre converter Oxygen sensor **(see illustrations)**.

23 Remove the crankcase emissions breather hose **(see illustration)**.

24 Remove the oil supply line from the turbocharger.

25 Disconnect the wiring plugs from the wastegate control module **(see illustration)** and the shut off solenoid.

26 Working from below remove the support bracket from the turbocharger **(see illustration)**.

27 Remove the coolant hose from the turbocharger.

28 Remove the oil return hose from the turbocharger.

29 Remove the engine stabiliser bar (pendulum) from the subframe.

30 To provide sufficient room to remove the turbocharger the engine must be pivoted

4.23 Remove the breather hose

4.25 Disconnect the wiring plug from the wastegate control

4.26 Unbolt the support bracket

4.31a Remove the turbocharger and...

4.31b ...recover the gasket

forward. Use a strap around the subframe and pull the bottom of the engine towards the subframe.

31 Remove the nuts from the turbocharger and lift the the turbocharger up and out of the engine bay **(see illustrations)**.

Refitting

32 Refit the turbocharger by following the removal procedure in reverse, noting the following points:

a) Renew all gaskets, sealing washers and O-rings.

b) Before reconnecting the oil supply pipe, fill the turbocharger with fresh oil using an oil can.

c) Tighten all nuts and bolts to the specified torque, where given.

d) Ensure that the air hose clips are securely tightened, to prevent air leaks.

e) Disable the ignition system and crank the engine over until the oil pressure warning light extinguishes.

f) When the engine is started after refitting, allow it to idle for approximately one minute to give the oil time to circulate around the turbine shaft bearings. Check for signs of oil or coolant leakage from the relevant unions.

5 Intercooler – general information

1 The intercooler is used to cool the pressurised inlet air before it enters the engine. On 2.0 litre engine a standard 'air to air' intercooler is fitted. On the 1.2 and 1.4 petrol engines an 'air to liquid' intercooler is fitted.

2 When the turbocharger compresses the inlet air, one side-effect is that the air is heated, causing the air to expand. If the inlet air can be cooled, a greater effective volume of air will be inducted, and the engine will produce more power.

3 On 2.0 litre engines, the compressed air from the turbocharger, which would normally be fed straight into the inlet manifold, is instead ducted around the engine to the base of the intercooler. The intercooler is mounted at the front of the car, in the airflow. The heated air entering the base of the unit rises upwards, and is cooled by the airflow over the intercooler fins, much as with the radiator. When it reaches the top of the intercooler, the cooled air is then ducted into the throttle housing.

4 On 1.2 and 1.4 litre engines the charge air entering the inlet manifold is cooled by a coolant filled heat exchanger, that is part of the inlet manifold. This functions in a similar manner to the engine cooling radiator. Air entering the inlet manifold passes over the heat exchanger (radiator) and is cooled. The heat recovered from the incoming air is transferred to the front panel mounted intercooler where it is dissipated through the cooling fins of the liquid filled intercooler (radiator). The circuit has an electrical coolant pump and is controlled by the engine management system.

5 On both types of intercooler the intercooler is mounted between the radiator and the AC condenser. The intercooler is removed with the radiator as described in Chapter 3 Section 3 or removed after the radiator is removed. Follow the procedure outlined in Chapter 3 if removal of the intercooler is required.

6 Exhaust system – component renewal

⚠️ *Warning: Allow ample time for the exhaust system to cool before starting work. In particular, note that the catalytic converter runs at very high temperatures. If there is any chance that the system may still be hot, wear suitable gloves. When removing the exhaust sections, take care not to damage*

the oxygen sensors if they are not removed from their locations.

Removal

1 The original Volkswagen system fitted in the factory is in three sections: the front section, the centre section (with silencer), and the rear section (with a silencer).The front section is part of the catalytic converter. The system is suspended on multiple flexible mounts.

2 To remove part of the system, first jack up the front or rear of the car and support it on axle stands (see *Jacking and vehicle support*). Alternatively, position the car over an inspection pit or on car ramps.

Front pipe and catalytic converter

Note: *Handle the flexible, braided section of the front pipe carefully, and do not bend it excessively.*

3 Before removing the front section of the exhaust, disconnect the wiring plugs from the oxygen sensors. The plugs are mounted on a bracket on the front of the plenum chamber.

4 Where practical remove the oxygen sensors before removing the convertor and front pipe. Alternatively remove the sensors after removing the converter and front pipe

5 Where fitted remove the heat shield from the right-hand driveshaft.

6 Remove the support bracket from the subframe **(see illustration)**.

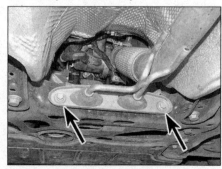

6.6 Remove the bracket

7 On 1.2 and 1.4 litre engines remove the support bracket from below the convertor.

8 Slacken the convertor mounting bolts, but do not remove them at this stage. Loosen the bolts at the exhaust sleeve type clamp **(see illustration)** and slide the clamp back onto the middle section of the exhaust system.

9 Note the angle of the bolt on the clamp and then slacken the clamp at the turbocharger. Push the clamp onto the turbocharger.

10 Remove the previously slackend converter mounting bolts and lower the converter and front pipe from the vehicle.

11 Recover the metal seal from the turbocharger

Centre pipe and silencer

12 Remove the transmission tunnel crossmember **(see illustration)**.

13 Unbolt the sleeve clamps and slide them onto the centre pipe – slide them onto the front pipe or rear silencer.

14 Unhook the silencer from the flexible mounting, or unbolt the bracket from body. Lower the silencer from the vehicle.

Rear silencer

Note: *There are several versions of the rear silencer fitted, depending on the engine size and the rear suspension type. Removal and refitting is essentially the same for all versions.*

15 Slacken the bolts on the sleeve type clamp and slide the clamp along the pipe.

16 Unhook the flexible mountings from the exhaust and remove it from the vehicle. Alternatively the mounting brackets can be removed. This is considerably easier if a specialist tool is not available.

17 Unscrew the bolts, and release the mounting(s) from the underside of the car. On models with two silencer mountings, it may prove sufficient to unbolt only one, and to prise the silencer from the remaining mounting, but for preference, both should be removed.

18 Where applicable, slide the clamp at the front end of the silencer section to release the pipe ends, and lower the silencer out of position.

Refitting

19 The catalytic converter and front pipe must be fitted stress free to avoid damaging the ceramic matrix of the converter.

a) Install the converter with a new sealing ring and loosely fit the clamp.

b) Fit the converter mounting bolts hand tight. It should be possible to move the converter.

c) Fully tighten the clamp at the turbocharger.

6.8 Note the orientation of the sleeve type clamp

The clamp must be in the previously noted position.

d) Fully tighten the converter mounting bolts.

e) Inspect the support bracket flexible hanger (replace them if necessary) and refit the bracket.

20 The middle and rear sections of the exhaust are fitted by a reversal of the removal sequence, noting the following points:

a) Ensure that all traces of corrosion have been removed from the flanges or pipe ends, and renew all necessary gaskets.

b) If necessary, renew the clamps, and use the markings on the pipes as a guide to the clamp's correct fitted position.

c) Inspect the mountings for signs of damage or deterioration, and renew as necessary.

d) If using exhaust assembly paste, make sure this is only applied to joints downstream of the catalyst.

e) Prior to tightening the exhaust system mountings and clamps, ensure that all rubber mountings are correctly located and that there is adequate clearance between the exhaust system and vehicle underbody. Try to ensure that no unnecessary twisting stresses are applied to the pipes – move the pipes relative to each other at the clamps to relieve this.

7 Catalytic converter – general information and precautions

1 The catalytic converter is a reliable and simple device which needs no maintenance in itself, but there are some facts of which an owner should be aware if the converter is to function properly for its full service life:

a) DO NOT use leaded or lead-replacement petrol in a car equipped with a catalytic converter – the lead (or other additives) will coat the precious metals, reducing their

6.12 Remove the crosmember

converting efficiency and will eventually destroy the converter.

b) Always keep the ignition and fuel systems well-maintained in accordance with the manufacturer's schedule (see Chapter 1A).

c) If the engine develops a misfire, do not drive the car at all (or at least as little as possible) until the fault is cured.

d) DO NOT push- or tow-start the car – this will soak the catalytic converter in unburned fuel, causing it to overheat when the engine does start.

e) DO NOT switch off the ignition at high engine speeds – ie, do not 'blip' the throttle immediately before switching off the engine.

f) DO NOT use fuel or engine oil additives – these may contain substances harmful to the catalytic converter.

g) DO NOT continue to use the car if the engine burns oil to the extent of leaving a visible trail of blue smoke.

h) Remember that the catalytic converter operates at very high temperatures. DO NOT, therefore, park the car in dry undergrowth, over long grass or piles of dead leaves after a long run.

i) Remember that the catalytic converter is FRAGILE – do not strike it with tools during servicing work, and take care handling it when removing it from the car for any reason.

j) In some cases, a sulphurous smell (like that of rotten eggs) may be noticed from the exhaust. This is common to many catalytic converter-equipped cars, and has more to do with the sulphur content of the brand of fuel being used than the converter itself.

k) The catalytic converter, used on a well-maintained and well-driven car, should last for between 50 000 and 100 000 miles – if the converter is no longer effective, it must be renewed.

Chapter 4 Part D
Emission control and exhaust systems – diesel engines

Contents

Section number

Catalytic converter/particulate filter – removal and refitting. 8
Crankcase emission system – general information 2
Exhaust Gas Recirculation (EGR) system – component removal. . . . 3
Exhaust system – component renewal. 9
General Information 1

Section number

Intercooler – general information, removal and refitting. 7
Turbocharger – general information and precautions. 4
Turbocharger and exhaust manifold – removal and refitting 5
Turbocharger charge control system components – description,
    removal and refitting. 6

Degrees of difficulty

Easy, suitable for novice with little experience 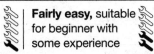	**Fairly easy,** suitable for beginner with some experience	**Fairly difficult,** suitable for competent DIY mechanic	**Difficult,** suitable for experienced DIY mechanic	**Very difficult,** suitable for expert DIY or professional

Specifications

Engine codes*

1.6 litre	CLHA, CLHB, CRKB, CXXA, CXXB and DBKA
2.0 litre	CKFC, CRBC, CRLB, CRLD, CRMB and CUNA

*See 'Vehicle identification' at the end of the manual for the location of the engine code markings

Emission control standards

1.6 litre engine code
CLHA and CLHB	EU5
CRKB	EU5 or EU6
CXXA and CXXB.	EU6
DBKA	EU6+

2.0 litre engine code
CKFC and CRBC	EU5
CRLB, CRMB and CUNA	EU6

Torque wrench settings

	Nm	lbf ft
Catalytic converter/particulate filter mounting bracket \ nuts/bolts (see text)	20	15
EGR control motor	9	6
EGR cooler	20	15
Exhaust gas temperature probe:		
1.6 litre engine	45	33
2.0 litre engine	60	44
Exhaust system clamp	30	22
Exhaust to filter clamp	7	5
Lambda (O2) sensor.	55	41
Particulate filter/catalytic converter clamp (to turbocharger).	8	6
Particulate filter pressure sensor line (at filter)	45	33
Particulate filter support bracket (to block)	40	30
Particulate filter support bracket (to manifold).	20	15
Turbocharger/manifold to cylinder head nuts*:		
Stage 1.	11	8
Stage 2.	22	16
Stage 3 (repeat stage 2)	22	16
Turbocharger oil feed banjo bolt	30	22
Turbocharger oil feed pipe (at turbo)	22	16
Turbocharger oil drain (at turbocharger) bolts	14	10
Turbocharger oil drain (at block) bolts	10	7

*Use new fixings

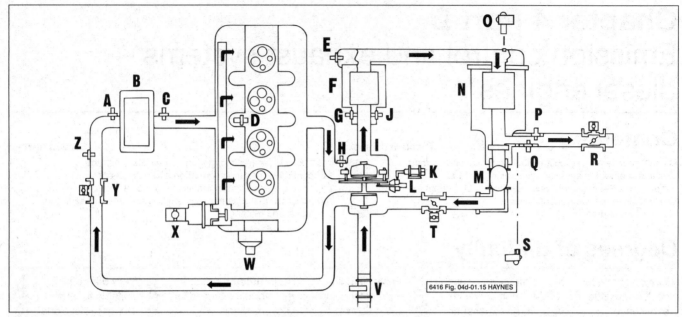

1.5 The EGR and air regulation system

A Inlet temperature sensor
B Charge air cooler
C Intercooler air temperature sensor (after intercooler)
D Camshaft position sensor
E Exhaust gas temperature sensor
F Catalytic convertor
G O2 (Lambda) sensor
H Exhaust gas temperature sensor

I Turbocharger (exhaust side with variable vane)
J Exhaust gas temperature sensor
K Boost pressure control solenoid
L Position sensor for turbocharger
M EGR cooler
N Particulate filter
O Differential pressure sensor
P Exhaust gas temperature sensor
Q O2 (Lambda) sensor (post convertor)

R Exhaust flap control
S Exhaust gas temperature sensor
T EGR control motor
U Turbocharger (compressor side)
V MAF (Mass Airflow) sensor
W VVT control (some models)
X EGR control (high pressure, some models only)
Y Throttle control
Z Boost pressure sensor

1 General Information

Emission control systems

1 All diesel engines covered by this manual have a crankcase emission control system, a close coupled catalytic converter, a Diesel Particulate Filter (DPF) and Exhaust Gas Recirculation (EGR). Models that are EU6 compliant have a low pressure and a high pressure EGR system fitted.

Crankcase emission control

2 To reduce the emission of unburned hydrocarbons from the crankcase into the atmosphere, the engine is sealed and the blow-by gases and oil vapour are drawn from inside the crankcase, through a wire mesh oil separator, into the inlet tract to be burned by the engine during normal combustion.
3 Under conditions of high manifold depression, the gases will be sucked positively out of the crankcase. Under conditions of low manifold depression, the gases are forced out of the crankcase by the (relatively) higher crankcase pressure. If the engine is worn, the raised crankcase pressure (due to increased

blow-by) will cause some of the flow to return under all manifold conditions.

Exhaust emission control

4 All models have an oxidation catalyst and DPF combined into a single 'emissions module' This has the effect of removing a large proportion of the gaseous hydrocarbons, carbon monoxide and particulates present in the exhaust gas.
5 A sophisticated Exhaust Gas Recirculation (EGR) and air regulation system is fitted to all models **(see illustration)**. This reduces the level of nitrogen oxides produced during combustion by introducing a proportion of the exhaust gas back into the inlet manifold under certain engine operating conditions. EU6 models also have a high pressure EGR system fitted (as well as the standard low pressure system). On the high pressure system a proportion of the exhaust gas is immediately fed back (via the cylinder head) into the combustion chamber. The system is controlled electronically by the diesel engine management ECU.

Exhaust systems

6 The exhaust system consists of the exhaust manifold, front flexible pipe with catalytic converter/particulate filter and rear pipe

section including silencer. The turbocharger is integral with the exhaust manifold, and is driven by the exhaust gases.
7 The system is supported by various metal brackets screwed to the vehicle floor, with rubber vibration dampers fitted to suppress noise.

2 Crankcase emission system – general information

1 The crankcase emission control system is fully integrated into the cylinder head cover **(see illustration)**.

2.1 Disconnecting the breather hose

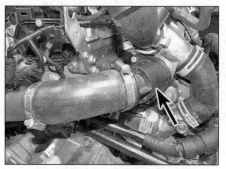

3.7 Remove the inlet elbow/resonator (shown with charge air pipe)

3.10 The EGR lower coolant hose

3.12 The main hose clip

2 The system requires no attention other than to check at regular intervals. Apart from the hose, in the event of failure the cylinder head cover must be replaced.

3 Exhaust Gas Recirculation (EGR) system – component removal

1 The EGR system consists of the EGR control valve, which controls the flow of exhaust gas from the exhaust to the inlet manifold. An EGR cooler is fitted before the control valve to lower the temperature of the exhaust gas. The control of the gas flow is all controlled by the engine management ECU. Note that EGR flow is all part of the integrated air regulation system **(see illustration 1.5)**.
2 The control valve is removed with the cooler, although it can be removed separately if required. Note that access to both components is limited.

EGR cooler

3 Remove the engine cover by pulling it up.
4 Jack up and support the front of the vehicle (see *Jacking and vehicle support*).
5 Drain the coolant as described in Chapter 1B Section 33 and then remove air filter housing (Chapter 4B Section 3) the battery and battery tray as described in Chapter 5A Section 3.
6 Remove the coolant hoses and the charge air pipe from the left-hand end of the engine.
7 Unbolt and remove the resonator **(see illustration)**.
8 Disconnect the gear selector cables, unbolt the mounting bracket and move the cable to the side.
9 Remove the heat shield and disconnect the wiring plug from the cooler.
10 Remove the upper and lower coolant hoses **(see illustration)**.
11 Remove the spring clips and then remove the air duct.
12 Slacken the large hose clip and push the clip onto the particulate filter **(see illustration)**.
13 Unscrew the mounting bolts and remove the cooler **(see illustration)**. Anticipate some coolant spillage as the cooler is removed.
14 Refitting is a reversal of removal, but

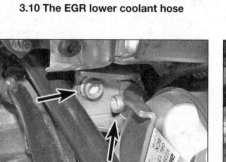

3.13 The EGR cooler mounting bracket bolts

use new gaskets and fit the main hose clip so that the tightening screw is angled downwards approximately 10 to 15 degrees below horizontal. Refill the cooling system as described in Chapter 1B Section 33 and lower the vehicle.

EGR control valves

Control valve 1

15 The valve is at the left-hand end of the inlet manifold, behind the throttle body. It is only fitted to models that have a high pressure EGR system fitted **(see illustration)**.
16 Remove the throttle body housing, as described in Chapter 4B Section 4.
17 Disconnect the wiring plug from the back of the EGR valve.
18 Drain the coolant as described in Chapter 1B Section 33, or alternatively clamp off the coolant hoses with hose clamps.

3.19a Remove the bolts...

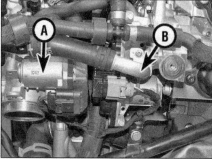

3.15 The throttle body (A) and the EGR valve (B)

Remove the coolant hoses. Anticipate some coolant loss.
19 Remove the bolts and remove the control valve. Recover the seal and gasket **(see illustrations)**.
20 Refitting is a reversal of removal, using a new EGR valve O-ring seal and gasket. Tighten the retaining bolts to the specified torque.

Control valve 2

21 The valve is part of the EGR cooler.
22 Remove the engine cover by pulling it up and then remove the turbocharger intake pipe (or remove the complete air filter housing, as described in Chapter 4B Section 3).
23 Remove the spring clips and remove the EGR cooler hose.
24 Move the heat insulation aside and then disconnect the wiring plug.
25 Remove the bolts and detach the control valve. Recover the seal.

3.19b ...and pull out the valve

3.29 The exhaust control flap

26 Refitting is a reversal of removal, but use a new seal.

EGR exhaust control flap

27 Jack up and support the front of the vehicle (see *Jacking and vehicle support*).
28 Where fitted remove the heat insulation sleeve and then disconnect the wiring plug.
29 Unscrew the bolts and remove the control unit **(see illustration)**.
30 Refitting is a reversal of removal, but where a new flap has been fitted, it must be adapted to the engine ECU using a diagnostic tool. Consult a Volkswagen dealer or suitably equipped garage.

4 Turbocharger – general information and precautions

General information

1 A turbocharger is fitted to all engines, and is integral with the exhaust manifold.
2 The turbocharger increases engine efficiency by raising the pressure in the inlet manifold above atmospheric pressure. Instead of the air simply being sucked into the cylinders, it is forced in.
3 Energy for the operation of the turbocharger comes from the exhaust gas. The gas flows through a specially shaped housing (the turbine housing) and in so doing, spins the turbine wheel. The turbine wheel is attached to a shaft, at the end of which is another

vaned wheel, known as the compressor wheel. The compressor wheel spins in its own housing, and compresses the inducted air on the way to the inlet manifold.
4 Between the turbocharger and the inlet manifold, the compressed air passes through an intercooler. This is an air to liquid intercooler and forms part of the inlet manifold. The purpose of the intercooler is to remove from the inducted air some of the heat gained in being compressed. Because cooler air is denser, removal of this heat further increases engine efficiency.
5 The turbocharger is a Variable Vane Turbocharger (VVT). Alternatively referred to as a Variable Geometry Turbocharger (VGT) or a Variable Nozzle Turbocharger (VNT). Boost pressure (the pressure in the inlet manifold) is controlled by altering the angle of the vanes of the turbocharger to the incoming exhaust gas. The angle of the vanes is controlled by a vacuum operated lever, that responds to commands from the engine control ECU. A position sensor is also incorporated into the controller to provide feedback to the ECU.
6 The turbo shaft is pressure-lubricated by an oil feed pipe from the engine oil filter mounting. The shaft 'floats' on a cushion of oil. Oil is returned to the sump through a return pipe that connects to the rear of the cylinder block.

Precautions

7 The turbocharger operates at extremely high speeds and temperatures. Certain precautions must be observed to avoid premature failure of the turbo, or injury to the operator.
● Do not operate the turbo with any parts exposed – foreign objects falling onto the rotating vanes could cause excessive damage and (if ejected) personal injury.
● Cover the turbocharger air inlet ducts to prevent debris entering, and clean using lint-free cloths only.
● Do not race the engine immediately after start-up, especially if it is cold. Give the oil a few seconds to circulate.
● Observe the recommended intervals for oil and filter changing, and use a reputable oil of the specified quality. Neglect of oil changing, or use of inferior oil, can cause

carbon formation on the turbo shaft and subsequent failure. Thoroughly clean the area around all oil pipe unions before disconnecting them, to prevent the ingress of dirt. Store dismantled components in a sealed container to prevent contamination.

5 Turbocharger and exhaust manifold – removal and refitting

Note: *This Section describes the removal of the turbocharger together with the exhaust manifold. The turbocharger cannot be removed from the exhaust manifold. Note that there is very little room to remove the emissions control module (the Catalytic converter and the particulate filter) and these must be removed before the turbocharger can be removed. Consideration should be given to removing the engine if extensive work is required at the back of the engine.*

Removal

1 Apply the handbrake, then jack up the front of the vehicle and support it on axle stands (see *Jacking and vehicle support*). Remove the engine compartment undertray and the engine cover.
2 Drain the coolant as described in Chapter 1B Section 33.
3 Remove the air filter assembly and ducting as described in Chapter 4B Section 3.
4 Remove the resonator **(see illustration 3.7)**.
5 Unclip and move aside the wiring plugs and connectors on the plenum chamber front – the number varies depending on the engine **(see illustration)**.
6 On vehicles that have a coolant pipe at the rear of the cylinder head, remove the mounting bracket bolts and the hose clips. Remove the hose from the vehicle.
7 Remove the coolant pipes from the EGR cooler **(see illustration)**.
8 Working underneath the vehicle, remove the heat shield from the right-hand driveshaft **(see illustration)**. Note that access can be improved if the right-hand driveshaft is removed as described in Chapter 8 Section 2.

5.5 Remove the wiring plugs and mounting bracket from the front of the plenum chamber

5.7 Remove the coolant hoses

5.8 Remove the driveshaft heat shield

5.13a The oil feed pipe (shown with driveshaft removed)

5.13b The oil drain pipe (shown with emissions module removed)

5.13c The oil feed and oil drain pipes at the turbocharger

5.13d Removing the oil drain pipe

5.14 Remove the bracket

5.15 Remove the heat shield

5.16a The manifold mounting bolts

5.16b Remove the turbocharger

13 Unbolt the oil feed pipe and the oil return line **(see illustrations)**. Seal the openings in the engine block.

14 Remove the bolts and remove the emissions control module support bracket **(see illustration)**.

15 Remove the upper heat shield **(see illustration)** and the disconnect the vacuum lines.

16 Remove the manifold bolts **(see illustrations)** and with the aid of an assistant remove the turbocharger from the cylinder head.

Refitting

17 Refit the turbocharger by following the removal procedure in reverse, noting the following points:

a) *Renew exhaust maniflold gaskets, sealing washers and O-rings* **(see illustration)**.

b) *Fit a new gasket to the oil return pipe upper flange* **(see illustration)**.

c) *Fit a new banjo bolt to the oil return pipe* **(see illustration)**.

9 Remove the exhaust down pipe as described in Section 9.

10 Remove the O2 sensors and the exhaust gas temperature sensors. The number varies according to the model.

11 Remove the coolant pipes from the rear of the engine and the left-hand side **(see illustration 5.7)**.

12 Remove the emission control module as described in Section 8.

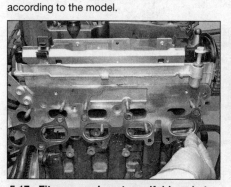

5.17a Fit a new exhaust manifold gasket...

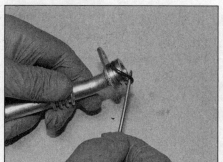

5.17b ...and renew the oil return pipe O-ring...

5.17c ...as well as the gasket

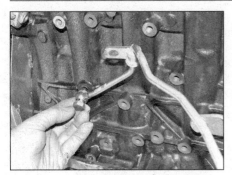

5.17d Fit new sealing washers to the oil supply banjo bolt

d) *Fit new sealing washers to the oil supply pipe* **(see illustration)**.

e) *Before reconnecting the oil supply pipe, fill the turbocharger with fresh oil using an oil can.*

f) *Tighten all nuts and bolts to the specified torque, where given.*

g) *Ensure that the air hose clips are securely tightened, to prevent air leaks.*

h) *When the engine is started after refitting, allow it to idle for approximately one minute to give the oil time to circulate around the turbine shaft bearings. Check for signs of oil or coolant leakage from the relevant unions.*

6 Turbocharger charge control system components – description, removal and refitting

Description

1 The turbocharger controller is operated by vacuum supplied by the vacuum pump (part of the oil pump). The vacuum supply is controlled by an electrically operated solenoid valve activated by the engine management ECU. The solenoid valve is mounted on the bulkhead at the rear of the engine compartment. The valve has three hoses connecting it to the air cleaner, turbocharger

and vacuum pump. It is important that the hoses are connected correctly to the solenoid valve **(see illustration 5.5)**.

Boost pressure sensor

2 Remove the engine cover.

3 The sensor is mounted remotely at the front left-hand end of the inlet manifold.

4 Disconnect the wiring plug **(see illustration)** and release the hose from the sensor. Unbolt the sensor and remove it.

5 Refitting is a reversal of removal.

Boost pressure control solenoid valve

6 The charge pressure solenoid valve is mounted at the rear of the engine compartment **(see illustration 5.5)** on the bulkhead.

7 Disconnect the wiring plug from the valve.

8 Undo the two retaining nuts and withdraw the solenoid valve away from the bulkhead.

9 Remove the vacuum hoses from the ports on the control solenoid valve, noting their order of connection carefully to aid correct refitting.

10 Refitting is a reversal of removal.

Boost pressure controller

11 There are various versions of the vacuum controller fitted. All operate in the same manner. Removal and refitting is essentially the same for all versions. If the controller is being removed (and will be refitted) precisely mark the position of the controller in relation to the turbocharger.

12 Remove the engine cover and disconnect the wiring plug from the controller.

13 Unplug the vacuum line and then remove the circlip from the operating arm. Remove the mounting bolts and lift out the vacuum controller **(see illustration)**.

14 Refitting is a reversal of removal, but use a new circlip and bolts.

Adjustment

15 Where a new controller has been fitted (or

if the position of the old one was not marked) the new controller must be adapted to the engine with a diagnostic tool.

16 Check the voltage (on the diagnostic tool) and then attach a vacuum pump to the vacuum supply line. Apply a 650-750 mbar vacuum to the controller with the pump.

17 Slacken the controller mounting bolts and adjust the position of the controller until the voltage at the diagnostic tool reads 0.75 volts (plus or minus 0.02 volts).

18 Fully tighten the bolts, remove the vacuum pump and reconnect the vacuum hose. Using the diagnostic tool clear any fault codes and then remove the tool.

7 Intercooler – general information, removal and refitting

1 All engines feature air to liquid intercoolers, with the intercooler mounted either between the radiator and condenser, or below the radiator. A separate electrical coolant pump is fitted that circulates coolant (depending on demand) from the intercooler to the inlet manifold heat exchanger.

2 Removal and refitting of the intercooler, required the removal of tha radiator and is described in Chapter 3 Section 3.

3 The heat exchanger is part of the inlet manifold and is removed with the manifold. If the cooler leaks or is faulty the manifold must be replaced, as described in Chapter 4B Section 6.

8 Catalytic converter/ particulate filter – removal and refitting

⚠ *Warning: Allow ample time for the exhaust system to cool before starting work. In particular, note that the catalytic converter runs at very high temperatures. If there is any chance*

6.4 Disconnect the wiring plug

6.13 The boost pressure controller (circlip and mounting bolts)

8.1a Open the heat shield…

8.1b …and disconnect the DPF sensors

8.1c Unbolt the sensors…

that the system may still be hot, wear suitable gloves.

 Warning: DO NOT use fuel or engine oil additives – these may contain substances harmful to the catalytic converter/particulate filter.

 Warning: DO NOT continue to use the car if the engine burns (engine) oil to the extent of leaving a visible trail of blue smoke.

 Warning: Remember that the catalytic converter and particulate filter are FRAGILE – do not strike them with tools during servicing work, and take care handling it when removing it from the car for any reason.

Note: *This Section describes removal of the catalytic converter and the particulate filter. The converter and particulate filter are a single assembly, called an 'emissions control module' by VW.*

Note: *A set of 'Crow's foot' sockets will be required to remove the sensors.*

1 Remove the engine cover and then (where fitted) open the insulation cover on the cylinder head cover and disconnect the wiring plugs. Unclip the connectors from the bracket and remove the bracket **(see illustrations)**.
2 Release the wiring loom from the retaining clips and then remove the upper and lower exhaust gas temperature sensors **(see illustration)**. Note that the sensors can be left

8.1d …and then unbolt the bracket

in position and simply disconnected, however there is a distinct possibility of damaging the sensors as the emissions module is removed.
3 Repeat the procedure for the third and fourth temperature sensors. Note that not all vehicles have four temperature sensors.
4 Trace the wiring loom from the oxygen (lambda) sensors (or single sensor on some models), disconnect the wiring plug(s) and remove the sensors **(see illustrations)**.
5 Disconnect the wiring plug from the coolant reservoir, unclip the coolant hoses, unclip the reservoir and move it to the side.
6 Trace the differential pressure sensor hose up from the module and disconnect it. Release the pipe/hose from the brackets and remove it complete with the sensor. Note that the location of the sensor, varies.

8.2 The upper exhaust gas temperature sensor

7 Jack up and support the front of the vehicle (see *Jacking and vehicle support*). Remove the engine undershield.
8 Drain the coolant as described in Chapter 1B Section 33.
9 Remove the EGR cooler as described in Section 3. and then (where fitted) remove the coolant pipe from the top of the emissions module.
10 With reference to Chapter 10 Section 22, remove the front subframe.
11 Remove the front section of the exhaust system as described in Section 9
12 Slacken the turbocharger to emissions module clamp and then either remove it or push it onto the module **(see illustration)**.
13 The module must now be supported. VW list a special tool for this purpose (T10511).

8.4a The post catalytic converter O2 sensor wiring plug is hidden behind the undertray

8.4b Disconnect the wiring plug

8.12 Slacken the clamp

8.13 The hook for the factory support tool

8.14 Remove the clamp (upper bolt hidden)

19 Tighten the upper rear bolt (20 Nm) and then using a hex key turn the upper bolt inner sleeve (by the cylinder head) clockwise until it meets the emissions control module. Turn the sleeve a quarter turn further and then fit the main bolt. Tighten this bolt to 20 Nm and then turn it 90 degrees (stage 2) and then a further 45 degrees (stage 3).
20 Refit the rest of the components in the reverse order to removal.

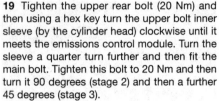
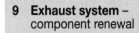

9 Exhaust system – component renewal

⚠️ *Warning: Allow ample time for the exhaust system to cool before starting work. In particular, note that the catalytic converter runs at very high temperatures. If there is any chance that the system may still be hot, wear suitable gloves.*

Removal

1 The original system fitted in the factory is in two sections. The front section includes the exhaust flap control (part of the emissions control system). The rear section, which connects to the front section under the centre of the vehicle has a silencer fitted. A flexible joint is fitted to the front section and the complete system is suspended on flexible (rubber) mountings.
2 To remove part of the system, first jack up the front or rear of the car and support it on axle stands (see *Jacking and vehicle support*). Alternatively, position the car over an inspection pit or on car ramps.

Front pipe

Caution: Handle the flexible, braided section of the front pipe carefully, and do not bend it excessively, if it is bent more than 10° it could get damaged.

3 Where fitted, remove the insulation sleeve from the exhaust control flap motor and disconnect the wiring plug **(see illustration)**.
4 Unbolt and remove the transmission tunnel cross member **(see illustration)**.
5 Remove the support bracket from the front cross member **(see illustration)**.

8.15a The upper mounting bolt

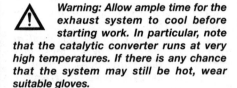

8.15b The lower mounting bolts (one shown, one hidden)

This is a bracket that bolts to the engine and supports the module using the hook fitted to the module **(see illustration)**. A similar home made tool can be fabricated. Alternatively support the module with an engine crane or support bar fitted between the strut towers.
14 Remove the large bracket from the EGR cooler outlet **(see illustration)**.
15 Remove the mounting bolts and swing the engine (with the aid of an assistant) so that the bottom of the module moves away from the engine block. Unhook the module form the support and lower it carefully from the engine **(see illustrations)**.

Refitting

Note: *To ensure that the module is fitted free of stresses, the module is mounted on special self adjusting bolts. As the main bolt is tightened*

the inner sleeve (with a left-hand thread) rises up to meet the under side of the module. These must be reset (by winding the outer sleeve fully in) before installing the module.
16 Reset the self-adjusting bolts by screwing in the outer sleeve. Fit a new gasket and slide the clamp onto the intake of the module.
17 Lift up the module from below and hang it from the support bracket. Install the clamp and tighten the clamp so that the module is in position, but is free to rotate around the clamp. Fit the lower self adjusting bolt and tighten it by hand and then back it off by a quarter turn.
18 Fully tighten the clamp (8 Nm) and then tighten the lower bolt (20 Nm). Fit the upper rear bolt (below the clamp) but do not tighten it. Insert the two end bolts and tighten them (20 Nm).

9.3 Disconnect the wiring plug

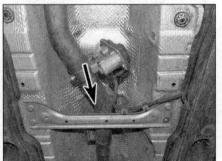

9.4 Remove the crossmember

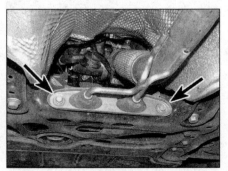

9.5 Remove the front exhaust support bracket

6 Slacken the exhaust sleeve clamp and slide it along the exhaust pipe **(see illustration)**. Remove the front exhaust pipe.

7 Mark the position of the clamp and then remove the clamp from the emissions control module. Lower the front exhaust pipe and recover the gasket **(see illustrations)**. Remove the pipe from the vehicle.

Rear pipe and silencer

8 Unbolt and remove the rear transmission tunnel cross member **(see illustration)**.

9 Slacken the sleeve clamp and slide it along the exhaust pipe **(see illustration 9.6)**.

10 Release the silencer from the rubber mountings. Use an exhaust mounting tool or unbolt the hangers from the body.

11 Lower the system and remove it.

Refitting

12 Each section is refitted by a reversal of the removal sequence, noting the following points:

a) *Ensure that all traces of corrosion have been removed from the flanges or pipe ends, and renew all necessary gaskets.*

b) *Align the exhaust so that the system hangs directly below the flexible mountings.*

c) *Fit a new clamp and gasket.*

d) *The new gasket must fit into the slot in the particulate filter.*

e) *The bolt of the clamp must sit directly above the cut out in the particulate filter. A 30 degree tolerance is acceptable.*

f) *The sleeve clamp should be installed with the bolts facing up and at an angle of 30 degrees below the horizontal.*

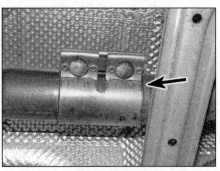

9.6 Slide the sleeve back, so that the joint is exposed

9.7a Remove the clamp. Note the paint marks

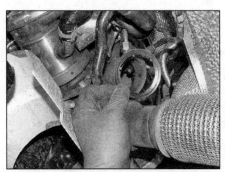

9.7b Recover the gasket

9.8 Remove the rear crossmember

g) *The design of the clamps used between the exhaust sections means that they play a greater role in ensuring a gas-tight seal – fit new clamps if they are in less than perfect condition.*

h) *Inspect the mountings for signs of damage or deterioration, and renew as necessary.*

i) *If using exhaust assembly paste, make sure this is only applied to joints downstream of the catalyst.*

Notes

Chapter 5 Part A
Starting and charging systems

Contents

Section number

Alternator – brush holder/regulator module renewal 6
Alternator – removal and refitting 5
Alternator/charging system – testing in vehicle 4
Battery – disconnecting, reconnecting, removal and refitting 3
Battery – testing and charging 2

Section number

General information and precautions 1
Starter motor – removal and refitting 8
Starter motor – testing and overhaul 9
Starting system – testing 7

Degrees of difficulty

Easy, suitable for novice with little experience	**Fairly easy,** suitable for beginner with some experience	**Fairly difficult,** suitable for competent DIY mechanic	**Difficult,** suitable for experienced DIY mechanic	**Very difficult,** suitable for expert DIY or professional

Specifications

Torque wrench settings	Nm	lbf ft
Alternator main lead nut	20	15
Alternator mounting bolts	24	18
Alternator mounting bracket:		
Petrol engines*	45	33
Stage 1	20	15
Stage 2	Angle-tighten a further 90°	
Diesel engines*		
Stage 1 (upper 2 bolts)	40	30
Stage 2	Angle-tighten a further 180°	
Stage 1 (lower 4 bolts)	40	30
Stage 2	Angle-tighten a further 45°	
Battery clamping plate bolt	22	16
Starter motor lead nut	20	15
Starter mounting bolts:		
Short bolt models	40	30
Long bolt models	80	60

*Use new nut/bolts

1 General information and precautions

General information

1 The engine electrical system consists of the charging and starting systems. Because of their engine-related functions, these are covered separately from the body electrical devices such as the lights, instruments, etc (which are covered in Chapter 12). On petrol engine models refer to Chapter 5B for information on the ignition system, and on diesel models refer to Chapter 5C for the preheating system.

2 The electrical system is of the 12 volt negative earth type.

3 The battery is a maintenance-free (sealed for life) type and is charged by the alternator, which is belt-driven from the crankshaft pulley.

4 The starter motor is of the pre-engaged type, with an integral solenoid. On starting, the solenoid moves the drive pinion into engagement with the flywheel ring gear before the starter motor is energised. Once the engine has started, a one-way clutch prevents the motor armature being driven by the engine until the pinion disengages from the flywheel.

5 Further details of the various systems are given in the relevant Sections of this Chapter. While some repair procedures are given, the usual course of action is to renew the component concerned.

Precautions

⚠️ *Warning: It is necessary to take extra care when working on the electrical system to avoid damage to semi-conductor devices (diodes and transistors), and to avoid the risk of personal injury. In addition to the precautions given in 'Safety first!', observe the following when working on the system:*

⚠️ *Warning: Always remove rings, watches, etc, before working on the electrical system. Even with the battery disconnected, capacitive discharge could occur if a component's live terminal is earthed*

through a metal object. This could cause a shock or nasty burn.

 Warning: Do not reverse the battery connections. Components such as the alternator, electronic control units, or any other components having semi-conductor circuitry could be irreparably damaged.

 Warning: Never disconnect the battery terminals, the alternator, any electrical wiring or any test instruments when the engine is running.

 Warning: Do not allow the engine to turn the alternator when the alternator is not connected.

⚠️ *Warning: Never test for alternator output by flashing the output lead to earth.*

⚠️ *Warning: Always ensure that the battery is disconnected when working on the electrical system.*

⚠️ *Warning: If the engine is being started using jump leads and a slave battery, connect the batteries positive-to-positive and negative-to-negative (see Jump starting at the beginning of the manual). This also applies when connecting a battery charger.*

⚠️ *Warning: Before using electric-arc welding equipment on the car, disconnect the battery, alternator and components such as the electronic control units (where applicable) to protect them from the risk of damage.*

2 Battery – testing and charging

Testing

1 All original equipment batteries are sealed for life maintenance-free batteries. These may be one of three types:

● Standard lead acid. Sealed for life with a visual charge indicator fitted.

● Absorbent Glass Mat (AGM) Lead acid battery with the electrolyte absorbed in a glass matrix. No visual indicator fitted.

● Enhanced Flooded Battery (EFB). Visual indicator fitted. Used on some stop-start models.

2 Topping-up and testing of the electrolyte in each cell is not possible. The condition of the battery can therefore only be tested using a battery condition indicator or a voltmeter.

3 All models (except those with AGM batteries) are fitted with a maintenance-free battery with a built-in charge condition indicator. The indicator is located in the top of the battery casing, and indicates the condition of the battery from its colour. If the indicator shows green, then the battery is in a good state of charge. If the indicator turns darker, eventually to black, then the battery requires charging, as described later in this Section. If the indicator shows clear/yellow, then the electrolyte level in the battery is too low to allow further use, and the battery should be renewed. Do not attempt to charge, load or jump-start a battery when the indicator shows clear/yellow.

Note: *From 2009 Volkswagen introduced batteries that only have a two colour visual indicator. If the indicator shows black there is sufficient electrolyte in the cell, if the indicator shows light yellow the electrolyte level is low and the battery must be replaced. Note that the indicator is only a guide to the electrolyte level on one cell and is not a guide to the state of charge.*

4 If testing the battery using a voltmeter, connect the voltmeter across the battery and note the voltage **(see illustration)**. The test is only accurate if the battery has not been subjected to any kind of charge for the previous six hours. If this is not the case, switch on the headlights for 30 seconds, then wait four to five minutes before testing the battery after switching off the headlights. All other electrical circuits must be switched off, so check that the doors and tailgate are fully shut when making the test.

5 If the voltage reading is less than 12.2 volts, then the battery is discharged, whilst a reading of 12.2 to 12.4 volts indicates a partially discharged condition. The battery should be recharged as described later in this Section.

6 The preferable method of testing the battery is to use a digital battery analyser. Most garages (and battery supply specialists) will have one. These machines are capable of assessing the condition and performance of the battery without removing it from the vehicle or disconnecting the battery terminals. Note also that many modern battery chargers will also have some ability to test the battery **(see illustration)**.

Charging

Note: *The following is intended as a guide only. Always refer to the manufacturer's recommendations (often printed on a label attached to the battery) before charging a battery.*

7 If the battery is to be recharged, we recommend that you use an 'intelligent' charger. Where an AGM or EFB battery is fitted it is essential that the charger is specifically capable

2.4 Checking the battery voltage

2.6 Modern battery chargers can often test battery capacity

3.2 Open the cover

3.3a Unbolt and then...

3.3b ...disconnect the battery negative terminal

of charging these types of battery. Whilst some chargers are capable of safely charging the battery with the battery connected to the vehicle, if you are unsure, always disconnect the battery. If the battery is disconnected (e.g. if it is to be removed and recharged on the bench), note that certain 'learned' values will be lost from the engine management ECU memory, requiring the car to be driven over a short distance after refitting the battery. Also, when the battery is reconnected, the warning lights for the ESP and electro-mechanical steering will light up and stay on. They will extinguish if you drive briefly in a straight line at a speed of 9 to 13 mph.

3 Battery – disconnecting, reconnecting, removal and refitting

Disconnecting the battery

⚠️ **Warning: There are two methods of battery disconnection: If working on the airbag system then the battery must be disconnected and reconnected with the ignition ON. When working on all other systems the battery must be disconnected and connected with the ignition OFF.**

1 Lower the drivers window and remove the key from the ignition. Note the warning above!
2 The battery is located on the left-hand side of the engine compartment. Open the cover to gain access to the battery **(see illustration)**.
3 Loosen the clamp nut and disconnect the battery negative lead (-) **(see illustrations)**.

4 Move the negative (earth) lead away from the terminal. Cover the lead (or battery terminal) with a suitable insulator (a plastic bag is ideal) or simply secure it to the side with a cable tie.

Reconnecting the battery

5 Reconnect the negative lead. Push it down until it is flush with the battery terminal post and then tighten the nut to the specified torque.
6 Refit the battery cover and close the bonnet.
7 Reach through the open drivers window and turn on the sidelights. Wait a minute or so to allow the on board computer systems to boot up and for the battery voltage to stabilise.
8 Start the vehicle (from outside where possible) and then open and close all the power windows. Adjust the clock time and

re-activate the audio unit by inserting the security code (where applicable).
9 To restore the electric window automatic opening/closing function (where fitted) ensure all windows and doors are closed, and then lock the vehicle via the driver's door. Now unlock the driver's door, and then lock it again – hold the key in the locking position for at least one second.
10 After reconnecting the battery and starting the vehicle the ESP (Electronic Stability Programme) the TCS (Traction Control System) and the power steering warning light will remain on until the vehicle is driven in a straight line at a speed of 10 mph or more.

Removal

11 Disconnect the battery negative cable as described above and then disconnect the battery positive cable **(see illustration)**.
12 Remove the cover and then unscrew the retaining clamp bolt. Lift the battery from the engine compartment **(see illustrations)**.

3.11 Unbolt and disconnect the positive lead

3.12a Remove the surround

3.12b Remove the retaining clamp bolt...

3.12c ...and remove the clamp

3.12d Lift out the battery

3.13a Remove the bolts...

3.13b ...and lift out the support tray

13 If necessary the battery tray can now be removed. Remove the air filter housing as described in Chapter 4A Section 3 (petrol engines) or Chapter 4B Section 3 (diesel engines). Unbolt and remove the battery tray **(see illustrations)**.

Refitting

14 Refit the battery by following the removal procedure in reverse.

4 Alternator/charging system – testing in vehicle

Note: *Refer to Section 1 of this Chapter before starting work.*

1 If the charge warning light fails to illuminate when the ignition is switched on, first check the alternator wiring connections for security. If the light still fails to illuminate, check the continuity of the warning light feed wire from the alternator to the bulbholder. If all is satisfactory, the alternator is at fault and should be renewed or taken to an auto-electrician for testing and repair.

2 Similarly, if the charge warning light comes on with the ignition, but is then slow to go out when the engine is started, this may indicate an impending alternator problem. Check all the items listed in the preceding paragraph, and refer to an auto-electrical specialist if no obvious faults are found.

3 If the charge warning light illuminates when the engine is running, stop the engine and check that the auxiliary drivebelt is not broken (see Chapter 1A Section 11 or Chapter 1B Section 11) and that the alternator connections are secure. If all is so far satisfactory, check the alternator brushes and slip-rings as described in Section 6. If the fault persists, the alternator should be renewed, or taken to an auto-electrician for testing and repair.

4 If the alternator output is suspect even though the warning light functions correctly, the regulated voltage may be checked as follows.

5 Connect a voltmeter across the battery terminals **(see illustration)**, and start the engine.

6 Increase the engine speed until the voltmeter reading remains steady; the reading should be approximately 12 to 14 volts, and no more than 15 volts.

7 Switch on as many electrical accessories (eg, the headlights, heated rear window and heater blower) as possible, and check that the alternator maintains the regulated voltage at around 13 to 14.9 volts **(see illustration)**. Note that variations are to be expected due to the specifications of the multimeter used.

8 If the regulated voltage is not as stated, this may be due to worn brushes, weak brush springs, a faulty voltage regulator, a faulty diode, a severed phase winding or worn or damaged slip-rings. The brushes and slip-rings may be checked, but if the fault persists, the alternator should be renewed or taken to an auto-electrician.

5 Alternator – removal and refitting

Removal

1 Disconnect the battery negative lead and position it away from the terminal as described in Section 3.

2 Where fitted, remove the engine cover from the top of the engine **(see illustration)**.

3 Remove the auxiliary drivebelt from the alternator pulley as described in Chapter 1A Section 30 (petrol engines) or Chapter 1B Section 30 (diesel engines). Mark the drivebelt for direction to ensure it is refitted in the same position.

1.2 and 1.4 petrol models and all diesel models

4 If not already done so, jack up and support the front of the vehicle (see *Jacking and vehicle support*). Remove the right-hand wheel and then remove the right-hand wing liner.

5 Unbolt and remove the auxiliary belt tensioner **(see illustration)**.

6 Disconnect the wiring plug from the AC compressor and then unbolt the compressor from the mounting bracket. DO NOT disconnect the refrigerant lines. Secure the compressor to the side with cable ties or similar.

7 Remove the alternator mounting bolts. Work the alternator free from the bracket, rotate the alternator to gain access to the wiring plug.

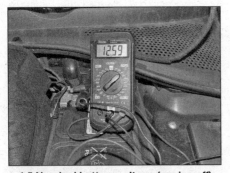

4.5 Nominal battery voltage (engine off)

4.7 The full load output of the alternator (14.79 volts)

5.2 Remove the engine cover – diesel model shown

5.5 Remove the tensioner

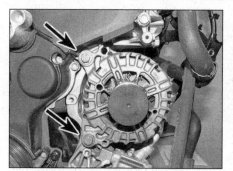

5.7a The alternator mounting bolts

5.7b Pull the alternator from the mounting

5.7c Remove the cap (to access the main cable nut), the cable clip and the control wire plug

Unbolt the main cable and then disconnect the control wire plug **(see illustrations)**.

2.0 litre petrol engines

8 If not already done so, jack up and support the front of the vehicle (see Jacking and support 13). Remove the right-hand wheel, the right-hand wing liner and the engine undershield.

9 Remove the radiator fan and cowl as described in Chapter 3 Section 5.

10 Remove the upper air inlet hose. Disconnect the boost pressure sensor wiring plug, move the coolant hose to the side and remove the boost pressure charge hose.

11 Disconnect the wiring plug from the AC compressor and then unbolt the compressor from the mounting bracket. DO NOT disconnect the refrigerant lines. Secure the compressor to the side with cable ties or similar.

12 Remove the upper and lower alternator mounting bolts, lower the alternator to gain access to the wiring plug and main cable.

13 Remove the cover from the main cable and then unbolt the cable, Disconnect the wiring plug from the control wire.

14 Remove the alternator downwards to remove.

Refitting

15 Refitting is a reversal of removal. Refer to Chapter 1A Section 30 (petrol engines) or Chapter 1B Section 30 (diesel engines) as applicable for details of refitting and tensioning the auxiliary drivebelt. Tighten the alternator mounting bolts to the specified torque.

6 Alternator – brush holder/ regulator module renewal

Removal

1 Remove the alternator, as described in Section 5.

2 Place the alternator on a clean work surface, with the pulley facing down.

Bosch

3 Undo the screw and the two retaining nuts,

and lift away the outer plastic cover **(see illustration)**.

4 Unscrew the three securing screws, and remove the voltage regulator **(see illustrations)**.

6.3 On the Bosch type, remove the outer cover...

6.4b ...and remove the brush holder/ regulator

6.6a ...undo the two screws and single nut...

Valeo

5 Prise off the spring clips, and remove the outer plastic cover **(see illustration)**.

6 Undo the two screws and single nut, and remove the voltage regulator **(see illustrations)**.

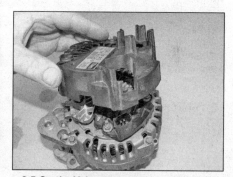

6.4a ...undo the screws...

6.5 On the Valeo type, remove the outer plastic cover...

6.6b ...and remove the voltage regulator

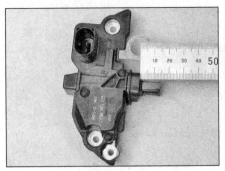

6.8 Measure the brush length

7 Slide off the brush cover by depressing the lugs on each side.

Inspection

8 Measure the free length of the brush contacts **(see illustration)**. Check the measurement with the Specifications; renew the module if the brushes are worn below the minimum limit.
9 Clean and inspect the surfaces of the slip-rings **(see illustration)**, at the end of the alternator shaft. If they are excessively worn, or damaged, the alternator must be renewed.

Refitting

Bosch

10 Refit the voltage regulator using a reversal of the removal procedure, tightening the screws securely. On completion, refer to Section 5 and refit the alternator.

Valeo

11 Depress the carbon brushes into the housing, then refit the voltage regulator and tighten the screws and nut securely. Slide on the brush cover until it is heard to engage. On completion, refer to Section 5 and refit the alternator.

---

7 Starting system – testing

Note: *Refer to Section 1 of this Chapter before starting work.*
1 If the starter motor fails to operate when

6.9 Clean and inspect the surfaces of the slip-rings

the ignition key is turned to the appropriate position, the following possible causes may be to blame:
a) *The battery is faulty.*
b) *The electrical connections between the switch, solenoid, battery and starter motor are somewhere failing to pass the necessary current from the battery through the starter to earth.*
c) *The solenoid is faulty.*
d) *The starter motor is mechanically or electrically defective.*
2 To check the battery, switch on the headlights. If they dim after a few seconds, this indicates that the battery is discharged – recharge (see Section 2) or renew the battery. If the headlights glow brightly, operate the ignition switch and observe the lights. If they dim, then this indicates that current is reaching the starter motor, therefore the fault must lie in the starter motor. If the lights continue to glow brightly (and no clicking sound can be heard from the starter motor solenoid), this indicates that there is a fault in the circuit or solenoid – see following paragraphs. If the starter motor turns slowly when operated, but the battery is in good condition, then this indicates that either the starter motor is faulty, or there is considerable resistance somewhere in the circuit.
3 If a fault in the circuit is suspected, disconnect the battery leads (including the earth connection to the body), the starter/solenoid wiring and the engine/transmission earth strap. Thoroughly clean the connections, and reconnect the leads and wiring, then use a voltmeter or test light to check that full battery voltage is available at the

battery positive lead connection to the solenoid, and that the earth is sound.
4 If the battery and all connections are in good condition, check the circuit by disconnecting the wire from the solenoid blade terminal. Connect a voltmeter or test light between the wire end and a good earth (such as the battery negative terminal), and check that the wire is live when the ignition switch is turned to the start position. If it is, then the circuit is sound – if not the circuit wiring can be checked as described in Chapter 12 Section 2.
5 The solenoid contacts can be checked by connecting a voltmeter or test light between the battery positive feed connection on the starter side of the solenoid, and earth. When the ignition switch is turned to the start position, there should be a reading or lighted bulb, as applicable. If there is no reading or lighted bulb, the solenoid is faulty and should be renewed.
6 If the circuit and solenoid are proved sound, the fault must lie in the starter motor. It may be possible to have the starter motor overhauled by a specialist, but check on the availability and cost of spares before proceeding, as it may prove more economical to obtain a new or exchange motor.

---

8 Starter motor – removal and refitting

Removal

1 Disconnect the battery negative lead – see Section 3.
2 Apply the handbrake, then jack up the front of the vehicle and support it on axle stands (see *Jacking and vehicle support*). Remove the engine undertray.
3 Where fitted remove the engine cover from the top of the engine **(see illustration 5.2)**.
4 Where required, remove the air filter housing as described in Chapter 4A Section 3 (petrol engines) or Chapter 4B Section 3 (diesel engines).
5 Disconnect the wiring plug from the solenoid. Remove the protective cover and then unscrew the nut and disconnect the battery positive lead from the starter motor **(see illustrations)**.

8.5a Release the locking tab…

8.5b …and disconnect the solenoid wiring plug

8.5c Remove the cover…

8.5d ...and then unbolt...

8.5e ...and remove the main supply cable from the starter motor

6 Unscrew the nut and disconnect the earth cable **(see illustration)**.

7 On some versions the lower bolt is best removed from below. On most versions the lower bolt can be removed from above **(see illustration)**.

8 Unscrew the upper mounting bolt noting and then guide the starter motor out of the bellhousing aperture. Depending on the engine fitted the starter motor can either be removed upwards or where easier downwards **(see illustrations)**.

Refitting

9 Refit the starter motor by following the removal procedure in reverse. Tighten the mounting bolts to the specified torque.

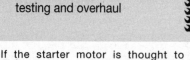

9 Starter motor –
testing and overhaul

1 If the starter motor is thought to be defective, it should be removed from the vehicle and taken to an auto-electrician for assessment. In the majority of cases, new starter motor brushes can be fitted at a reasonable cost. However, check the cost of repairs first as it may prove more economical to purchase a new or exchange motor.

8.6 Unbolt the earth cable

8.7 Removing the lower bolt from above

8.8a Unscrew the upper mounting bolt...

8.8b ...then guide the starter motor out of the bellhousing

Notes

Chapter 5 Part B
Ignition system – petrol engines

Contents

Section number

General Information 1
HT coil(s) – removal and refitting 3

Section number

Ignition system – testing. 2
Ignition timing – checking and adjusting 4

Degrees of difficulty

Easy, suitable for novice with little experience	**Fairly easy,** suitable for beginner with some experience	**Fairly difficult,** suitable for competent DIY mechanic	**Difficult,** suitable for experienced DIY mechanic	**Very difficult,** suitable for expert DIY or professional

Specifications

System type

1.2 litre engines	Bosch motronic ME17.5.21
1.4 litre engines:	
Engine codes CHPA, CHPB, CMBA, CPTA, CXSA, CZDA, CZDD and CZEA.	Bosch motronic ME17
Engine code CZCA.	Bosch motronic ME17.5.21
2.0 litre engines:	
Engine codes CHHA and CHHB	Bosch Motronic MED 17.5
Engine codes CJXE and CXDA	N/A

Ignition coil

Type (all engines):	Coil over plug (COP). One coil per spark plug

Spark plugs

Spark plugs	*See Chapter 1A Section 1*

Torque wrench settings

	Nm	lbf ft
Ignition coil mounting bolts:		
1.2 and 1.4 litre engines	5	3
2.0 litre engines	10	7
Spark plugs:		
1.2 and 1.4 litre engines	22	16
2.0 litre engines	30	22

1 General Information

1 The Bosch systems are self-contained engine management systems, which control both the fuel injection and ignition. This Chapter deals with the ignition system components only – refer to Chapter 4A for details of the fuel system components.
2 The ignition systems fitted are of the 'distributorless' (DIS – Distributorless Ignition System) type. All engines have four separate coils, one fitted to each spark plug. This arrangement is often referred to as 'Coil over plug' (COP) ignition.
3 The ignition timing cannot be adjusted by conventional means, and the advance and retard functions are carried out by the Electronic Control Unit (ECU).
4 The ignition system consists of the spark plugs, the ignition coils, crankshaft position sensor, camshaft position sensor and the ECU together with its associated sensors and wiring. These are the primary inputs, but all the engine management components will influence the ignition timing.
5 The basic operation is the same for all models: the ECU supplies a voltage to the input stage of the ignition coil, which causes the primary windings in the coil to be energised. The supply voltage is periodically interrupted by the ECU and this results in the collapse of primary magnetic field, which then induces a much larger voltage in the secondary coil, called the HT voltage. This voltage is directed to the spark plug in

the cylinder currently on its ignition stroke. The spark plug electrodes form a gap small enough for the HT voltage to arc across, and the resulting spark ignites the fuel/air mixture in the cylinder. The timing of this sequence of events is critical, and is regulated solely by the ECU.
6 The ECU calculates and controls the ignition timing primarily according to engine speed, crankshaft position, camshaft position, and inlet airflow rate information, received from sensors mounted on and around the engine. Other parameters that affect ignition timing are throttle position and rate of opening, inlet air temperature, coolant temperature and engine knock, monitored by sensors mounted on the engine. Note that most of these sensors have a dual role, in that the information they provide is equally useful in determining the

fuelling requirements as well as deciding the optimum ignition or firing point – therefore, removal of some of the sensors mentioned below is described in Chapter 4A.

7 The ECU computes engine speed and crankshaft position from toothed impulse ring attached to the engine crankshaft, with an engine speed sensor whose inductive head runs just above ring. As the crankshaft rotates, the ring 'teeth' pass the engine speed sensor, which transmits a pulse to the ECU every time a tooth passes it. At the top dead centre (TDC) position, there is one missing tooth in the ring periphery, which results in a longer pause between signals from the sensor. The ECU recognises the absence of a pulse from the engine speed sensor at this point, and uses it to establish the TDC position for No 1 piston. The time interval between pulses, and the location of the missing pulse, allow the ECU to accurately determine the position of the crankshaft and its speed. The camshaft position sensor enhances this information by detecting whether a particular piston is on an inlet or an exhaust cycle.

8 Information on engine load is supplied to the ECU by the inlet manifold pressure sensor, and from the throttle position sensor. The engine load is determined by computation based on the quantity of air being drawn into the engine. Further engine load information is sent to the ECU from the knock sensor(s). These sensors are sensitive to vibration, and detect the knocking which occurs when the engine starts to 'pink' (pre-ignite). If pre-ignition occurs, the ECU retards the ignition timing of the cylinder that is pre-igniting in steps until the pre-ignition ceases. The ECU then advances the ignition timing of that cylinder in steps until it is restored to normal, or until pre-ignition occurs again.

9 Sensors monitoring coolant temperature, throttle position, camshaft position, roadspeed, and (where applicable) air conditioning system operation. From all this constantly changing data, the ECU selects, and if necessary modifies, a particular ignition advance setting from a map of ignition characteristics stored in its memory.

10 The ECU also uses the ignition timing

to finely adjust the engine idle speed, in response to signals from the air conditioning switch (to prevent stalling), or if the alternator output voltage falls too low.

11 In the event of a fault in the system due to loss of a signal from one of the sensors, the ECU reverts to an emergency ('limp-home') program. This will allow the car to be driven, although engine operation and performance will be limited. A warning light on the instrument panel will illuminate if the fault is likely to cause an increase in harmful exhaust emissions.

12 It should be noted that comprehensive fault diagnosis of all the engine management systems described in this Chapter is only possible with dedicated electronic test equipment. In the event of a sensor failing or other fault occurring, a fault code will be stored in the ECU's fault log, which can only be extracted from the ECU using a dedicated fault code reader. A Volkswagen dealer will obviously have such a reader, as will most garages. Low cost diagnostic tools are available in the aftermarket, but at the lower end of the market these may be limited to only displaying the mandatory emissions related fault codes **(see illustration)**. Once the fault has been identified, the removal/refitting sequences detailed in the following Sections will then allow the appropriate component(s) to be renewed as required.

2 Ignition system – testing

> ⚠️ **Warning: Extreme care must be taken when working on the system with the ignition switched on; it is possible to get a substantial electric shock from a vehicle's ignition system. Persons with cardiac pacemaker devices should keep well clear of the ignition circuits, components and test equipment. Always switch off the ignition before disconnecting or connecting any component and when using a multimeter to check resistances.**

1 If a fault appears in the engine management (fuel injection/ignition) system which is thought to ignition related, first ensure that the fault is not due to a poor electrical connection or poor maintenance; ie, check that the air cleaner filter element is clean, the spark plugs are in good condition, that the engine breather hoses are clear and undamaged, referring to Chapter 1A for further information. If the engine is running very roughly, check the compression pressures as described in Chapter 2A Section 2 (1.2 and 1.4 litre engines) or Chapter 2B Section 3 (2.0 litre engines).

2 If these checks fail to reveal the cause of the problem, the vehicle should be taken to a Volkswagen dealer or well equipped garage for testing. A diagnostic connector is incorporated in the engine management circuit into which a special electronic diagnostic tester can be plugged **(see illustration 1.12)**. The tester will help a skilled technician locate the fault, alleviating the need to test all the system components individually which is a time consuming operation. However it is important to note that because a fault for the camshaft position sensor is logged (as an example) it does not necessarily mean that the sensor is at fault. The wiring could be faulty or the ECU may not be responding to the output signal from the sensor. The wiring should be checked carefully and testing of the output signal of the sensor should be checked at the ECU wiring plug.

3 The only ignition system checks which can be carried out by the home mechanic are those described in Chapter 1A Section 29, relating to the spark plugs. If necessary, the system wiring and wiring connectors can be checked as described in Chapter 12 Section 2 ensuring that the ECU wiring connector(s) have first been disconnected.

3 HT coil(s) – removal and refitting

1 Removal of the ignition coils is covered in the spark plug renewal procedure in Chapter 1A Section 29, since the coils must be removed for access to the plugs **(see illustration)**.

4 Ignition timing – checking and adjusting

1 The ignition timing is under the control of the engine management system ECU and is not manually adjustable without access to dedicated electronic test equipment. A basic setting cannot be quoted because the ignition timing is constantly being altered to control engine idle speed (see Section 1 for details).

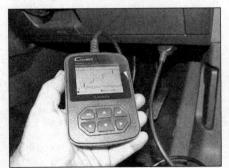

1.12 Checking for fault codes with a low cost code reader

3.1 Ignition coils on the 1.4 litre engine

Chapter 5 Part C
Preheating system

Contents

Section number

General Information 1
Glow plug control unit – removal and refitting 3

Section number

Glow plugs – testing, removal and refitting 2

Degrees of difficulty

Easy, suitable for novice with little experience	Fairly easy, suitable for beginner with some experience	Fairly difficult, suitable for competent DIY mechanic	Difficult, suitable for experienced DIY mechanic	Very difficult, suitable for expert DIY or professional

Specifications

Glow plugs
Electrical resistance .... 1.0 ohm
Current consumption (typical – no value quoted by VW)........... 8 amps (per plug)

Torque wrench setting	Nm	lbf ft
Glow plug to cylinder head	17	13
Glow plug (models with compression sensor glow plug on cylinder 3) .	12	9

1 General Information

1 To assist cold starting and to control emissions during the warm up phase, diesel engine models are fitted with a preheating system, which consists of four glow plugs, a glow plug control unit, a facia-mounted warning light and the associated electrical wiring. The glow plug control unit/relay located in the fusebox in the engine compartment (see Section 3).

2 The glow plugs are miniature electric heating elements, encapsulated in a metal case with a probe at one end and electrical connection at the other. Each inlet tract has a glow plug threaded into it, which is positioned directly in line with the incoming spray of fuel. When the glow plug is energised, the fuel passing over it is heated, allowing its optimum combustion temperature to be achieved more readily in the combustion chamber.

3 The duration of the preheating period is governed by the ECU, which monitors the temperature of the engine through the coolant temperature sensor and alters the preheating time to suit the conditions. Pre-heating only takes place at coolant temperature below 9°C.

4 A facia-mounted warning light informs the driver that preheating is taking place. The light extinguishes when sufficient preheating has taken place to allow the engine to be started, but power will still be supplied to the glow plugs for a further period until the engine is started. If no attempt is made to start the engine, the power supply to the glow plugs is switched off to prevent battery drain and glow plug burn-out. If the warning light flashes, or comes on during normal driving, this indicates a fault with the diesel engine management system, which should be investigated by a Volkswagen dealer or suitably equipped garage as soon as possible.

5 After the engine has been started, the glow plugs continue to operate for a further period of time. This helps to improve fuel combustion whilst the engine is warming-up, resulting in quieter, smoother running and reduced exhaust emissions. On models fitted with a DPF (Diesel Particulate Filter) the glow plugs are used to assist with filter cleaning when regeneration of the filter takes place.

6 Models that meet the EU6 emission standards have a special glow plug fitted to number 3 cylinder. The glow plug has the ability to calculate the cylinder combustion pressure. This information is used by the ECU to modify the fuel injection timing and fuel quantity.

2 Glow plugs – testing, removal and refitting

 Warning: A correctly functioning glow plug will become red-hot in a very short time. This should be in mind when removing the glow plugs, if they have recently been in use. If a glow plug is dropped, it may be damaged internally, which could result in ceramic fragments entering the engine causing extensive damage. Do not fit a glow plug that has been dropped.

Testing
Caution: DO NOT apply 12 volts to the glow plugs. The glow plugs are not designed to run on battery voltage.

1 A faulty glow plug should set a fault code. Check for any fault codes with a diagnostic tool. Where no suitable tool is available have the fault code memory checked by the dealer or a suitably equipped garage.

2 Where no diagnostic tool is available the glow plugs can be checked with a multimeter set to resistance (Ohms). A good quality meter capable of reading below 5 Ohms will be required.

3 Remove the engine cover and disconnect

2.8a Pull up the connector (note the correct gripping point)...

2.8b ...and remove it (note different connector on number 3 glow plug)

2.10a Remove the glow plugs

2.10b The special compression sensing glow plug (cylinder number 3)

the wiring connector from the glow plugs. Connect a suitable multimeter between the glow plug and a good earth.

4 Select the Ohms range on the multimeter and check each plug in turn. Each plug should have a resistance of 5 Ohms or less. Replace any plugs that have a higher resistance or ore open circuit.

5 If a suitable ammeter is available, connect it between the glow plug and its wiring connector, and measure the steady-state current consumption (ignore the initial current surge, which will be about 50% higher). As a guide, high current consumption (or no current draw at all) indicates a faulty glow plug.

6 As a final check, remove the glow plugs and

inspect them visually, as described below. A badly burned or charred stem may be an indication of a faulty fuel injector.

Removal

Note: *Refer to the Warning at the start of this Section before proceeding.*

7 Remove the engine cover.

Note: *The glow plugs tend to be easier to remove from a warm engine. Snapping a glow plug whilst removing it will likely lead to the need to remove the cylinder head.*

8 Disconnect the wiring plugs from the injectors. A small lip is visible at the top of the injector wiring plug. Grasp the connector close to this lip to remove the wiring plug. DO NOT grab the base of the connector or it will be damaged **(see illustrations)**. Note that VW list a special pair of pliers (VAG tool 3314) that are designed to fit into the grasp lip to release the wiring plug.

9 Clean the area around the glow plugs; use a vacuum cleaner if possible. Spray brake cleaner (or similar) around the glow plug opening, letting it penetrate briefly, and then blow out with compressed air.

Caution: Always wear protective goggles to protect your eyes, when using compressed air.

10 Using a universal joint, extension and a deep 10mm socket (12mm for the number three cylinder where a compression sensing plug is fitted), unscrew and remove the glow plug(s) from the cylinder head **(see illustrations)**. Note that the plug must be kept 'straight' when being removed, as it can be easily damaged.

Refitting

11 Refitting is a reversal of removal, but tighten the glow plugs to the specified torque.

3 Glow plug control unit – removal and refitting

Removal

1 The glow plug control unit is located in the engine compartment fusebox **(see illustration)**.

2 Remove the cover and pull out the controller **(see illustration)**.

Refitting

3 Refitting is a reversal of removal.

3.1 Glow plug control unit location

3.2 Pull out the control unit

Chapter 6 Part A
Clutch – manual transmission

Contents

Section number

Clutch friction disc and pressure plate – removal, inspection and
   refitting 5
Clutch pedal and master cylinder – removal and refitting 3
General Information 1

Section number

Hydraulic system – bleeding 2
Release bearing and lever – removal, inspection and refitting...... 6
Slave cylinder – removal and refitting........................ 4

Degrees of difficulty

Easy, suitable for novice with little experience	Fairly easy, suitable for beginner with some experience	Fairly difficult, suitable for competent DIY mechanic	Difficult, suitable for experienced DIY mechanic	Very difficult, suitable for expert DIY or professional

Specifications

General

Type:
Luk clutch..	Single dry friction disc, diaphragm spring with spring-loaded hub, self-adjusting pressure plate (SAC)
Sachs clutch...	Single dry friction disc, diaphragm spring with spring-loaded hub
Clutch operation......................................	Hydraulic with master and slave cylinders

Torque wrench settings

	Nm	lbf ft
Clutch pedal crash bar bolt	20	15
Clutch pedal mounting bracket nuts*.....................	25	18
Clutch pressure plate-to-flywheel bolts*:		
M7 bolt	20	15
M6 bolt	13	10
Clutch release bearing guide sleeve bolts		
(transmissions with an external slave cylinder only)*:		
Stage 1	5	4
Stage 2	Angle-tighten a further 90°	
Concentric release bearing bolts*:		
Metal housing, with locking fluid	12	9
Plastic housing, with locking fluid	15	11
Clutch slave cylinder bolts.............................	20	15

*Use new bolts/nuts

1 General Information

1 The clutch is of single dry plate type, incorporating a diaphragm spring pressure plate, and is hydraulically operated.

2 The pressure plate is bolted to the rear face of the flywheel, and the friction disc is located between the pressure plate and the flywheel friction surface. The friction disc hub is splined to the transmission input shaft and is free to slide along the splines. Friction lining material is riveted to each side of the disc, and the disc hub incorporates cushioning springs to absorb transmission shocks and ensure a smooth take-up of drive.

3 On all transmissions except 02Q (6 speed transmission), when the clutch pedal is depressed, the slave cylinder pushrod moves the release lever forwards. On 02Q transmissions, the slave cylinder is fitted concentrically around the transmission input shaft within the bellhousing. The release bearing is forced onto the pressure plate diaphragm spring fingers. As the centre of the diaphragm spring is pushed in, the outer part of the spring moves out and releases the pressure plate from the friction disc. Drive then ceases to be transmitted to the transmission.

4 When the clutch pedal is released, the diaphragm spring forces the pressure plate into contact with the linings on the friction disc, and at the same time pushes the disc slightly forward along the input shaft splines into engagement with the flywheel. The friction disc is now firmly sandwiched between the pressure plate and flywheel. This causes drive to be taken up.

5 As the linings wear on the friction disc, the pressure plate rest position moves closer to the flywheel resulting in the 'rest' position of the diaphragm spring fingers being raised. The hydraulic system requires no adjustment since the quantity of hydraulic fluid in the circuit automatically compensates for wear every time the clutch pedal is operated.

2 Hydraulic system – bleeding

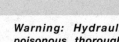

⚠️ *Warning: Hydraulic fluid is poisonous, thoroughly wash off spills from bare skin without delay. Seek immediate medical advice if any fluid is swallowed or gets into the eyes. Certain types of hydraulic fluid are inflammable and may ignite when brought into contact with hot components. Hydraulic fluid is also an effective paint stripper. If spillage occurs onto painted bodywork or fittings, it should be washed off immediately, using copious quantities of cold water. It is also hygroscopic (i.e. it can absorb moisture from the air) which then renders it useless. Old fluid may have suffered contamination, and should never be re-used.*

1 If any part of the hydraulic system is dismantled, or if air has accidentally entered the system, the system will need to be bled. The presence of air is characterised by the pedal having a spongy feel and it results in difficulty in changing gear.

2 On 02Q transmissions (fitted with a concentric clutch slave cylinder) the design of the clutch hydraulic system makes bleeding using the conventional method of pumping the clutch pedal hard to achieve. In order to remove all air present in the system, the best approach is to use pressure bleeding equipment. This is available from auto accessory shops at relatively low cost. An alternative method is to reverse bleed the clutch by pushing fluid back towards the master cylinder using a large syringe filled with brake/clutch fluid. Conventional bleeding is possible on models fitted with an external slave cylinder (see illustration).

3 When pressure bleeding equipment is used, should be connected to the brake/clutch hydraulic fluid reservoir in accordance with the manufacturer's instructions. The system is bled through the bleed screw of the clutch slave cylinder (all transmissions except 02Q), which is located on the top of the transmission housing. On 02Q transmissions, the slave cylinder bleed screw is located at the front of the transmission, above the starter motor (see illustrations) and can be accessed by removing the air filter housing as described in Chapter 4A Section 3 or Chapter 4B Section 3

4 Bleed the system until the fluid being ejected is free from air bubbles. Close the bleed screw, then disconnect and remove the bleeding equipment.

5 Check the operation of the clutch to see that it is satisfactory. If air still remains in the system, repeat the bleeding operation.

6 Discard any fluid that is bled from the system, even if it looks clean. Hydraulic fluid absorbs water and its re-use can cause internal corrosion of the master and slave cylinders, leading to excessive wear and failure of the seals.

3 Clutch pedal and master cylinder – removal and refitting

Removal

Note: *The complete pedal assembly and clutch master cylinder are removed as a single item.*

1 Move the driver's seat fully to the rear, and adjust the steering column to its highest position.

2 Disconnect the battery negative lead and position it away from the terminal – see Chapter 5A Section 3.

3 Remove the driver's side lower facia trim panel and knee airbag as described in Chapter 12 Section 24. Remove the footwell air distribution duct and then unbolt and remove the pedal crash bar.

4 Anticipate the loss of some brake/clutch fluid and cover the area below the brake and clutch master cylinders with shop towels.

5 Working under the bonnet (and where fitted) remove the insulated cover from the clutch master cylinder and then disconnect the clutch fluid supply hose from the clutch master cylinder. Alternatively the hose can be clamped with a hose clamp, but note that it will deform, but can be manipulated back into shape after the clamp is removed.

6 Pull out the circlip and disconnect the

2.2 Preparing to bleed the clutch on 02S transmissions

2.3a Clutch slave cylinder bleed screw – 02S transmissions

2.3b Clutch bleed screw – 02Q transmissions

clutch outlet hose. Seal all the openings with suitable plugs.

7 Disconnect the wiring plug from the clutch pedal position switch.

8 Anticipate the loss of some brake/clutch fluid and cover the area below the clutch pedal with shop towels.

9 Undo the mounting nuts **(see illustration)** and remove the pedal assembly.

10 Remove the clutch position sensor by unclipping it. Note that when the sensor is refitted it must fit with and audible click.

11 Working at each side of the clutch pedal, release and push out the retaining clips to disengage the master cylinder and push rod from the pedal. Remove the master cylinder.

12 If required the clutch pedal can also be removed by firstly unhooking the over centre and return springs. Using a 14mm hex socket, remove the pivot pin and lift out the pedal. Note that the pivot pin will be destroyed and must be replaced.

Refitting

13 Refitting is a reversal of removal, bearing in mind the following points:
a) The master cylinder pivot pins must be replaced if removed.
b) If the pedal was removed the main pivot pin must be replaced.
c) If a new clutch position switch is fitted, it must be configured (adapted) to the vehicle using diagnostic equipment.
d) Tighten all fixings to the specified torque, where given.
e) Bleed the clutch as described in Section 2.
f) On completion, check the brake/clutch fluid level, and top-up if necessary.
g)

4 Slave cylinder – removal and refitting

Removal

Note: No spare parts are available from Vokswagon for the slave cylinder. If the slave cylinder is faulty or worn, the complete assembly must be renewed.

Transmissions with an external slave cylinder

1 The slave cylinder is located on the top of the transmission casing **(see illustration)**.

2 Remove the air filter housing, as described in Chapter Section (petrol engines) or Chapter 4B Section 3 (diesel engines).

3 Remove the the battery and battery tray with reference to Chapter 5A Section 3.

4 Disconnect the gear selector cables from the gear selector levers, as described in Chapter 7A Section 2.

5 Prise out the retaining clips and remove the outer cables from the mounting bracket, then unbolt the mounting bracket from the top of the transmission.

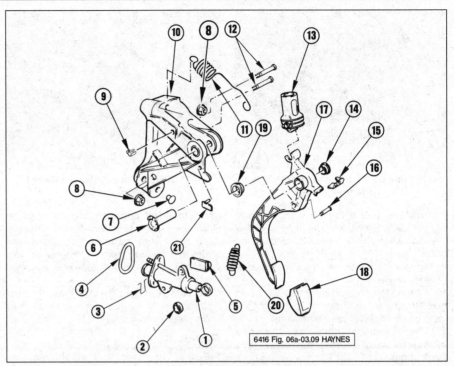

3.9 Clutch pedal assembly

1 Clutch mastercylinder
2 Bush
3 Clip
4 Seal (self- adhesive)
5 Position sensor
6 Pivot pin (must be replaced after removal)
7 Bump stop
8 Mounting nut (X3)
9 Ball socket
10 Mounting bracket
11 Return spring
12 Pivot for master cylinder (must be replaced after removal)
13 Over centre spring
14 Bush
15 Slide bush (some versions only)
16 Pivot for master cylinder plunger (must be replaced after removal)
17 Clutch pedal
18 Pedal rubber
19 Bush
20 Spring
21 Damper

Caution: Refer to the warning at the beginning of Section 2 regarding the hazards of working with hydraulic fluid.

6 Place shop towels beneath the fluid line connection on the slave cylinder to catch escaping fluid.

7 Release the fluid pipe retaining clip from the union on the slave cylinder, then pull the pipe from the union. Position the fluid pipe clear of the slave cylinder, and plug the end. Be prepared for some fluid spillage.

8 Unscrew the two bolts securing the slave cylinder to the transmission casing, and withdraw the slave cylinder from the transmission **(see illustration)**.

Transmissions with an internal slave cylinder/release bearing

Note: The slave cylinder and release bearing are a single item, often referred to as a concentric slave cylinder (CSC).

Note: As the transmission must be removed to access the bearing, always check the clutch friction material, the clutch cover and the condition of the flywheel. This is particularly

4.1 Clutch slave cylinder

4.8 Removing the clutch slave cylinder from the transmission

4.10 Prise up the clip and pull the bleed valve from place

4.11 Slave cylinder/release bearing retaining bolts

important on models fitted with a dual mass flywheel. Always replace the slave cylinder/release bearing with the clutch and clutch cover.

9 Remove the transmission as described in Chapter 7A Section 3.

10 Release the retaining clip and pull the fluid bleeder connection from the outside of the transmission casing **(see illustration)**.

11 Undo the bolts and remove the slave cylinder/release bearing assembly **(see illustration)**.

Refitting

12 Refitting is a reversal of removal, bearing in mind the following points:
a) *Tighten all fixings to the specified torque where given.*
b) *On completion, bleed the clutch hydraulic system as described in Section 2.*

---

5 Clutch friction disc and pressure plate – removal, inspection and refitting

⚠ **Warning: Dust created by clutch wear and deposited on the clutch components may contain asbestos, which is a health hazard. DO NOT blow it out with compressed air or inhale any of it. DO NOT use petrol or petroleum-based solvents to clean off the dust. Brake system cleaner**

or methylated spirit should be used to flush the dust into a suitable receptacle. After the clutch components are wiped clean with clean rags, dispose of the contaminated rags and cleaner in a sealed container.
Note: *Always inspect the dual mass flywheel (as described in the relevant engine Chapter) and replace it if necessary.*

Removal

1 Access to the clutch is obtained by removing the transmission as described in Chapter 7A Section 3.

2 If the clutch is to be refitted, mark the clutch pressure plate and flywheel in relation to each other.

3 Hold the flywheel stationary, and then unscrew the clutch pressure plate bolts ¼ of a turn at a time **(see illustration)**. With the bolts unscrewed two or three turns, check that the pressure plate is not binding on the dowel pins. If necessary, use a screwdriver to release the pressure plate. On models with the Sachs clutch, as the bolts are removed the stop pin must slacken. If it doesn't, press the pin towards the flywheel **(see illustration)**.

4 Remove all the bolts, then lift the clutch pressure plate and friction disc from the flywheel.

Inspection

Note: *Due to the amount of work necessary to remove and refit clutch components, it is*

usually considered good practice to renew the clutch friction disc, pressure plate assembly and release bearing as a matched set, even if only one of these is actually worn enough to require renewal. It is also worth considering the renewal of the clutch components on a preventative basis if the engine and/or transmission have been removed for some other reason.

5 Clean the pressure plate friction surface, clutch friction disc and flywheel. Do not inhale the dust, as it may contain asbestos which is dangerous to health.

6 Examine the fingers of the diaphragm spring for wear or scoring. If the depth of wear exceeds half the thickness of the fingers, a new pressure plate assembly must be fitted.

7 Examine the pressure plate for scoring, cracking, distortion and discoloration. Light scoring is acceptable, but if excessive, a new pressure plate assembly must be fitted **(see illustration)**. If the distortion of the friction surface exceeds 1.0 mm, renew it.

8 Examine the friction disc linings for wear and cracking, and for contamination with oil or grease. The linings are worn excessively if they are worn down to, or near, the rivets. Check the disc hub and splines for wear by temporarily fitting it on the transmission input shaft. Renew the friction disc as necessary.

9 Examine the flywheel friction surface for scoring, cracking and discoloration (caused by overheating). If excessive, it may be possible to have the flywheel machined by an engineering works, otherwise it should be renewed.

10 Ensure that all parts are clean, and free of oil or grease, before reassembling. Apply just a small amount of lithium-based grease (VAG No. G000100) to the splines of the friction disc hub. Do not use copper-based grease. Note that new pressure plates and clutch covers may be coated with protective grease. It is only permissible to clean the grease away from the friction disc lining contact area. Removal of the grease from other areas will shorten the service life of the clutch.

Refitting

11 Commence reassembly by locating the friction disc on the flywheel, with the raised

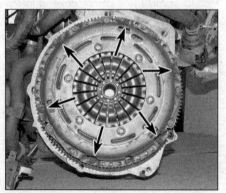

5.3a Undo the pressure plate retaining screws

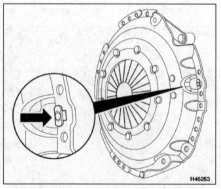

5.3b Ensure the stop pin is free to move

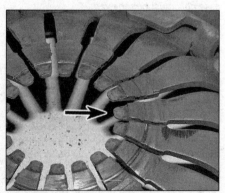

5.7 A worn and damaged clutch cover should always be replaced

side of the hub facing outwards (normally marked 'Getriebeseite' or 'Gearbox side'). If possible, the centralising tool (see paragraph 20) should be used to hold the disc on the flywheel at this stage (see illustration).

Models with self-adjusting clutch (SAC)

12 On models with a Self-adjusting clutch (SAC), where a new friction disc is fitted, but the pressure plate is to be re-used, it is necessary to reset the pressure plate adjusting ring prior to assembly as follows.

13 Insert three 8 mm bolts into the pressure plate mounting holes at intervals of 120°. The bolts should be inserted from the flywheel side, and retained by nuts (see illustration).

14 Place the pressure plate face down on the bed of an hydraulic press so that only the heads of the bolts make contact with the press bed, then place a circular spacer over the ends of the diaphragm springs fingers.

15 Use 2 screwdrivers to attempt to rotate the adjuster ring anti-clockwise. Apply just enough pressure with the hydraulic press until it's just possible to move the adjuster ring (see illustration).

16 Once the adjuster ring edges are between the notches, relieve the pressure. The ring is now reset. **Note:** *New pressure plates are supplied in this reset position.*

All models

17 Locate the clutch pressure plate on the

5.11 The friction disc should be marked 'Getriebeseite' or 'Gearbox side'

disc, and fit it onto the location dowels (see illustration). If refitting the original pressure plate, make sure that the previously-made marks are aligned.

18 Insert the bolts finger-tight to hold the pressure plate in position.

19 The friction disc must now be centralised, to ensure correct alignment of the transmission input shaft with the disc centre. To do this, a proprietary tool may be used, or alternatively, use a wooden mandrel made to fit inside the friction disc and the hole in the centre of the crankshaft. Insert the tool through the friction disc into the crankshaft, and make sure that it is central.

20 Tighten the pressure plate bolts progressively and in diagonal sequence, until the specified torque setting is achieved, then remove the centralising tool (see illustration).

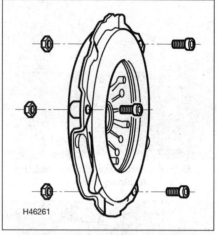

5.13 Insert three 8 mm bolts from the flywheel side, and secure with nuts

21 Check the release bearing in the transmission bellhousing for smooth operation – if the clutch is to be replaced always renew the release bearing (the bearing is normally part of the clutch kit). Renew it with reference to Section 4 (CSC type) or Section 6.

22 Refit the transmission with reference to Chapter 7A Section 3.

6 Release bearing and lever – removal, inspection and refitting

Removal

1 Remove the transmission as described in Chapter 7A Section 3.

2 Using a screwdriver, prise the release lever from the ball-stud on the transmission housing. If this proves difficult, push the retaining spring from the release lever first (see illustration). Where applicable, remove the plastic pad from the stud.

3 Slide the release bearing, together with the lever, from the guide sleeve, and withdraw it over the transmission input shaft.

5.15 The edges of the adjuster ring (B) must be between the notches (A)

5.17 Fit the pressure plate over the locating dowel pins

5.20 With the pressure plate screws tightened, remove the centralising tool

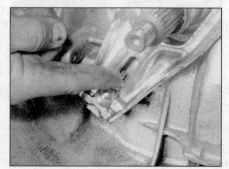

6.2 Push the spring clip to release the arm from the ball-stud

6.4a Use a screwdriver to depress the retaining tags...

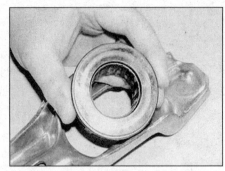

6.4b ...then remove the release bearing from the arm

6.5 Guide sleeve on the transmission

6.6 Typical release bearing failure

6.8 Fit the new guide sleeve

4 Separate the release bearing from the lever **(see illustrations)**.
5 If the guide sleeve is worn excessively, unbolt it and remove the O-ring seal **(see illustration)**. Note that a new guide bush may be included with the new clutch assembly.

Inspection

6 Spin the release bearing by hand, and check it for smooth running **(see illustration)**.

Any tendency to seize or run rough will necessitate renewal of the bearing. If the bearing is to be re-used, wipe it clean with a dry cloth; the bearing should not be washed in a liquid solvent, as this will remove the internal grease. Note that a new replacement release bearing is always included in a new clutch kit.
7 Clean the release lever, ball-stud and guide sleeve.

Refitting

8 If the guide sleeve was removed fit the new guide sleeve and tighten the bolts to the specified torque **(see illustration)**. If preferred, the guide sleeve may be assembled to the release bearing and lever, and the components fitted over the input shaft as one unit.
9 Lubricate the ball-stud in the transmission bellhousing with molybdenum sulphide-based grease.
10 Push the operating arm onto the pivot ball stud **(see illustration)**.
11 Slide the bearing over the guide sleeve and clip it into the operating arm **(see illustrations)**.
12 Replacement clutch kits are usually supplied with a lubricant suitable for the guide sleeve and the splines of the input shaft. Where no lubricant is supplied lubricate the transmission input shaft with light oil – DO NOT use grease.
13 Check that the bearing slides smoothly up and down the guide sleeve and then refit the transmission as described in Chapter 7A Section 3.

6.10 Fit the arm onto the stud

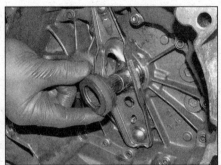

6.11a Slide on the bearing...

6.11b ...and clip it onto the arm

Chapter 6 Part B
Clutch – DSG transmission

Contents

Section number

6 Speed transmission clutch (OD9) – removal and refitting 2
7 Speed transmission clutch (OCW) – removal and refitting 3

General information 1

Section number

Degrees of difficulty

Easy, suitable for novice with little experience	Fairly easy, suitable for beginner with some experience	Fairly difficult, suitable for competent DIY mechanic	Difficult, suitable for experienced DIY mechanic	Very difficult, suitable for expert DIY or professional

Specifications

Type:
6 speed DSG (OD9) . . . . Wet, dual multi-plate clutch
7 speed transmission (OCW) . . . . Dual dry clutch assembly

Torque wrench settings   **Nm**   **lbf ft**
7 speed transmission:
 Release lever K2 bolts*:
  Stage 1 8   6
  Stage 2 . . . . Angle-tighten a further 90º
Use new bolts/nuts

1 General information

1 The six speed transmissions (code OD9) all have a 'wet' multiplate clutch assembly and the seven speed transmissions (code OCW) all have a 'dry' dual clutch fitted. They are not interchangeable.
2 Before removing the transmission, it is vitally important that a full diagnostic code read is performed on the vehicle. This will require professional level diagnostic equipment. The factory diagnostic tool will be more than capable, but several aftermarket tools should also give access to not only the DSG fault codes (if there are any), but also the 'live data'. The 'live data is' the actual information coming live (as the vehicle is driven) from the engine management ECU. This information can help identify any potential, or real problems.

2 6 Speed transmission clutch (OD9) – Removal and refitting

Clutch cover
Removal
1 Remove the transmission as described in Chapter 7B Section 2.

Note: *Special tool T10302 will be required before starting work.*
2 The clutch cover must be removed to access the clutch. Release the large circlip and then (working through the starter motor opening) lever up the cover, anticipating some oil spillage. Note that once removed the cover must be replaced.
Refitting
Caution: Do not lubricate or touch the centre seal. Only hold the cover at the edges and do not use any tools to install the new cover.
3 Where required clean the sealing surface of the driveplate.
4 The sealing lip of the new cover must be moved to the installation position. Place the guide sleeve (T10302) on a flat surface

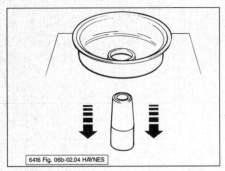

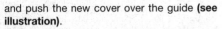

2.4 Push the new cover over the guide sleeve and then pull out the sleeve

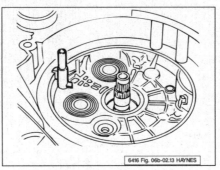

2.13 The tool correctly positioned

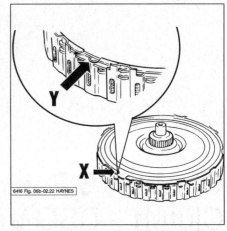

2.22 Locate the circlip 'ears' (X) at either side of the lug (Y)

and push the new cover over the guide (see illustration).

5 Fit the guide sleeve to the clutch shaft and then install the new cover over the shaft. Press evenly around the cover to seat it. Do not use a hammer, but it is permissible to lever the cover into position with screwdriver at the edge.

6 Fit a new circlip and then remove the guide sleeve.

Clutch

Removal

Note: *Special tool T10303, a dial gauge and support stand will be required to replace the clutch assembly.*

7 Remove the clutch cover as described above.

8 Remove the large circlip from the perimeter and lift out the driveplate.

9 Remove the centre circlip and lift out the dual clutch.

10 Remove the central pump shaft by pulling it up. Set it to the side.

Refitting

11 Remove the new clutch from the packaging and check that the hub seals are correctly seated. The seal gaps should be positioned offset to each over and must move freely. Adjust them if required.

12 Check that the lug on the driveplate sits between the coloured marks on the outer plate. If these marks are not present, use a permanent marker and provide your own.

13 Fit the special tool (T10303) to the bell housing (see illustration).

14 With an assistant holding the retaining pin, fit the new clutch housing. A certain amount of rocking and slight rotating maybe required to lower it fully into position. Do not drop the clutch into position.

15 Remove the outer circlip from the new dual clutch and lift out the driveplate. Note that this circlip may be reused.

16 Select the 2 mm circlip from the assortment supplied with the new clutch and fit it to the shaft.

17 A dial gauge must now be set up to measure the axial play. Bolt a meat plate to the bellhousing and then set up the dial gauge with a magnetic stand, so that the pointer of the gauge rest on the edge of the input shaft. Zero the gauge and then lift the clutch to the stop and note down the movement on the dial gauge.

18 Repeat the procedure, but with the probe of the gauge resting on the hub of the clutch carrier. This is the gap between the 2 mm circlip. Note down the measurement.

19 The thickness of the new circlip is calculated by subtracting the first measurement from the second and then adding 1.85 mm. This figure is the thickness of the correct circlip. Measure the circlips provided with the clutch and select the one closest to the calculated dimension.

20 Remove the 2.0 mm circlip and install the calculated one.

21 Refit the pump shaft and then refit the driveplate, so that the lug is correctly aligned with the marks.

22 Refit the outer circlip, with the ends of the circlip installed on either side of the driveplate

lug (see illustration). Settle the circlip by pushing it fully home with a screwdriver.

23 Remove the special tool and fit the new clutch cover as described in this Section.

24 Refit the transmission as described in Chapter 7B Section 2.

3 7 Speed transmission clutch (OCW) – removal and refitting

Removal

1 Remove the transmission as described in Chapter 7B Section 2.

2 A set of special tools will be required from either a Volkswagen dealer or the aftermarket (see illustration). These tools are essential. Note that some of the available tools adopt a unique approach to both removing the clutch and calculating the required shims. These tools will be supplied with their own instructions.

3 If not done during removal of the transmission, remove the breather plugs from the transmission and mechatronic unit and seal the breathers. The mechatronic breather will likely be damaged during removal, so a new breather will be required on refitting.

4 Support the transmission in an upright position on the workbench.

5 Note the position of the central hub circlip and remove it (see illustrations).

3.2 An aftermarket set of the essential clutch tools

3.5a Note the position of the circlip

3.5b Remove the circlip

3.6a Lift up…

3.6b …and remove the clutch hub

3.8a Install the tool and compress the clutch assembly

3.8b Remove the tool and remove the circlip

3.9a Install the special tool and…

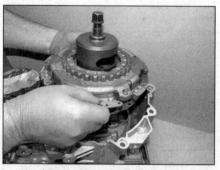

3.9b … pull out the clutch

6 Lift out the central hub (clutch) using a hooked tool (fabricated from welding rod or similar) **(see illustrations)**.

7 If the clutch is to be replaced, then the position of the bearings should be measured now – see the adjustment Section.

8 Remove the now exposed circlip. If the circlip can not be released then fit the special tool (T10323) with the forcing screw and thrust plate across the bell housing and compress the clutch by tightening the screw by hand ONLY. Remove the special tool and remove the circlip **(see illustrations)**.

9 With the circlip removed, install the special tool and pull out the clutch **(see illustrations)**.

10 Recover the shims and bearing **(see illustrations)**.

Refitting

11 If any parts of the clutch assembly are

replaced, then the adjustment procedure (detailed below) must be carried out.

12 Replace the shims, exactly as removed.

13 Refit the main clutch plate with the assembly tool and wind out the forcing screw to lower the clutch into position.

14 Refit the thrust piece, bridge and forcing screw. Feed in the forcing screw, whilst rocking the clutch slightly with one hand. The clutch will lose all play when the limit stop is reached, at this point, remove the special tool. Do not overtighten the forcing screw or the clutch will be damaged.

15 Remove the tool and fit the new circlip. The circlip must be fitted with the narrower face of the circlip on top.

16 Install the puller (T10373A) from the special tool kit and (using the tool) pull up the clutch assembly with one hand, whilst pushing the clutch in the normal direction of rotation.

The clutch should slide up into contact with the circlip. Note that the circlip may already be in contact with the clutch, so this procedure may not be strictly necessary.

17 Refit the central hub – it will only fit in one position. Fit the large circlip.

18 Check that the clutch is free to rotate. If the clutch does not turn freely then the clutch has been not installed correctly. If the clutch has been replaced, the correct shims may not have been fitted. Remove the clutch and refit it.

19 Refit the transmission as described in Chapter 7B Section 2.

Adjustment

20 If any parts of the clutch assembly have been replaced the adjustment procedure must be carried out.

21 With the clutch assembly removed, clean

3.10a Remove the bearing…

3.10b …the large shim (K1)…

3.10c …and the small shim

3.22 A straight edge will be required

3.23 Measure the distance to the top of the outer input shaft

3.24 Measure the distance to the top of the circlip (X1 in the table)

3.28 Install the large release arm

out the bellhousing using brake cleaner and then remove the operating arm ball pin. The pin can be removed with pliers and must be replaced. Fit the new pin and tap it into position with a soft faced hammer or block of wood.

22 Install the old circlip to the outer input shaft and then place a straight edge across the face of the bellhousing (see illustration).

23 Using a depth gauge (a digital or mechanical vernier gauge is ideal) measure the distance to the top of the input outer shaft (see illustration). Note down this number, or if using a digital gauge, then 'zero' the gauge. Note: This measurement can also be taken with the clutch hub removed, but with the main clutch still installed.

24 Next measure the distance to the top of the circlip and note down this number (see illustration). Subtract the first number from the second and note this down. If a digital vernier is used simply note down the measurement. Repeat the procedure on the opposite side of the shaft.

25 To get the average height divide the measurements by two. Note down the number. The table below shows the method used to calculate the first stage of determining the shim thickness for clutch K1. Note that the numbers given in the table are arbitrary – they are not actual measurements.

Distance to circlip (X1)	57.50mm
Distance to top of outer shaft (X2)	54.90mm
Calculated dimension (X1 – X2 = T1)	2.60mm
Distance to circlip (Y1)*	57.45mm
Distance to to top of outer shaft (Y2)*	54.84mm
Calculated dimension (Y1 – Y2 = T2)	2.61mm
Average dimension (T1 + T2/2)	2.605mm
* Taken 180 degrees from the first measurements (X1 and X2)	

26 Remove the circlip and dispose of it – a new one will be required for refitting.

27 The procedure must now be repeated, but the second measurement is now taken to the top edge of the installed gauge block (T10466) This forms part of the special tool kit.

28 If removed, install the large release arm with no shims (see illustration). The arm must be correctly seated.

29 Install the gauge block, press down on the block and rotate it to fully engage it.

30 Next measure the distance to the top of the gauge block and note down this number. Subtract the first number (derived from the average distance to the top of the circlip – T1 + T2 divided by 2 in our table example) from the second and note this down. If a digital vernier is used simply note down the measurement. Repeat the procedure on the opposite side of the shaft.

31 To get the average height divide the measurements by two. Note down the number.

32 The bearing tolerance can now be calculated. Subtract the first measurement noted down (paragraph 6) from the second (paragraph 13) to find the tolerance. Note down this number.
33 On the new clutch read the tolerance value for the bearing 'K1' **(see illustration)**.
34 Take the calculated height of the bearing (the figure derived in paragraph 31) and add the tolerance value taken from the new clutch. Note that the value on the new clutch may be a minus figure and must be subtracted, not added.
35 This calculated figure is the thickness of the shim required. A total of eleven shims are available (see the table). Select the shim closest to the available size.

3.33 The K1 tolerance

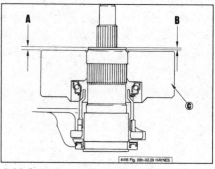

3.39 Calculating the shim for thickness for bearing K2.

A = Calculated height (see text)
B = Previously calculated height
C = Gauge block

K1 Bearing – calculated shim thickness (in millimetres)	Available shim (in millimetres)
1.21 to 1.60	1.50
1.61 to 1.80	1.70
1.81 to 2.00	2.10
2.21 to 2.40	2.30
2.41 to 2.60	2.50
2.61 to 2.80	2.70
2.81 to 3.00	2.90
3.01 to 3.20	3.10
3.21 to 3.40	3.30
3.41 to 3.80	3.50

36 Remove the gauge block and the large engagement lever in preparation for calculating the shim for the smaller operating lever (K2 bearing).
37 The second shim thickness is calculated in a similar manner to the first. Install the smaller release arm. Note that new release arms may be supplied with the guide sleeve in the unlocked position. Rotate it to lock it in place – the holes of the guide will be at 90 degrees to the major axis when the sleeve is correctly installed.
38 Insert the new bolts and tighten them to the specific torque and then install the gauge block (T10466). Rotate the gauge block to fully engage it.
39 Measure the height to the gauge block **(see illustration)**. Subtract the measured distance from the input shaft (T1 + T2 divided by 2 in our example table) from the measured distance to the gauge block and note down the measurement. On the illustration this is dimension A, minus dimension B.
40 Repeat the procedure on the opposite side and calculate the average by dividing by 2.
41 On the new clutch note the 'K2' tolerance and add it to the calculated tolerance. Note that the new clutch tolerance may be minus and so must be subtracted from the calculated tolerance.
42 Select the correct shim from the available ones (see the table).

K2 Bearing – calculated bearing thickness (in millimetres)	Available shims (in millimetres)
0.31 to 0.90	0.80
0.91 to 1.10	1.00
1.11 to 1.30	1.20
1.31 to 1.50	1.40
1.51 to 1.70	1.60
1.71 to 1.90	1.80
1.91 to 2.10	2.00
2.11 to 2.30	2.20
2.31 to 2.50	2.40
2.51 to 2.70	2.60
2.71 to 3.30	2.80

43 With both new shim thicknesses calculated the clutch assembly can be installed with the new shims as described above.

Chapter 7 Part A
Manual transmission

Contents

Section number

Gear change housing and cable – removal, refitting and adjustment . . 2
General Information 1
Reversing light and neutral switches – testing, removal and refitting. . 6

Section number

Transmission – removal and refitting 3
Transmission oil – removal refilling and level checking 4
Transmission overhaul – general information 5

Degrees of difficulty

Easy, suitable for novice with little experience | **Fairly easy,** suitable for beginner with some experience | **Fairly difficult,** suitable for competent DIY mechanic | **Difficult,** suitable for experienced DIY mechanic | **Very difficult,** suitable for expert DIY or professional

Specifications

General

Type . . . . Five or six speed, transversely-mounted, front-wheel-drive layout with integral transaxle differential/final drive and 1 reverse gear

Code:
5-speed 0A4/0AF/0AH
6-speed 02Q/0BB/0FB/02S/0AJ

Oil capacities

0A4 transmission* . . . . 1.7 litres
0AF transmission* . . . . 2.0 litres
0AH transmission* . . . . 2.2 litres
0AJ transmission* . . . .
02Q/0BB/0FB transmission* . . . . 2.3 litres
02S transmission* . . . . 1.9 litres
* Capacities are the refill amounts for a previously fitted transmission

Torque wrench settings

	Nm	lbf ft
Flywheel cover plate (where fitted).	10	7
Gearchange cable support bracket	20	15
Gear lever housing to body:		
M6 nuts.	8	6
M8 nuts.	25	18
Left-hand mounting bracket bolts:		
To transmission: *		
Stage 1	40	30
Stage 2	Angle-tighten a further 90°	
Bracket to body:		
Stage 1	60	45
Stage 2	Angle-tighten a further 90°	
Pendulum mount: *		
To transmission:		
Stage 1	50	37
Stage 2	Angle-tighten a further 90°	
To subframe:		
Stage 1	130	96
Stage 2	Angle-tighten a further 90°	
Reversing light switch	20	15
Transmission to engine:		
M12 bolts	80	59
M10 bolt	40	30
Oil filler/level plug		
Plug with 12 point socket	45	33
Plug with hex head	30	22

*Do not re-use

1 General Information

1 The manual transmission is bolted directly to the left-hand end of the engine. This layout has the advantage of providing the shortest possible drive path to the front wheels, as well as locating the transmission in the airflow through engine bay, optimising cooling. The unit is cased in aluminium alloy.

2 Drive from the crankshaft is transmitted through the clutch to the gearbox input shaft, which is splined to accept the clutch friction disc.

3 All forward gears are fitted with synchromesh. The floor-mounted gear lever is connected to the gearbox by shift cables.

4 Levers on the transmission actuate internal selector forks, which are connected to the synchromesh sleeves. The sleeves are locked to the gearbox shafts but can slide axially by means of splined hubs, and they press baulk rings into contact with the respective gear/pinion. The coned surfaces between the baulk rings and the pinion/gear act as a friction clutch, that progressively matches the speed of the synchromesh sleeve (and hence the gearbox shaft) with that of the gear/pinion. This allows gearchanges to be carried out smoothly.

5 Drive is transmitted to the differential crownwheel, which rotates the differential case and planetary gears, thus driving the sun gears and driveshafts. The rotation of the differential planetary gears on their shaft allows the inner roadwheel to rotate at a slower speed than the outer roadwheel during cornering.

Note: *There is no recommendation from Volkswagen with regards to changing or checking the transmission oil level. The transmission should be checked for leaks at service time and the conscientious owner might consider changing the oil on a high mileage vehicle.*

2 Gear change housing and cable – removal, refitting and adjustment

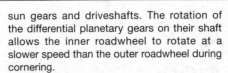

Removal

1 Remove the air filter housing as described in Chapter 4A Section 3 (petrol engines) or Chapter 4B Section 3 (diesel engines).

2 Remove the battery and battery tray as described Chapter 5A Section 3.

3 Prise out the clips (where fitted) securing the inner cable to the lever on the transmission, and the outer cable to the support bracket **(see illustrations)**. Withdraw the cable from the support bracket and discard the clips – new ones must be fitted. Note that on five speed transmissions the cable support bracket must be unbolted before releasing the selector cables from the selector shaft.

4 Working inside the vehicle, remove the centre console, as described in Chapter 11

Section 26.

5 Remove the insulation around the base of the gear change housing to access the mounting nuts.

6 Raise the front of the vehicle and support it securely on axle stands (see *Jacking and vehicle support*).

7 Remove the centre tunnel front heat shield from the underside of the vehicle to gain access to the base of the selector lever housing and cables. It may be necessary to separate the exhaust downpipe from the intermediate pipe with reference Chapter 4C Section 6 (petrol engines) or Chapter 4D Section 9 (diesel engines).

8 Working back inside the vehicle, undo the retaining nuts, then remove the bracket and lower the gear change housing downwards. Withdraw it complete with selector cables out from under the vehicle. It may be useful having the aid of an assistant at this point, to be under the vehicle when lowering the gear change housing.

9 To remove the cables from the gear change housing, prise out the clips securing the inner cable to the lower part of the gear lever, and then withdraw the securing clips from the outer cable to the gear change housing. Withdraw the cables and discard the clips – new ones must be fitted.

Refitting

10 Refitting is the reversal of the removal procedure, noting the following points:

a) *Ensure that the cables are correctly routed and secured, as noted on removal.*

b) *Take care not to bend or kink the cables.*

c) *Carry out the cable adjustment procedure described below before reconnecting the cable at the transmission end.*

d) *When refitting the cables, use new clips.*

Adjustment

11 Remove the engine top cover (where fitted), air cleaner housing, and air ducting for access to the top of the transmission. If required remove the battery and battery tray, as described in Chapter 5A Section 3.

12 With the gearchange set in the neutral position, push the two locking collars (one on each cable) forwards to compress the springs,

2.3a Release the gear change inner cable retaining clip

2.3b Release the cable adjustment collar and prise off the gate selector cable

2.3c Remove the circlips to release the cables...

2.3d ...or unbolt and...

2.3e ...lift off the support bracket

2.12 Push the collar down and lock in position

2.13 The transmission locking pin (6 speed shown, but 5 speed transmission is similar)

2.15 Release the two locking collars back into position

turn them clockwise (looking from the driver's seat) to lock into position **(see illustration)**.

13 Press down on the selector shaft on the top of the transmission, and push the locking pin into the transmission while turning it clockwise, until it engages and the selector shaft cannot move **(see illustration)**.

14 Working inside the vehicle, unclip the gear lever gaiter from the centre console -as described in Chapter 11 Section 26. Still in the neutral position, move the gear lever as far to the left as possible and insert the locking pin (or drill bit) through the hole in the insulation, into the base of the gear lever and down into the hole in the housing.

15 Working back in the engine bay, turn the two locking collars on the cables anti-clockwise so that the springs will release them back into position and lock the cables **(see illustration)**.

16 With the cable adjustment set, the locking pin in the transmission housing, can now be turned anti-clockwise to its original position pointing upwards.

17 Inside the vehicle, remove the locking pin from the gear lever, and then check the operation of the selector mechanism. When

the gear lever is at rest in neutral, it should be central, ready to select 3rd or 4th. The gear lever gaiter can now be refitted to the centre console.

18 Refit the air ducting, air filter housing, battery tray, battery and engine cover (where fitted).

3 Transmission – removal and refitting

Note: *A safe method of supporting the engine while the transmission is removed will be required. The recommended method of removing the transmission is to support both the engine and transmission with a support bar that fits across the engine bay. Support bars are readily available in the aftermarket, however the special extensions and fittings specified by Volkswagen are not available (see illustration). Where the correct support bar is not available the best alternative for the home mechanic is to support the engine with an engine crane (installed from the side) and then support the transmission with a*

trolley jack or ideally a transmission jack (see illustration). Consideration should also be given to removing the complete transmission and engine as a single unit (as described in Chapter 2D Section 4) especially on diesel engines fitted with a 6 speed transmission as removal of the transmission on these engines requires the removal of the front subframe. Whichever method is used the aid of an assistant is essential.

Removal

1 Select a solid, level surface to park the vehicle upon. Give yourself enough space to move around it easily. Apply the handbrake and chock the rear wheels.

2 Raise the front of the vehicle and support it securely on axle stands (see *Jacking and vehicle support*). Remove the engine/transmission undertray sections. Position a suitable container beneath the transmission, then unscrew the drain plug and drain the transmission oil.

3 Remove the engine top cover (where fitted). Remove the air filter housing as described in Chapter 4A Section 3 (petrol engines) or Chapter 4B Section 3 (diesel engines) On turbocharged models remove the charge air pipes from the turbocharger/intercooler.

4 Remove the battery and battery tray with reference to Chapter 5A Section 3. Where necessary, unclip the EVAP canister (petrol models) or the fuel filter (diesel models). This will avoid any damage to the filter or canister

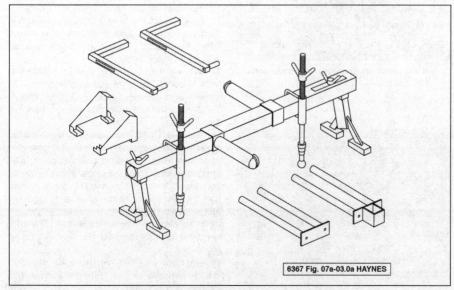

6367 Fig. 07a-03.0a HAYNES

3.0a Engine support bar and extensions

3.0b Transmission support jack

3.6 Remove the support bracket

3.7a Unbolt and then...

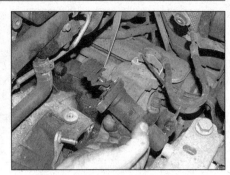

3.7b ...remove the slave cylinder

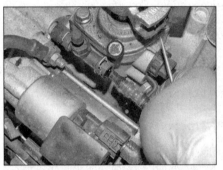

3.8 Prise up the clip a little and pull the hose from the connection – 02Q transmissions

3.9 Unbolt the earth cable

as the engine is moved. There is no need to disconnect the fuel lines.

5 Release the retaining clips and disconnect the gear selector cables from the gear selector levers, as described in Section 2. Unbolt and remove the cable mounting bracket from the top of the transmission.

6 Undo the retaining bolts, and then remove the support bracket **(see illustration)**, from the top of the transmission.

7 On models with the clutch slave cylinder on the top of the transmission, undo the retaining bolts, remove the cylinder and secure it out of harms way **(see illustrations)**.

8 On 02Q transmissions, seal the slave cylinder flexible hose using a hose clamp, then prise out the clip and pull the fluid pipe from the bleeder connection on the slave cylinder supply pipe **(see illustration)**.

9 Unbolt the earth cable from the engine/ transmission or subframe **(see illustration)**.

10 With reference to Chapter 5A Section 8, remove the starter motor.

11 Remove the upper bolts securing the transmission to the engine.

12 Remove the left-hand wheel arch liner.

13 Disconnect the wiring from the reversing light switch **(see illustrations)**, and where fitted, the neutral position switch on vehicles with a start/stop system.

14 Where fitted unbolt the metal shield from around the right-hand driveshaft. On models with gas discharge headlights (Xenon) disconnect the ride height sensor and secure it to the side.

15 Slacken the clamp securing the exhaust intermediate pipe to the rear section and undo the front mounting bracket bolts **(see illustrations)**. This will allow the engine to be moved forwards and backwards during the transmission removal and alignment procedures. Disconnect the exhaust system as described in Chapter 4C Section 6 (petrol engines) or Chapter 4D Section 9 (diesel engines).

16 Unscrew and remove the bolts securing the driveshafts to the transmission output flanges. Tie the right-hand driveshaft to one side, and then tie the left-hand driveshaft to the suspension strut, so that the shaft is as high

3.13a Reversing light switch on the OAF type transmission...

3.13b ...and on the O2Q transmission

3.15a Slacken the exhaust clamp...

3.15b ...and undo the exhaust mounting bracket bolts

3.16 Support the driveshafts

3.18 Unbolt the engine rear mounting torque arm

3.19 Remove the plate (where fitted)

as possible **(see illustration)**. Alternatively, completely remove the driveshafts as described in Chapter 8 Section 2.

17 Remove the radiator cooling fans (as described in Chapter 3 Section 5). Cover the rear of the radiator/cooling fans to prevent it from being damaged as the engine/transmission is moved forward. On models with an AC pressure switch at the front of the engine, remove the switch – there is a schraeder valve below the switch, so no refrigerant should escape.

18 Unbolt the engine rear mounting torque arm from the bottom of the transmission **(see illustration)**. On diesel engines remove the front subframe as described in Chapter 10 Section 22.

19 Where applicable, unbolt the flywheel cover plate from the transmission bellhousing **(see illustration)**.

20 Using a suitable hoist (see the note at the beginning of this Section) support the weight of the engine and then unscrew the bolts securing the transmission mounting to the body. Also, unbolt the mounting bracket from the transmission **(see illustrations)**. A block of wood should be fitted between the back of the engine and the subframe to push the engine forward as the assembly is lowered.

21 Lower the engine/transmission assembly slightly and, using a trolley jack/transmission jack, support the transmission. Position the jack so that it can be withdrawn from the left-hand side of the car. As the engine/transmission is moved, make sure any wiring or hoses are not damaged.

22 Unscrew and remove the remaining lower transmission to engine mounting bolts, including the bolt located on the left-hand rear of the engine **(see illustration)**.

23 Carefully pull the transmission directly away from the engine, taking care not to allow its weight to rest on the clutch friction disc hub. A second person is helpful to pull the left-hand end of the engine as far forwards as possible.

24 On models with driveshafts that have a bolted flange, it will be necessary to manouvre the right-hand driveshaft flange, from around the flywheel on removal. If required, hold the drive flange in position and undo the centre securing bolt, then the drive flange can be removed **(see illustrations)**, making removal of the transmission easier.

3.20a Transmission end mounting bracket

3.20b Remove the bracket from the transmission

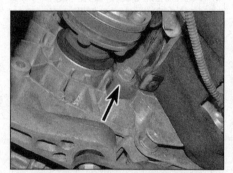

3.22 Undo the rear mounting bolt

3.24a Hold the drive flange in position ...

3.24b ...whilst removing the centre bolt ...

3.24c ...then slide the drive flange from the transmission

⚠️ *Warning: Support the transmission to ensure that it remains steady on the jack head. Keep the transmission level until the input shaft is fully withdrawn from the clutch friction disc.*

25 When the transmission is clear of the locating dowels and clutch components, lower the transmission to the ground and withdraw from under the car.

Refitting

26 Refitting the transmission is essentially a reversal of the removal procedure, but note the following points:

a) Apply a smear of high melting-point grease to the clutch friction disc hub splines; take care to avoid contaminating the friction surfaces.

b) In order to align the transmission with the flywheel, gently pull the engine forward as the transmission is manoeuvred into place.

c) Tighten the transmission to engine bolts to the specified torque.

d) Refer to the relevant part of Chapter 2 and tighten the engine mounting bolts to the correct torque.

e) Refer to Chapter 8 Section 2, and then tighten the driveshaft bolts to the specified torque.

f) On completion, refer to Section 2 and check the gearchange linkage/cable adjustment.

g) Refill the transmission with the correct grade and quantity of oil. Refer to 'Lubricants and fluids' and Section 4.

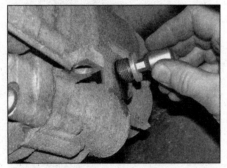

4.3a Removing the oil level/filler plug on 02Q transmissions

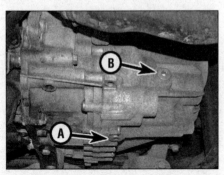

4.8 The oil drain plug (A) and filler level plug (B) on 02Q transmissions

4 Transmission oil – removal refilling and level checking

Oil level checking
02Q and 0AF transmissions

1 The vehicle must be on level ground to check the transmission oil level. This can be accomplished by using wheel ramps to raise the front of the vehicle and then raising the rear of the vehicle using a jack and axle stands (see *Jacking and vehicle support*). The alternative method is to remove the air filter housing and check the level from above. Access is restricted, but possible.

2 Where the vehicle has been jacked up to access the filler plug, remove the engine undershield.

3 The oil level should reach the lower edge of the filler/level hole. A certain amount of oil will have gathered behind the filler/level plug, and will trickle out when it is removed **(see illustrations)**. This does not necessarily indicate that the level is correct. To ensure that a true level is established, wait until the initial trickle has stopped, then add oil as necessary until a trickle of new oil can be seen emerging. The level will be correct when the flow ceases; use only good-quality oil of the specified type.

4 If the transmission has been overfilled so that oil flows out when the filler/level plug is removed, check that the car is completely level (front-to-rear and side-to-side), and allow the surplus to drain off into a suitable container.

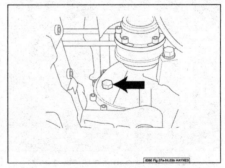

4.3b The plug location on 0AF and 0AH transmissions

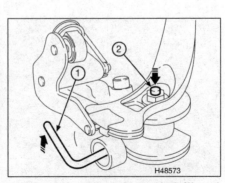

4.17 Press down the selector shaft (2), and rotate the locking rod (1) upwards

5 When the oil level is correct, refit the filler/level plug and tighten it to the specified torque. Note that two versions of the oil filler plug are fitted and they have different torque settings.

6 Wipe off any spilt oil then refit the engine undertray (if removed), tighten the retaining screws securely. Lower the car to the ground. If access has been gained from above, refit the air filter housing.

0A4 and 02S transmissions

7 On these transmissions, it is impossible to check the level of the oil through the 'filler' plug, due to the engine/transmission installation angle; the level of the fluid is above the lower edge of the filler hole. The only method of ensuring the correct fluid level is to completely drain and refill the transmission – as described below.

Draining and refilling
02Q and 0AF/0AH transmissions

8 Raise the front of the vehicle and support it securely on axle stands (see *Jacking and vehicle support*). Remove the engine/transmission undershield. Position a suitable container beneath the transmission, then unscrew the drain plug and drain the transmission oil **(see illustration)**. On 0AF and 0AH transmissions the drain plug is below the filler/level plug on the differential housing.

9 Remove the filler/level plug from the transmission **(see illustrations 4.3a and 4.3b)**.

10 Refit the drain plug and tighten it to the specified torque. Note that two versions of the oil filler plug are fitted and they have different torque settings.

11 Fill the transmission with oil until it is just below the level of the filler plug. Allow time for the oil to drain down into the transmission and then re-check the level.

12 Fit the engine undershield and lower the vehicle to the ground (if only the front was raised). Remove the air filter housing and (with the vehicle on level ground) check the oil level from above. Add oil as required and then refit the filler/level plug. Again note that two versions of the filler/level plug are fitted.

13 Refit the air filter housing.

0A4 and 02S transmissions

14 The vehicle must be on level ground to check/fill the transmission. This can be accomplished by using wheel ramps to raise the front of the vehicle and then raising the rear of the vehicle using a jack and axle stands (see *Jacking and vehicle support*).

15 Undo the fasteners and remove the engine undertray.

16 Remove the air filter housing as described in Chapter 4A Section 3 or Chapter 4B Section 3.

17 In order to drain the transmission, the pivot pin must be removed from the underside of the transmission casing. However, to prevent the position of the selector forks being altered, press the selector shaft down, then turn the angled locking rod upwards, and lock the shaft in position **(see illustration)**.

18 Place a container under the transmission casing.

19 Unscrew the drain plug from the base of the differential housing and allow the oil to drain **(see illustration)**.

20 Then undo the retaining bolt, pull out the pivot pin nearest the passenger's roadwheel and allow the oil to drain **(see illustration 4.19)**. The pivot pin O-ring seal must be renewed.

21 When the oil has finished draining, clean the surrounding area, refit the drain plug and tighten it to the specified torque.

22 Rotate the selector-shaft locking rod to its original position.

23 Unscrew the reversing light switch from the top of the transmission casing.

24 Using a 600 mm length of 10 mm (external) diameter hose, and funnel, add 1.7 litres of new oil to the transmission.

25 Refit the reversing light switch, and tighten it to the specified torque.

5 Transmission overhaul – general information

1 The overhaul of a manual transmission is a complex (and often expensive) task for the DIY home mechanic to undertake, which requires access to specialist equipment. It involves dismantling and reassembly of many small components, measuring clearances precisely and if necessary, adjusting them by selecting shims and spacers. Internal transmission components are also often difficult to obtain and in many instances, extremely expensive. Because of this, if the transmission develops a fault or becomes noisy, the best course of action is to have the unit overhauled by a specialist repairer or to obtain an exchange reconditioned unit.

2 Nevertheless, it is not impossible for the more experienced mechanic to overhaul the transmission if the special tools are available and the job is carried out in a deliberate step-by-step manner, to ensure nothing is overlooked.

3 The tools necessary for an overhaul include internal and external circlip pliers, bearing pullers, a slide hammer, a set of pin punches, a dial test indicator and possibly a hydraulic press. In addition, a large, sturdy workbench and a vice will be required.

4 During dismantling of the transmission, make careful notes of how each component is fitted to make reassembly easier and accurate.

5 Before dismantling the transmission, it will help if you have some idea of where the problem lies. Certain problems can be closely related to specific areas in the transmission, which can make component examination and renewal easier. Refer to the Fault finding Section in this manual for more information.

6 Reversing light and neutral switches – testing, removal and refitting

Note: The neutral switch is only fitted to vehicles with the Stop/Start system.

Testing

1 Ensure that the ignition switch is turned to the OFF position.

2 Unplug the wiring harness from the reversing light switch (or the neutral switch) at the connector. The switch is located on the front or top of the casing **(see illustrations)**

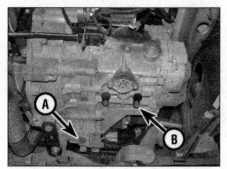

4.19 Oil drain plug (A) and pivot pin (B)

3 Connect the probes of a continuity tester, or multimeter set to the resistance measurement function, across the terminals of the reversing light switch.

4 The switch contacts are normally open, so with any gear other than reverse selected, the tester/meter should indicate an open circuit or infinite resistance. When reverse gear is selected, the switch contacts should close, causing the tester/meter to indicate continuity or zero resistance.

5 If the switch does not operate correctly, it should be renewed.

Removal

6 Ensure that the ignition switch is turned to the OFF position.

7 Unplug the wiring harness from the reversing light switch at the connector.

8 Unscrew the switch from the transmission casing, and recover the sealing ring.

Refitting

9 Refitting is a reversal of removal.

6.2a The reverse light switch on 0A4 transmissions...

6.2b ...on 0AF transmissions...

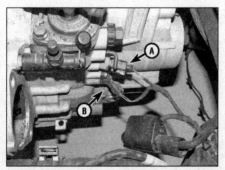

6.2c ...and on 02Q transmissions. Reverse light switch (A) and neutral switch (B)

Chapter 7 Part B
DSG semi-automatic transmission

Contents

Section number

Emergency release of selector lever 5
General Information 1
Selector lever housing and cable – removal, refitting and adjustment 4

Spigot bearing – renewal 7
Transmission – removal and refitting 2
Transmission oil renewal 6
Transmission overhaul – general information 3

Degrees of difficulty

Easy, suitable for novice with little experience | **Fairly easy,** suitable for beginner with some experience | **Fairly difficult,** suitable for competent DIY mechanic | **Difficult,** suitable for experienced DIY mechanic | **Very difficult,** suitable for expert DIY or professional

Specifications

General
Transmission type:
0D9	6 speed. Multi-plate wet clutch.
0CW	7 speed. Dual dry clutch.

Transmission capacity:
0D9 (6 speed)
- Initial fill (at factory) .... 6.9 to 7.2 litres (dependant on production date)
- Change quantity .... 5.2 litres (approximately)
- Change quantity (mechatronic unit, after removal and refit) ...... 3.0 to 4.0 litres

0CW (7 speed)
- After draining (for general repair) .... 1.9 litres
- After draining and extracting oil for removal of the mechatronic control unit .... 2.1 litres
- Mechatronic hydraulic oil .... 1.0 litre

Torque wrench settings

	Nm	lbf ft
Oil filter housing (0D9 transmission only)	20	15
Transmission-to-engine bolts:		
M10 bolts	40	30
M12 bolts	80	59
Transmission mounting bracket to transmission bolts*:		
Stage 1	40	30
Stage 2	Angle-tighten a further 90°	
Mounting to body bolts*:		
Stage 1	60	44
Stage 2	Angle-tighten a further 90°	
Pendulum mount*		
To transmission:		
Stage 1	50	37
Stage 2	Angle-tighten a further 90°	
To subframe:		
Stage 1	130	96
Stage 2	Angle-tighten a further 90°	
Drain plug (0CW transmission)	30	22
Drain/level plug (0D9 transmission)	45	31
Oil level tube (0D9 transmission)	3	2

*Do not reuse

1 General Information

1 The VW semi-automatic Direct Shift Gearbox (DSG) has six or seven-forward speeds (and one reverse). In contrast to traditional automatic transmissions where a fluid flywheel (torque converter) transmits the power from the engine to the gearbox, the DSG has a multi-plate clutch in the six-speed transmission and a twin-clutch in the seven-speed transmission (see illustrations). The main advantages of the DSG transmission, is near-instant gear changes, with seamless, highly efficient drive, resulting in less exhaust emissions and improved fuel consumption.

2 On the front of the transmission housing is a mechatronic unit, this is made up of mechanical and electronic components. The electronic part of the unit uses information from sensors (e.g. engine speed, road speed, driving mode etc.) to determine the optimum gear and shift commands, the mechanical part then selects the correct gear required. On 6-speed transmissions, the unit is inside the transmission housing with a pressed steel cover, bolted to the front of the transmission casing. On 7-speed transmissions, it is a sealed unit, and is bolted to the front of the transmission.

3 On 6-speed transmissions, the clutch is of a multi-plate type, which runs in the transmission oil. It is made up of four outer plates, which have teeth on the outer edge to locate in the clutch housing, four inner plates with teeth on the inner edge that locate on the clutch inner hub, and one drive plate that is located on the outside of the clutch plate assembly. The four larger outer plates (C1)

operate 1st, 3rd, 5th and reverse gears, and then the four smaller inner plates (C2) operate 2nd, 4th and 6th gears. With this system whilst 'C1' has a gear engaged, then 'C2' will pre-select the next gear ready to change gear. The assembly requires special care, as all the components in the assembly are balanced together, during manufacture. The clutch assembly is sealed inside the bell housing by a clutch end cover, which also forms a seal, to prevent loss of oil. If the end cover is removed for any reason, it will need to be renewed.

4 On 7-speed transmissions, the clutch is of a dual-clutch dry plate type, which has two friction discs and a spring loaded centre hub (see illustration). The clutch friction disc nearest the engine is operated by the larger outer release lever (K1) and operates 1st, 3rd, 5th & 7th gears. The clutch friction disc nearest the transmission is operated by the smaller inner release lever (K2) and

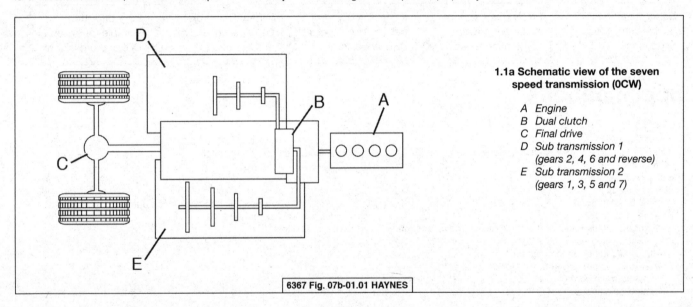

1.1a Schematic view of the seven speed transmission (0CW)

A Engine
B Dual clutch
C Final drive
D Sub transmission 1
   (gears 2, 4, 6 and reverse)
E Sub transmission 2
   (gears 1, 3, 5 and 7)

6367 Fig. 07b-01.01 HAYNES

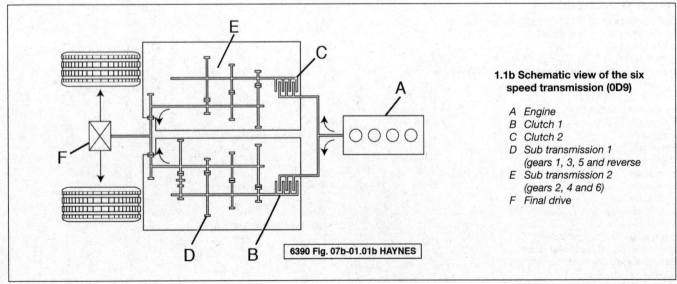

1.1b Schematic view of the six speed transmission (0D9)

A Engine
B Clutch 1
C Clutch 2
D Sub transmission 1
   (gears 1, 3, 5 and reverse
E Sub transmission 2
   (gears 2, 4 and 6)
F Final drive

6390 Fig. 07b-01.01b HAYNES

operates 2nd, 4th, 6th & Reverse gears. With this system whilst 'K1' has a gear engaged, then 'K2' will pre-select the next gear ready to change gear. The clutch assembly can only be purchased as a complete unit, and if renewed, new release levers will also be needed.

5 A fault diagnosis system is integrated into the control unit, but analysis can only be undertaken with specialised equipment. It is important that any transmission fault be identified and rectified at the earliest possible opportunity. A Volkswagen dealer or suitably equipped specialist can 'interrogate' the ECM fault memory for stored fault codes, enabling him to pinpoint the fault quickly. Once the fault has been corrected and any fault codes have been cleared, normal transmission operation is restored.

6 Because of the need for special test equipment, the complexity of some of the parts, and the need for scrupulous cleanliness when these transmissions, the work which the owner can do is limited. Most major repairs and overhaul operations should be left to a Volkswagen dealer or specialist, who will be equipped with the necessary equipment for fault diagnosis and repair. The information in this Chapter is therefore limited to a description of the removal and refitting of the transmission as a complete unit. The removal, refitting and adjustment of the selector cable is also described.

7 In the event of a transmission problem occurring, consult a Volkswagen dealer or transmission specialist before removing the transmission from the vehicle, since the majority of fault diagnosis is best carried out with the transmission still in the vehicle.

2 Transmission – removal and refitting

Note: *A safe method of supporting the engine while the transmission is removed will be required. The recommended method of removing the transmission is to support both the engine and transmission with a support bar that fits across the engine bay. Support bars are readily available in the aftermarket, however the special extensions and fittings specified by Volkswagen are not available. Where the correct support bar is not available the best alternative for the home mechanic is to support the engine with an engine crane (installed from the side) and then support the transmission with a trolley jack or ideally a transmission jack (see illustration). Consideration should also be given to removing the complete transmission and engine as a single unit (as described in Chapter 2D Section 4) as removal of the DSG transmission requires the removal of the front subframe. Whichever method is used the aid of an assistant is essential.*

1.4 Clutch assembly – 0CW transmission

 Warning: The mechatronic unit on the front of the 7-speed (0CW) transmission is a sealed unit. If any oil is lost from this mechatronic unit, it will need to be renewed, as it cannot be refilled. Remove the breather cap from the top of the unit and cover with blanking plug, to prevent any loss of oil.

Removal

1 The transmission is removed downwards from the engine compartment. First, select a solid, level surface to park the vehicle upon. Give yourself enough space to move around it easily. Select P, apply the handbrake, and chock the rear wheels.

2 Loosen the front wheel bolts, and the driveshaft hub bolts. Do not undo the hub bolt more than 90° at this point; otherwise the wheel bearing could be damaged, whilst the weight is still on the wheels.

3 Raise the front of the vehicle and rest it securely on axle stands (see *Jacking and vehicle support*). Remove the front wheels. Allow a suitable working clearance underneath for the eventual withdrawal of the transmission. Undo the fasteners and remove the engine/transmission undershield.

4 Remove the air filter housing as described in Chapter 4A Section 3 (petrol engine) or Chapter 4B Section 3 (diesel engine) and then remove the battery and support tray Chapter 5A Section 3.

5 Where fitted remove the breather plug from the top of the transmission and fit a sealing

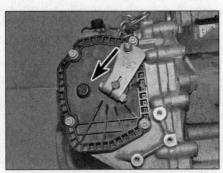

2.5 Fit a blanking plug to the breather

2.0 Transmission support jack

plug **(see illustration)**. The vent plug will more than likely be damaged on removal, so a new one will be required for refitting.

6 Undo the retaining clips and remove the turbocharger intake hose and charge air pipe to the intercooler or air filter as described in Chapter 4C Section 4 (petrol engines) or Chapter 4D Section 5 (diesel engines)

7 On some 6 speed models a protective cover is fitted to the base of the transmission. Remove this where fitted.

8 Remove the earth cable **(see illustration and illustration 2.11a)** and then remove the starter motor as described in Chapter 5A Section 8. Note that on 6 speed (0D9) transmissions there is a bell housing bolt inside the starter motor housing. Remove the bolt.

9 Disconnect the selector cable from the selector shaft lever on the top of the transmission, as described in Section 4. Position the cable to one side, noting that the retaining clip/circlip on 6 speed transmissions must be renewed.

10 On 6-speed transmissions there is a fluid cooler and control valve located on top of the transmission. Clamp off the cooler hoses with brake hose type clamps. Release the retaining clips and detach the hoses from the cooler. Disconnect the wiring plug, unbolt the control valve and move it to the side. Take great care not to spill any coolant into the transmission unit, as this will cause damage.

11 Disconnect the wiring plug connectors from the front of the transmission **(see**

2.8 Remove the earth cable

2.11a Wiring plug (and earth cable) – 6 transmissions

2.11b Slide up the locking collar (7 speed transmissions)

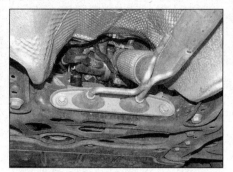

2.14 Undo the exhaust mounting retaining bolts

illustrations). Detach the wiring loom and remove the mounting brackets from the transmission.

a) *6-speed transmissions – rotate the collar anti-clockwise to disconnect.*

b) *7-speed transmissions – slide the locking lever upwards to disconnect.*

12 Remove the upper engine to transmission mounting bolts.

13 Remove the radiator cooling fan assembly as described in Chapter 3 Section 5.

14 Undo the bolts and slide rearwards the exhaust pipe connecting piece between the front and rear sections of the exhaust system. Also undo the retaining bolts and remove the exhaust front mounting bracket **(see illustration)**. **Note:** *On some models the exhaust must be detached at the turbocharger and removed.*

15 Where fitted, disconnect the wiring plug from the engine oil level/temperature sensor on the sump **(see illustration)**. This will prevent the sensor from damage when the engine moves forward.

16 With reference to Chapter 8 Section 2, unscrew and remove the bolts securing the driveshafts to the transmission output flanges. Tie the right-hand driveshaft to one side, and then tie the left-hand driveshaft to the suspension strut, so that the shaft is as high as possible **(see illustration)**. Alternatively, completely remove the driveshaft.

17 Remove the front subframe, complete with the track control arms as described in Chapter 10 Section 22. The steering rack can either be removed with the subframe or detatched from the subframe and left in place.

18 Support the engine with a hoist or (where available) with the factory support bar located on the suspension strut towers and inner wings. Depending on the engine, temporarily remove components as necessary to attach the hoist.

19 Position a trolley jack underneath the transmission, and raise it to just take the weight of the unit.

20 Undo and remove the bolts securing the left-hand transmission mounting. Lower the engine and transmission slightly and remove the bracket from the transmission **(see illustration)**.

21 Where fitted, undo the retaining bolt and remove the small cover plate located above the right-hand driveshaft flange.

22 Lower the engine/transmission until there is sufficient clearance between the upper edge of the transmission and the left-hand chassis member.

23 Unscrew and remove the lower bolts securing the transmission to the engine, noting the bolt locations, as they are of different sizes and lengths.

24 Check that all the fixings and attachments are clear of the transmission. Enlist the aid of an assistant to help in guiding and supporting the transmission during its removal.

25 The transmission is located on engine alignment dowels, and if stuck on them, it may be necessary to carefully tap and prise the transmission free of the dowels to allow separation. Once the transmission is disconnected from the location dowels, swivel the unit out and lower it out of the vehicle.

Note that the transmission must be turned to allow the driveshaft flange to clear the engine block. This is a difficult manoeuvre as the transmission must be supported at all times and not allowed to hang on the transmission input shaft.

⚠ *Warning: Support the transmission to ensure that it remains steady on the jack head.*

26 When the transmission is clear of the locating dowels and clutch components, lower the transmission to the ground and withdraw from under the car. Make sure that the transmission does not fall and lose any transmission oil. Also make sure that the clutch assembly comes away with the transmission, and stays inside the bell-housing.

Refitting

27 Refitting the transmission is essentially a reversal of the removal procedure, but note the following points:

a) *Always replace the spigot bearing as described in Section 7.*

b) *When reconnecting the transmission to the engine, ensure that the location dowels are in position, and that the transmission is correctly aligned with them before pushing it fully into engagement with the engine.*

c) *Tighten all retaining bolts to their specified torque wrench settings.*

d) *Be sure to guide the selector cable into the support bracket as the transmission is refitted – renew the retaining clips.*

e) *Adjust the selector cable, as described in Section 4.*

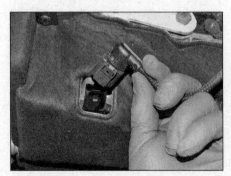

2.15 Disconnect the oil level/temperature sensor wiring connector

2.16 Fasten the driveshaft to one side

2.20 Remove the bracket from the transmission

4.5 Selector cable clip and outer cable circlip

4.6 Prise the inner cable from the ball joint

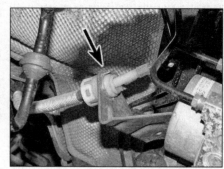

4.7 Release the outer cable securing clip

f) *Refer to Chapter 8 Section 2, and then tighten the driveshaft bolts to the specified torque.*
g) *On completion, check the coolant level.*
h) *If a new transmission unit has been fitted, it will be necessary to have the transmission ECM 'matched' to the engine management ECM electronically, to ensure correct operation – seek the advice of your VAG/ Seat dealer or suitably equipped specialist.*
i) *Refill the transmission with the correct grade and quantity of oil, as described in Section 6.*

3 Transmission overhaul – general information

1 In the event of a fault occurring, it will be necessary to establish whether the fault is electrical, mechanical or hydraulic in nature, before repair work can be contemplated. Diagnosis requires detailed knowledge of the transmission's operation and construction, as well as access to specialised test equipment, and so is deemed to be beyond the scope of this manual. It is therefore essential that problems with the automatic transmission be referred to a Volkswagen dealer or specialist for assessment.
2 Note that a faulty transmission should not be removed before the vehicle has been assessed by a dealer or specialist, as fault diagnosis is best carried out with the transmission still in the vehicle.

4 Selector lever housing and cable – removal, refitting and adjustment

Note: *The selector lever housing and cable should not be separated, remove the housing and cable as a complete unit.*

Removal

1 Move the selector lever to the P position, and remove the battery and battery tray as described in Chapter 5A Section 3.
2 Remove the air filter housing as described in Chapter 4A Section 3 (petrol engine) or Chapter 4B Section 3 (diesel engine).
3 Working inside the vehicle, remove the centre console and gear selector knob, as described in Chapter 11 Section 26.

6-speed (0D9) transmission

4 Working inside the engine compartment, slacken the adjustment screw on the cable end fitting at the transmission end.
5 Prise out the clips securing the cable to the lever on the transmission, and the outer cable to the support bracket **(see illustration)**. Withdraw the cable from the support bracket and discard the clips – new ones must be fitted.

7-speed (0CW) transmission

6 Working inside the engine compartment, use a pair of long-nose pliers to release the cable end fitting from the ball head on the selector lever **(see illustration)**.
7 Prise out the clip securing the outer cable

and withdraw the cable from the support bracket on the transmission **(see illustration)**. Discard the retaining clip – as a new one must be fitted.

All transmissions

8 Raise the front of the vehicle and support it securely on axle stands (see *Jacking and vehicle support*).
9 Remove the centre tunnel front heat shield from the underside of the vehicle to gain access to the base of the selector lever housing and cable. It may be necessary to separate the exhaust downpipe from the intermediate pipe.
10 Working inside the vehicle, undo the retaining nuts **(see illustrations)**, then remove the bracket and lower the gear selector housing downwards. Withdraw it complete with selector cable out from under the vehicle. It may be useful having the aid of an assistant at this point, to be under the vehicle when lowering the selector housing.

Refitting

11 Refitting is the reversal of the removal procedure, noting the following points:
a) *DO NOT grease the cable end fittings.*
b) *Ensure that the cable is correctly routed and secured, as noted on removal.*
c) *Take care not to bend or kink the cable.*
d) *Carry out the cable adjustment procedure described below before reconnecting the cable at the transmission end.*
e) *When refitting the outer cable to the support bracket, use new clips.*

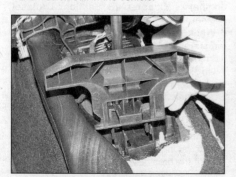

4.10a Remove the rear bracket (where fitted)...

4.10b ...and then remove the front...

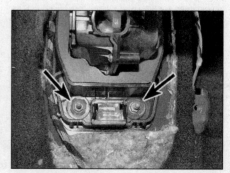

4.10c ...and rear mounting nuts

4.15a Secure the outer cable in the bracket ...

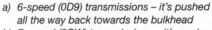

4.15b ...and slacken the cable adjustment screw

4.17 Push the lever in the direction show

Adjustment

12 Inside the car, move the selector lever to the P position.

13 If not already done, disconnect the cable from the selector lever on the transmission.

14 Move the selector lever inside the vehicle from 'P' to 'S' and back, repeatedly, to check that everything moves easily. Seat recommend that you do not grease the cable.

15 Reconnect the cable to the lever at the transmission, and then slacken the cable adjusting bolt (see illustrations).

16 Check that both the selector lever inside the car and the lever on the transmission are in their P positions. Gently rock the levers backwards and forwards to make sure the cable is settled. Do not move either lever out of the P position.

17 The transmission lever is in the P position when:

a) 6-speed (0D9) transmissions – it's pushed all the way back towards the bulkhead
b) 7-speed (0CW) transmissions – it's pushed back towards the selector cable mounting bracket (see illustration).

18 When in position, tighten the cable adjusting bolt.

19 Verify the operation of the selector lever by shifting through all gear positions and checking that every gear can be selected smoothly and without delay.

5 Emergency release of selector lever

1 If the vehicles battery is disconnected or discharged, it is possible to release the selector lever from its locked position.

2 Carefully prise up the selector lever gaiter

surround trim from the console and move it to one side (see illustration).

3 Press the yellow plastic wedge downwards (see illustration). It should now be possible to move the selector lever to the desired position.

6 Transmission oil renewal

7-speed dual clutch 0CW transmission

Note: The transmission oil is filled for life. There is no requirement to change the oil.

1 Take the vehicle on a short journey to warm the transmission oil, and then park the car on a level surface. For improved access to the drain plug, apply the handbrake, then jack up the front of the vehicle and support it on axle stands (see Jacking and vehicle support), but note that the rear of the vehicle should also be raised to ensure all oil is drained.

2 Undo the retaining screws and remove the engine undertray. Wipe clean the area around the transmission drain plug, which is situated on the lower rear of the transmission (see illustration).

3 Place a container under the transmission casing, then unscrew the drain plug from the base of the differential housing, and allow the oil to drain.

4 Remove the battery and battery tray as described in Chapter 5A Section 3.

5 Remove the air cleaner housing as described in Chapter 4A Section 3 (petrol engine) or Chapter 4B Section 3 (diesel engine).

6 When the oil has finished draining, clean the surrounding area, refit the drain plug and tighten it to the specified torque.

7 Unclip the breather cap from the selector cover plate on the top of the transmission casing (see illustration).

8 Using a length of hose, and funnel, add 1.7 litres of new oil to the transmission. Only use the correct Volkswagen oil, for 7-speed transmission.

9 Refit the breather cap, making sure that it is secure. Renew if damaged.

10 The remainder of refitting is a reversal of removal.

5.2 Prise up the selector lever gaiter surround trim

5.3 Press down the yellow plastic peg

6.2 Transmission oil drain plug

6.7 Breather cap on selector cover – 0CW transmissions

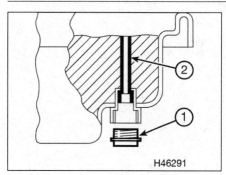

6.13 Transmission fluid level check

1 Level plug   2 Level tube

6-speed dual clutch 0D9 transmission

Checking oil level

Note: *An accurate fluid level check can only be made with the transmission fluid at a temperature of between 35°C and 45°C, and if it is not possible to ascertain this temperature, it is strongly recommended that the check be made by a Volkswagen dealer who will have the instrumentation to check the temperature and to check the transmission electronics for fault codes. Over-filling or under-filling adversely affects the function of the transmission.*

11 Take the vehicle on a short journey to warm the transmission oil. And then park the vehicle on level ground and engage P with the selector lever. Raise the front and rear of the vehicle and support it on axle stands (see *Jacking and vehicle support*), ensuring the vehicle is kept level. Undo the retaining screws and remove the engine undertray to gain access to the base of the transmission unit.

12 Start the engine and run it at idle speed until the transmission fluid temperature reaches 35°C. Note that the level is checked with the engine running.

13 Unscrew the fluid level plug from the bottom of the transmission sump **(see illustration)**.

14 If fluid continually drips from the level tube as the fluid temperature increases, the fluid level is correct and does not need to be topped-up. Note that there will be some fluid already present in the level tube, and it will be necessary to observe when this amount has drained before making the level check. Make sure that the check is made before the fluid temperature reaches 45°C.

15 If no fluid drips from the level tube, even when the fluid temperature has reached 45°C, it will be necessary to add fluid. Volkswagen technicians use an adaptor which screws into the bottom of the transmission sump, however, a tube inserted up through the drain plug (into the space above the fluid); will allow fluid to be added. Ideally, the fluid should be allowed to cool before adding the fluid.

16 Check the condition of the seal on the level plug and renew it if necessary by cutting off the old seal and fitting a new one. Refit the plug and tighten to the specified torque.

17 Refit the engine undertray, tighten the retaining screws securely, and lower the vehicle to the ground.

Oil and filter change

18 The recommended oil and filter change is at every 37,000 miles (60,000 kilometres). The oil and filter should always be replaced if the clutch has been replaced or there is any evidence of metal particles in the oil.

19 Start the engine and run it at idle speed until the transmission fluid temperature reaches 35°C. The temperature must not be above 50°C.

20 Engage 'Park on the transmission and remove the complete air filter housing as described in Chapter 4A Section 3 (petrol engines) or Chapter 4B Section 3 (diesel engines).

21 Remove the battery and battery tray as described in Chapter 5A Section 3.

22 Place shop towels around the filter housing and slacken the filter housing, so that the seal is just broken. This will allow most of the oil in the filter to drain into the transmission. Allow the oil to drain and then fully remove the filter housing.

23 Clean the area around the housing and remove the shop towels. Fit the new filter and then refit (with a new seal) the filter housing and tighten it to the specified torque.

24 Raise the front and rear of the vehicle and support it on axle stands (see *Jacking and vehicle support*), ensuring the vehicle is kept level. Undo the retaining screws and remove the engine undertray to gain access to the base of the transmission unit.

25 Unscrew the fluid level plug from the bottom of the transmission sump and then remove the overflow pipe (8 mm hex key required) and allow the oil to drain **(see illustration 6.13)**.

26 Refit the overflow pipe and then fill the transmission with 5.5 litres of DSG transmission fluid. Refit the drain plug.

27 Refit the air filter, battery tray and battery and then start the engine. Depress the brake pedal and move the selector lever through all the positions several times.

28 Select park and then check the oil level as described at the start of this section. Top up as required.

29 Refit the engine undertray, tighten the retaining screws securely, and lower the vehicle to the ground.

7 Spigot bearing – renewal

1 The spigot bearing must always be replaced on DSG transmissions.

2 As a reference measure the depth of the installed bearing before removal **(see illustration)**. The factory setting is 2.0 mm inside the end of the crankshaft.

3 An internal bearing puller and slide hammer are required to remove the bearing. Select a suitable expanding mandrel and pull out the bearing **(see illustrations)**.

4 Fit the new bearing by driving in into the crankshaft using a socket that bears only on the outer edge of the bearing. Check that the bearing is set to the correct depth and refit the transmission as described in Section 2.

7.2 Check the depth of the bearing before removal.

7.3a Select the correct puller,...

7.3b ...pull out the bearing...

7.3c ... and remove it

Chapter 8
Driveshafts

Contents

Section number

Driveshaft gaiters – renewal 3
Driveshaft overhaul – general information 4

Driveshafts – removal and refitting 2
General Information 1

Section number

Degrees of difficulty

Easy, suitable for novice with little experience	Fairly easy, suitable for beginner with some experience	Fairly difficult, suitable for competent DIY mechanic	Difficult, suitable for experienced DIY mechanic	Very difficult, suitable for expert DIY or professional

Specifications

General
Driveshaft type . . . .

Steel shafts with outer constant velocity joints and inner tripod or constant velocity joints (according to type).

Type code differences:
VL 100 . . . .

CV joints each end, inner joint diameter 90 mm or 100 mm bolted to transmission drive flanges on each side

VL 107 . . . .

CV joints each end, inner joint diameter 107 mm bolted to transmission drive flanges on each side

AAR 3300i . . . .

CV outer joint, tripod inner joint body bolted to transmission drive flanges on each side or inserted into transmission

Lubrication
Overhaul and repair . . . . Use only special grease supplied in sachets with gaiter/overhaul kits
Joint grease type . . . . Refer to a Vokswagon dealer
Joint grease quantity:
Outer joint . . . . 80 g
Inner joint . . . . 130 g

Torque wrench settings

	Nm	lbf ft
Driveshaft-to-transmission flange bolts:		
Stage 1	10	7
Stage 2:		
M8 x 48 bolts* – (VL100 type joint)	40	30
M10 x 52 bolts* – (VL107 type joint)	70	52
M10 x 23 bolts – (AAR 3300i type joint)	70	52
Hub bolt: *		
Stage 1	200	148
Stage 2	Angle-tighten a further 180°	
Lower arm-to-balljoint nuts: *		
Stage 1	40	30
Stage 2	Angle-tighten a further 45°	
Wheel bolts	120	89

*Use new bolts/nuts

1 General Information

1 Drive is transmitted from the differential to the front wheels by means of two steel driveshafts of either solid or hollow construction (depending on model, and which side of the vehicle). Both driveshafts are splined at their outer ends, to accept the wheel hubs, and are secured to the hub by a large bolt. The inner end of each driveshaft is either bolted to a transmission drive flange or splined directly onto the differential splined shaft.

2 The outer ends of each driveshaft are fitted with ball-bearing type constant velocity (CV) joints, to ensure the smooth and efficient transmission of drive at all the angles possible, as the roadwheels move up-and-down with the suspension, and as they turn from side to side under steering.

3 The inner ends of each driveshaft (except for the AAR 3300i type joints) are fitted with ball and cage type constant velocity (CV) joint. The AAR 3300i driveshafts have a triple roller type (tripod) joint fitted to the inner end of the driveshaft.

4 Hytrel (thermoplastic elastomer) gaiters are fitted over the CV joints with steel clips. These gaiters combine the flexibility of rubber with the strength and durability of thermoplastics. The gaiters contain the grease that lubricates the joints, and also protect the joints from the entry of dirt and debris.

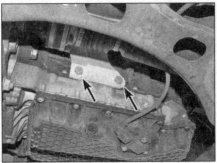

2.3a Unbolt and...

2.3b ...remove the heat shield

2 Driveshafts – removal and refitting

Removal

1 Remove the wheel trim/centre cap (as applicable) then apply the handbrake, and partially unscrew the relevant hub bolt with the vehicle resting on its wheels, by a maximum of 90º – note that the bolt is very tight, and a suitable extension bar will probably be required to aid unscrewing (see illustration 2.4). Also slacken the road wheel securing bolts by half a turn. Note: Do not loosen the bolt more than 90º with the vehicle standing on the ground, as the wheel bearings may be damaged.

2 Apply the handbrake, then jack up the front of the vehicle and support it on axle stands

(see Jacking and vehicle support). Remove the appropriate front roadwheel.

3 Remove the retaining screws and/or clips, and remove the undershields from beneath the engine/transmission unit to gain access to the driveshafts. Where necessary, also unbolt the heat shield from the transmission housing to improve access to the driveshaft inner joint (see illustrations).

4 Fully unscrew and remove the hub bolt (see illustration). Note: Discard the bolt and obtain a new one.

5 Unscrew the three nuts securing the front suspension lower arm balljoint to the lower arm (see illustrations). Discard the nuts, as new ones must be used on refitting. Disconnect the anti-roll bar drop link from the anti-roll bar and on models with Zenon headlights unbolt the ride height sensor from the control arm.

6 Lever the lower arm downwards to release it from the balljoint studs, then pull the hub carrier outwards, and at the same time withdraw the driveshaft outer constant velocity joint from the hub (see illustration). If the joint splines are a tight fit in the hub, tap the joint out of the hub using a soft-faced mallet and drift. If this fails to free the driveshaft from the hub, the joint will have to be pressed out using a suitable tool bolted to the hub.

7 On some models, in order to gain the necessary clearance required to withdraw the left-hand driveshaft, it may be necessary to unbolt the rear engine transmission mounting from the subframe (see illustration), and move the engine slightly.

2.4 A 12 point (Bi-hex) socket will be required

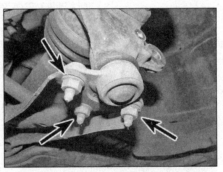

2.5a Undo the lower ball joint retaining nuts...

2.5b ...and lower the control arm

2.6 Slide the driveshaft out from the hub assembly

2.7 Unbolt the rear pendulum mounting

2.9a Make alignment marks…

2.9b …and remove the drive flange bolts and plates

2.16 Locate a new gasket on the inner joint

8 Proceed as follows according to driveshaft type.

Caution: Support the driveshaft by suspending it with wire or string – do not allow it to hang under its own weight, or the joint may be damaged.

Inner joint with drive flange – VL100 and VL107

9 Mark the inner joint in relation to the drive flange for refitting. Using a multi-splined tool, unscrew and remove the six bolts securing the inner driveshaft joint to the transmission flange and, recover the retaining plates from underneath the bolts **(see illustrations)**.

Inner joint splined to differential drive shaft – VL107

10 Position a container beneath the transmission to catch spilt oil, and then pull out the driveshaft. The internal driveshaft circlip may be tight in the transmission side gear, in which case careful use of a lever against the transmission casing will be required. Lever against a block of wood to prevent damage to the casing, and take care not to damage the oil seal as the driveshaft is being removed. **Note:** *Pull only on the inner joint body, not the driveshaft itself; otherwise the gaiter may be damaged.*

Inner joint triple roller (tripod) located in joint body – AAR 3300i

11 Mark the inner joint body and driveshaft in relation to each other, as the tripod joint will need to be refitted in the joint body in the same position. Loosen the larger retaining clip, ease off the rubber gaiter, and pull the triple roller out of the joint body.

All types

12 Manoeuvre the driveshaft out from underneath the vehicle and (where fitted) recover the gasket from the end of the inner constant velocity joint. **Note:** *Discard the gasket and obtain a new one.*

Caution: Do not allow the vehicle to rest on its wheels with one or both driveshaft(s) removed, as damage to the wheel bearings may result.

13 If moving the vehicle is unavoidable, temporarily insert the outer end of the driveshaft(s) in the hub(s), and tighten the driveshaft retaining bolt(s); in this case, the

inner end(s) of the driveshaft(s) must be supported, for example by suspending with string from the vehicle underbody.

Refitting

14 Where applicable, check the condition of the circlip on the inner end of the driveshaft, and if necessary, renew it.

15 As applicable, clean the splines on each end of the driveshaft and in the hub and apply a little oil, and where applicable wipe clean the oil seal in the transmission casing. Check the oil seal and if necessary renew it.

Inner joint with bolted drive flange – VL100 and VL107

16 Ensure that the transmission flange and inner joint mating surfaces are clean and dry. Where necessary, fit a new gasket to the joint by peeling off its backing foil and sticking it in position **(see illustration)**.

17 Manoeuvre the driveshaft into position, aligning the previously made marks **(see illustration)**, and then align the inner joint holes with those on the transmission flange. Refit the new retaining bolts and locking plates, and then tighten the retaining bolts to the specified torque.

Inner joint splined to differential drive shaft – AAR3300i

18 Locate the inner end of the driveshaft into the transmission – turn the driveshaft as necessary to engage the splines. Press in the driveshaft until the internal circlip engages the groove. Check that the circlip is engaged by

2.17 Align the markings made on removal when refitting

attempting to pull out the driveshaft with only moderate force.

Inner joint triple roller (tripod) located in joint body – AAR 3300i

19 Fill the inner joint with the specified quantity of grease, and then locate the driveshaft tripod into the joint body, aligning the previously made marks. Ease the gaiter onto the joint body, and secure the gaiter with a new retaining clip.

All types

20 With the lower arm levered downwards, engage the outer joint with the hub. Fit the new hub bolt and use it to draw the joint fully into position.

21 Align the balljoint studs with the holes in the lower arm, then release the arm and fit the three new nuts. Tighten the nuts to the specified torque.

22 Where applicable, refit the lower rear mounting-to-transmission bolts, and then tighten the new bolts to the specified torque.

23 Tighten the driveshaft bolt to the Stage 1 torque setting. **Note:** *The bolt must be tightened with the wheel clear of the ground. There are three different types of bolts fitted, one is ribbed under the face of the bolt head and one is smooth.*

24 Refit the roadwheel and lower the vehicle to the ground, then angle-tighten the driveshaft bolt through the Stage 2 angle (see Specifications Section).

25 Once the driveshaft bolt is correctly tightened, tighten the wheel bolts to the specified torque and refit the wheel trim/centre cap.

3 Driveshaft gaiters – renewal

1 Remove the driveshaft from the car, as described in Section 2. Continue as described under the relevant sub-heading. Driveshafts with a tripod type inner joint can be identified by the shape of the inner CV joint; the driveshaft retaining bolt holes are in extensions from the joint, giving it a six-pointed star-shaped exterior, in

3.1a Driveshaft components – models with VL100 CV joint

1 Hub bolt
2 Outer joint gaiter
3 Gaiter securing clip
4 Driveshaft
5 Inner joint
6 Flange bolts
7 Bolt retaining plate
8 Thrust washer
9 Circlip
10 Washer
11 Gasket
12 Inner joint gaiter
13 Outer joint

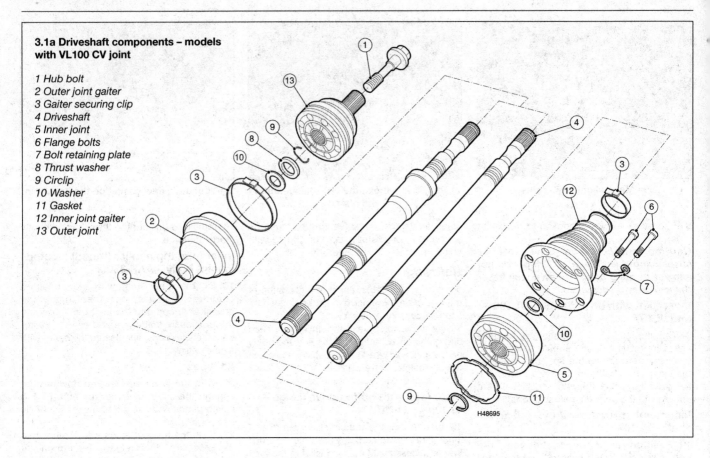

3.1b Driveshaft joint components – models with VL107 CV joint

1 Hub bolt
2 Outer joint
3 Circlip
4 Gaiter securing clip
5 Gaiter
6 Gaiter securing clip
7 Driveshaft
8 Gaiter securing clip
9 Gaiter
10 Gaiter securing clip
11 Locking plate
12 Cap
13 Inner joint
14 Circlip
15 End cover
16 Bolt

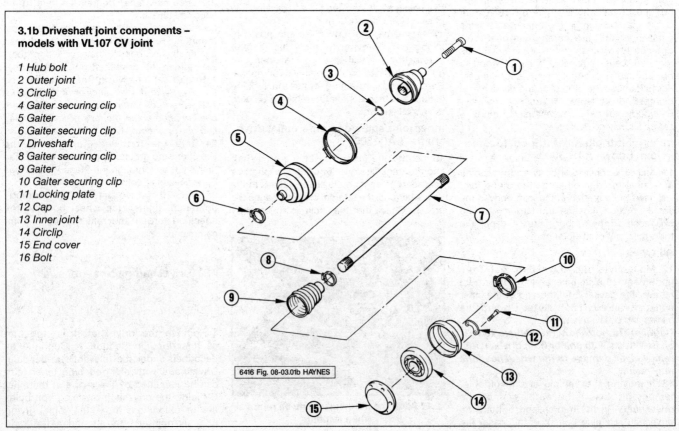

6416 Fig. 08-03.01b HAYNES

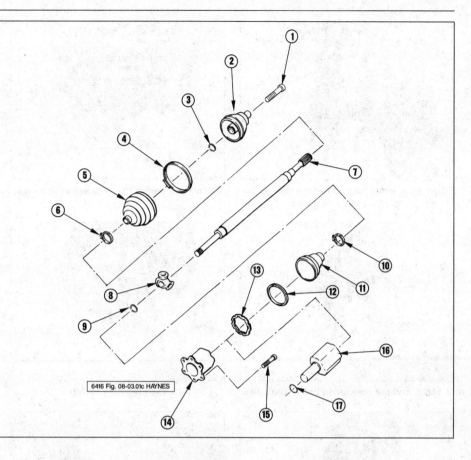

**3.1c Driveshaft joint components –
models with AAR3300i triple roller joints**

1 Hub bolt
2 Outer joint
3 Circlip
4 Gaiter securing clip
5 Gaiter
6 Gaiter securing clip
7 Driveshaft
8 Tripod roller
9 Circlip
10 Gaiter securing clip
11 Inner joint gaiter
12 Gaiter securing clip
13 Adaptor
14 Inner joint body
15 Bolt
16 Inner joint body
17 Circlip

6416 Fig. 08-03.01c HAYNES

contrast to the smooth, circular shape of the ball-and-cage joint **(see illustrations)**.

Outer CV joint gaiter – All types of driveshafts

2 Secure the driveshaft in a vice equipped with soft jaws, and release the two outer joint gaiter retaining clips **(see illustration)**. If necessary, the retaining clips can be cut to release them.
3 Slide the rubber gaiter down the shaft to expose the constant velocity joint, and scoop out excess grease **(see illustration)**.
4 Using a soft-faced mallet, tap the joint off the end of the driveshaft **(see illustration)**.
5 Remove the circlip from the driveshaft groove. Where fitted slide off the thrustwasher and dished washer, noting which way around they are fitted **(see illustration)**.

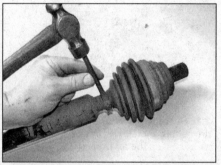

3.2 Release the outer joint gaiter clips…

6 Slide the rubber gaiter off the driveshaft and discard it **(see illustration)**.
7 Thoroughly clean the constant velocity

3.3 …and slide the gaiter away from the joint

joint(s) using paraffin, or a suitable solvent, and dry thoroughly. Carry out a visual inspection as follows.

3.4 Use a mallet to drive the outer joint from the driveshaft

3.5 Removing the circlip, thrustwasher and dished washer

3.6 Removing the outer gaiter

3.11 Temporarily tape over the splines to protect the new gaiter

3.14a Pack half of the grease in the joint...

3.14b ...and the remaining half in the gaiter

3.15a Fit a new circlip...

3.15b ...then refit the outer joint

3.16 Seat the gaiter on the outer joint and driveshaft, then lift its inner lip to equalise the air pressure

worn or damaged, it will be necessary to renew the complete joint assembly. If the joint is in satisfactory condition, obtain a new gaiter and retaining clips, a constant velocity joint circlip and the correct type of grease. Grease is often supplied with the joint repair kit – if not, use good-quality molybdenum disulphide grease.

11 Tape over the splines on the end of the driveshaft, to protect the new gaiter as it is slid into place **(see illustration)**.

12 Slide the new gaiter onto the end of the driveshaft, then remove the protective tape from the driveshaft splines.

13 Slide on the dished washer, making sure its convex side is innermost, followed by the thrustwasher.

14 Pack the joint with half the quantity of the specified type of grease. Work the grease well into the bearing tracks whilst twisting the joint, and fill the rubber gaiter with the remaining half **(see illustrations)**.

15 Fit a new circlip to the driveshaft, then tap the joint onto the driveshaft until the circlip engages in its groove **(see illustrations)**. Make sure that the joint is securely retained by the circlip.

16 Ease the gaiter over the joint, and ensure that the gaiter lips are correctly located on both the driveshaft and constant velocity joint. Lift the outer sealing lip of the gaiter to equalise air pressure within the gaiter **(see illustration)**.

17 Fit the large metal retaining clip to the gaiter. Pull the clip as tight as possible, and locate the hooks on the clip in their slots. Remove any slack in the gaiter retaining clip by carefully compressing the raised section of the clip. In the absence of the special tool, a pair of side-cutters may be used, taking care not to cut the clip **(see illustrations)**. Secure the small retaining clip using the same procedure.

18 Check the constant velocity joint moves freely in all directions, then refit the driveshaft to the vehicle, as described in Section 2.

Inner gaiter with bolted drive flange – VL100 and VL107

19 Secure the driveshaft in a vice equipped with soft jaws, then release the gaiter small securing clip, securing the gaiter to the driveshaft **(see illustration)**.

8 Move the inner splined driving member from side-to-side to expose each ball in turn at the top of its track. Examine the balls for cracks, flat spots or signs of surface pitting.
9 Inspect the ball tracks on the inner and outer members. If the tracks have widened,

the balls will no longer be a tight fit. At the same time, check the ball cage windows for wear or cracking between the windows.
10 If on inspection any of the constant velocity joint components are found to be

3.17a Fit the large metal retaining clip...

3.17b ...and use a suitable tool to tighten it

3.19 Release the gaiter small securing clip...

3.20 ...drive the metal ring from the joint outer member

3.22 Remove the circlip...

3.23a ...followed by the joint...

20 Using a hammer and a small drift, carefully drive the gaiter metal ring from the joint outer member **(see illustration)**.

21 Slide the gaiter down the driveshaft to expose the constant velocity joint, and scoop out excess grease.

22 Remove the circlip from the end of the driveshaft using circlip pliers **(see illustration)**.

23 Press or drive the driveshaft from the joint, taking great care not to damage the joint. Recover the dished washer fitted between the constant velocity joint and the gaiter **(see illustrations)**.

24 Slide the gaiter from the end of the driveshaft **(see illustration)**.

25 Proceed as described previously in paragraphs 7 to 12 **(see illustrations)**.

26 Slide the dished washer onto the driveshaft, making sure its convex side is innermost.

27 Fit the joint to the end of the driveshaft, noting that the chamfered edge of the internal splines on the joint should face towards the driveshaft. Drive or press the joint into position until it contacts the shoulder on the driveshaft.

28 Fit a new circlip to retain the joint on the end of the driveshaft.

29 If the left-hand driveshaft is being worked on, mark the final installation position of the gaiter outboard end on the driveshaft using tape or paint – do not scratch the surface of the driveshaft.

30 Pack the joint with the half the recommended quantity of grease (see Specifications), and then pack the gaiter with the remaining half **(see illustrations)**.

3.23b ...dished washer...

3.24 ...and gaiter

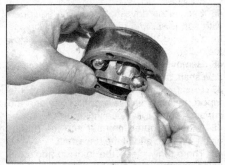

3.25a Tilt the splined hub and cage to remove the ball-bearings...

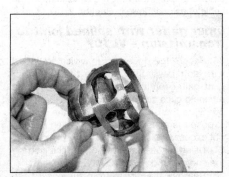

3.25b ...then separate the hub from the cage

3.25c Inner CV joint gaiter repair kit

3.30a Pack the inner joint with half of the grease...

3.30b ...then pack the gaiter with the remaining half

3.31a Temporarily fit one of the flange bolts to ensure the bolt holes are correctly aligned...

3.31b ...then drive the metal ring onto the joint outer member

31 Slide the gaiter up the driveshaft, and press or drive the gaiter metal ring onto the joint outer member. To ensure the bolt holes are correctly positioned, temporarily fit a couple of flange bolts (see illustrations).

32 If the left-hand driveshaft is being worked on, slide the outboard end of the gaiter into position using the mark made previously (see paragraph 29), then secure the outer gaiter securing clip in position as described in paragraph 17.

33 If the right-hand driveshaft is being worked on, slide the outboard end of the gaiter into position on the driveshaft, then secure the outer gaiter securing clip in position as described in paragraph 17.

34 Check the driveshaft joint moves freely in all directions, then refit the driveshaft to the vehicle, as described in Section 2.

Inner gaiter with splined joint to transmission – VL107

35 Secure the driveshaft in a vice equipped with soft jaws, and release the two inner joint gaiter retaining clips. If necessary, the retaining clips can be cut to release them.

36 Slide the rubber gaiter down the shaft to expose the constant velocity joint, and scoop out excess grease.

37 Using a soft-faced mallet, tap the joint off the end of the driveshaft.

38 Remove the circlip from the end of the driveshaft groove, and then slide the rubber gaiter off the driveshaft and discard it.

39 Proceed as described previously in paragraphs 7 to 12.

40 Pack the joint with half the quantity of the specified type of grease. Work the grease well into the bearing tracks whilst twisting the joint, and fill the rubber gaiter with the remaining half.

41 Fit a new circlip to the driveshaft, then tap the joint onto the driveshaft until the circlip engages in its groove. Make sure that the joint is securely retained by the circlip.

42 Ease the gaiter over the joint, and ensure that the gaiter lips are correctly located on both the driveshaft and constant velocity joint. Lift the outer sealing lip of the gaiter to equalise air pressure within the gaiter.

43 Fit the large metal retaining clip to the gaiter, as described in paragraph 17. Secure the small retaining clip using the same procedure.

44 Check the constant velocity joint moves freely in all directions, then refit the driveshaft to the vehicle, as described in Section 2.

Inner gaiter with triple roller (tripod) joint – AAR 3300i

45 Secure the driveshaft in a vice equipped with soft jaws, and clean out the old grease from around the triple roller joint and inside the gaiter.

46 Remove the circlip from the end of the driveshaft.

47 Press or drive the driveshaft from the tripod, taking great care not to damage the surfaces of the roller locating arms.

48 Slide the outer member and the rubber gaiter from the end of the driveshaft.

49 Thoroughly clean the joint components using paraffin, or a suitable solvent, and dry thoroughly. Carry out a visual inspection as follows.

50 Inspect the tripod rollers and the joint outer member for signs of wear, pitting or scuffing on their mating surfaces. Check that the joint rollers rotate smoothly, with no traces of roughness.

51 If the rollers or outer member shown signs of wear or damage, it will be necessary

to renew the complete driveshaft, since the joint is not available separately. If the joint is in satisfactory condition, obtain a repair kit, consisting of a new gaiter, retaining clips, circlip, and the correct type and quantity of grease.

52 Tape over the splines on the end of the driveshaft, to protect the new gaiter as it is slid into place, and then slide the new gaiter over the end of the driveshaft and secure the smaller end in place with a new retaining clip. Remove the protective tape from the driveshaft splines.

53 Press or drive the tripod onto the end of the driveshaft until it contacts the stop, ensuring that the marks made on the end of the driveshaft and the tripod before dismantling are aligned. Note that the chamfered edge of the internal splines on the tripod should face towards the driveshaft.

54 Fit the new circlip to retain the tripod on the end of the driveshaft.

55 Check the triple roller joint moves freely, then refit the driveshaft to the vehicle, as described in Section 2.

4 Driveshaft overhaul – general information

1 If any of the checks described in this Chapter reveal wear in any driveshaft joint, first remove the roadwheel trim or centre cap (as applicable) and check that the hub bolt is tight. If the bolt is loose, obtain a new one, and tighten it to the specified torque (see Section 2). If the bolt is tight, refit the centre cap/trim, and repeat the check on the other hub bolt.

2 Road test the vehicle, and listen for a metallic clicking from the front of the vehicle as the vehicle is driven slowly in a circle on full-lock. If a clicking noise is heard, this indicates wear in the outer constant velocity joint; this means that the joint must be renewed.

3 If vibration consistent with roadspeed is felt through the car when accelerating, there is a possibility of wear in the inner constant velocity joints.

4 To check the joints for wear, remove the driveshafts, then dismantle them as described in Section 3. If any wear or free play is found, the affected joint must be renewed. Refer to a Volkswagen dealer or aftermarket supplier for information on the availability of driveshaft components.

Chapter 9
Braking system

Contents

Anti-lock braking system (ABS) – general information
and precautions 18
Anti-lock braking system (ABS) components – removal and
refitting 19
Brake disc – inspection, removal and refitting 6
Brake light switch – removal and refitting 17
Brake pedal assembly – removal and refitting 10
Front brake caliper – removal, overhaul and refitting 5
Front brake disc shield – removal and refitting 7
Front brake pads – renewal 4
General information and precautions 1

Handbrake control switch – removal and refitting 16
Handbrake control unit – removal and refitting 15
Handbrake motor – removal and refitting 14
Hydraulic pipes and hoses – renewal 3
Hydraulic system – bleeding 2
Master cylinder – removal, overhaul and refitting 13
Rear brake caliper – removal, overhaul and refitting 9
Rear brake pads – renewal 8
Servo non-return valve – testing, removal and refitting 12
Servo unit – testing, removal and refitting 11
Vacuum pump – testing, removal and refitting 20

Degrees of difficulty

Easy, suitable for novice with little experience	**Fairly easy,** suitable for beginner with some experience	**Fairly difficult,** suitable for competent DIY mechanic	**Difficult,** suitable for experienced DIY mechanic	**Very difficult,** suitable for expert DIY or professional

Specifications

Front brakes

Caliper type	PC57, FS III, or C60
Disc diameter:	
FS III	276 mm
PC57:	
15" wheels	288 mm
16" wheels	312 mm
C60	340 mm
Disc thickness.	
New:	
FS III	24.0 mm
PC57	25.0 mm
C60	30.0 mm
Minimum permissible thickness:	
FS III	21.0 mm
PC57	22.0 mm
C60	27 mm
Maximum disc run-out	0.1 mm
Brake pad lining thickness (all models):	
New	12 – 14.0 mm
Minimum	2.0 mm

Rear disc brakes

Caliper type	FNc-M38 (15") or FNc-M42 (17")
Disc diameter:	
FNc-M38	272 mm
FNc-M42	310 mm
Disc thickness:	
New:	
FNc-M38	10.0 mm
FNc-M42	22.0 mm
Minimum thickness:	
FNc-M38	08.0 mm
FNc-M42	20.0 mm
Maximum disc run-out	0.1 mm
Brake pad lining thickness:	
All versions	11 mm
Minimum	2.0 mm

Torque wrench settings

	Nm	lbf ft
ABS control unit retaining bolts	8	6
ABS control unit mounting bracket nuts	20	15
ABS control unit to hydraulic unit mounting bolts*		
Stage 1 (seal settling)	1-1.5	0.7 – 1
Stage 2	2.5	1.85
ABS wheel sensor retaining bolts	8	6
Brake light switch	5	4
Brake pedal mounting bracket	25	18
Brake disc shield bolts	12	9
Front brake caliper:		
FS III brake guide pins	30	22
PC57 and C60 caliper bolts*	35	26
Mounting bracket bolts (PC57 and C60 calipers)	200	148
Hydraulic brake line to caliper banjo bolt	35	26
Hydraulic brake line union nuts	14	10
Master cylinder mounting nuts*	16	12
Rear brake caliper:		
Guide pin bolts	35	26
Mounting bracket bolts: *		
Stage 1	90	66
Stage 2	Angle-tighten a further 90°	
Parking motor to caliper bolts	8	6
Roadwheel bolts	120	89
Servo unit mounting bolts	25	18
Vacuum pump bolts (2.0 litre petrol engines only): *		
Stage 1	8	6
Stage 2	Angle-tighten a further 180°	

*Use new fasteners

1 General information and precautions

General information

1 The braking system is of servo-assisted, diagonal dual-circuit hydraulic type. The arrangement of the hydraulic system is such that each circuit operates one front and one rear brake from a tandem master cylinder. Under normal circumstances, both circuits operate in unison, but, if there is hydraulic failure in one circuit, full braking force will still be available at two wheels. On petrol engines, vacuum for the servo unit is supplied from the inlet manifold on 1.2 and 1.4 litre engines.

On 2.0 litre engines vacuum is supplied from a camshaft driven vacuum pump (see Section 20). On diesel engines the vacuum pump is combined with the engine oil pump that is fitted in the sump. Removal and refitting of the oil/vacuum pump is covered in Chapter 2C Section 13.

2 All models covered by this manual are equipped with disc brakes at the front and rear. ABS is fitted as standard to all models (refer to Section 18 for further information on ABS operation).

3 The front disc brakes are actuated by single-piston sliding type calipers, which ensure that equal pressure is applied to each disc pad.

4 The rear brakes are also actuated by single-piston sliding calipers. The handbrake is operated by a motor mounted to the rear brake caliper. Note that rear brake pad replacement requires the use of a suitable diagnostic tool.

Precautions

When servicing any part of the system, work carefully and methodically; also observe scrupulous cleanliness when overhauling any part of the hydraulic system. Always renew components in axle sets (where applicable) if in doubt about their condition, and use only genuine Volkswagen parts, or at least those of known good quality. Note the warnings given in and at relevant points in this Chapter concerning the dangers of asbestos dust and hydraulic fluid.

2 Hydraulic system – bleeding

⚠️ *Warning: Hydraulic fluid is poisonous; wash off immediately and thoroughly in the case of skin contact, and seek immediate medical advice if any fluid is swallowed or gets into the eyes. Certain types of hydraulic fluid are flammable, and may ignite when allowed into contact with hot components; when servicing any hydraulic system, it is safest to assume that the fluid is flammable, and to take precautions against the risk of fire as though it is petrol that is being handled. Hydraulic fluid is also an effective paint stripper, and will attack plastics; if any is spilt, it should be washed off immediately, using copious quantities of fresh water. Finally, it is hygroscopic (it absorbs moisture from the air) – old fluid may be contaminated and unfit for further use. When topping-up or renewing the fluid, always use the recommended type, and ensure that it comes from a freshly opened sealed container.*

Note: *VW specify that at least 0.25 litre of brake fluid should be expelled from each caliper.*

General

1 The correct operation of any hydraulic system is only possible after removing all air from the components and circuit; this is achieved by bleeding the system. Since the clutch hydraulic system also uses fluid from the brake system reservoir, it should also be bled at the same time by referring to Chapter 6.

2 During the bleeding procedure, add only clean, unused hydraulic fluid of the recommended type; never re-use fluid that has already been bled from the system. Ensure that sufficient fluid is available before starting work.

3 If there is any possibility of incorrect fluid being already in the system, the brake components and circuit must be flushed completely with uncontaminated, correct fluid, and new seals should be fitted to the various components.

4 If hydraulic fluid has been lost from the system, or air has entered because of a leak, ensure that the fault is cured before continuing further.

5 Park the vehicle on level ground, then chock the wheels and release the handbrake.

6 Check that all pipes and hoses are secure, unions tight and bleed screws closed. Clean any dirt from around the bleed screws.

7 Unscrew the master cylinder reservoir cap, and top the reservoir up to the MAX level line; refit the cap loosely, and remember to maintain the fluid level at least above the MIN level line throughout the procedure, or there is a risk of further air entering the system.

8 There is a number of one-man, do-it-yourself brake bleeding kits currently available from motor accessory shops. It is recommended that one of these kits is used whenever possible, as they greatly simplify the bleeding operation, and reduce the risk of expelled air and fluid being drawn back into the system. If such a kit is not available, the basic (two-man) method must be used, which is described in detail below.

9 If a kit is to be used, prepare the vehicle as described previously, and follow the kit manufacturer's instructions, as the procedure may vary slightly according to the type being used; generally, they are as outlined below in the relevant sub-section.

10 Whichever method is used, the same sequence must be followed (paragraph 12) to ensure the removal of all air from the system.

Bleeding sequence

11 If the system has been only partially disconnected, and suitable precautions were taken to minimise fluid loss, it should be necessary only to bleed that part of the system.

12 If the complete system is to be bled, then it should be done working in the following sequence:

a) Left-hand front brake.
b) Right-hand front brake.
c) Left-hand rear brake.
d) Right-hand rear brake.

13 If the system is completely empty of fluid, repeat the sequence up to five times, or until the brake pedal feels firm and has an acceptable amount of travel.

Bleeding

Basic (two-man) method

14 Collect together a clean glass jar of reasonable size, a suitable length of plastic or rubber tubing which is a tight fit over the bleed screw, and a ring spanner to fit the screw. The help of an assistant will also be required.

15 Remove the dust cap from the first screw in the sequence **(see illustration)**. Fit the spanner and tube to the screw, place the other end of the tube in the jar, and pour in sufficient fluid to cover the end of the tube.

16 Ensure that the master cylinder reservoir fluid level is maintained at least above the MIN level line throughout the procedure.

17 Have the assistant fully depress the brake pedal several times to build-up pressure, and then maintain it on the final downstroke.

18 While pedal pressure is maintained, unscrew the bleed screw (approximately one turn) and allow the compressed fluid and air to flow into the jar. The assistant should maintain pedal pressure, following it down to the floor if necessary, and should not release it until instructed to do so. When the flow stops, tighten the bleed screw again, have the assistant release the pedal slowly, and recheck the reservoir fluid level.

19 Repeat the steps given in paragraphs 16 and 17 until the fluid emerging from the bleed screw is free from air bubbles. If the master cylinder has been drained and refilled, and air is being bled from the first screw in the sequence, allow approximately five seconds between cycles for the master cylinder passages to refill.

20 When no more air bubbles appear, tighten the bleed screw securely, remove the tube and spanner, and refit the dust cap. Do not overtighten the bleed screw.

21 Repeat the procedure on the remaining screws in the sequence, until all air is removed from the system and the brake pedal feels firm again.

Using a one-way valve kit

22 As their name implies, these kits consist of a length of tubing with a one-way valve fitted, to prevent expelled air and fluid being drawn back into the system; some kits include a translucent container, which can be positioned so that the air bubbles can be more easily seen flowing from the end of the tube.

23 The kit is connected to the bleed screw, which is then opened. The user returns to the driver's seat, depresses the brake pedal with a smooth, steady stroke, and slowly releases it; this is repeated until the expelled fluid is clear of air bubbles **(see illustration)**.

24 Note that these kits simplify work so much that it is easy to forget the master cylinder reservoir fluid level; ensure that this is maintained at least above the MIN level line at all times.

Using a pressure-bleeding kit

25 These kits are usually operated by the reservoir of pressurised air contained in

2.15 Remove the dust cap from the first bleed screw in the sequence

2.23 Bleeding a brake using a one-way valve kit

3.6a Brake hose retaining clip

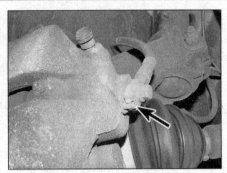

3.6b Locating peg for brake hose end fitting

the spare tyre. However, note that it will be probably necessary to reduce the pressure to less than 1.0 bar (14.5 psi); refer to the instructions supplied with the kit.

26 By connecting a pressurised, fluid-filled container to the master cylinder reservoir, bleeding can be carried out simply by opening each screw in turn (in the specified sequence), and allowing the fluid to flow out until no more air bubbles can be seen in the expelled fluid.

27 This method has the advantage that the large reservoir of fluid provides an additional safeguard against air being drawn into the system during bleeding.

28 Pressure-bleeding is particularly effective when bleeding 'difficult' systems, or when bleeding the complete system at the time of routine fluid renewal.

All methods

29 When bleeding is complete, and firm pedal feel is restored, wash off any spilt fluid, tighten the bleed screws securely, and refit their dust caps.

30 Check the hydraulic fluid level in the master cylinder reservoir, and top-up if necessary (see *Weekly checks*).

31 Discard any hydraulic fluid that has been bled from the system; it will not be fit for re-use.

32 Check the feel of the brake pedal. If it feels at all spongy, air must still be present in the system, and further bleeding is required. Failure to bleed satisfactorily after a reasonable repetition of the bleeding procedure may be due to worn master cylinder seals.

3 Hydraulic pipes and hoses – renewal

Note: *Refer to the note in Section 2 concerning the dangers of hydraulic fluid.*

1 If any pipe or hose is to be renewed, minimise fluid loss by first removing the master cylinder reservoir cap, then tightening it down onto a piece of polythene to obtain an airtight seal. Alternatively, flexible hoses can be sealed, if required, using a proprietary

brake hose clamp; metal brake pipe unions can be plugged (if care is taken not to allow dirt into the system) or capped immediately they are disconnected. Place a wad of rag under any union that is to be disconnected, to catch any spilt fluid.

2 If a flexible hose is to be disconnected, where applicable unscrew the brake pipe union nut before removing the spring clip which secures the hose to its mounting bracket.

3 To unscrew the union nuts, it is preferable to obtain a brake pipe spanner of the correct size; these are available from most large motor accessory shops. Failing this, a close-fitting open-ended spanner will be required, though if the nuts are tight or corroded, their flats may be rounded-off if the spanner slips. In such a case, a self-locking wrench is often the only way to unscrew a stubborn union, but it follows that the pipe and the damaged nuts must be renewed on reassembly. Always clean a union and surrounding area before disconnecting it. If disconnecting a component with more than one union, make a careful note of the connections before disturbing any of them.

4 If a brake pipe is to be renewed, it can be obtained, cut to length and with the union nuts and end flares in place, from VW dealers. All that is then necessary is to bend it to shape, following the line of the original, before fitting it to the car. Alternatively, most motor accessory

shops can make up brake pipes from kits, but this requires very careful measurement of the original, to ensure that the new pipe is of the correct length. The safest answer is usually to take the original to the shop as a pattern.

5 On refitting, do not overtighten the union nuts. It is not necessary to exercise brute force to obtain a sound joint.

6 Ensure that the pipes and hoses are correctly routed, with no kinks, and that they are secured in the clips or brackets provided **(see illustrations)**. After fitting, remove the polythene from the reservoir, and bleed the hydraulic system as described in Section 2. Wash off any spilt fluid, and check carefully for fluid leaks.

4 Front brake pads – renewal

⚠ *Warning: Renew both sets of front brake pads at the same time – never renew the pads on only one wheel, as uneven braking may result. Note that the dust created by wear of the pads may contain asbestos, which is a health hazard. Never blow it out with compressed air, and don't inhale any of it. An approved filtering mask should be worn when working on the brakes. DO NOT use petrol or petroleum-based solvents to clean brake parts; use a proprietary brake cleaner only.*

1 Two types of front caliper are fitted to the Golf range – see Specifications. There are minor differences, but removal and refitting of the brake pads is essentially the same for all types of caliper. Note however that FS III type brakes have an inner and outer brake pad with spring clips attached. On these brakes the pads are removed with caliper **(see illustrations)**.

2 Apply the handbrake, then slacken the front roadwheel nuts. Jack up the front of the vehicle and support it on axle stands. Remove both front roadwheels.

4.1a Removing the outer pad from FS III type front brakes

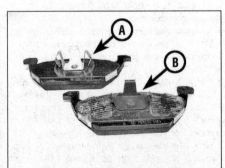

4.1b Note the that the brake pads have different spring clips and must be fitted correctly. A = Inner (piston side) pad and B = outer pad

3 Follow the accompanying photos **(illustrations 4.3a to 4.3t)** for the actual pad renewal procedure. Be sure to stay in order and read the caption under each illustration, and note the following points:

a) *New pads may have an adhesive foil on the backplates. Remove this foil prior to installation.*

b) *Thoroughly clean the caliper guide surfaces, and apply a little brake assembly (polycarbamide) grease. DO NOT use a copper based grease.*

c) *When pushing the caliper piston back to accommodate new pads, keep a close eye on the fluid lever in the reservoir.*

d) *If there is any doubt as to the condition of the brake pads, always replace them.*

4 Depress the brake pedal repeatedly, until the pads are pressed into firm contact with the brake disc, and normal (non-assisted) pedal pressure is restored.

5 Repeat the above procedure on the remaining front brake caliper.

6 Refit the roadwheels, then lower the vehicle to the ground and tighten the roadwheel nuts to the specified torque.

7 Check the hydraulic fluid level as described in *Weekly checks*.

Caution: New pads will not give full braking efficiency until they have bedded-in. Be prepared for this, and avoid hard braking as far as possible for the first hundred miles or so after pad renewal.

4.3a Where fitted disconnect the pad wear warning light wiring plug

4.3b Using a spanner to counter hold the guide pin, remove the lower…

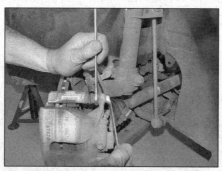

4.3c …and then the upper guide pin bolts. Dispose of the bolts

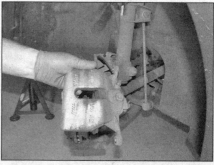

4.3d Lift off the caliper. Rocking the caliper as it is removed will help push the piston back, allowing the pads to clear the brake disc

4.3e Secure the caliper to the front strut to avoid straining the brake hose

4.3f Remove the outer brake pad…

4.3g …and the inner brake pad

4.3h Inspect the brake disc and then clean the brake pad mounting surfaces…

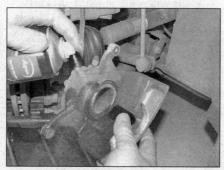

4.3i …and the caliper. Use a proprietary brake cleaner

4.3j Check that the guide pins slide freely in the caliper bracket (upper guide pin shown). Lubricate them with lithium grease if required

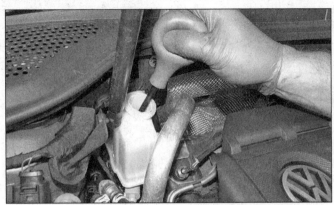

4.3k Check the fluid level in the master cylinder. The level will rise as the piston is pushed back and it may be necessary to remove some fluid from the reservoir. Avoid spilling brake fluid and clean any spills immediately with shop towels and brake cleaner

4.3l Push the piston into the caliper with a piston retraction tool. A 'G' clamp and a block of wood can also be used if the tool is not available

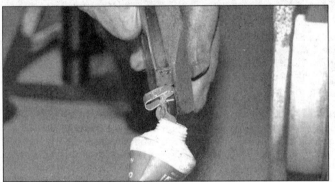

4.3m Apply a little brake lubricant ('cera-tec') grease to the pad mounting surfaces. DO NOT use a copper based grease

4.3n Fit the new outer brake pad…

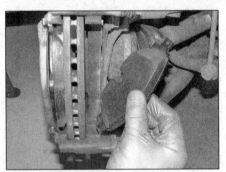

4.3o … and then the inner

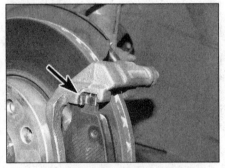

4.3p The anti-rattle springs must locate correctly in the caliper bracket

4.3q Refit the caliper

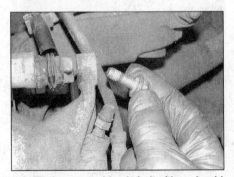

4.3r Fit the new guide pin bolts (they should be supplied with the new brake pads)

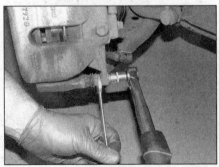

4.3s Tighten the new bolts to the specified torque

4.3t Where fitted connect the wiring plug for the brake pad wear warning light

5 Front brake caliper – removal, overhaul and refitting

Note: *Before starting work, refer to the note at the beginning of Section 2 concerning the dangers of hydraulic fluid, and to the warning at the beginning of Section concerning the dangers of asbestos dust.*

Removal

1 Apply the handbrake, then jack up the front of the vehicle and support it on axle stands (see *Jacking and vehicle support*). Remove the appropriate roadwheel.
2 Minimise fluid loss by first removing the master cylinder reservoir cap, and then tightening it down onto a piece of polythene, to obtain an airtight seal. Alternatively, use a brake hose tool to clamp the flexible hose **(see illustration)**.
3 Clean the area around the union, and then loosen the brake hose union nut.
4 Remove the brake pads as described in Section 4.
5 Unscrew the caliper from the end of the brake hose and remove it from the vehicle.

Overhaul

6 With the caliper on the bench, wipe away all traces of dust and dirt, but avoid inhaling the dust, as it is injurious to health.
7 Withdraw the partially ejected piston from the caliper body, and remove the dust seal.
8 Using a small screwdriver, extract the piston hydraulic seal, taking great care not to damage the caliper bore **(see illustration)**.
9 Thoroughly clean all components, using only methylated spirit, isopropyl alcohol or clean hydraulic fluid as a cleaning medium. Never use mineral-based solvents such as petrol or paraffin, as they will attack the hydraulic system rubber components. Dry the components immediately, using compressed air or a clean, lint-free cloth. Use compressed air to blow clear the fluid passages.
10 Check all components, and renew any

that are worn or damaged. Check particularly the cylinder bore and piston; these should be renewed if they are scratched, worn or corroded in any way (note that this means the renewal of the complete caliper body assembly). Similarly check the condition of the spacers/guide pins and their bushes/bores (as applicable); both spacers/pins should be undamaged and (when cleaned) a reasonably tight sliding fit in their bores. If there is any doubt about the condition of any component, renew it.
11 If the assembly is fit for further use, obtain the appropriate repair kit; the components are available from Volkswagen dealers in various combinations.
12 Renew all rubber seals, dust covers and caps disturbed on dismantling as a matter of course; these should never be re-used.
13 On reassembly, ensure that all components are clean and dry.
14 Thinly coat the piston and piston seal with brake fitting paste (VAG part no G 052 150 A2). This should be included in the caliper overhaul/repair kit.
15 Fit the new piston (fluid) seal, using only your fingers (no tools) to manipulate it into the cylinder bore groove. Fit the new dust seal to the piston, and refit the piston to the cylinder bore using a twisting motion; ensure that the piston enters squarely into the bore. Press the piston fully into the bore, then press the dust seal into the caliper body.

Refitting

16 Screw the caliper fully onto the flexible hose union.
17 Refit the brake pads as described in Section 4.
18 Securely tighten the brake pipe union nut.
19 Remove the brake hose clamp or polythene, as applicable, and bleed the hydraulic system as described in Section 2. Note that, providing the precautions described were taken to minimise brake fluid loss, it should only be necessary to bleed the relevant front brake.
20 Refit the roadwheel, then lower the vehicle to the ground and tighten the roadwheel bolts to the specified torque.

6 Brake disc – inspection, removal and refitting

Note: *Before starting work, refer to the note at the beginning of Section concerning the dangers of asbestos dust.*
Note: *If either disc requires renewal, BOTH should be renewed at the same time, to ensure even and consistent braking. New brake pads should also be fitted.*

Front brake disc

Inspection

1 Apply the handbrake, then jack up the front of the car and support it on axle stands (see *Jacking and vehicle support*). Remove the appropriate front roadwheel.
2 Slowly rotate the brake disc so that the full area of both sides can be checked; remove the brake pads if better access is required to the inboard surface. Light scoring is normal in the area swept by the brake pads, but if heavy scoring or cracks are found, the disc must be renewed.
3 It is normal to find a lip of rust and brake dust around the perimeter of the disc; this can be scraped off if required. If, however, a lip has formed due to excessive wear of the brake pad swept area, then the disc thickness must be measured using a micrometer. Take measurements at several places around the disc, at the inside and outside of the pad swept area; if the disc has worn at any point to the specified minimum thickness or less, the disc must be renewed.
4 If the disc is thought to be warped, it can be checked for run-out. Either use a dial gauge mounted on any convenient fixed point, while the disc is slowly rotated, or use feeler blades to measure (at several points all around the disc) the clearance between the disc and a fixed point, such as the caliper mounting bracket. If the measurements obtained are at the specified maximum or beyond, the disc is excessively warped, and must be renewed; however, it is worth checking first that the hub bearings are in good condition. If the run-out is excessive, the disc must be renewed **(see illustration)**.

5.2 Clamp the brake flexible hose

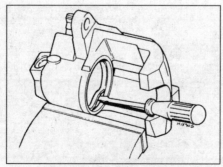

5.8 Use a small screwdriver to extract the caliper piston hydraulic seal

6.4 Using a DTI gauge to measure disc run-out

6.7a Remove the bolts and...

6.7b ...lift off the caliper mounting bracket

6.8a Undo the retaining screw...

6.8b ...and remove the front brake disc

5 Check the disc for cracks, especially around the wheel bolt holes, and any other wear or damage, and renew if necessary.

Removal

6 Remove the brake pads as described in Section 4. Using a piece of wire or string, tie the caliper to the front suspension coil spring, to avoid placing any strain on the brake hose.
7 Unscrew the two bolts securing the brake caliper mounting bracket to the hub **(see illustrations)**.
8 Use chalk or paint to mark the relationship of the disc to the hub, then remove the screw securing the brake disc to the hub, and remove the disc **(see illustrations)**. If it is tight, apply penetrating fluid, and tap its rear

face gently with a hide or plastic mallet. The use of excessive force could cause the disc to be damaged.

Refitting

9 Refitting is the reverse of the removal procedure, noting the following points:
a) Ensure that the mating surfaces of the disc and hub are clean and flat.
b) Align (if applicable) the marks made on removal, and securely tighten the disc retaining screw.
c) If a new disc has been fitted, use a suitable solvent to wipe any preservative coating from the disc, before refitting the caliper.
d) Slide the caliper into position over the disc, making sure the pads pass either

side of the disc. Tighten the caliper bracket mounting bolts to the specified torque.
e) Fit the pads as described in Section 4.
f) Refit the roadwheel, then lower the vehicle to the ground and tighten the roadwheel bolts to the specified torque. On completion, repeatedly depress the brake pedal until normal (non-assisted) pedal pressure returns.

Rear brake disc

Inspection

10 Firmly chock the front wheels, then jack up the rear of the car and support it on axle stands. Remove the appropriate rear road-wheel.
11 Inspect the disc as described in paragraphs 1 to 5.

Removal

12 Unscrew the two bolts securing the brake caliper mounting bracket in position, then slide the caliper assembly off the disc. Using a piece of wire or stout cord, secure the caliper to the to avoid placing any strain on the hydraulic brake hose **(see illustrations)**.
13 Use chalk or paint to mark the relationship of the disc to the hub, then remove the screw securing the brake disc to the hub, and remove the disc **(see illustration)**. If it is tight, apply penetrating fluid, and tap its rear face gently with a hide or plastic mallet. The use

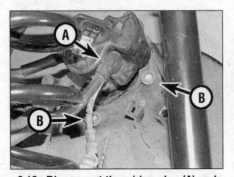

6.12a Disconnect the wiring plug (A) and remove the bolts (B)

6.12b Secure the caliper and mounting bracket

6.13 Remove the rear brake disc

7.2 Remove the bolts

of excessive force could cause the disc to be damaged.

Refitting

14 Refitting is a reversal of the removal procedure, noting the following points:

a) Ensure that the mating surfaces of the disc and hub are clean and flat.

b) Align (if applicable) the marks made on removal, and securely tighten the disc retaining screw.

c) If a new disc has been fitted, use a suitable solvent to wipe any preservative coating from the disc, before refitting the caliper.

d) Slide the caliper into position over the disc, making sure the pads pass either side of the disc. Tighten the caliper bracket mounting bolts to the specified torque. If new discs have been fitted and there is insufficient clearance between the pads to accommodate the new, thicker disc, it may

be necessary to push the piston back into the caliper body as described in Section 4.

e) Refit the roadwheel, then lower the vehicle to the ground and tighten the roadwheel bolts to the specified torque. On completion, repeatedly depress the brake pedal until normal (non-assisted) pedal pressure returns.

7 Front brake disc shield – removal and refitting

Removal

1 Remove the brake disc as described in Section 6.

2 Unscrew the securing bolts **(see illustration)** and remove the brake disc shield.

Refitting

3 Refitting is a reversal of removal. Tighten the shield retaining bolts to the specified torque. Refit the brake disc with reference to Section 6.

8 Rear brake pads – renewal

⚠️ **Warning: Renew both sets of rear brake pads at the same time – never renew the pads on only one wheel, as uneven braking may result. Note that the dust created by wear**

of the pads may contain asbestos, which is a health hazard. Never blow it out with compressed air, and don't inhale any of it. An approved filtering mask should be worn when working on the brakes. DO NOT use petrol or petroleum-based solvents to clean brake parts; use brake cleaner or methylated spirit only.

Note: A suitable vehicle specific diagnostic tool (or dedicated brake caliper reset tool) will be required to retract the brake parking motor to the service position. Note that the diagnostic tool only moves the piston internal spindle back – the piston will still be extended. A standard brake caliper wind back tool will then be required to push the piston back.

1 There are two versions of the rear brake caliper fitted, depending on the wheel size fitted (see the Section at the start of this Chapter).

2 Chock the front wheels, slacken the rear road wheel nuts, then jack up the rear of the vehicle and support it on axle stands (see *Jacking and vehicle support*). Remove the rear wheels.

3 Follow the accompanying photos **(see illustrations 8.3a to 8.3v)** for the actual pad renewal procedure. Be sure to stay in order and read the caption under each illustration, and note the following points:

a) If re-installing the original pads, ensure they are fitted to their original position.

b) Thoroughly clean the caliper guide surfaces and guide bolts.

c) If new pads are to be fitted, use a piston retraction tool to push the piston back – keep an eye on the fluid level in the reservoir whilst retracting the piston.

8.3a Move the caliper motor to the service position with the service tool

8.3b Unhook the retaining spring

8.3c Remove the upper...

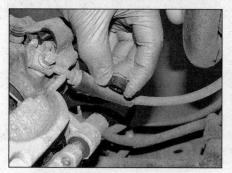

8.3d ...and lower bolt covers

8.3e Unbolt the guide bolts (M7 Hex) and...

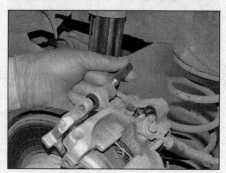

8.3f ...remove them

8.3g Disconnect the wiring plug…

8.3h … and lift off the caliper

8.3i Secure the caliper so the brake hose is not under any strain and then…

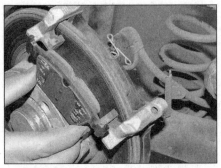

8.3j …remove the outer brake pad…

8.3k …followed by the inner. Note the spring fitted to the inner brake pad

8.3l Use a wire brush and brake cleaner to clean the caliper…

8.3m …and the caliper bracket

8.3n Install the wind back tool and push the piston back into the caliper – check the fluid level in the master cylinder reservoir as the piston is pushed back. Remove brake fluid from the reservoir if necessary to avoid any spillage

8.3o Apply a little brake grease ('cera-tec' or similar) to the mounting points. DO NOT use a copper based grease.

8.3p Fit the new inner brake pad…

8.3q …followed by the outer brake pad

8.3r Refit the caliper and then…

8.3s ...fit the caliper guide bolts

8.3t Tighten the bolts to the specified torque

8.3u Refit the guide bolt covers...

8.3v ...and then refit the retaining spring, ensuring it is correctly located

4 Repeat the above procedure on the remaining brake caliper.

5 Using the brake reset tool move the pistons forward, following the instructions on the tool as required.

6 Refit the roadwheels, then lower the vehicle to the ground and tighten the roadwheel nuts to the specified torque.

7 Check the hydraulic fluid level as described in *Weekly checks*.

Caution: New pads will not give full braking efficiency until they have bedded-in. Be prepared for this, and avoid hard braking as far as possible for the first hundred miles or so after pad renewal.

9 Rear brake caliper – removal, overhaul and refitting

Note: *Before starting work, refer to the note at the beginning of Section 2 concerning the dangers of hydraulic fluid, and to the warning at the beginning of Section concerning the dangers of asbestos dust.*

Removal

1 Chock the front wheels, then jack up the rear of the vehicle and support on axle stands (see *Jacking and vehicle support*). Remove the relevant rear wheel.

2 Minimise fluid loss by first removing the master cylinder reservoir cap, and then tightening it down onto a piece of polythene, to obtain an airtight seal. Alternatively, use a

brake hose clamp, a G-clamp or a similar tool to clamp the flexible hose.

3 Clean the area around the union on the caliper, and then loosen the brake hose union nut.

4 Disconnect the wiring plug from the handbrake motor.

5 Lift the caliper from the brake pads as described in Section 8.

6 Unscrew the caliper from the end of the flexible hose and remove it from the vehicle.

Overhaul

Note: *It is not possible to fully overhaul the brake caliper. If the mechanism is faulty, or fluid is leaking from the seal the caliper assembly must be renewed.*

7 With the caliper on the bench, wipe away all traces of dust and dirt, but avoid inhaling the dust, as it is injurious to health.

8 Using a small screwdriver, carefully prise out the dust seal from the caliper, taking care not to damage the piston. Note that this is only part of the hydraulic side of the caliper that is replaceable.

9 Withdraw the guide pins from the caliper, and remove the guide sleeve gaiters.

10 Unbolt the handbrake motor and recover the o-ring seal.

11 Thoroughly clean all components, using a proprietary brake cleaner. Dry the components immediately, using compressed air or a clean, lint-free cloth.

12 Check the caliper for any physical damage and then fit a new dust seal, motor O-ring seal and guide pin bushes.

Refitting

13 Screw the caliper fully onto the flexible hose union.

14 Refit the caliper over the brake pads as described in Section 8.

15 Securely tighten the brake pipe union nut.

16 Remove the brake hose clamp or remove the polythene from the fluid reservoir, as applicable, and bleed the hydraulic system as described in Section 2. Note that, providing the precautions described were taken to minimise brake fluid loss, it should only be necessary to bleed the relevant rear brake.

17 Refit the roadwheel, then lower the vehicle to the ground and tighten the roadwheel bolts to the specified torque. On completion, check the hydraulic fluid level as described in *Weekly checks*.

10 Brake pedal assembly – removal and refitting

Removal

1 Disconnect the battery negative lead as described in Chapter 5A Section 3.

2 Remove the wipers arms, the windscreen cowl panel (plenum chamber cover) and then remove the wiper motor – all as described in Chapter 12 Section 15 and Chapter 12 Section 16.

3 Remove the now accessible single bolt from the bulkhead **(see illustration)**.

4 Remove the facia end panel, the lower trim panel, the storage compartment and the main facia lower panel as described in Chapter 11 Section 25.

5 Where fitted remove the knee airbag (Chapter 12 Section 24).

6 Undo the retaining screw and remove the footwell air vent from above the pedal assembly.

7 Unbolt and remove the crash protector from the above the pedal.

8 It is now necessary to release the brake pedal from the ball on the vacuum servo pushrod. To do this, a Volkswagen special tool is available (T10159B), but a suitable alternative can be improvised. Note that the plastic lugs in the pedal are very stiff, and it will not be possible to release them by hand. Depress

10.3 Remove the bolt

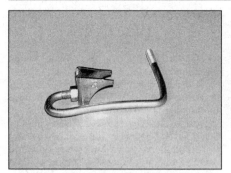

10.8a Improvised special tool constructed from a modified exhaust clamp, used to release the brake pedal from the servo pushrod

10.8b Using the tool to release the brake pedal from the servo pushrod

10.8c Rear view of the brake pedal showing plastic lugs securing the pedal to the servo pushrod

and hold down the pedal, then, using the tool, release the securing lugs, and pull the pedal from the servo pushrod **(see illustrations)**.

9 Disconnect the wiring plugs from the pedal and the accelerator module. The number will vary, depending on the equipment level of the vehicle.

10 Unbolt and remove the accelerator pedal.

11 The brake servo and master cylinder should now be supported with cable ties or a suitable wooden wedge.

12 Release the wiring loom from the brackets and then unbolt and remove the pedal assembly.

13 If required the pivot shaft can now be removed by rotating it clockwise until the retaining tabs break off. Pull out and discard the pivot pin – a new one must be used.

14 Carefully clean all components, and renew any that are worn or damaged.

Refitting

15 If the pivot pin was removed, then refit the new pin by rotating it anticlockwise until the tabs locate in the stop – an audible sound should be heard. DO NOT lubricate the pin or the bushes.

16 The remainder of the refitting procedure is the opposite of the removal.

11 Servo unit – testing, removal and refitting

Testing

1 To test the operation of the servo unit, depress the footbrake several times to exhaust the vacuum, then start the engine whilst keeping the pedal firmly depressed. As the engine starts, there should be a noticeable 'give' in the brake pedal as the vacuum builds-up. Allow the engine to run for at least two minutes, and then switch it off. If the brake pedal is now depressed, it should feel normal, but further applications should result in the pedal feeling firmer, with the pedal stroke decreasing with each application.

2 If the servo does not operate as described, first inspect the servo unit non-return valve

as described in Section 12. On diesel models check the operation of the vacuum pump as described in 2C Section 13.

3 If the servo unit still fails to operate satisfactorily, the fault lies within the unit itself. Repairs to the unit are not possible – if faulty, the servo unit must be renewed.

Removal

4 Remove the master cylinder as described in Section 13.

5 Where applicable remove the heat shield from the servo, then carefully ease the vacuum hose out from the sealing grommet in the front of the servo. Where applicable, also disconnect the wiring from the servo vacuum sensor, then extract the retaining circlip with a screwdriver, and withdraw the sensor from the servo.

6 The brake pedal must be separated from the servo as described in Section 10. With the pedal released from the servo remove the two lower pedal assembly nuts.

7 Jack up and support the front of the vehicle (see *Jacking and vehicle support*), and then remove the engine undershield.

8 To gain enough room to extract the servo on diesel engines remove:

● The battery and battery tray (Chapter 5A Section 3).
● The front subframe and steering rack (Chapter 10 Section 22).
● The front section of the exhaust system (Chapter 4D Section 9).
● Drain the coolant and remove the coolant pipes from the rear of the engine.
● The EGR cooler (Chapter 4D Section 3).
● The exhaust gas temperature sensors.

9 On petrol engines remove the catalytic converter (Chapter 4C Section 6), drain the cooling system and remove the coolant pipes from the rear of the engine.

10 The original factory fitted brake servo maybe bonded to the bulkhead, so the seal must be broken to allow the servo to be removed. Pull the servo away from the bulkhead to break the seal and then lower it from the vehicle.

Refitting

11 Where the original servo was bonded to the bulkhead, use a hot air gun to soften the adhesive. Remove the softened adhesive with

a paint scraper, taking care not to damage the paintwork. The adhesive does not require replacing.

12 Check the servo unit vacuum hose sealing grommet for signs of damage or deterioration, and renew if necessary.

13 Where applicable, fit a new gasket to the rear of the servo unit, and then reposition the unit in the engine compartment.

14 From inside the vehicle, ensure that the servo unit pushrod is correctly engaged with the brake pedal, and push the pedal onto the pushrod ball. Check the pushrod ball is securely engaged, then refit the servo unit mounting nuts and tighten them to the specified torque.

15 Refit the facia trim panels.

16 Carefully ease the vacuum hose back into position in the servo, taking great care not to displace the sealing grommet. Refit the heat shield to the servo and, where applicable, refit the vacuum sensor and wiring.

17 Refit the master cylinder as described in Section 13 of this Chapter.

18 On completion, start the engine and check for air leaks at the vacuum hose-to-servo unit connection.

12 Servo non-return valve – testing, removal and refitting

1 The non-return valve is located in the vacuum hose close to the brake servo **(see illustration)**.

12.1 Typical Non-return valve in the vacuum pipe

Removal

2 Where fitted, disconnect the wiring plug from the vacuum sensor and then ease the vacuum hose out of the servo unit, taking care not to displace the grommet.

3 Note the routing of the hose and then slacken the retaining clip(s) and disconnect the opposite end of the hose assembly from the manifold (petrol engines) or at the junction with the hose leading to the oil/vacuum pump (diesel engines) and remove it from the car.

Testing

4 Examine the check valve and vacuum hose for signs of damage, and renew if necessary.

5 The valve may be tested by blowing through it in both directions; air should flow through the valve in one direction only; when blown through from the servo unit end of the valve. Renew the valve if this is not the case.

6 Examine the servo unit rubber sealing grommet for signs of damage or deterioration, and renew as necessary.

Refitting

7 Ensure that the sealing grommet is correctly fitted to the servo unit.

8 Ease the hose union into position in the servo, taking great care not to displace or damage the grommet.

9 Ensure that the hose is correctly routed, and connect it to the inlet manifold/vacuum pump, ensuring the hose is secured in the retaining clips.

10 On completion, start the engine and check the valve to servo unit connection for signs of air leaks.

---

13 Master cylinder – removal, overhaul and refitting

Note: *Before starting work, refer to the warning at the beginning of Section 2 concerning the dangers of hydraulic fluid. A new master cylinder O-ring will be required on refitting.*

Removal

1 Disconnect the battery negative lead as described in Chapter 5A Section 3 and then (where fitted) remove the engine cover.

Diesel models

2 Place shop towels around the fuel lines and then disconnect the fuel lines at the right-hand inner wing – close to the coolant reservoir. Seal the fuel lines as soon as they are disconnected.

3 Unclip the fuel lines form the side of the coolant reservoir and from the top of the engine and then unbolt the fuel filter housing (there is no need to disconnect the fuel lines at the fuel filter) and move it to the side.

4 Disconnect the wiring plug from the coolant reservoir and then unclip the reservoir and secure it to the side.

5 Remove the timing belt upper cover as described in Chapter 2C Section 6.

All models

6 Where fitted remove the heat shield from the front of the plenum chamber.

7 On manual transmission models disconnect the fluid supply line to the clutch master cylinder. Seal the pipe and immediately clean up ay spilt brake fluid, using a shop towel and brake cleaner.

Note: *On models fitted with Air Conditioning (AC) the system must be evacuated using specialist equipment. Most garages will have the necessary equipment to perform this task at a reasonable cost. Mobile AC specialists may also operate in your area.*

 Warning: It is a criminal offence to knowingly discharge refrigerant to the atmosphere.

8 Where AC is fitted, disconnect the AC refrigerant lines at the junction in front of the master cylinder. Seal the lines immediately and move them to the side.

9 Remove the master cylinder reservoir cap and then syphon the hydraulic fluid from the reservoir. **Note:** *Do not syphon the fluid by mouth, as it is poisonous; use a syringe or an old antifreeze tester.*

10 Where fitted remove the heat shield from the reservoir and then disconnect the wiring plugs from the brake light switch and the fluid level warning light switch.

11 Wipe clean the area around the brake pipe unions on the side of the master cylinder, and place absorbent rags beneath the pipe unions to catch any leaking fluid. Remove the plastic pin securing the reservoir to the master cylinder and then pull up the reservoir and remove it from the master cylinder.

12 Make a note of the correct fitted positions of the unions, then unscrew the union nuts and carefully withdraw the pipes. Plug or tape over the pipe ends and master cylinder orifices, to minimise the loss of brake fluid, and to prevent the entry of dirt into the system. Wash off any spilt fluid immediately with brake cleaner.

13 Unscrew and remove the two nuts and washers securing the master cylinder to the vacuum servo unit, remove the heat shield (where fitted), then withdraw the unit from the engine compartment **(see illustration)**.

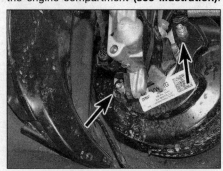

13.13 Master cylinder securing nuts

Remove the O-ring from the rear of the master cylinder, and check it for damage, renew if required.

Overhaul

14 If the master cylinder is faulty, it must be renewed. Repair kits are not available.

15 The only items that can be renewed are the mounting seals for the fluid reservoir; if these show signs of deterioration, prise them out with a screwdriver. Lubricate the new seals with clean brake fluid, and press them into the master cylinder ports.

Refitting

16 Remove all traces of dirt from the master cylinder and servo unit mating surfaces, and fit a new O-ring to the groove on the master cylinder body.

17 Fit the master cylinder to the servo unit, ensuring that the servo unit pushrod enters the master cylinder bore centrally. Refit the heat shield (where applicable) and the master cylinder mounting nuts and then tighten them to the specified torque.

18 Wipe clean the brake pipe unions, then refit them to the master cylinder ports and tighten them securely.

19 Refit the hydraulic fluid reservoir; making sure is it entered correctly in the rubber grommets.

20 On manual transmission models, reconnect the clutch master cylinder supply hose to the reservoir.

21 Refill the master cylinder reservoir with new fluid, and bleed the complete hydraulic system as described in Section 2.

22 Reconnect the wiring to the brake level sender unit and brake light switch as applicable.

23 Refit the engine cover (where necessary), and then reconnect the battery negative lead.

---

14 Handbrake motor – removal and refitting

Note: *All models covered by this manual have an electromechanical handbrake (parking brake) fitted. On these systems an electrical motor pushes the brake caliper piston out, forcing the brake pads into contact with the brake disc. The footbrake is a completely independent standard hydraulic system. A diagnostic tool will be required to replace the brake pads and the motor body.*

Removal

1 Chock the front wheels, release the handbrake, turn off the ignition and wait at least 20 seconds before commencing work.

2 Raise the rear of the vehicle and support it on axle stands – see *Jacking and vehicle support*.

3 Remove the appropriate road wheel

14.3 Disconnect the wiring plug

14.4 Remove the bolts and lift off the motor

14.5 Back off the adjuster

and disconnect the motor wiring plug **(see illustration)**.

4 Remove the bolts and pull the motor from the caliper **(see illustration)**. Recover the seal.

5 In the event of motor failure and where the handbrake is locked on, remove the motor as described and then back off the adjuster **(see illustration)**. This will allow the pads to be released from the brake disc and the vehicle moved.

Refitting

6 Clean the sealing ring mounting groove with brake cleaner. Grease the new seal and fit it to the groove.

7 Grease the socket on the motor, align it with the bolt holes and push the motor onto the caliper body. If the motor will not seat properly remove it, and (using a E11 torx socket) adjust the position of the input shaft on the caliper. DO NOT use the mounting bolts to draw the motor onto the caliper as the motor will be damaged and DO NOT twist the motor to align it as the seal may be damaged.

8 Reconnect the wiring plug, refit the wheel(s) and lower the vehicle to the ground.

9 The handbrake system must now be reset using the diagnostic tool. Where the tool is not available entrust this task to a VW dealer or suitably equipped garage.

15 Handbrake control unit – removal and refitting

1 The control unit is integrated into the ABS control unit and cannot be replaced separately. If a fault develops in the control unit the complete ABS control unit must be replaced as described in Section 19.

16 Handbrake control switch – removal and refitting

Removal

1 The switch is fitted to the centre console. Remove the centre console as described in Chapter 11 Section 26 to access the switch.

2 If not already done so disconnect the wiring plug and then release the switch locking tabs. Remove the switch **(see illustration)**.

Refitting

3 Refitting is a reversal of removal.

17 Brake light switch – removal and refitting

Removal

1 The brake light switch is located on the lower part of the master cylinder **(see illustration)**. Follow the procedure described Section 13 (Master cylinder) but do not drain or remove the master cylinder.

2 Disconnect the wiring from the switch.

3 Unscrew the mounting bolt, then pull the switch from the bottom of the master cylinder, and remove it from the locking lug at the top.

Refitting

4 Refitting is a reversal of removal, but tighten the mounting bolt to the specified torque.

18 Anti-lock braking system (ABS) – general information and precautions

1 The anti-lock braking system (ABS) fitted as standard to all models, prevents wheel lock-up under heavy braking, and not only optimises stopping distances, but also improves steering control. By electronically monitoring the speed of each roadwheel in relation to the other

wheels, the system can detect when a wheel is about to lock-up, before control is actually lost. The brake fluid pressure applied to that wheel's brake caliper is then decreased and restored ('modulated') several times a second until control is regained. The system components are: four wheel-speed sensors, a hydraulic unit with integral Electronic Control Unit (ECU), brake lines and a dashboard-mounted warning light. The four wheel-speed sensors are active sensors integrated into the wheel bearings. Unlike the older generation 'passive' wheel speed sensors, 'active' sensors can determine if the vehicle has stopped and if the sensor is faulty. Active sensors produce a square wave form which is then transmitted to the ECU, and used to calculate the rotational speed of each wheel. The ECU has a self-diagnostic facility, to inhibit the operation of the ABS if a fault is detected, lighting the dashboard-mounted warning light. The braking system will then revert to conventional, non-ABS operation. If the nature of the fault is not immediately obvious upon inspection, the vehicle must be taken to a Volkswagen dealer (or suitably equipped garage), who will have the diagnostic equipment required to interrogate the ABS ECU electronically.

2 The operation of the ABS system is entirely dependent on electrical signals. To prevent the system responding to any inaccurate signals, a built-in safety circuit monitors all signals received by the ECU. If an inaccurate signal or low battery voltage is detected, the ABS system is automatically shut down, and the warning light on the instrument panel is illuminated, to inform the driver that the ABS system is not operational. Normal braking will still be available, however.

16.2 Remove the switch

17.1 Brake light switch

19.2 Remove the battery tray

19.4 Release the wiring plug

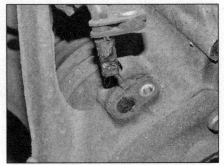

19.10 Remove the front wheel sensor

19 Anti-lock braking system (ABS) components – removal and refitting

Hydraulic unit and electronic control

Removal

1 The hydraulic unit (valve block) and electronic control (modulator) are combined in a single assembly. The unit is mounted on the left-hand side of the engine bay behind the battery.

2 Disconnect and then remove the battery and battery tray **(see illustration)** as described in Chapter 5A Section 3.

3 A brake pedal depressor must now be installed. Jack up and support the front left-hand wheel and the rear left-hand wheel. Remove both wheels and connect a hose and collection bottle to both front and rear bleed nipples. Open the bleed nipples and depress the brake pedal a minimum of 60 mm. Hold the brake pedal in this position using the brake pedal depressing tool. Do not remove the brake pedal depressor. Close the bleed nipples.

4 Identify and mark the position of the brake lines on the ABS hydraulic unit. Place shop towels below the unit and then disconnect the wiring plug from the ABS modulator **(see illustration)**. Seal the plug in a clean plastic bag if there is any chance it will be contaminated by brake fluid.

5 Remove the brake lines from the unit. Seal all the brake lines and the hydraulic unit openings with suitable plugs. Unbolt the complete assembly from the mounting bracket and remove it from the vehicle.

Note: *There is a slight chance that the control unit may be damaged by static electricity, so all work should be carried out on an Electro Static Discharge (ESD) safe work mat. Before commencing work touch a know good ground (earth) and avoid directly touching the electronic components.*

6 On the bench (and with the control unit on the top) unbolt the electronic control modulator from the valve block. Remove the control module by pulling it vertically upwards. DO NOT tilt the valve block or control unit. Recover the seals. Seal the modulator in a plastic bag and keep the hydraulic unit (valve block) upright at all times.

Refitting

7 Refitting is a reversal of removal noting the following points:

a) *The electronic control unit (modulator) can be replaced as a separate item, but if the hydraulic valve block is faulty both the control unit and the valve block must be replaced.*

b) *If a new control unit is fitted it must be programmed to the vehicle using suitable diagnostic equipment.*

c) *Bleed the brakes, using pressure bleeding equipment if possible.*

Front wheel sensor

Removal

8 Chock the rear wheels, then firmly apply the handbrake, jack up the front of the car and support on axle stands (see *Jacking and vehicle support*). Remove the appropriate front roadwheel.

9 Disconnect the wiring plug from the sensor.

10 Slacken and remove the bolt securing the sensor to the hub carrier, and remove the sensor from the car **(see illustration)**.

Refitting

11 Ensure that the sensor and hub carrier sealing faces are clean.

12 Apply a thin coat of multi-purpose grease to the mounting hole inner surface, then fit the sensor to the hub carrier. Refit the retaining bolt and tighten it to the specified torque.

13 Ensure that the sensor wiring is correctly routed and retained by all the necessary clips, and reconnect the wiring connector.

14 Refit the roadwheel, then lower the car to the ground and tighten the roadwheel bolts to the specified torque.

Rear wheel sensor

Removal

15 Chock the front wheels, then jack up the rear of the car and support it on axle stands (see *Jacking and vehicle support*). Remove the appropriate roadwheel.

16 Disconnect the wiring plug, remove the bolt and pull the sensor from the hub **(see illustrations)**.

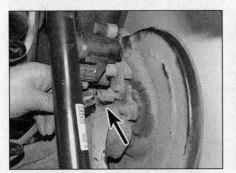

19.16a Disconnect the wiring plug...

19.16b ...remove the bolt...

19.16c ...and pull out the sensor

Refitting

17 Refit the sensor as described above in paragraphs 6 to 9.

Reluctor rings

18 The reluctor rings are integral with the wheel bearings (front and rear) and can only be inspected after removal of the hub assembly. If faulty, the bearings must be renewed as described in Chapter 10 Section 3 (front) and Chapter 10 Section 10 (rear).

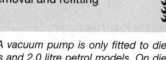

20 Vacuum pump – testing, removal and refitting

Note: *A vacuum pump is only fitted to diesel vehicles and 2.0 litre petrol models. On diesel models the vacuum pump is part of the oil pump (located in the sump). Removal and refitting of the oil pump is covered in Chapter 2C Section 13. On 2.0 litre petrol models the vacuum pump is fitted to the end of the exhaust camshaft and is driven directly by the camshaft.*

Testing

1 The basic test should be to first exhaust the vacuum by pressing the brake pedal repeatedly – the pedal will feel hard with little travel once the vacuum is exhausted. Start the engine whilst keeping your foot on the brake. The pedal should move down slightly as the vacuum builds up. Further comprehensive testing is described below.

2 A comprehensive test of the braking system vacuum pump requires a vacuum gauge. Where fitted, remove the engine cover to access the vacuum hose.

3 Disconnect the vacuum hose at the quick release connector (or at the brake servo) and connect the gauge to the vacuum line using a suitable length of hose.

4 Start the engine and allow it to idle, and then measure the vacuum created by the pump. As a guide, after one minute, a minimum of approximately 500 mm Hg should

20.7 Disconnect the vacuum hose

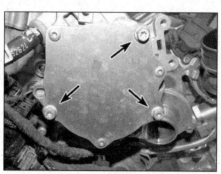

20.10a Remove the bolts...

be recorded. If the vacuum registered is significantly less than this, it is likely that the pump is faulty. However, seek the advice of a VW dealer before condemning the pump.

5 Reconnect the vacuum hose. Overhaul of the vacuum pump is not possible, since no major components are available separately for it. If faulty, the complete pump (and oil pump on diesel models) must be renewed.

Removal (2.0 litre petrol engines only)

6 Remove the engine cover by pulling it up and then remove the air filter housing as described in Chapter 4A Section 3.

7 Disconnect the vacuum hose from the vacuum pump **(see illustration)**.

20.8 Unbolt the rigid coolant pipe (at both ends)

20.10b ...and lift off the vacuum pump

8 Unbolt the rigid coolant pipe **(see illustration)** from the pump and cylinder head and move it to the side.

9 Remove the high pressure fuel pump as described in Chapter 4A Section 4.

10 Remove the mounting bolts and pull off the vacuum pump **(see illustrations)**.

Refitting

11 Clean the mounting surfaces and fit a new gasket to the pump **(see illustration)**.

12 Line up the pump with the drive dog and bolt the pump into position **(see illustrations)**. Tighten the bolts to the specified torque.

13 Fit the remaining components in reverse order to to removal.

20.11 Fit a new gasket

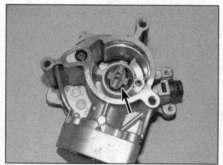

20.12a Line up the drive dog...

20.12b ...with the slot in the camshaft and refit the pump

Chapter 10
Suspension and steering systems

Contents

Section number

Front anti-roll bar – removal and refitting 7
Front anti-roll bar drop link – removal and refitting 8
Front hub bearings – renewal. 3
Front suspension lower arm – removal, overhaul and refitting. 5
Front suspension lower arm balljoint – removal, inspection
   and refitting. 6
Front suspension strut – removal, overhaul and refitting 4
Front wheel bearing housing (swivel hub) – removal and refitting . . . 2
General Information 1
Ignition switch/lock cylinder – removal and refitting 21
Rear anti-roll bar and drop link – removal and refitting 16
Rear coil spring – removal and refitting 14
Rear hub/wheel bearings – checking and renewal. 10

Section number

Rear shock absorber – removal and refitting 15
Rear subframe (multi-link suspension) – removal and refitting 18
Rear track control rod – removal and refitting 11
Rear trailing arm and bracket – removal, overhaul and refitting. 13
Rear transverse links – removal and refitting 12
Rear wheel bearing housing/stub axle – removal and refitting 9
Steering column – removal, inspection and refitting 20
Steering gear assembly – removal, overhaul and refitting 22
Steering gear gaiters and track rods – renewal 23
Steering wheel – removal and refitting. 19
Torsion beam axle – removal and refitting 17
Track rod end – removal and refitting. 24
Wheel alignment and steering angles – general information 25

Degrees of difficulty

Easy, suitable for novice with little experience	Fairly easy, suitable for beginner with some experience	Fairly difficult, suitable for competent DIY mechanic	Difficult, suitable for experienced DIY mechanic	Very difficult, suitable for expert DIY or professional

Specifications

Front suspension
Type . . . .   Independent, with MacPherson struts incorporating coil springs, telescopic shock absorbers and anti-roll bar

Rear suspension
Type . . . .   Trailing arm with Multi-link transverse arms, separate gas-filled telescopic shock absorbers, coil springs and anti-roll bar on models with greater than 90 Kw output. Torsion beam axle on models up to 89 Kw output.

Steering
Type . . . .   Rack-and-pinion. Electro-mechanical power assistance standard

Wheel alignment and steering angles*
Front wheel:
Camber.	- 0°30' ± 30'
Maximum difference between sides.	0°30'
Castor	7° 23' ± 30'
Toe setting	0°10' ± 10'
Toe-out on turns (20° left or right).	1° 19' ± 20'

Rear wheel (beam axle):
Camber angle.	-1° ± 10'
Maximum difference between sides.	0°30'
Total track	0°+20' ± 12'
Maximum difference between sides.	0°20'

Rear wheel (multi-link suspension)
Camber angle.	-1° 20' ± 30'
Maximum difference between sides.	0° 30'
Total track.	10' ± 10'

*Figures are for standard suspension. Refer to Volkswagenfor alternative suspension and the latest figures.

Vehicle ride height

Basic model	385 mm ± 10 mm
Sport model	370 mm ± 10 mm
Raised ride model	400 mm ± 10 mm
GTD and GTI	370 mm ± 10 mm
Blue motion models	370 mm ± 10 mm
GTE	395 mm ± 10 mm
'R' models	365 mm ± 10 mm

Torque wrench settings

	Nm	lbf ft
Front suspension		
Anti-roll bar link nuts*	65	48
Anti-roll bar to subframe: *		
Stage 1	20	15
Stage 2	Angle-tighten a further 80°	
Driveshaft hub bolt: *		
Stage 1	200	148
Stage 2	Angle-tighten a further 180°	
Hub to wheel bearing housing: *		
Stage 1	70	52
Stage 2	Angle-tighten a further 90°	
Lower arm:		
Front and rear bolts: *		
Stage 1	70	52
Stage 2	Angle-tighten a further 180°	
Balljoint nuts: *		
Stage 1	40	30
Stage 2	Angle-tighten a further 45°	
Subframe support bracket to body : *		
Stage 1	50	37
Stage 2	Angle-tighten a further 90°	
Subframe support bracket to subframe: *		
Stage 1	70	52
Stage 2	Angle-tighten a further 180°	
Subframe to body: *		
Front bolt		
Stage 1	70	52
Stage 2	Angle-tighten a further 180°	
Rear bolts		
Stage 1	20	15
Stage 2	Angle-tighten a further 180°	
Splash plate to wheel bearing housing	10	7
Suspension strut:		
Pinch nut/bolt (to hub): *		
Stage 1	70	52
Stage 2	Angle-tighten a further 180°	
Upper mounting (to body): *		
Stage 1	15	11
Stage 2	Angle-tighten a further 90°	
Upper piston rod nut*	60	44
Vehicle level sender to subframe and lower arm	9	7
Always use new nut/bolts		
Rear suspension (beam axle models)		
ABS speed sensor	8	6
Axle pivot bolt: *		
Stage 1	70	52
Stage 2	Angle-tighten a further 360°	
Axle mounting bracket to body: *		
Stage 1	50	37
Stage 2	Angle-tighten a further 45°	
Hub to wheel bearing housing bolt: *		
Stage 1	200	148
Stage 2	Angle-tighten a further 90°	
Shock absorber: *		
To body:		
Stage 1	50	37
Stage 2	Angle-tighten a further 45°	

To axle:		
Stage 1	70	52
Stage 2	Angle-tighten a further 180°	
Stub axle bolts: *		
Stage 1	30	22
Stage 2	Angle-tighten a further 90°	
Vehicle level sender	5	4

Always use new nut/bolts

Rear suspension (multi-link suspension models)

Anti-roll bar (to subframe) bolts: *		
Stage 1	20	15
Stage 2	Angle-tighten a further 90°	
Anti-roll bar (to link) nut	55	
Anti-roll bar link to lower arm: *		
Stage 1	20	15
Stage 2	Angle-tighten a further 180°	
Shock absorber (lower nut/bolt): *		
Stage1	70	55
Stage 2	Angle-tighten a further 180°	
Shock absorber (upper bolts): *		
Stage 1	50	37
Stage 2	Angle-tighten a further 45°	
Subframe bolts: *		
Long bolts		
Stage 1	70	55
Stage 2	Angle-tighten a further 180°	
Short bolts		
Stage 1	50	37
Stage 2	Angle-tighten a further 45°	
Trailing arm: *		
To hub bolts		
Stage 1	70	55
Stage 2	Angle-tighten a further 90°	
To bracket/bush bolt		
Stage 1	90	68
Stage 2	Angle-tighten a further 90°	
Bracket to body bolts		
Stage 1	50	37
Stage 2	Angle-tighten a further 45°	
Transverse link (upper to hub): *		
Stage 1	130	98
Stage 2	Angle-tighten a further 180°	
Transverse link (upper to subframe)	95	72
Transverse link (lower to hub): *		
Stage 1	70	55
Stage 2	Angle-tighten a further 180°	
Transverse link (lower to subframe: *	95	72
Wheel bearing/hub nut: *		
Stage 1	200	148
Stage 2	Angle-tighten a further 90°	

Always use new nut/bolts

Steering

Crash bar (above pedals)		
Steering column:		
To crossmember*	20	15
To rack (pinch bolt): *		
Stage 1	20	15
Stage 2	Angle-tighten a further 90°	
Steering rack to subframe: *		
Stage 1	70	52
Stage 2	Angle-tighten a further 90°	
Steering wheel to column: *		
Stage 1	30	22
Stage 2	Angle-tighten a further 90°	
Track rod end to track rod	70	52
Track rod end: *		
Stage 1	20	15
Stage 2	Angle-tighten a further 90°	
Track rod (to steer rack)	100	74

Always use new nuts/bolts

1 General Information

1 The independent front suspension is of the MacPherson strut type, incorporating coil springs and integral telescopic shock absorbers. The struts are located by transverse lower suspension arms, which use rubber inner mounting bushes, and incorporate a balljoint at the outer ends. The front wheel bearing housings, which carry the wheel bearings, brake calipers and the hub/disc assemblies, are attached to the MacPherson struts by clamp bolts, and connected to the lower arms through the balljoints. A front anti-roll bar is fitted to all models. The anti-roll bar is rubber-mounted, and is connected to both lower suspension arms by short links.

2 Two types of rear suspension are fitted to the Golf Mk7 range of vehicles. Vehicles with a power output up to 89 Kw have a simple torsion beam suspension fitted, vehicles with an output greater than 89 Kw (90 Kw and over) have a multi-link suspension system fitted (see illustration).

3 The torsion beam suspension consist of the beam axle, mounted to brackets and fitted with bonded rubber bushes at the front. with, Coil springs and separate shock absorbers complete the suspension. A stub axle is bolted to the beam. No anti-roll bar is fitted. The suspension geometry is fixed – no adjustment possible.

4 The multi-link rear suspension consists of a trailing arm, rubber-mounted at its front end to the underbody, a wheel bearing housing, lower main transverse link and coil spring, track control rod, upper transverse link, and separate shock absorber. A rear anti-roll bar is fitted to all models. The anti-roll bar is rubber-mounted on the rear subframe, and is connected to the wheel bearing housings on each side by a short connecting link.

5 The safety steering column incorporates an intermediate shaft at its lower end. The intermediate shaft is connected to both the steering column and steering gear by universal joints, although the shaft is supplied as part of the column assembly and cannot be separated. Both the inner steering column and intermediate shaft have splined sections that collapse during a major frontal impact. The outer column is also telescopic with two sections, to facilitate reach adjustment.

6 The steering gear is mounted onto the front subframe, and is connected by two track rods, with balljoints at their inner and outer ends, to the steering arms projecting rearwards from the wheel bearing housings. The track rod ends are threaded to the track rods in order to allow adjustment of the front wheel toe setting. The steering gear has electro-mechanical assistance, and incorporates an integral control unit. It is only functional when the engine is running. There are no hydraulic components, and steering assistance is automatically matched to the vehicle speed, steering wheel torque and steering wheel angle.

7 All models are fitted with an Anti-lock Brake System (ABS), and can also be fitted with a Traction Control System (TCS), an Electronic Differential Lock (EDL) system and an Electronic Stability Program (ESP). The ABS may also be referred to as including EBD (Electronic Brake Distribution), which means it adjusts the front and rear braking forces according to the weight being carried. The TCS may also be referred to as ASR (Anti Slip Regulation).

8 The TCS system prevents the front wheels

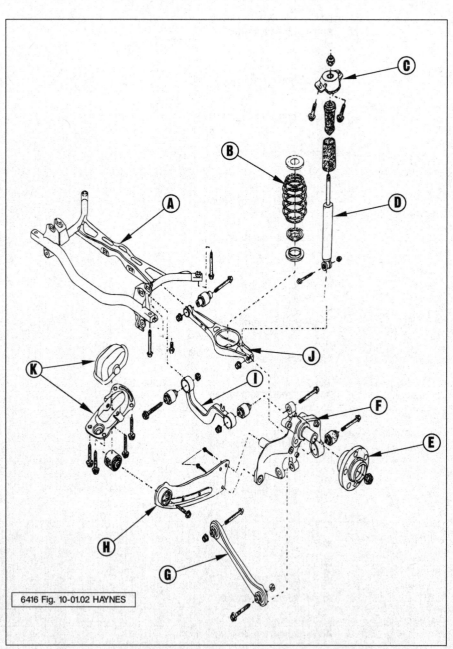

6416 Fig. 10-01.02 HAYNES

1.2 The component parts of the multi-link rear suspension

A Subframe
B Coil spring and mounts
C Shock absorber
D Shock absorber top mount
E Hub
F Wheel bearing housing
G Control rod
H Trailing arm
I Upper transverse link
J Lower transverse link
K Trailing arm mounting bracket

1.11 Check the ride height by measuring from the centre of the hub nut vertically to the wheel arch

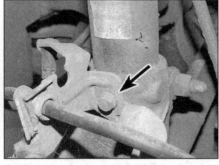

2.4 Remove the brake hose/wiring bracket

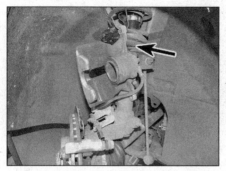

2.5 Suspend the caliper from the front suspension spring

from losing traction during acceleration by reducing the engine output. The system is switched on automatically when the engine is started, and it utilises the ABS system sensors to monitor the rotational speeds of the front wheels.

9 The ESP system extends the ABS, TCS and EDL functions to reduce wheel spin in difficult driving conditions. It does this by using highly sensitive sensors that monitor the speed of the vehicle, lateral movement of the vehicle, the brake pressure, and the steering angle of the front wheels. If, for example, the vehicle is tending to oversteer, the brake will be applied to the front outer wheel to correct the situation. If the vehicle is tending to understeer, the brake will be applied to the rear inside wheel. The steering angle of the front wheels is monitored by an angle sensor on the top of the steering column.

10 The TCS/ESP systems should always be switched on, except when driving with snow chains, driving in snow or driving on loose surfaces, when some wheel spin may be advantageous. The ESP switch is located in the centre of the facia.

11 Some models are also fitted with an Electronic Differential Lock (EDL), which reduces unequal traction from the front wheels. If one front wheel spins 100 rpm or more faster than the other, the faster wheel is slowed down by applying the brake to that wheel. The system is not the same as the traditional differential lock, where the actual differential gears are locked. Because the system applies a front brake, in the event of a brake disc overheating the system will shut down until the disc has cooled. No warning light is displayed if the system shuts down. As is the case with the TCS system, the EDL system uses the ABS sensors to monitor front wheel speeds.

Note: *As a general rule all suspension component fixings, should only be fully tightened when the unladen vehicle is on it's wheels, with the tyres at the correct pressure. Always check the ride height before and after completion of any work (see illustration). The ride height can also be compared to the ride height given in the specifications. It is possible in most cases to raise the suspension*

(with a trolley jack) to the correct height to fully tighten the suspension bolts, however extreme caution is required as achieving the correct height may start to lift the vehicle off the axle stands.

2 Front wheel bearing housing (swivel hub) – removal and refitting

Note: *Renewal of the hub bearings does not require removal of the wheel bearing housing (see Section 3). This Section describes removal of the wheel bearing housing leaving the suspension strut in situ, however, if necessary it can be removed together with the suspension strut, and then separated on the bench. All self-locking nuts and bolts disturbed on removal must be renewed as a matter of course.*

Removal

1 Remove the wheel trim/hub cap (as applicable) and loosen the driveshaft retaining bolt (hub bolt) by 90° with the vehicle resting on its wheels. Also loosen the wheel bolts. **Note:** *Do not loosen the hub bolt more than 90° at this stage, or the wheel bearing may be damaged.*

2 Apply the handbrake, then jack up the front of the vehicle and support it on axle stands (see *Jacking and vehicle support*). Remove the front roadwheel.

3 Unscrew and remove the driveshaft

retaining bolt. Check that the driveshaft moves freely in the hub before proceeding.

4 Remove the ABS wheel sensor as described in Chapter 9 Section 19. Also, unbolt the brake hose/wiring bracket from the strut **(see illustration)**.

5 Remove the brake disc as described in Chapter 9 Section 6. This procedure includes removing the brake caliper; however do not disconnect the hydraulic brake hose from the caliper. Using a piece of wire or string, tie the caliper to the front suspension coil spring, to avoid placing any strain on the hydraulic brake hose **(see illustration)**.

6 Unbolt the splash plate from the wheel bearing housing.

7 Loosen the nut securing the steering track rod balljoint to the wheel bearing housing. To do this, fit a ring spanner to the nut, and then hold the balljoint pin stationary using an Allen key. With the nut removed, it may be possible to release the balljoint from the wheel bearing housing by turning the balljoint pin with an Allen key. If not, leave the nut on by a few turns to protect the threads, then use a universal balljoint separator to release the balljoint. Remove the nut completely once the taper has been released.

8 Where fitted unbolt the headlight level sensor. Unscrew the front suspension lower balljoint-to-lower arm retaining nuts **(see illustrations)**, then lever the lower arm down to release the balljoint studs from the arm. Now use a soft-faced mallet to tap the driveshaft from the hub splines while pulling out the

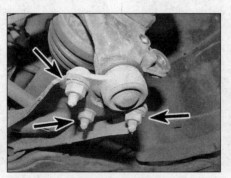

2.8a Remove the lower ball joint securing nuts…

2.8b …and lower the control arm

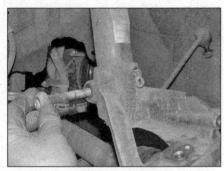

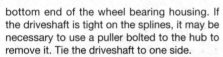

2.9 Remove the bolt

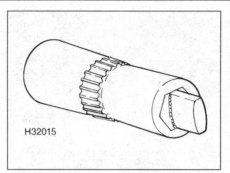

2.10a Tool used by Volkswagon technicians to open up the split wheel bearing housing

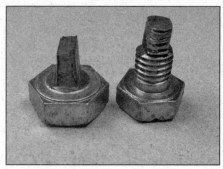

2.10b A home made version of the factory tool can also be used

bottom end of the wheel bearing housing. If the driveshaft is tight on the splines, it may be necessary to use a puller bolted to the hub to remove it. Tie the driveshaft to one side.

9 Note which way round it is fitted, then unscrew the nut and remove the clamp bolt securing the wheel bearing housing to the bottom of the strut **(see illustration)**.

10 The wheel bearing housing must now be released from the strut. To do this, Volkswagon technicians insert a special tool into the split wheel bearing housing, and turn it through 90° to open up the clamp. A similar tool can be made out of an old screwdriver or bolt. Alternatively a suitable cold chisel can be driven into the split as a wedge. Slightly press inwards the top of the wheel bearing housing, and then push it downwards from the bottom of the strut **(see illustrations)**.

Refitting

11 Ensure that the driveshaft outer joint and hub splines are clean and dry, and then lubricate the splines with fresh engine oil. Also lubricate the threads and contact surface of the hub nut/bolt with oil.

12 Lift the wheel bearing assembly into position, and engage the hub with the splines on the outer end of the driveshaft. Fit the new hub bolt, tightening it by hand only at this stage.

13 Engage the wheel bearing housing with

the bottom of the suspension strut; making sure that the hole in the side plate aligns with the holes in the split housing. Remove the tool used to open the split.

14 Insert the strut-to-wheel bearing housing clamp bolt from the front, and fit the new retaining nut. Tighten the nut to the specified torque.

15 Refit the lower arm balljoint to the lower arm, and tighten the nuts to the specified torque.

16 Refit the track rod balljoint to the wheel bearing housing, then fit a new retaining nut and tighten it to the specified torque. If necessary, hold the balljoint pin with an Allen key while tightening the nut.

17 Refit the splash plate and tighten the bolts.

18 Refit the brake disc and caliper with reference to Chapter 9 Section 6.

19 Refit the ABS wheel sensor as described in Chapter 9 Section 19.

20 Ensure that the outer joint is drawn fully into the hub, and then refit the roadwheel.

21 Have an assistant depress the brake pedal, and then tighten the driveshaft retaining bolt in the stages given in the Specifications. It is recommended that an angle gauge be used to ensure the correct tightening angle. **Note:** *The car must not be standing on its wheels when tightening the bolt, or the wheel bearing may be damaged.*

22 Lower the vehicle to the ground, tighten the roadwheel bolts, and refit the wheel trim/ hub cap.

3 Front hub bearings – renewal

Note: *The bearing is a sealed, pre-adjusted and pre-lubricated, double-row roller type, and requires no maintenance. It is bolted to the wheel bearing housing.*

1 Remove the wheel trim/hub cap (as applicable) and loosen the driveshaft retaining bolt (hub bolt) with the vehicle resting on its wheels. **Note:** *Do not loosen the hub bolt more than 90° at this stage, or the wheel bearing may be damaged. Also loosen the wheel bolts.*

2 Apply the handbrake, then jack up the front of the vehicle and support it on axle stands (see *Jacking and vehicle support*). Remove the front roadwheel.

3 Fully unscrew and remove the driveshaft retaining bolt.

4 Remove the ABS wheel sensor as described in Chapter 9 Section 19.

5 Remove the brake disc as described in Chapter 9 Section 6. This procedure includes removing the brake caliper; however do not disconnect the hydraulic brake hose from the

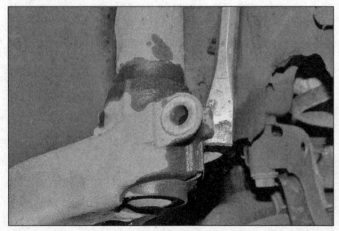

2.10c Using a cold chisel to open up the wheel bearing housing and release the suspension strut

2.10d Withdrawing the wheel bearing housing from the bottom of the suspension strut

3.8a Remove the bolts...

3.8b ...and pull the bearing from the housing

caliper. Using a piece of wire or string, tie the caliper to the front suspension coil spring, to avoid placing any strain on the hydraulic brake hose **(see illustration 2.5)**.

6 Unbolt the anti-roll bar drop link from the suspension strut. Where fitted disconnect the Zenon headlight level sensor from the lower arm.

7 Remove the lower control arm bolts **(see illustration 2.8a and 2.8b)** and remove the arm from the hub. Pull the swivel hub forward and remove the driveshaft from the bearing housing/swivel hub. Secure the driveshaft to the side and temporarily refit the hub to the control arm.

8 Tun the swivel hub to access the bolts. Unbolt and remove the bearing housing **(see illustrations)**.

9 Store the hub with the bearing up and avoid contact with anything magnetic.

10 Fit the new wheel bearing to the housing and tighten the bolts to the specified torque.

11 Refit the driveshaft and tighten the new driveshaft hub nut until the hub rotates. Do not attempt to fully tighten the bolt at this stage

12 Refit the brake disc and caliper with reference to Chapter 9 Section 6.

13 Refit the ABS wheel sensor with reference to Chapter 9 Section 19.

14 Ensure that the outer joint is drawn fully into the hub, and then refit the roadwheel.

15 Tighten the new driveshaft retaining bolt in the stages given in the Specifications. It is recommended that an angle gauge be used to ensure the correct tightening angle. Have an assistant apply the brakes and tighten the bolt to the first stage. **Note:** *The car must not be standing on its wheels when tightening the bolt, or the wheel bearing maybe be damaged. Lower the vehicle to the ground and tighten the bolt to the second stage.*

16 Tighten the roadwheel bolts to the specified torque.

4 Front suspension strut – removal, overhaul and refitting

Note: *This section describes removal of the suspension strut leaving the wheel bearing housing in situ, however, if necessary it can be removed together with the wheel bearing housing, then separated on the bench. All self-locking nuts and bolts disturbed on removal must be renewed as a matter of course.*

Removal

1 Remove the wheel trim/hub cap (as applicable) and loosen the driveshaft retaining bolt (hub bolt) with the vehicle resting on its wheels. **Note:** *Do not loosen the hub bolt more than 90° at this stage, or the wheel bearing may be damaged. Also loosen the wheel bolts.*

2 Apply the handbrake, then jack up the front of the vehicle and support it on axle stands (see *Jacking and vehicle support*). Remove the appropriate roadwheel.

3 Unscrew the nut and disconnect the anti-roll bar drop link from the strut **(see illustration)**.

4 Release the ABS sensor wiring/brake hose bracket from the strut **(see illustration 2.4)**.

5 Unbolt the brake caliper and secure it to the side so that the brake is is not strained.

6 Unscrew and remove the driveshaft retaining bolt **(see illustration)**.

7 Where fitted unbolt the level sensor form the control arm (models with Xenon headlights only).

8 Unscrew the front suspension lower balljoint to control arm retaining nuts, then lever the lower arm down to release the balljoint studs. Now use a soft-faced mallet to tap the driveshaft from the hub splines while pulling out the bottom end of the wheel bearing housing **(see illustrations 2.8a and 2.8b)**. If the driveshaft is tight on the splines, it may be necessary to use a puller bolted to the hub to remove it. Secure the driveshaft to one side.

9 Note which way round it is fitted, then unscrew the nut and remove the clamp bolt securing the wheel bearing housing to the bottom of the strut **(see illustration)**.

4.3 Disconnect the anti-roll bar drop link from the strut

4.6 Unscrew and remove the driveshaft retaining bolt

4.9 Remove the clamp bolt...

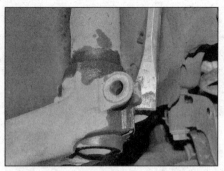

4.11a ...then use a suitable tool to expand the split...

4.11b ...so that the strut can be pulled from the wheel bearing housing.

10 Before removing the strut from the swivel hub, prevent the hub from rotating by locking it in place with a screwdriver inserted into the brake disk vents. The screwdriver should rest against the brake caliper mounting bracket. Position a trolley jack under the brake disk. The jack will support the weight of the hub when it is removed from the strut. Note that if the track rod end is removed from the hub (as described in Section 24) then the complete hub can be removed from the vehicle.

11 The wheel bearing housing/swivel hub must now be released from the strut. To do this, VW technicians insert a special tool into the split wheel bearing housing, and turn it through 90° to open up the clamp (see illustrations 2.10a and 2.10b). A similar tool such as an Allen key can be used, or alternatively a suitable cold chisel can be driven into the split as a wedge. Slightly press inwards the top of the wheel bearing housing, and then push it downwards from the bottom of the strut (see illustrations). Adjust the trolley jack to take the weight of the hub as soon as it is released from the strut.

12 Remove the wiper arms, windscreen cowl as described in Chapter 12 Section 15 and Chapter 12 Section 16.

13 To ensure correct refitting, note the mark and arrows on the strut (see illustration). If the reason for removing the strut is overhaul, remover the cover cap and then loosen the upper mounting centre nut one turn, while holding the piston rod with an Allen key.

14 Support the strut, then unscrew the upper mounting bolts and lower the strut from under the wheel arch (see illustrations).

Overhaul

⚠️ *Warning: Before attempting to dismantle the suspension strut, a suitable tool to hold the coil spring in compression must be obtained. Adjustable coil spring compressors are readily available, and are recommended for this operation. Any attempt to dismantle the strut without such a tool is likely to result in damage or personal injury.*

15 With the strut removed from the car, clean away all external dirt. If necessary, mount it upright in a vice during the dismantling procedure.

16 Fit the spring compressor, and compress the coil spring until all tension is relieved from the upper spring seat (see illustration).

17 Unscrew and remove the upper centre retaining nut, whilst retaining the strut piston with a suitable Allen key, then remove the mounting, thrust bearing, and coil spring (see illustrations).

4.13 The mark and arrows must always be inboard

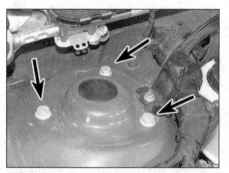

4.14a Unscrew the upper mounting bolts...

4.14b ...and lower the strut from under the wheel arch

4.16 Compress the coil spring with the compressor tool

4.17a Unscrew the upper centre nut...

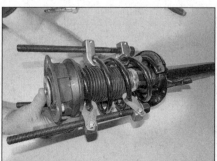

4.17b ...then remove the mounting, thrust bearing and coil spring

4.18a Remove the protective sleeve...

4.18b ...and upper bearing race...

4.18c ...then remove the bump stop from the upper mounting

18 Remove the protective sleeve and upper bearing race, and then remove the bump stop from the upper mounting **(see illustrations)**.
19 With the strut assembly now completely dismantled, examine all the components for wear, damage or deformation, and check the bearing for smoothness of operation. Renew any of the components as necessary.
20 Examine the strut for signs of fluid leakage. Check the strut piston for signs of pitting along its entire length, and check the strut body for signs of damage. While holding it in an upright position, test the operation of the strut by moving the piston through a full stroke, and then through short strokes of 50 to 100 mm. In both cases, the resistance felt should be smooth and continuous. If the resistance is jerky, or uneven, or if there is any visible sign of wear or damage to the strut, renewal is necessary.
21 If any doubt exists about the condition of the coil spring, carefully remove the spring compressors, and check the spring for distortion and signs of cracking. Renew the spring if it is damaged or distorted, or if there is any doubt as to its condition.
22 Inspect all other components for signs of damage or deterioration, and renew as necessary.
23 Assemble the bump stop to the upper

4.24 Locate the end of the spring on the stop

mounting, and then refit the upper bearing race and protective sleeve to the mounting. The larger diameter of the bump stop must be against the upper mounting.
24 Fit the coil spring (together with the compressor tool) onto the strut, making sure its lower (larger diameter) end is correctly located against the spring seat stop **(see illustration)**.
25 Refit the thrust bearing and upper mounting, then screw on a new retaining nut. Tighten the nut to the specified torque while holding the piston rod with an Allen key.

Refitting

26 Manoeuvre the strut into position under the wheel arch, and locate in the suspension strut turret in the previously noted position **(see illustration 4.13)**. Insert the bolts and tighten them to the specified torque.
27 Refit the plenum chamber cover and wiper arms.
28 Engage the swivel hub with the bottom of the suspension strut. Ensure that the hole in the side plate aligns with the holes in the split housing. Raise the housing, while pressing it inwards to assist entry. Use a trolley jack if necessary. When fully entered, remove the tool used to open the split.
29 Insert the new strut to swivel hub bolt from the rear. The nut should be at the front of the vehicle. Tighten the nut to the specified torque.
30 Insert the outer end of the driveshaft through the hub and engage it with the splines. Fit the new hub bolt, tightening it by hand only at this stage.
31 Refit the swivel hub to the control arm lower arm, and tighten the nuts to the specified torque. Where applicable, refit the headlight range control sensor arm to the lower arm and tighten the nut.
32 Refit the anti-roll bar drop link, using a new nut and tighten to the specified torque.
33 Refit the ABS wheel sensor as described in Chapter 9 Section 19.

34 Ensure that the outer joint is drawn fully into the hub, and then refit the roadwheel.
35 Tighten the new driveshaft retaining bolt in the stages given in the Specifications. It is recommended that an angle gauge be used to ensure the correct tightening angle. Have an assistant apply the brakes and tighten the bolt to the first stage. **Note:** *The car must not be standing on its wheels when tightening the bolt, or the wheel bearing maybe be damaged. Lower the vehicle to the ground and tighten the bolt to the second stage.*
36 Lower the vehicle to the ground and tighten the roadwheel bolts.

5 Front suspension lower arm – removal, overhaul and refitting

Note: *Before dismantling any suspension component, check the vehicle ride height by measuring the distance from the centre of the front hub to the wheel arch. Note down this figure.*

Removal

1 Apply the handbrake, then jack up the front of the vehicle and support it on axle stands (see *Jacking and vehicle support*). Remove the appropriate front roadwheel and the engine compartment undertray.
2 Where fitted remove the ride height sensor (models with Xenon headlights only).
3 Unscrew the front suspension lower balljoint to lower arm retaining nuts, then lever down the lower arm to release the arm from the balljoint studs **(see illustration 2.8a and 2.8b)**.
4 If working on the left-hand arm on vehicles fitted with the six speed DSG transmission (OD9) unbolt the exhaust bracket from the rear of the subframe and then unbolt the engine pendulum mount. This will allow the transmission to be moved sufficiently to allow the arm to be removed.
5 Unscrew and remove the mounting bolts

5.5a The control arm bolts

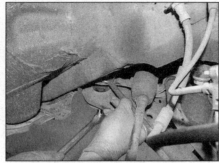

5.5b Counterhold the rear bolt...

5.5c ...and remove it. Recover the nut

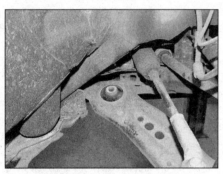

5.6 Remove the control arm

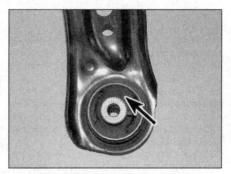

5.8a Before removing the bush, note the alignment marks on the rear bush

5.8b A suitable setup for bush removal. The old bush is pulled into the large socket

5.8c Two sockets are used to allow clearance for the lip of the bush

5.8d Adjust the position of the bush so that it protrudes equally on both sides

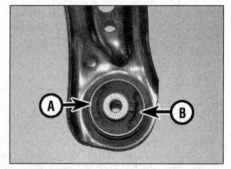

5.8e Fill the voids (A and B) in the bush with grease

from the subframe **(see illustrations)**. A spanner will be required to counterhold the rear mounting bolt nut.

6 Pivot the arm and remove it from the subframe **(see illustration)**. Manoeuvre it past the swivel hub to remove it completely. If working on the left-hand arm on a vehicle fitted with the 6 speed DSG transmission the transmission and engine must be pushed forward to allow enough clearance to remove the arm.

Overhaul

7 Thoroughly clean the lower arm, then check carefully for cracks or any other signs of wear or damage, paying particular attention to the rubber mounting bushes.

8 The removal and fitting of new bushes is essentially the same for both front and rear bushes A range of sockets and a length of threaded bar will be required. Where

available a hydraulic press can also be used **(see illustrations)**. The voids in the rear bush should be filled with grease. VW G 052150 A2 is recommended or a commercial available lithium grease that confirms to VWs specifications.

Refitting

9 Locate the rear bush into the subframe and pivot the control arm around and into position.

10 Insert the mounting bolts using a new nut on the rear bolt. Tighten the bolts hand tight only at this stage.

11 Lever down the lower arm and locate the balljoint studs in their holes. Fit the new nuts and tighten to the specified torque.

12 Where remove, refit the ride height sensor (Xenon headlights only).

13 Raise the arm using a suitable jack until the suspension is in the unladen position.

Measure the distance from the hub nut centre to the wheel arch and adjust the distance to that noted down at the beginning of the work **(see illustration)**. Alternatively check the ride

5.13 Raise the arm until the distance from the hub centre to the wheel arch is the same as noted down

height against the specifications given at the start of this Chapter.

Caution: Exercise extreme care as the vehicle may be lifted off the axle stand during this procedure. An alternative approach is to refit the wheel and tighten the arm bolts with the vehicle on the ground (or wheel ramps).

14 Tighten the mounting bolts to the specified torque.

15 Refit the roadwheel and undertray, and lower the car to the ground.

6 Front suspension lower arm balljoint – removal, inspection and refitting

Note: *All self-locking nuts and bolts disturbed on removal must be renewed as a matter of course.*

Removal

Method 1

1 Remove the wheel bearing housing/swivel hub as described in Section 2.

2 Unscrew and remove the balljoint retaining nut **(see illustration)**, then release the balljoint from the wheel bearing housing using a universal balljoint separator. Withdraw the balljoint.

Method 2

3 Remove the wheel trim/hub cap (as applicable) and loosen the driveshaft retaining bolt (hub bolt) with the vehicle resting on its wheels. **Note:** *Do not loosen the hub bolt more than 90° at this stage, or the wheel bearing may be damaged. Also loosen the wheel bolts.*

4 Apply the handbrake, then jack up the front of the vehicle and support it on axle stands (see *Jacking and vehicle support*). Remove the appropriate roadwheel.

5 Unscrew and remove the driveshaft retaining bolt.

6 Unscrew the front suspension lower balljoint-to-lower arm retaining nuts, then lever the lower arm down to release the balljoint studs. Now use a soft-faced mallet to tap the driveshaft from the hub splines while pulling out the bottom end of the

wheel bearing housing. If the driveshaft is tight on the splines, it may be necessary to use a puller bolted to the hub to remove it. It is not necessary to remove the driveshaft completely from the hub. Retain the wheel bearing housing away from the lower arm by inserting a block of wood between the strut and the inner body panel.

7 Unscrew and remove the balljoint retaining nut, then release the balljoint from the wheel bearing housing using a universal balljoint separator. Withdraw the balljoint.

Inspection

8 With the balljoint removed, check that it moves freely, without any sign of roughness. Check also that the balljoint rubber gaiter shows no sign of deterioration, and is free from cracks and splits. Renew as necessary.

Refitting

Method 1

9 Fit the balljoint to the wheel bearing housing and fit the new retaining nut. Tighten the nut to the specified torque setting, noting that the balljoint shank can be retained with an Allen key if necessary to prevent it from rotating.

10 Refit the wheel bearing housing with reference to Section 2.

Method 2

11 Fit the balljoint to the wheel bearing housing and fit the new retaining nut. Tighten the nut to the specified torque setting, noting that the balljoint shank can be retained with an Allen key if necessary to prevent it from rotating.

12 Remove the wooden block and move the strut inwards, then refit the balljoint to the lower arm using new nuts, and tighten them to the specified torque.

13 Refit the driveshaft retaining bolt and tighten it sufficiently to draw the driveshaft fully into the hub, then refit the roadwheel.

14 Tighten the new driveshaft retaining bolt in the stages given in the Specifications. It is recommended that an angle gauge be used to ensure the correct tightening angle. Have an assistant apply the brakes and tighten the bolt to the first stage. **Note:** *The car must not be standing on its wheels when tightening the bolt, or the wheel bearing maybe be damaged.*

6.2 Front suspension lower arm balljoint retaining nut

Lower the vehicle to the ground and tighten the bolt to the second stage. Tighten the roadwheel bolts to the specified torque.

7 Front anti-roll bar – removal and refitting

Note: *As the subframe must be lowered during this procedure, Volkswagen subframe locating pins (T10486/1) or similar are required ensuring correct front wheel alignment. All self-locking nuts and bolts disturbed on removal must be renewed as a matter of course.*

Note: *The subframe is lowered, leaving the steering rack in position. However it maybe more convenient to lower the subframe with the steering rack still attached to the subframe.*

Removal

1 Apply the handbrake, then jack up the front of the vehicle and support it on axle stands (see *Jacking and vehicle support*). Remove both front roadwheels and the engine compartment undertray.

2 Unbolt the rear engine pendulum bracket from the transmission (as described in Chapter 2A Section 17, Chapter 2B Section 17 or Chapter 2C Section 16) and then unbolt the exhaust support bracket from the rear of the subframe **(see illustrations)**.

3 Unscrew the nuts securing the drop links to the anti-roll bar **(see illustration)**.

4 On models fitted with Zenon headlights

7.2a Unbolt the pendulum bracket...

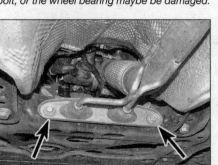

7.2b ...and remove the exhaust support bracket

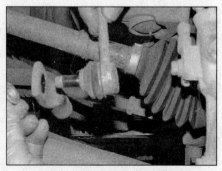

7.3 Disconnect the drop link from the anti-roll bar

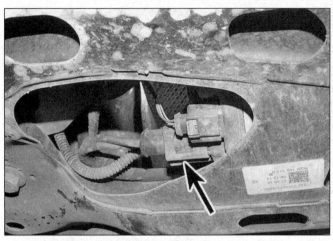

7.6 If the subframe is lowered with the steering rack, the wiring plugs must be disconnected

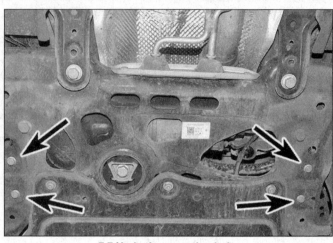

7.7 Undo the mounting bolts

disconnect the wiring plug from the ride height sensor and then unbolt the sensor from the control arm.

5 Working on each side in turn, unscrew the front suspension balljoint to control lower arm retaining nuts, then disconnect the track rod ends with reference to Section 24.

6 Work along the subframe and unclip the wiring loom **(see illustration)** and (where necessary) the fuel line.

7 Unscrew the bolts securing the anti-roll bar clamps to the subframe **(see illustration)**. Mark the anti-roll bar to indicate which way round it is fitted, and the position of the rubber mounting bushes as an aid to refitting.

8 Remove the steering rack mounting bolts and (using a pry bar) lift the steering rack off the locating dowels. Secure the steering rack with cable ties to the bulkhead before lowering the subframe.

9 Support the subframe with a trolley jack and block of wood. If not using the special Volkswagen locating pins T10486/1, accurately mark the position of the subframe to ensure correct wheel alignment **(see illustrations)**.

10 Unscrew the mounting bolts **(see illustrations)** and slightly lower the subframe, taking care not to damage the electrical wiring. Where the subframe pins are available

they should be fitted in turn as each subframe mounting bolt is removed

11 Lower the subframe sufficiently to allow the anti-roll bar to be removed. There is no need to remove it completely from the vehicle.

12 Carefully examine the anti-roll bar components for signs of wear, damage or deterioration, paying particular attention to the rubber mounting bushes. Renew worn components as necessary.

Refitting

13 Refitting is a reversal of removal but tighten all nuts and bolts to the specified torque where given. When refitting the subframe, align it with the marks made on removal, or use the special location pins before tightening the mounting bolts. Have the front wheel alignment checked at the earliest opportunity.

7.9a Mark the position of the subframe around each mounting bolt

7.9b Where available fit the subframe alignment pins (shown after removal of the subframe)

8 Front anti-roll bar drop link – removal and refitting

Note: *All self-locking nuts and bolts disturbed on removal must be renewed as a matter of course.*

Removal

1 Apply the handbrake, then jack up the front

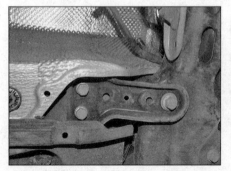

7.10a Remove the support brackets from each side

7.10b Remove the front...

7.10c ...and rear subframe mounting bolts (at both sides)

8.2a Counterhold the shank, unbolt...

8.2b ...and remove the link from the strut

8.2c Repeat the procedure at the anti-roll bar

of the vehicle and support it on axle stands (see *Jacking and vehicle support*). Remove the relevant front roadwheel.

2 Unscrew and remove the nuts securing the link to the strut and anti-roll bar **(see illustrations)**.

3 Inspect the link rubbers for signs of damage or deterioration. If evident, renew the link complete.

Refitting

4 Refitting is a reversal of removal, but tighten the nuts to the specified torque.

9 Rear wheel bearing housing/ stub axle – removal and refitting

Multi-link rear suspension

Removal

1 Chock the front wheels, then jack up the rear of the vehicle and support it on axle stands (see *Jacking and vehicle support*).

2 Remove the rear hub/wheel bearing housing as described in Section 10.

3 Remove the dust shield and then remove the coil spring as described in Section 14.

4 Where fitted remove the ride height sensor (models with Xenon headlights only). On models fitted with a plastic stone protector, remove the 'scrivets' and remove the guard.

5 Disconnect the wiring plugs from the ABS sensor and the handbrake motor.

6 Support the housing with a trolley jack and

then remove the upper and lower trailing arm bolts.

7 Unscrew the bolts securing the upper transverse link and lower transverse links to the rear wheel bearing housing.

8 Unscrew the bolt securing the rear track control rod to the rear wheel bearing housing.

9 Withdraw the rear wheel bearing housing from the car.

Refitting

Note: *All bolts that pass through suspension components that have bonded bushes should only be hand tightened initially. They are fully tightened when the vehicle ride height is correctly set (see text).*

10 Attach the rear wheel bearing housing to the rear track control rod, and the upper and lower transverse links, and hand-tighten the bolts.

11 Fit the wheel bearing housing to the trailing arm and fit the bolts hand tight only.

12 Refit the splash plate and tighten the bolts to the specified torque.

13 Refit the rear hub with reference to Section 10.

Caution: Exercise extreme care as the vehicle may be lifted off the axle stand during this procedure. An alternative approach is to refit all the components and tighten the suspension bolts with the vehicle on the ground (or wheel ramps).

14 Place a trolley jack under the hub. Position the centre of the rear hub to the ride-height distance noted at the beginning of the procedure, using the trolley jack to adjust

the position **(see illustration)**.

15 Tighten all the bolts except the trailing arm bolts to the specified torque.

16 Remove the trolley jack, then refit the rear coil spring with reference to Section 14.

17 Refit the ABS sensor and handbrake motor wiring plugs.

18 Fully tighten the trailing arm mounting bolts. The bolts must be tightened with the suspension in the extended position, not with the suspension raised.

19 Refit the roadwheel, then lower the vehicle to the ground, tighten the roadwheel bolts, and refit the wheel trim/hub cap. Have the rear wheel alignment checked and if necessary adjusted by a VW dealer or suitably equipped garage.

Torsion beam axle

Removal

20 On models fitted with a torsion beam axle the wheel bearing housing is a simple stub axle.

21 Remove the rear hub as described in Section 10.

22 Unbolt and remove the stub axle **(see illustration)**.

Refitting

23 Refitting is a reversal of removal, but use new bolts and tighten them to the specified torque.

10 Rear hub/wheel bearings – checking and renewal

Note: *The rear wheel bearings cannot be renewed independently of the rear hub, because the outer races are formed in the hub itself. If excessive wear is evident, the rear hub must be renewed complete. The rear hub bolt must always be renewed after removal.*

Note: *Removal and refitting of the rear wheel bearing is essentially the same for both the multi-link rear suspension and the torsion beam rear suspension.*

Removal

1 Chock the front roadwheels, then jack up the rear of the vehicle and support on axle stands (see *Jacking and vehicle support*).

9.14 Adjust the wheel arch to hub distance as required before tightening the fixings

9.22 The stub axle mounting bolts

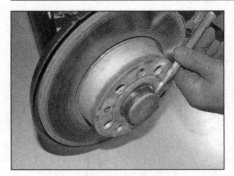

10.4 Remove the dust cap

10.5a Slacken and then...

10.5b ...remove the bolt

Release the handbrake and remove the relevant rear roadwheel.

2 Remove the rear brake caliper and mounting bracket with reference to Chapter 9 Section 9. Do not disconnect the hydraulic brake pipe. Move the caliper just clear of the brake disc, without bending the hydraulic pipe excessively, and support it with welding rod or on an axle stand.

3 Undo the crosshead screw then withdraw the brake disc from the hub.

4 Remove the dust cap from the centre of the hub using a cold chisel **(see illustration)**. Dispose of the cap – a new one will be required for refitting.

5 Unscrew and remove the hub bolt, using a multi-spline tool **(see illustrations)**. Note that it is tightened to a high torque and a socket extension bar may be required to loosen it. The bolt must be renewed whenever removed.

6 Pull the hub from the stub axle **(see illustration)**. It may be necessary to use a suitable puller to pull the hub and bearings from the stub axle.

7 Examine the hub and bearings for wear, pitting and damage. If any damage is evident, renew the hub complete.

Refitting

8 Check the condition of the stub axle. Wipe clean the stub axle and fit the hub.

9 Screw on the new bolt and tighten it to the specified torque.

10 Fit the new dust cap. Use a hammer on a large socket to carefully tap the cap into the hub. **Note:** *A badly fitting dust cap will allow*

moisture to enter the bearing, reducing its service life.

11 Refit the brake disc and tighten the crosshead screw.

12 Refit the rear brake mounting bracket and caliper with reference to Chapter 9 Section 9.

13 Refit the roadwheel and lower the vehicle to the ground.

11 Rear track control rod – removal and refitting

Note: *Multi-link rear suspension only.*

Removal

1 Check the vehicle ride height by measuring the distance from the centre of the wheel arch to the centre of the hub. Note down this dimension.

2 Chock the front roadwheels, then jack up the rear of the vehicle and support on axle stands (see *Jacking and vehicle support*). Remove the relevant rear roadwheel.

3 Where required, remove the anti-roll bar clamp bracket **(see illustration)** from the anti-roll bar on the appropriate side.

4 Remove the outer mounting nut and bolt.

5 Note the orientation of the rear track control rod and then remove the inner nut and bolt **(see illustration)**. The anti-roll bar may need to be levered out of the way to allow the bolt to be removed.

Refitting

6 Refit the control rod, using new bolts where

specified. Tighten the bolts hand tight only at this stage.

7 Place a trolley jack under the hub. Position the centre of the rear hub to the ride height distance noted at the beginning of the procedure, using the trolley jack to adjust the position.

Caution: Exercise extreme care as the vehicle may be lifted off the axle stand during this procedure. An alternative approach is to refit all the components and tighten the suspension bolts with the vehicle on the ground (or wheel ramps).

8 With the suspension raised or the vehicle on the ground, tighten the bolts to the specified torque.

9 If not already done so, refit the wheel and tighten the bolts to the specified torque. Have the rear wheel alignment checked and if necessary adjusted by a Volkswagen dealer or suitably equipped garage.

12 Rear transverse links – removal and refitting

Note: *Multi-link rear suspension only.*

Upper link

Removal

1 Check the ride height by measuring the distance from the centre of the wheel arch to the centre of the hub before raising the vehicle.

10.6 Remove the hub

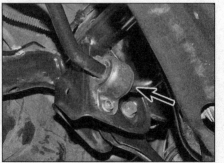

11.3 Remove the bracket

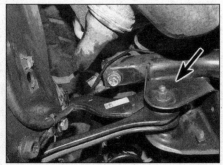

11.5 Track control inner mounting

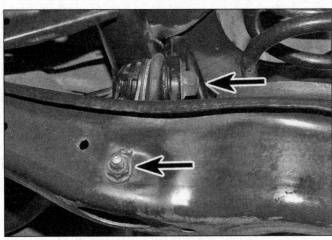

12.13 Unbolt the anti-roll bar drop link

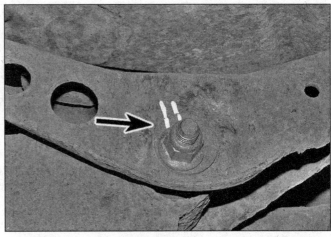

12.16 The eccentric bolt marked up for adjustment of the rear suspension

2 Chock the front roadwheels, then jack up the rear of the vehicle and support on axle stands (see *Jacking and vehicle support*). Remove the roadwheel.
3 Remove the rear coil spring as described in Section 14.
4 Release the ABS speed sensor wiring from the upper link, and then unscrew the bolt securing the link to the wheel bearing housing.
5 At the inner end of the upper link, mark the position of the eccentric bolt and subframe in relation to each other. This alignment determines the camber setting of the rear wheels.
6 Note which way round the eccentric bolt is fitted, then unscrew and remove it and withdraw the upper link.

Refitting
7 Refitting is a reversal of removal, but delay fully-tightening the mounting bolts until the rear suspension is in the unladen position. Make sure the eccentric bolt is correctly aligned as previously noted and then raise the rear suspension using a trolley jack under hub. Raise the jack until the ride height is correct and then tighten the bolts to the specified torque.
Caution: Exercise extreme care as the vehicle may be lifted off the axle stand during this procedure. An alternative approach is to refit all the components and tighten the suspension bolts with the vehicle on the ground (or wheel ramps).
8 Fit the wheel and lower the vehicle to the ground. Tighten the bolts to the specified torque. Have the rear wheel alignment checked and if necessary adjusted by a Volkswagen dealer or suitably equipped garage.

Lower transverse link
Removal
9 Check the ride height by measuring the distance from the centre of the wheel arch to the centre of the hub before raising the vehicle.

10 Chock the front roadwheels, then jack up the rear of the vehicle and support on axle stands (see *Jacking and vehicle support*). Remove the roadwheel.
11 Where fitted unbolt the ride height sensor from the link arm (Xenon headlight models only).
12 Remove the rear coil spring as described in Section 12.
13 Unbolt the anti-roll bar drop link from the arm **(see illustration)** and then unbolt the lower shock absorber mounting bolt.
14 Where required remove the rear exhaust silencer as described in Chapter 4C Section 6 or Chapter 4D Section 9.
15 Unscrew the bolt securing the lower transverse link to the wheel bearing housing.
16 At the inner end of the lower link, mark the position of the eccentric bolt and subframe in relation to each other **(see illustration)**. This alignment determines the camber setting of the rear wheels.
17 Unscrew and remove the inner bolt and withdraw the lower transverse link from under the car.

Refitting
18 Refitting is a reversal of removal, but delay fully-tightening the mounting bolts until the rear suspension is in the unladen position. Make sure the eccentric bolt is correctly aligned as previously noted and then raise the rear suspension using a trolley jack under hub. Raise the jack until the ride height is correct and then tighten the bolts to the specified torque.
Caution: Exercise extreme care as the vehicle may be lifted off the axle stand during this procedure. An alternative approach is to refit all the components and tighten the suspension bolts with the vehicle on the ground (or wheel ramps).
19 Fit the wheel and lower the vehicle to the ground. Tighten the bolts to the specified torque. Have the rear wheel alignment checked and if necessary adjusted by a Volkswagen dealer or suitably equipped garage.

13 Rear trailing arm and bracket – removal, overhaul and refitting

Note: *Multi-link rear suspension only.*

Removal
1 Chock the front roadwheels, then jack up the rear of the vehicle and support on axle stands (see *Jacking and vehicle support*). Remove the roadwheel.
2 Remove the rear coil spring as described in Section 14.
3 Unclip the wiring loom from the trailing arm and the mounting bracket.
4 Unscrew the bolts securing the trailing arm to the rear wheel bearing housing.
5 Mark the position of the trailing arm front mounting bracket in relation to the underbody **(see illustration)**.
6 Support the front mounting bracket on a trolley jack, then unscrew the bolts, lower the assembly and withdraw the rear trailing arm and bracket from under the vehicle.

Overhaul
7 Thoroughly clean the trailing arm and bracket, then unscrew the front pivot bolt and separate the arm from the bracket. Check carefully for cracks or any other signs of wear or damage, paying particular attention to the rubber mounting bush.

13.5 Rear trailing arm mounting bracket

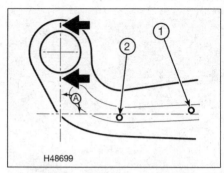

13.8a Make a vertical line along holes (1) and (2) on the arm as shown…

Angle (A) = 90°

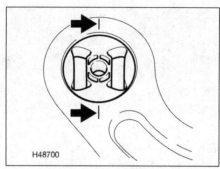

13.8b …then press in the new bush so that the centre line is as shown

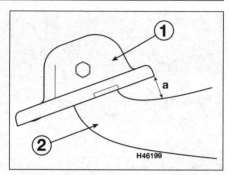
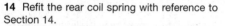

13.9 Mounting bracket assembly to trailing arm

1 Mounting bracket   2 Trailing arm
a = 37.0 mm

8 If the bush requires renewal, take the arm to a Volkswagen dealer or suitably equipped garage. Alternatively, a hydraulic press and suitable spacers may be used to press the bush out of the arm, and to install the new one. Dip the bush in a mild solution of washing-up liquid and water. When fitting the new bush to the front of the trailing arm, it is important to position it correctly. Make a vertical line on the arm as shown in the accompanying illustration, and then press in the new bush so that the line is between the two projections shown **(see illustrations)**.
9 With the new bush in position, locate the front of the arm in the bracket, and insert the

bolt. Position the arm in relation to the bracket as shown **(see illustration)** then tighten the bolt/nut to the specified torque.

Refitting

10 Fit the trailing arm to the wheel bearing housing and insert the bolts loosely.
11 Raise the front mounting bracket and locate it on the underbody in its previously noted position. Insert the new bolts and tighten to the specified torque.
12 Lower the jack then tighten the arm-to-housing bolts to the specified torque.
13 Refit the wiring loom to the retaining clips.

14 Refit the rear coil spring with reference to Section 14.
15 Refit the roadwheel and lower the vehicle to the ground. Have the rear wheel alignment checked and if necessary adjusted by a Volkswagen dealer or suitably equipped garage.

14 Rear coil spring – removal and refitting

⚠️ *Warning: Adjustable coil spring compressors are readily available, and are recommended for this operation. Any attempt to remove the coil spring without such a tool is likely to result in damage or personal injury.*
Note: *To ensure even rear suspension, both rear coil springs should be renewed at the same time.*

Removal

Note: *The removal procedure is essentially the same for both the torsion beam suspension and the multi-link suspension.*
1 Chock the front roadwheels, then jack up the rear of the vehicle and support on axle stands (see *Jacking and vehicle support*). Remove the relevant rear road-wheel.
2 On torsion beam models prise up the retaining clip from the centre of the coil spring **(see illustration)**.
3 On multi-link suspension models remove the shock absorber top mounting bolts as described in Section 15.
4 Fit the tool to the coil spring and compress it until it can be removed from the transverse arm and underbody **(see illustrations)**. With the coil spring on the bench, carefully release the tension of the tool and remove it.
5 With the coil spring removed, recover the upper and lower spring seats and check

14.2 Remove the central peg

14.4a The rear coil spring

14.4b Compress the rear coil spring with the special tool…

14.4c …then remove it from the trailing arm and underbody

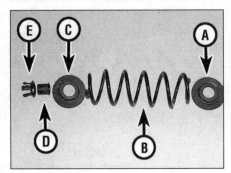

14.5 The component parts of the coil spring (torsion beam model)

A Upper spring seat   D Locking peg
B Coil spring   E Locking peg
C Lower spring seat   housing

them for damage **(see illustration)**. Obtain new ones if necessary, but note that they are different, the lower one having a location pin that enters a hole in the lower transverse link. Also clean thoroughly the spring locations on the underbody and trailing arm.

Refitting

6 Refitting is a reversal of removal, but make

15.2 Remove the wing liner

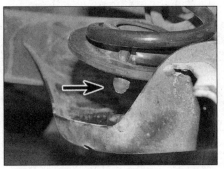

14.6a The spring seat locating peg (torsion beam axle)

sure that the lug on the lower spring seat engages in the hole in the lower transverse link or axle beam and the lower end of the coil spring abuts the stop on the seat. Also make sure the upper seat is correctly engaged with the lug on the underbody **(see illustrations)**. **Note:** *To ensure even rear suspension, both rear coil springs should be renewed at the same time.*

15 Rear shock absorber – removal and refitting

Note: *All self-locking nuts and bolts disturbed on removal must be renewed as a matter of course.*
Note: *To ensure even rear suspension, both rear shock absorbers should be renewed at the same time.*

Removal

Note: *The removal procedure is essentially the same for both the torsion beam suspension and the multi-link suspension.*
1 Before removing the shock absorber, an

14.6b The upper spring seat (multi-link suspension)

idea of how effective it is can be gained by depressing the rear corner of the car. If the shock absorber is in good condition, the body should rise then settle in its normal position. If the body oscillates more than this, the shock absorber is defective.
2 Chock the front roadwheels, then jack up the rear of the vehicle and support on axle stands (see *Jacking and vehicle support*). Remove the relevant rear roadwheel and wing liner **(see illustration)**.
3 Position a trolley jack beneath the trailing arm or shock absorber lower mounting (torsion beam suspension) and raise the arm so that the shock absorber is slightly compressed. Note on some models, it may be necessary to remove the plastic stone protection guard first. Where fitted, unbolt the ride height sensor (Zenon headlight models only).
4 Unscrew the lower mounting bolt, then unscrew the upper mounting bolts and withdraw the shock absorber **(see illustrations)**.
5 With the shock absorber on the bench, remove the cap, then unscrew the nut from the top of the piston rod and remove the upper mounting bracket, followed by the bump stop,

15.4a Unscrew the rear shock absorber lower mounting bolt (torsion beam axle shown)...

15.4b ...and upper mounting bolts

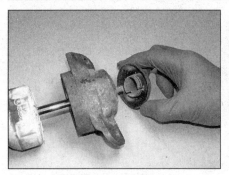

15.5a Remove the cap...

15.5b ... and unscrew the nut while counterholding the piston

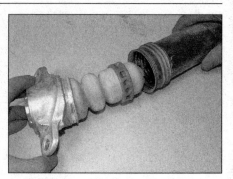

15.5c Remove the protective sleeve...

15.5d ...and bump stop

15.10 Set the ride height before fully tightening the lower mounting

support ring (where fitted), protective tube, and protective cap **(see illustrations)**.
6 If necessary, the action of the shock absorber can be checked by mounting it upright in a vice. Fully depress the rod, and then pull it up fully. The piston rod must move smoothly over its complete length.

Refitting

7 Locate the components removed from the top of the shock absorber in their correct order, and screw on a new nut. Tighten the nut and fit the cap.
8 Locate the shock absorber in the rear wheel arch, then insert the upper mounting bolts and tighten to the specified torque.
9 Extend the shock absorber if necessary, and insert the lower mounting bolt loosely.
10 Use the jack to raise the vehicle to the installation ride height (see Specifications)

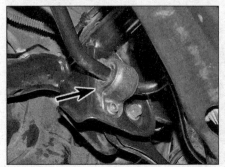

16.5 Rear anti-roll bar mounting clamp bolts

and fully tighten the shock absorber lower mounting bolt **(see illustration)**.
Caution: Exercise extreme care as the vehicle may be lifted off the axle stand during this procedure. An alternative approach is to refit all the components and tighten the suspension bolts with the vehicle on the ground (or wheel ramps).
11 Refit the wing liner and roadwheel. Lower the vehicle to the ground.

16 Rear anti-roll bar and drop link – removal and refitting

Note: *Multi-link suspension models only.*

Removal

1 Chock the front roadwheels, then jack up the rear of the vehicle and support on axle

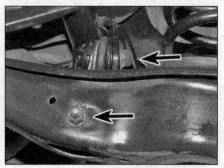

16.6 The drop link mounting bolts

stands (see *Jacking and vehicle support*). Remove both rear roadwheels.
2 Working on each side in turn, unscrew the nut and detach the connecting links from the anti-roll bar.
3 To make access easier, undo the retaining nuts and securing clips and remove the plastic shield from below the anti-roll bar – where fitted.
4 Mark the anti-roll bar to indicate which way round it is fitted, and the position of the rubber mounting bushes; this will aid refitting.
5 Unscrew the bolts securing the anti-roll bar clamps to the rear subframe, and recover the clamps **(see illustration)**.
6 To remove the anti-roll bar drop link, unbolt it from the lower transverse link arm **(see illustration)**.

Refitting

7 Refitting is a reversal of removal but tighten all nuts and bolts to the specified torque.

17 Torsion beam axle – removal and refitting

Removal

1 Chock the front wheels, then jack up the rear of the vehicle and support on axle stands (see *Jacking and vehicle support*). Remove both rear wheels.
2 Disconnect the wiring plugs from both wheel speed sensors and the both handbrake motors. Unclip the loom from the brackets.
3 Unbolt both rear brake calipers and suspend them from the bodywork, so that the brake flexible hose is not under any strain.
4 On models with Zenon headlights disconnect the wiring plug from the ride height sensor and unclip the wiring loom. Unbolt the sensor from the axle.
5 Unclip the brake line from the axle. The retaining clip will be destroyed and a new one will be required for refitting.
6 Remove both rear springs (Section 14) and both rear shock absorbers (Section 15).
7 Support the axle assembly on a jack (a transmission style scissor jack is ideal) and then with the aid of an assistant unbolt the axle from the body and lower it from the vehicle.

19.5a Using a splined tool …

19.5b …unscrew and remove the bolt

19.6 The steering wheel should be marked for its central position

Refitting

8 Refitting is a reversal of removal, but renew the retaining nuts. Before tighten the components raise the axle to the correct ride height **(see illustration 15.10)** and then tighten to the bolts to the specified torque.

18 Rear subframe (multi-link suspension) – removal and refitting

Removal

1 Chock the front wheels, then jack up the rear of the vehicle and support on axle stands (see Jacking and support 13). Remove both rear wheels.
2 Disconnect the wiring plugs from both wheel speed sensors and the both handbrake motors. Unclip the wiring loom from the brackets and move it clear of the subframe and trailing arm.
3 Remove the spring clip from the brake flexible hose at the junction with the rigid brake line. Remove the brake line from the holder. DO NOT disconnect the brake line.
4 Unbolt both rear brake calipers and suspend them from the bodywork, so that the brake flexible hose is not under any strain.
5 On models with Zenon headlights disconnect the wiring plug from the ride height sensor and unclip the wiring loom. Unbolt the sensor from the axle.
6 Unclip the brake line from the axle. The retaining clip will be destroyed and a new one will be required for refitting.
7 Remove both rear springs (Section 14) and both rear shock absorbers (Section 15).
8 Remove the rear exhaust as described in Chapter 4C Section 6 or Chapter 4D Section 9.
9 Make alignment marks around the trailing arm brackets and the subframe mounting points.
10 Support the axle assembly on a jack (a transmission style scissor jack is ideal) and then with the aid of an assistant unbolt the trailing arm brackets from the body.
11 Unbolt the subframe mounting bolts and lower the subframe slowly until the brake line on top of the subframe can be unclip. Lower the subframe to the floor.

Refitting

12 Refitting is a reversal of removal, but renew the retaining nuts. Before tighten the components raise the axle to the correct ride height **(see illustration 15.10)** and then tighten to the bolts to the specified torque.

19 Steering wheel – removal and refitting

⚠ **Warning: During the airbag removal and refitting procedures, avoid sitting in the front seats.**

Removal

1 Set the front wheels in the straight-ahead position, and release the steering lock by inserting the ignition key.
2 Disconnect the battery as described in Chapter 5A Section 3.
3 Adjust the steering column to its highest position, then extend it into the passenger compartment as far as possible, and lock it in this position.
Caution: To prevent any discharge of static electricity into the airbag circuit, temporarily touch the vehicle bodywork before disconnecting the wiring.
4 Remove the driver's airbag as described in Chapter 12 Section 24.

⚠ **Warning: Position the airbag in a safe and secure place, away from the work area.**

5 Using a multi-spline socket, unscrew and remove the retaining bolt, while holding the steering wheel stationary **(see illustrations)**. Discard the retaining bolt – it must be replaced.
6 Check if the steering wheel is marked in relation to the column. If not, use a dab of paint to mark them, and then ease the steering wheel from the column splines by firmly rocking it side-to-side **(see illustration)**.

Refitting

7 Locate the steering wheel on the column splines making sure that the previously made marks are correctly aligned.
8 Fit a new bolt and tighten to the specified torque while holding the steering wheel stationary.

9 Refit the driver's airbag with reference to Chapter 12 Section 24.
10 Reconnect the battery as described in Chapter 5A Section 3.

20 Steering column – removal, inspection and refitting

Removal

1 Disconnect the battery as described in Chapter 5A Section 3.
2 Remove the steering wheel as described in Section 19.
3 Return the steering to the straight-ahead position. Adjust the steering column to its lowest position and extend it into the passenger compartment as far as possible, and then lock it in this position.
4 Remove the upper shroud and lower shrouds from the steering column as described in Chapter 11 Section 25.
5 Remove the lower drivers side panel from the facia and knee airbag as described in Chapter 11 Section 25 and Chapter 12 Section 24.
6 Undo the retaining screw and remove the footwell heater ducting from above the pedals **(see illustration)**.
7 Remove the switch assembly from the top of the steering column as described in Chapter 12 Section 5.
8 Disconnect the wiring connector from the transponder around the ignition switch, and then release the wiring retaining clips from the steering column.
9 Follow the wiring loom down the length of the

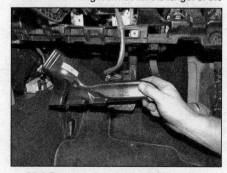

20.6 Remove the air distribution duct

20.9a Unclip the wiring loom conduit...

20.9b ...and release the loom clips

20.9c Remove the support bracket

20.10 Remove the panel

Inspection

15 The steering column is designed to collapse in the event of a front-end crash, to prevent the steering wheel injuring the driver. Before refitting the steering column, examine the column and mountings for signs of damage and deformation.

16 Check the inner column sections for signs of free play in the column bushes. If any damage or wear is found on the steering column bushes, the column must be renewed as an assembly.

17 The intermediate shaft is permanently attached to the inner column and cannot be renewed separately. Inspect the universal joints for excessive wear. If evident, the complete steering column must be renewed.

Refitting

18 Where removed, refit the ignition switch/steering column lock/switch carrier with reference to Section 21.

19 Refit the steering column to the bulkhead bracket, making sure it located on the locating lug. Insert the mounting bolts, and tighten to the specified torque, starting with the upper bolts first and then the lower bolts.

20 Attach the universal joint on the steering gear pinion splines, making sure the road wheels and steering wheel are in the correct position. Insert the new clamp bolt, and tighten to the specified torque.

21 Refit the wiring harness under the steering column.

22 Reconnect the wiring to the ignition switch transponder and secure the wiring in its retaining clips.

23 Refit the footrest trim and footwell vent under the steering column.

24 Refit the light switch assembly with reference to Chapter 12 Section 5.

25 Where the lower facia panel and knee airbag, as described in Chapter 11 Section 25 and Chapter 12 Section 24.

26 Refit the lower and upper shrouds, as described in Chapter 11 Section 25.

27 Refit the steering wheel with reference to Section 19.

28 Refit the airbag as described in Chapter 12 Section 24.

29 Reconnect the battery lead as described in Chapter 5A Section 3.

steering column, undo the earth cable retaining nut, release the retaining clips and remove the wiring loom from under the steering column, noting its fitted position **(see illustrations)**.

10 Working in the footwell, release the plastic fixings and remove the footrest panel **(see illustration)**. Fold back the carpet

11 Undo the clamp bolt from the steering column lower universal joint. Unscrew the clamp bolt and pull the universal joint from the steering gear pinion. Note that the pinion shaft has a cut-out to enable fitting of the clamp bolt, and the splined pinion shaft incorporates a flat making it impossible to assemble the joint to the shaft in the wrong position **(see illustration)**. Discard the clamp bolt; a new one should be used on refitting.

12 Note that the inner and outer columns, and the intermediate shaft, are telescopic, to facilitate the reach adjustment. It is important

to keep the splined sections of the inner steering column engaged with each other while the steering column is removed. If they become detached due to the outer column sections being separated, especially on a vehicle, which has completed a high mileage, it is possible that rattling noises may occur.

13 Support the steering column, then unscrew and remove the mounting bolts. Withdraw the steering column from inside the car **(see illustrations)**.

Caution: Do not carry the steering column by suspending it from the universal joint or intermediate shaft, as this will damage the universal joint and steering column bushes. Also, do not bend the joints by more than 90°.

14 If necessary, remove the ignition switch/steering column lock with reference to Section 21.

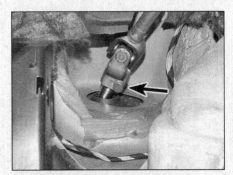

20.11 The column pinch bolt

20.13a Undo the mounting bolts (lower bolts shown)...

20.13b ...and withdraw the steering column

21 Ignition switch/lock cylinder – removal and refitting

Ignition switch

Removal

1 Disconnect the battery as described in Chapter 5A Section 3.
2 Remove the lower shroud from the steering column, as described in Chapter 11 Section 25.
3 Release the retaining clip and disconnect the wiring plug from the rear of the ignition switch **(see illustration)**.
4 Using two small screwdrivers in the slots in the outer housing release the two retaining clips, and then withdraw the ignition electrical switch **(see illustrations)**.

Refitting

5 Refit the switch to the steering lock housing and press in until the two retaining clips engage. Making sure the slot in the rear of the switch is aligned correctly.
6 Reconnect the wiring plug to the ignition switch.
7 Refit the lower shroud and tighten the screws.
8 Reconnect the battery.

Lock cylinder

Removal

9 Carry out the procedures as described in paragraphs 1 and 3.
10 Disconnect the wiring connector from the transponder around the ignition switch **(see illustration 20.8a)**.
11 Insert the ignition key and turn the lock cylinder to the drive/on position (which is 90° from off position).
12 Insert a piece of wire 1.2 mm in diameter in the drilling next to the ignition key, slide it in to release the locking lever, then withdraw the lock cylinder from the housing **(see illustrations)**. To make the piece of wire locate in the locking lever easier, file an angle on the end of the wire.

Refitting

13 Refit the lock cylinder with the ignition key in the Drive position, then remove the wire.
14 Reconnect the wiring connector to the transponder.
15 Refit the upper and lower shrouds, and tighten the screws.
16 Refit the steering wheel with reference to Section 19.
17 Reconnect the battery negative lead.

Ignition switch/lock cylinder housing

Removal

18 The ignition switch/lock housing is integral with the switch assembly carrier, which is secured to the steering column with shear-head bolts **(see illustration)**.

21.3 Disconnect the wiring plug

21.4b ...to release the two securing clips...

19 To remove the housing first remove the steering column as described in Section 20.
20 The switch/lock carrier is secured by shear-head bolts, and the heads are broken off in the tightening procedure. To remove the old bolts, either drill them out, or use a sharp cold chisel to cut off their heads or turn them

21.12a Hole provided in the ignition switch

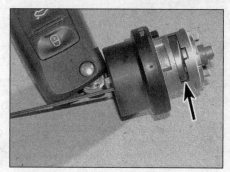

21.12c ...to release the locking lever

21.4a Insert two thin screwdrivers in the recesses...

21.4c ...and withdraw the electrical switch

anti-clockwise. Withdraw the carrier from the steering column.
21 When refitting locate the switch/lock carrier on the steering column, and insert the new shear-head bolts. Tighten the bolts until their heads break off.
22 The remaining procedure is a reversal of removal.

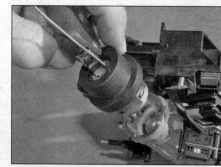

21.12b insert a thin rod through the hole ...

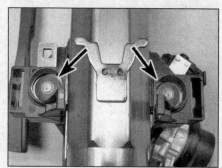

21.18 Steering lock housing shear bolts

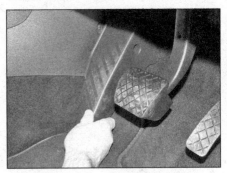

22.4a Remove the footrest panel...

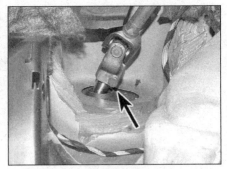

22.4b ...fold back the carpet and remove the pinch bolt

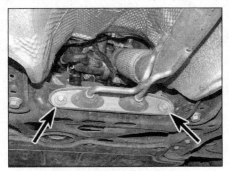

22.5a Remove the bracket...

22 Steering gear assembly – removal, overhaul and refitting

Note: *The steering rack is removed with the subframe. Volkswagen subframe locating pins (T10486/1) or similar are required to ensure correct front wheel alignment. Alternatively the position of the subframe in relation to the body should be marked up before removal. New subframe mounting bolts, track rod balljoint nuts, steering gear retaining bolts, and an intermediate shaft universal joint clamp bolt will be required on refitting.*

Removal

1 Apply the handbrake, then jack up the front of the vehicle and support it on axle stands positioned on the underbody, leaving the subframe free (see *Jacking and vehicle support*). Position the steering straight-ahead, and then remove both front wheels. Remove the engine compartment undertray.

2 Remove the ignition key and engage the steering wheel lock. On models with keyless entry and stop/start turn the ignition off and open the driver's door. This will engage the steering lock.

3 Disconnect the battery as described in Chapter 5A Section 3.

4 Inside the vehicle, remove the footrest panel,

22.5b ...and the torque strap bolts from the transmission

fold back the carpet and remove the steering rack pinion pinch bolt **(see illustrations)**. Pull the universal joint from the pinion splines. **Note:** *The steering gear pinion incorporates a cut-out for the clamp bolt, and therefore the joint can only be fitted in one position. Discard the clamp bolt; a new one should be used on refitting.*

5 Remove the exhaust support bracket from the rear of the subframe and then remove the engine rear torque strap (pendulum) from the transmission **(see illustrations)**.

6 On both sides unbolt the anti-roll bar drop links from the anti-roll bar.

7 Remove the nuts from the control arm balljoint and lever the control arm out of the swivel hub **(see illustration)**.

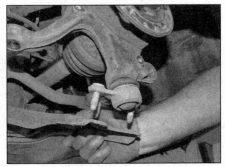

22.7 Release the control arm

8 With reference to Section 24, disconnect the track rod ends from the swivel hub (at both sides).

9 Where fitted (Xenon headlight models only) disconnect the wiring plug from the vehicle ride height sensor.

10 Disconnect the wiring plug from the oil level/temperature sensor (on the sump) and where fitted, disconnect the wiring plug from the coolant pump.

11 Work along the subframe and unclip the wiring loom from the subframe as required **(see illustration)**.

12 Fit the subframe alignment pins if available or mark the position of the subframe in relation to the body **(see illustration)**.

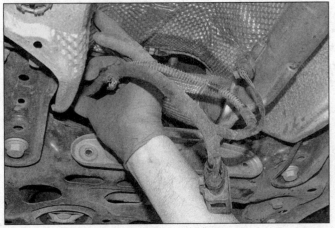

22.11 Unclip the wiring loom

22.12 Mark the exact position of the subframe

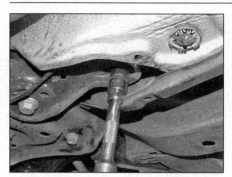

22.13a Remove the support brackets...

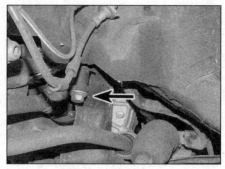

22.13b ...the front...

22.13c ...and rear bolts

22.13d With the subframe lowered slightly disconnect the steering rack wiring plugs

13 Position a suitable jack under the subframe, remove the mounting bolts and lower the subframe slightly so that the wiring plugs can be removed from the steering rack (see illustrations).

14 Check that all wiring has been removed from the subframe and then lower the subframe to the ground.

15 Remove the subframe from the vehicle. Remove the heat shield and then unbolt the subframe from the steering rack.
Caution: Do not touch the wiring terminals on the electronic control unit, as a static electricity discharge may damage the internal components.

Overhaul

16 Examine the steering gear assembly for signs of wear or damage, and check that the rack moves freely throughout the full length of its travel, with no signs of roughness or excessive free play between the steering gear pinion and rack.

17 It is not possible to overhaul the steering gear assembly housing components, and if it is faulty, the assembly must be renewed. The only components that can be renewed individually are the steering gear gaiters, the track rod end balljoints and the track rods, as described later in this Chapter.

Refitting

18 Refitting is a reversal of removal, noting the following points:
a) Align the subframe with the marks made on removal, or use the special Volkswagen location pins before tightening the mounting bolts.
b) Make sure that all mounting bolts are tightened to the specified torque.
c) Make sure wiring connections are secure and that the wiring loom is routed correctly.
d) Have the front wheel alignment checked at the earliest opportunity.
e) The steering angle sensor basic settings must be set by a Volkswagen dealer (or suitably equipped garage) using specialist diagnostic equipment.
f) If a new steering gear has been fitted, it must also be adapted to the vehicle by a Volkswagen dealer (or suitably equipped garage) using suitable diagnostic equipment.

23 Steering gear gaiters and track rods – renewal

Steering gear rubber gaiters

1 Remove the track rod end balljoint as described in Section 24. Also, unscrew the locking nut from the track rod arm, after noting its position.

2 Wipe clean the rubber gaiter to prevent entry of dirt or moisture. Note the fitted position of the gaiter on the track rod, then release the retaining clips and slide the gaiter off the steering gear housing and track rod (see illustration).

3 Wipe clean the track rod and the steering gear housing, and then apply a film of suitable grease to the surface of the rack. To do this, turn the steering wheel as necessary to fully extend the rack from the housing, then reposition it in its central position.

4 Carefully slide the new gaiter onto the track rod, and locate it on the steering gear housing. Position the gaiter as previously noted on removal, making sure that it is not twisted, then lift the outer sealing lip of the gaiter to equalise air pressure within the gaiter.

5 Secure the gaiter in position with new retaining clips. Where crimped-type clips are used, pull the clip as tight as possible, and locate the hooks in their slots. Remove any slack in the clip by carefully compressing the raised section. In the absence of the special crimping tool, a pair of side-cutters may be used, taking care not to cut the clip.

6 Screw on the locking nut, then refit the track rod end balljoint as described in Section 24.

Track rods

7 Remove the relevant steering gear rubber gaiter as described earlier. If there is insufficient working room with the steering gear mounted in the car, remove it as described in Section 22 and hold it in a vice while renewing the track rod.

8 Hold the steering rack stationary with one spanner on the flats provided, then loosen the balljoint nut with another spanner. Fully unscrew the nut and remove the track rod from the rack.

9 Locate the new track rod on the end of the steering rack and screw on the nut. Hold the rack stationary with one spanner and tighten the balljoint nut to the specified torque. A crow's foot adapter may be required since the track rod prevents access with a socket, and care must be taken to apply the correct torque in this situation.

10 Refit the steering gear or rubber gaiter with reference to the earlier paragraphs or Section 22. On completion check and, if necessary, adjust the front wheel alignment as described in Section 25.

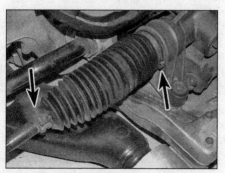

23.2 Steering rack gaiter securing clips

24 Track rod end – removal and refitting

Note: *A new balljoint retaining nut will be required on refitting.*

Removal

1 Apply the handbrake, then jack up the front of the vehicle and support it on axle stands (see *Jacking and vehicle support*). Remove the relevant roadwheel.

2 If the track rod end is to be re-used, mark its position in relation to the track rod to facilitate refitting.

3 Unscrew the track rod end locknut by a quarter of a turn **(see illustration)**. Do not move the locknut from this position, as it will serve as a handy reference mark on refitting.

4 Loosen and remove the nut securing the track rod end balljoint to the wheel bearing housing, and release the balljoint tapered shank using a universal balljoint separator.

Note that the balljoint shank has a hexagon hole – hold the shank with an Allen key while loosening the nut **(see illustrations)**.

5 Counting the exact number of turns necessary to do so, unscrew the track rod end from the track rod **(see illustration)**.

6 Carefully clean the balljoint and the threads. Renew the balljoint if its movement is sloppy or too stiff, if excessively worn, or if damaged in any way; carefully check the stud taper and threads. If the balljoint gaiter is damaged, the complete balljoint assembly must be renewed; it is not possible to obtain the gaiter separately.

Refitting

7 Screw the track rod end onto the track rod by the number of turns noted on removal. This should bring the track rod end to within a quarter of a turn of the locknut, with the alignment marks that were made on removal (if applicable) lined up. Tighten the locknut.

8 Refit the balljoint shank to the steering arm on the wheel bearing housing, then fit a new

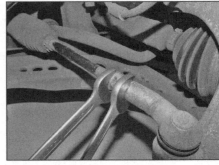

24.3 Slacken the lock nut

retaining nut and tighten it to the specified torque. Hold the shank with an Allen key if necessary.

9 Refit the roadwheel, then lower the car to the ground and tighten the roadwheel bolts to the specified torque.

10 Check and, if necessary, adjust the front wheel toe setting as described in Section 25.

24.4a Using an Allen key to hold the ball joint shank while loosening the nut

24.4b Release the track rod ball joint

24.4c Use a ball joint separator to release the track rod ball joint if it is a tight fit

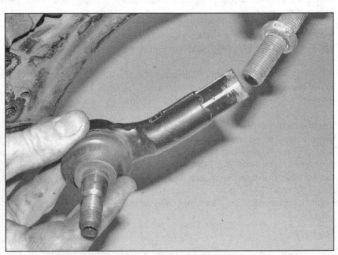

24.5 Unscrewing the track rod end from the track rod

25 Wheel alignment and steering angles – general information

Definitions

1 A car's steering and suspension geometry is defined in three basic settings – all angles are expressed in degrees; the steering axis is defined as an imaginary line drawn through the axis of the suspension strut, extended where necessary to contact the ground **(see illustration).**

2 *Camber* is the angle between each roadwheel and a vertical line drawn through its centre and tyre contact patch, when viewed from the front or rear of the car. Positive camber is when the roadwheels are tilted outwards from the vertical at the top; negative camber is when they are tilted inwards.

3 The front Camber angle is only adjustable by loosening the front suspension subframe mounting bolts and moving it slightly to one side. The camber angle can be checked using a camber checking gauge. This will also alter the Castor angle.

4 The rear Camber angle is only adjustable by loosening the upper transverse inner mounting nut, then turning the eccentric bolt (this can be turned left or right to a maximum range of 90º). The camber angle can be checked using a camber checking gauge. This will also alter the Castor angle.

5 *Castor* is the angle between the steering axis and a vertical line drawn through each roadwheel's centre and tyre contact patch, when viewed from the side of the car. Positive castor is when the steering axis is tilted so that it contacts the ground ahead of the vertical; negative castor is when it contacts the ground behind the vertical. Slight castor

angle adjustment is possible by loosening the front suspension subframe bolts and moving it slightly to one side. This also alters the Camber angle.

6 Castor is not easily adjustable, and is given for reference only; while it can be checked using a castor checking gauge, if the figure obtained is significantly different from that specified, the car must be taken for careful checking by a professional, as the fault can only be caused by wear or damage to the body or suspension components.

7 *Toe* is the difference, viewed from above, between lines drawn through the roadwheel centres and the car's centre-line. Toe-in is when the roadwheels point inwards, towards each other at the front, while toe-out is when they splay outwards from each other at the front.

8 The front wheel toe setting is adjusted by screwing the track rod(s) in/out of the outer balljoint(s) to alter the effective length of the track rod assembly.

9 Rear wheel toe setting is adjusted by loosening the lower transverse inner mounting nut, and then turning the eccentric bolt (this can be turned left or right to a maximum range of 90º).

10 If the figures obtained are significantly different from that specified, the car must be taken for careful checking by a professional, as the fault can only be caused by wear or damage to the body or suspension components.

Checking and adjustment

11 Due to the special measuring equipment necessary to check the wheel alignment, and the skill required to use it properly, the checking and adjustment of these settings is best left to a Volkswagen dealer or similar expert. Note that most tyre-fitting centres now possess sophisticated checking equipment.

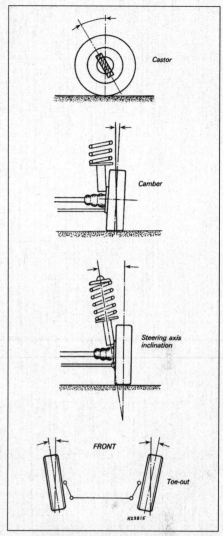

25.1 Front wheel geometry

Notes

Chapter 11
Bodywork and fittings

Contents

Section number

Body exterior fittings – removal and refitting 21
Bonnet – removal, refitting and adjustment 8
Bonnet lock – removal and refitting 10
Bonnet release cable – removal and refitting 9
Central locking components – description, removal and refitting . . . 17
Centre console – removal and refitting. 26
Crossmember – removal and refitting 28
Door – removal, refitting and adjustment 11
Door handle and lock components – removal and refitting 13
Door inner trim panel – removal and refitting 12
Door window glass and regulator – removal and refitting 14
Facia panel assembly – removal and refitting 27
Front bumper cover – removal and refitting 6
General information 1

Section number

Interior trim – removal and refitting 25
Maintenance – bodywork and underframe. 2
Maintenance – upholstery and carpets 3
Major body damage – repair 5
Minor body damage – repair 4
Mirrors and associated components – removal and refitting 18
Rear bumper cover – removal and refitting 7
Seat belt components – removal and refitting 24
Seat belt tensioning mechanisms – general information 23
Seats – removal and refitting 22
Sunroof – general information 20
Tailgate and support struts – removal and refitting 15
Tailgate lock components – removal and refitting 16
Windscreen and rear window glass – general information. 19

Degrees of difficulty

| Easy, suitable for novice with little experience | Fairly easy, suitable for beginner with some experience | Fairly difficult, suitable for competent DIY mechanic | Difficult, suitable for experienced DIY mechanic | Very difficult, suitable for expert DIY or professional |

Specifications

Torque wrench settings	Nm	lbf ft
Bonnet hinge nuts	22	16
Bonnet lock bolts	12	9
Door hinges:		
Hinge bolts**	50	37
Hinge pin bolt	23	17
Door check strap:		
To door	30	22
To body	9	7
Door lock	18	13
Door striker pin bolts	20	15
Crossmember bolts/nuts	20	15
Front seat belt adjuster bolt	20	15
Front seat belt lower mounting bolt	40	30
Front seat belt stalk to seat frame bolt*	20	15
Front seat mounting bolts	40	30
Inertia reel mounting bolts	40	30
Rera seat belt and stalk anchorage bolts.	40	30
Tailgate hinge bolts.	10	7

*Renew the bolts
** Loosen once for adjustment. Replace if loosened again

1 General Information

1 The body shell is made of pressed-steel sections, with many of the structural panels being made from high tensile steel. Most components are welded together, either by traditional spot welding or where increased rigidity is required by continuous laser welding. Structural adhesives are used to bond some body panels.

2 Extensive use is made of plastic materials, mainly in the interior, but also in exterior components. The front and rear bumpers, and front grille, are injection-moulded from a synthetic material that is very strong and yet light. Plastic components such as wheel arch liners are fitted to the underside of the vehicle, to improve the body's resistance to corrosion.

2 Maintenance – bodywork and underframe

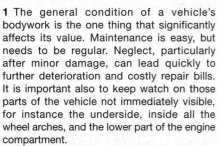

1 The general condition of a vehicle's bodywork is the one thing that significantly affects its value. Maintenance is easy, but needs to be regular. Neglect, particularly after minor damage, can lead quickly to further deterioration and costly repair bills. It is important also to keep watch on those parts of the vehicle not immediately visible, for instance the underside, inside all the wheel arches, and the lower part of the engine compartment.

2 The basic maintenance routine for the bodywork is washing – preferably with a lot of water, from a hose. This will remove all the loose solids, which may have stuck to the vehicle. It is important to flush these off in such a way as to prevent grit from scratching the finish. The wheel arches and underframe need washing in the same way, to remove any accumulated mud, which will retain moisture and tend to encourage rust. Paradoxically enough, the best time to clean the underframe and wheel arches is in wet weather, when the mud is thoroughly wet and soft. In very wet weather, the underframe is usually cleaned of large accumulations automatically, and this is a good time for inspection.

3 Periodically, except on vehicles with a wax-based underbody protective coating, it is a good idea to have the whole of the underframe of the vehicle steam-cleaned, engine compartment included, so that a thorough inspection can be carried out to see what minor repairs and renovations are necessary. Steam cleaning is available at many garages, and is necessary for the removal of the accumulation of oily grime, which sometimes is allowed to become thick in certain areas. If steam-cleaning facilities are not available, there are some excellent grease solvents available which can be brush-applied; the dirt can then be simply hosed off. Note that these methods should not be used on vehicles with wax-based underbody protective coating, or the coating will be removed. Such vehicles should be inspected annually, preferably just prior to Winter, when the underbody should be washed down, and any damage to the wax coating repaired. Ideally, a completely fresh coat should be applied. It would also be worth considering the use of such wax-based protection for injection into door panels, sills, box sections, etc, as an additional safeguard against rust damage, where such protection is not provided by the vehicle manufacturer.

4 After washing paintwork, wipe off with a chamois leather to give an unspotted clear finish. A coat of clear protective wax polish will give added protection against chemical pollutants in the air. If the paintwork sheen has dulled or oxidised, use a cleaner/polisher combination to restore the brilliance of the shine. This requires a little effort, but such dulling is usually caused because regular washing has been neglected. Care needs to be taken with metallic paintwork, as special non-abrasive cleaner/polisher is required to avoid damage to the finish. Always check that the door and ventilator opening drain holes and pipes are completely clear, so that water can be drained out. Brightwork should be treated in the same way as paintwork. Windscreens and windows can be kept clear of the smeary film that often appears, by the use of proprietary glass cleaner. Never use any form of wax or other body or chromium polish on glass.

3 Maintenance – upholstery and carpets

1 Mats and carpets should be brushed or vacuum-cleaned regularly, to keep them free of grit. If they are badly stained, remove them from the vehicle for scrubbing or sponging, and make quite sure they are dry before refitting. Seats and interior trim panels can be kept clean by wiping with a damp cloth. If they do become stained (which can be more apparent on light-coloured upholstery), use a little liquid detergent and a soft nail brush to scour the grime out of the grain of the material. Do not forget to keep the headlining clean in the same way as the upholstery. When using liquid cleaners inside the vehicle, do not over-wet the surfaces being cleaned. Excessive damp could get into the seams and padded interior, causing stains, offensive odours or even rot.

2 If the inside of the vehicle gets wet accidentally, it is worthwhile taking some trouble to dry it out properly, particularly where carpets are involved. Do not leave oil or electric heaters inside the vehicle for this purpose.

4 Minor body damage – repair

Scratches

1 If the scratch is very superficial, and does not penetrate to the metal of the bodywork, repair is very simple. Lightly rub the area of the scratch with a paintwork renovator, or a very fine cutting paste, to remove loose paint from the scratch, and to clear the surrounding bodywork of wax polish. Rinse the area with clean water.

2 Apply touch-up paint to the scratch using a fine paintbrush; continue to apply fine layers of paint until the surface of the paint in the scratch is level with the surrounding paintwork. Allow the new paint at least two weeks to harden, and then blend it into the surrounding paintwork by rubbing the scratch area with a paintwork renovator or a very fine cutting paste. Finally, apply wax polish.

3 Where the scratch has penetrated right through to the metal of the bodywork, causing the metal to rust, a different repair technique is required. Remove any loose rust from the bottom of the scratch with a penknife, and then apply rust-inhibiting paint to prevent the formation of rust in the future. Using a rubber or nylon applicator, fill the scratch with bodystopper paste. If required, this paste can be mixed with cellulose thinners to provide a very thin paste that is ideal for filling narrow scratches. Before the stopper-paste in the scratch hardens, wrap a piece of smooth cotton rag around the top of a finger. Dip the finger in cellulose thinners, and quickly sweep it across the surface of the stopper-paste in the scratch; this will ensure that the surface of the stopper-paste is slightly hollowed. The scratch can now be painted over as described earlier in this Section.

Dents

4 When deep denting of the vehicle's bodywork has taken place, the first task is to pull the dent out, until the affected bodywork almost attains its original shape. There is little point in trying to restore the original shape completely, as the metal in the damaged area will have stretched on impact, and cannot be reshaped fully to its original contour. It is better to bring the level of the dent up to a point, which is about 3 mm below the level of the surrounding bodywork. In cases where the dent is very shallow anyway, it is not worth trying to pull it out at all. If the underside of the dent is accessible, it can be hammered out gently from behind, using a mallet with a wooden or plastic head. Whilst doing this, hold a suitable block of wood firmly against the outside of the panel, to absorb the impact from the hammer blows and thus prevent a large area of the bodywork from being 'belled-out'.

5 Should the dent be in a section of the

bodywork that has a double skin, or some other factor making it inaccessible from behind, a different technique is called for. Drill several small holes through the metal inside the area – particularly in the deeper section. Then screw long self-tapping screws into the holes, just sufficiently for them to gain a good purchase in the metal. Now the dent can be pulled out by pulling on the protruding heads of the screws with a pair of pliers.

6 The next stage of the repair is the removal of the paint from the damaged area, and from an inch or so of the surrounding 'sound' bodywork. This is accomplished most easily by using a wire brush or abrasive pad on a power drill, although it can be done just as effectively by hand, using sheets of abrasive paper. To complete the preparation for filling, score the surface of the bare metal with a screwdriver or the tang of a file, or alternatively, drill small holes in the affected area. This will provide a really good 'key' for the filler paste.

7 To complete the repair, see the Section on filling and respraying.

Rust holes or gashes

8 Remove all paint from the affected area, and from an inch or so of the surrounding 'sound' bodywork, using an abrasive pad or a wire brush on a power drill. If these are not available, a few sheets of abrasive paper will do the job most effectively. With the paint removed, you will be able to judge the severity of the corrosion, and therefore decide whether to renew the whole panel (if this is possible) or to repair the affected area. New body panels are not as expensive as most people think, and it is often quicker and more satisfactory to fit a new panel than to attempt to repair large areas of corrosion.

9 Remove all fittings from the affected area, except those, which will act as a guide to the original shape of the damaged bodywork (e.g. headlight shells etc). Then, using tin snips or a hacksaw blade, remove all loose metal and any other metal badly affected by corrosion. Hammer the edges of the hole inwards, in order to create a slight depression for the filler paste.

10 Wire-brush the affected area to remove the powdery rust from the surface of the remaining metal. Paint the affected area with rust-inhibiting paint, if the back of the rusted area is accessible, treat this also.

11 Before filling can take place, it will be necessary to block the hole in some way. This can be achieved by the use of aluminium or plastic mesh, or aluminium tape.

12 Aluminium or plastic mesh, or glassfibre matting, is probably the best material to use for a large hole. Cut a piece to the approximate size and shape of the hole to be filled, then position it in the hole so that its edges are below the level of the surrounding bodywork. It can be retained in position by several blobs of filler paste around its periphery.

13 Aluminium tape should be used for small or very narrow holes. Pull a piece off the roll, trim it to the approximate size and shape required, then pull off the backing paper (if used) and stick the tape over the hole; it can be overlapped if the thickness of one piece is insufficient. Burnish down the edges of the tape with the handle of a screwdriver or similar, to ensure that the tape is securely attached to the metal underneath.

Filling and respraying

14 Before using this Section, see the Sections on dent, deep scratch, rust holes and gash repairs.

15 Many types of bodyfiller are available, but generally speaking, those proprietary kits, which contain a tin of filler paste and a tube of resin hardener, are best for this type of repair. A wide, flexible plastic or nylon applicator will be found invaluable for imparting a smooth and well-contoured finish to the surface of the filler.

16 Mix up a little filler on a clean piece of card or board – measure the hardener carefully (follow the maker's instructions on the pack), otherwise the filler will set too rapidly or too slowly. Using the applicator, apply the filler paste to the prepared area; draw the applicator across the surface of the filler to achieve the correct contour and to level the surface. As soon as a contour that approximates to the correct one is achieved, stop working the paste – if you carry on too long, the paste will become sticky and begin to 'pick-up' on the applicator. Continue to add thin layers of filler paste at 20-minute intervals, until the level of the filler is just proud of the surrounding bodywork.

17 Once the filler has hardened, the excess can be removed using a metal plane or file. From then on, progressively finer grades of abrasive paper should be used, starting with a 40-grade production paper, and finishing with a 400-grade wet-and-dry paper. Always wrap the abrasive paper around a flat rubber, cork, or wooden block – otherwise the surface of the filler will not be completely flat. During the smoothing of the filler surface, the wet-and-dry paper should be periodically rinsed in water. This will ensure that a very smooth finish is imparted to the filler at the final stage.

18 At this stage, the dent should be surrounded by a ring of bare metal, which in turn should be encircled by the finely 'feathered' edge of the good paintwork. Rinse the repair area with clean water, until all of the dust produced by the rubbing-down operation has gone.

19 Spray the whole area with a light coat of primer – this will show up any imperfections in the surface of the filler. Repair these imperfections with fresh filler paste or bodystopper, and once more smooth the surface with abrasive paper. Repeat this spray-and-repair procedure until you are satisfied that the surface of the filler, and the feathered edge of the paintwork, are perfect.

Clean the repair area with clean water, and allow to dry fully.

20 The repair area is now ready for final spraying. Paint spraying must be carried out in a warm, dry, windless and dust-free atmosphere. This condition can be created artificially if you have access to a large indoor working area, but if you are forced to work in the open, you will have to pick your day very carefully. If you are working indoors, dousing the floor in the work area with water will help to settle the dust, which would otherwise be in the atmosphere. If the repair area is confined to one body panel, mask off the surrounding panels; this will help to minimise the effects of a slight mis-match in paint colours. Bodywork fittings (e.g. chrome strips, door handles etc) will also need to be masked off. Use genuine masking tape, and several thicknesses of newspaper, for the masking operations.

21 Before commencing to spray, agitate the aerosol can thoroughly, and then spray a test area (an old tin, or similar) until the technique is mastered. Cover the repair area with a thick coat of primer; the thickness should be built up using several thin layers of paint, rather than one thick one. Using 400-grade wet-and-dry paper, rub down the surface of the primer until it is really smooth. While doing this, the work area should be thoroughly doused with water, and the wet-and-dry paper periodically rinsed in water. Allow to dry before spraying on more paint.

22 Spray on the top coat, again building up the thickness by using several thin layers of paint. Start spraying at one edge of the repair area, and then, using a side-to-side motion, work until the whole repair area and about 2 inches of the surrounding original paintwork is covered. Remove all masking material 10 to 15 minutes after spraying on the final coat of paint.

23 Allow the new paint at least two weeks to harden, then, using a paintwork renovator, or a very fine cutting paste, blend the edges of the paint into the existing paintwork. Finally, apply wax polish.

Plastic components

24 With the use of more and more plastic body components by the vehicle manufacturers (e.g. bumpers. spoilers, and in some cases major body panels), rectification of more serious damage to such items has become a matter of either entrusting repair work to a specialist in this field, or renewing complete components. Repair of such damage by the DIY owner is not really feasible, owing to the cost of the equipment and materials required for effecting such repairs. The basic technique involves making a groove along the line of the crack in the plastic, using a rotary burr in a power drill. The damaged part is then welded back together, using a hot-air gun to heat up and fuse a plastic filler rod into the groove. Any excess plastic is then removed, and the area rubbed down to a smooth finish. It is important that a filler rod of the correct plastic is used, as body components can be made of a variety of different types (e.g. polycarbonate, ABS, polypropylene).

25 Damage of a less serious nature (abrasions, minor cracks etc) can be repaired by the DIY owner using a two-part epoxy filler repair material. Once mixed in equal proportions, this is used in similar fashion to the bodywork filler used on metal panels. The filler is usually cured in twenty to thirty minutes, ready for sanding and painting.

26 If the owner is renewing a complete component himself, or if he has repaired it with epoxy filler, he will be left with the problem of finding a suitable paint for finishing which is compatible with the type of plastic used. At one time, the use of a universal paint was not possible, owing to the complex range of plastics encountered in body component applications. Standard paints, generally speaking, will not bond to plastic or rubber satisfactorily. However, it is now possible to obtain a plastic body parts finishing kit, which consists of a pre-primer treatment, a primer and coloured top coat. Full instructions are normally supplied with a kit, but basically, the method of use is to first apply the pre-primer to the component concerned, and allow it to dry for up to 30 minutes. Then the primer is applied, and left to dry for about an hour before finally applying the special-coloured top coat. The result is a correctly coloured component, where the paint will flex with the plastic or rubber, a property that standard paint does not normally possess.

6.2a Remove the screws from both ends, unclip...

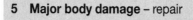

5 Major body damage – repair

1 Where serious damage has occurred, or large areas need renewal due to neglect, it means that complete new panels will need welding-in, and this is best left to professionals. If the damage is due to impact, it will also be necessary to check completely the alignment of the body shell, and this can only be carried out accurately by a VW dealer using special jigs. If the body is left misaligned, it is primarily dangerous, as the car will not handle properly, and secondly, uneven stresses will be imposed on the steering, suspension and possibly transmission, causing abnormal wear, or complete failure, particularly to such items as the tyres.

6.2b ...and remove the grille

6 Front bumper cover – removal and refitting

Note: *Depending on the year of production and the trim level slight changes to the removal and refitting procedures may be necessary.*

Removal

1 Apply the handbrake, then jack up the front of the vehicle and support it on axle stands (see *Jacking and vehicle support*).
2 Open the bonnet. Remove the screws from the grille panel, unclip the panel from the bumper cover and remove it **(see illustrations)**.
3 Turn the steering from lock to lock (or remove the wheels) and remove the fixings from the trailing edge of the bumper **(see illustration)**.
4 Remove the engine undershield.
5 Work along the base of the bumper cover and remove the lower fixings **(see illustration)**.
6 Release the trailing edge of the bumper cover from the front wing – at both sides. The bumper is a tight fit in the mounting bracket. Consider protecting the paint work with masking tape and if necessary, remove the wing liner and partially release the bumper from the rear of the bracket **(see illustrations)**.
7 Pull the bumper forward and release it from the lock carrier panel. With the aid of an assistant remove the bumper **(see illustration)**. Where fitted disconnect the

6.3 Remove the screws

6.5 Remove the lower fixings

6.6a Release the bumper cover from the front wings

6.6b A detailed view of the locking tabs that must be released (three per side)

6.7 Remove the bumper

wiring plugs from the parking sensors, foglights and the hose from the headlight washers as the cover is removed.

Refitting

8 Refitting is a reverse of the removal procedure, ensuring that the bumper ends engage correctly with the locating clips on the edge of the front wing panels.

7 Rear bumper cover – removal and refitting

Note: *Depending on the model, it is possible that slight changes to the removal and refitting procedures may be necessary.*

Removal

1 To improve access, chock the front wheels, and then jack up the rear of the vehicle and support it on axle stands (see *Jacking and vehicle support*).
2 Remove the rear light clusters as described in Chapter 12 Section 8.
3 Remove the fixings securing the rear of the wheel arch liners to the bumper ends. Access is possible without removing the wheels. Fold back the wing liner and remove the upper screw securing the bumper to the rear wing **(see illustrations)**.
4 Remove the fixings from the lower edge of the cover and disconnect the wiring plug **(see illustrations)**.
5 With the help of an assistant, release the bumper cover from the rear wing panels at both sides. The cover is a tight fit and

should be carefully worked free from the wing mounted support bracket. Withdraw the bumper from the rear of the vehicle **(see illustrations)**.

Refitting

6 Refitting is a reverse of the removal procedure, ensuring that the bumper ends engage correctly with the rear wing panels, as the bumper is refitted.

8 Bonnet – removal, refitting and adjustment

Removal

1 Open the bonnet and using a pencil or felt tip pen, mark the outline of each bonnet hinge

7.3a Remove the liner fixings

7.3b Remove the partially hidden upper fixing

7.4a Remove the trim clips and...

7.4b ...the liners screws

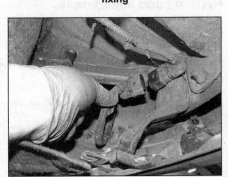

7.4c Disconnect the wiring plug

7.5a A large trim tool helps release the bumper cover from the rear wing

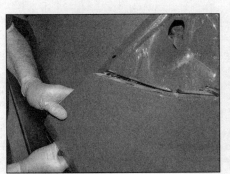

7.5b Work the bumper free from the bracket

7.5c Release the cover from the upper section of the bracket...

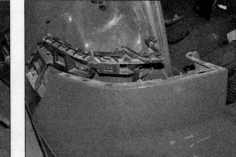

7.5d ...unclip it from the centre support panel and remove it

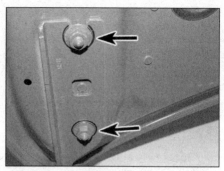

8.1 Mark the position of the hinges or the flange nuts

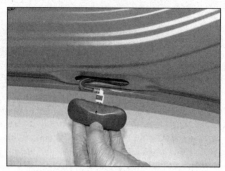

8.2a Remove the washer jets and...

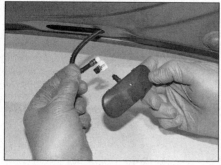

8.2b ...and unclip the washer hose

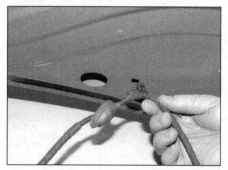

8.2c Pull out and unclip the hose

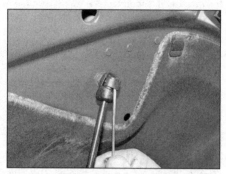

8.3 Unclip the gas strut

8.5 Mark the position of the hinges

(or nut) relative to the bonnet, to use as a guide on refitting (see illustration).

2 Unclip the washer jets. Release the hoses and on models fitted with heated washer jets disconnect the wiring plug. Pull the hose from the bonnet (see illustrations).

3 Slacken the bonnet hinge bolts and then with an assistant to support the bonnet unclip the bonnet gas strut (see illustration).

4 Undo the under bonnet retaining nuts and then (with the aid of an assistant) carefully lift the bonnet clear. Store the bonnet out of the way in a safe place.

5 Inspect the bonnet hinges for signs of wear and free play at the pivots, and if necessary renew. Each hinge is secured to the body by bolts (see illustration). Mark the position of the hinge on the body then undo the retaining

bolts and remove the hinge. On refitting, align the new hinge with the marks and tighten the retaining bolts.

Refitting and adjustment

6 With the aid of an assistant, offer up the bonnet and loosely fit the retaining bolts. Align the hinges with the marks made on removal, and then tighten the retaining bolts/nuts securely.

7 Refit the gas support strut.

8 Refit the washer hose and wiring in the reverse order of removal.

9 Close the bonnet, and check for alignment with the adjacent panels. If necessary, unscrew the hinge bolts and re-align the bonnet. Once the bonnet is correctly aligned, tighten the hinge bolts. Check that the bonnet fastens and releases satisfactorily.

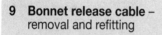

9 Bonnet release cable –
    removal and refitting

Removal

1 The bonnet release cable is in two sections, with a coupling located over the right-hand headlight. To remove the shorter front section cable, remove the bonnet lock as described in Section 10.

2 Working inside the vehicle, locate the release lever and pull it out slightly, then insert a small screwdriver into the gap between the release lever and its securing clip. Let the lever return to its original position, then release the clip with a screwdriver (see illustrations).

3 Remove the 'scrivet'. Prise up (with difficulty) the trim panel and remove it.

9.2a Remove the clip and...

9.2b ...slide off the handle

9.3 Remove the screw/clip ('scrivet)

9.4 Unscrew the release handle mounting bracket screws

9.5 Unclip the release cable from the lever

9.10 Slide the securing clip into the handle before refitting

4 Undo the two retaining screws and withdraw the bonnet release lever from the bottom of the A-pillar **(see illustration)**.
5 Release the outer cable from the mounting bracket, and then detach the inner cable from the lever **(see illustration)**.
6 Working along the length of the cable and noting its correct routing, free it from any retaining clips/ties and release the cable sealing grommet from the bulkhead.
7 Tie a length of string to the end of the cable inside the vehicle, and then withdraw the cable through into the engine compartment.

8 Once the cable is free, untie the string and leave it in position in the vehicle; the string can then be used to draw the new cable back into position.

Refitting

9 Tie the inner end of the string to the end of the cable, and then use the string to draw the bonnet release cable back from the engine compartment. Once the cable is through, untie the string.
10 Refitting is a reversal of removal. **Note:** *Before refitting the bonnet release lever, fit*

the securing clip back into the lever first **(see illustration)** *and then push the lever back into place.*
11 Ensure the rubber grommet in the bulkhead is fitted correctly, and the cable is correctly routed and secured to all the relevant retaining clips.
12 Before closing the bonnet, check the operation of the release lever and cable.

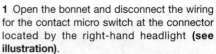

10 Bonnet lock – removal and refitting

Removal

1 Open the bonnet and disconnect the wiring for the contact micro switch at the connector located by the right-hand headlight **(see illustration)**.
2 Disconnect the bonnet cable at the join adapter located by the right-hand headlight. Unclip the cover and release the two parts of the cable **(see illustrations)**.
3 Unbolt the panel from above the headlight, turn it over and using pliers release the cable housing from the panel **(see illustration)**.

10.1 Disconnect the bonnet lock wiring plug

10.2a Open the cover…

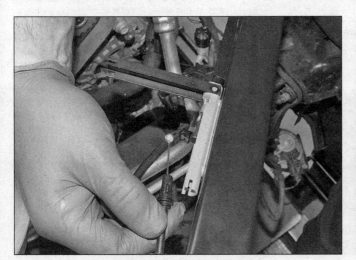

10.2b and unhook the cable

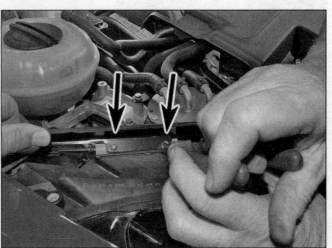

10.3 Remove the cable housing

10.4a Release the upper hidden clips with a small screwdriver

10.4b Release the bottom clips and lift off the grille

10.4c Remove the air intake top cover...

10.4d ...and then the lower cover

10.6a Mark the position of the lock

4 Unscrew and unclip the grille from the bumper cover and then remove both sections of the air intake duct (see illustrations).
5 Release the cable from the lock carrier by using a small screwdriver through the lock carrier to release the cable clips.
6 Mark the position of the lock, remove the bolts and lift out the lock (see illustrations).
7 Unhook the cable from the lock and unclip the microswitch (see illustration).

Refitting

8 Refitting is a reversal of removal. Check that the bonnet fastens and releases satisfactorily. If adjustment is necessary, loosen the bonnet lock retaining bolts, and adjust the position of the lock to suit. Finally, tighten the bolts.

11 Door – removal, refitting and adjustment

Removal

1 Before removing the door, measure the door gaps and mark them as required.
2 Open the door then disconnect the wiring plug at the A- or B-pillar and then unbolt the check strap (see illustrations).
3 With an assistant supporting the door, remove the cover (where fitted) and then

10.6b Lift out the lock with the cable and the microswitch wiring

10.7 Remove the cable

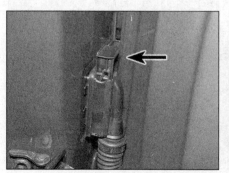

11.2a Lift up the latch...

11.2b ...and release the wiring plug

11.2c Unbolt the door check strap

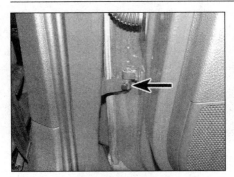

11.3 Remove the bolts

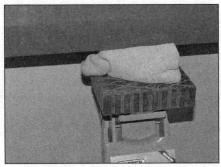

11.4 Protect the door from damage and use a jack to lift the door off the hinges

remove the bolts from the hinge pins **(see illustration)**.
4 With the aid of an assistant, lift the door up and off the hinges. Alternatively raise the door off the hinges with a trolley jack and then remove it **(see illustration)**.
5 Examine the hinges for signs of wear or damage. If renewal is necessary accurately mark the position of the hinges as a guide to refitting.

Refitting

6 Where renewed, fit the hinges and tighten the bolts to the specified torque.
7 With the aid of an assistant, offer up the door to the vehicle and locate it on the hinge

pins. Fit the hinge bolts and tighten to the specified torque.
8 Reconnect the wiring plug and secure with the locking lever.

Adjustment

9 Close the door and check the door alignment with the surrounding body panels. There must be an even gap all around, and the door must be level with the surrounding body panels.
10 Adjustment is made at the door pillars and at the door. To access the left-hand A-pillar hinge the glovebox and fusebox must be removed. To access the right-hand hinge the lower trim panel and storage compartment must be removed. The lower hinge can be

accessed after the lower A-trim panels are removed. Removal and refitting of the facia panels is described in Section 27.
11 If working on the rear doors the B-pillar trim must be removed as described in Section 25.
12 Check that the striker enters the door lock centrally as the door is closed, and if necessary adjust the position of the striker by loosening its mounting bolts.

12 Door inner trim panel – removal and refitting

Removal

1 Switch off the ignition, before disconnecting any wiring connectors.

Front door

2 Remove the pull handle cover and then remove the screw. Remove the screw from beneath the armrest. **(see illustrations)**.
3 At the bottom of the panel release the turnbuckle **(see illustration)**.
4 Working around the panel with a trim tool release the panel retaining clips. Note that the upper rear clip is on and extension and the panel must be released from the extension and not from the door skin. This upper clip is best released by pushing up the panel after all the other clips have been released **(see illustrations)**.
5 With all the clips released, push up the panel to release it from the weatherseal.

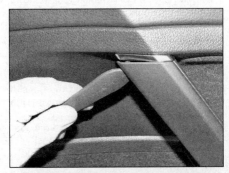

12.2a Prise up the cover with a trim tool…

12.2b …and remove it

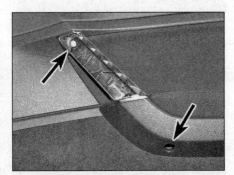

12.2c Remove the screws

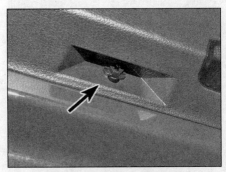

12.3 Release the turnbuckle

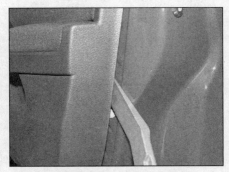

12.4a Release the panel clips

12.4b Note the upper rear panel clip

12.5a Unclip the door release cable

12.5b Disconnect the wiring plugs

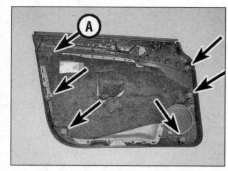

12.5c The location of the panel clips. Note the fitting point of the upper rear panel clip (A)

12.7a Lever out the trim piece...

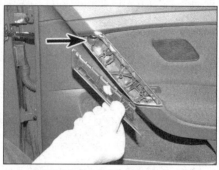

12.7b ...and remove the screw

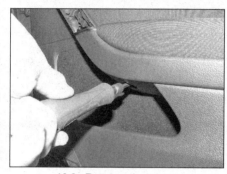

12.8a Remove the screw

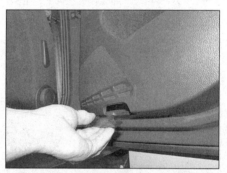

12.8b Unclip the reflector

12.8c Rotate the turnbuckle a quarter turn

Support the panel and unclip the bowden cable and the wiring plugs (see illustrations).

Rear doors

6 On vehicles fitted with manual rear windows release the winder handle by sliding the locking clip away from the handle. Release the handle from the shaft.

7 Lever out the pull handle trim and then remove the now exposed screw (see illustrations).

8 Remove the lower screw and then unclip the reflector from the panel. Rotate the turnbuckle (see illustrations).

9 Work around the panel with a trim tool and release the panel clips (see illustrations).

12.9a Use a trim tool to...

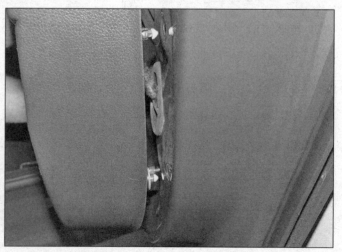

12.9b ...release the panel trim clips

10 Push up the panel to release it. Note that the panel is a tight fit at the quarter light. Support the panel and disconnect the release cable, follwed by the wiring plugs **(see illustrations)**. Remove the panel.

Refitting

11 The Refitting of the trim panel is then a reversal of removal. Where required reset the door trim clips by pushing the central peg into the body of the clip **(see illustration)**. If the panel clip will not reset it should be replaced.
12 Check the operation of the door electrical equipment.
13 On models with manual windows refit the winder handle so that it is approximately 30 degrees below horizontal with the window fully closed.

13 Door handle and lock components – removal and refitting

Note: *The exterior handle and cylinder lock (or cover) can be removed from the outside of the door.*

Removal

Front door lock cylinder and handle

1 Open the door, then remove the blanking plug from the rear edge of the door to access the retaining screws **(see illustration)**.
2 Remove the inner screw completely and then slacken the outer screw (to the stop). Push in the outer screw to release the lock

cylinder. Pull out the lock cylinder **(see illustrations)**.
3 Note that on most models the lock cylinder is hidden beneath the cosmetic cover. The ignition key can be used to flick off the cover – avoid twisting the key in the slot at the bottom

of the cover as this may damage the paintwork **(see illustration)**. The ignition key can be used to access the vehicle in the event of a failure of the remote key or central locking.
4 Unhook and then slide out the handle **(see illustration)**.

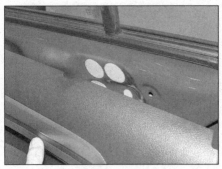
12.10a Release the panel...

12.10b ...unclip the release cable...

12.10c ...and disconnect the wiring plugs

12.11 The clip on the left shows the correct position of the clip before refitting

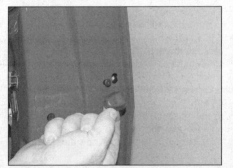
13.1 Remove the cover

13.2a Remove the inner screw

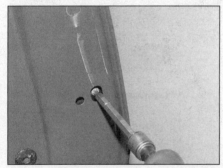
13.2b Slacken the retaining screw (and then push in)...

13.2c ...and pull out the lock cylinder (shown with the cover removed)

13.3 Use the key to remove the cover

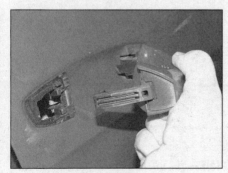
13.4 Remove the handle

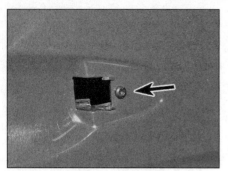

13.6 Remove the screw

13.7 Remove the cover

13.8a Disconnect the wiring plug

13.8b Remove the bolts

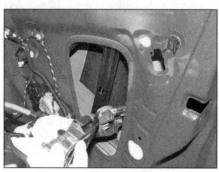

13.9a Remove the complete assembly

Front door lock and support bracket

5 Remove the door trim panel as described in Section 12.
6 Remove the outer door handle as described above and then remove the frame screw **(see illustration)**.
7 Remove the cover and then feed the release handle cable through the cover **(see illustration)**.
8 Disconnect the wiring plug and then remove the lock mounting bolts **(see illustrations)**.
9 Unhook the inner frame from the outer door panel (and recover the gasket) and then remove the inner frame and lock from the door **(see illustrations)**.
10 If required the handle frame can now be removed from the lock **(see illustrations 19a, 19b and 19c)**.

Rear door handle

11 Open the door and remove the blanking grommet (or sticker) from the end of the door. The weatherseal will require partial removal **(see illustration)**.
12 A hook tool must now be fabricated from welding rod or coat hanger wire. This should be around 90mm long, with a mark placed at 44 mm. Insert the tool through the door frame to the 44 mm mark and (with difficulty) locate and release the lock/unlock section of the door handle inner frame **(see illustrations)**.

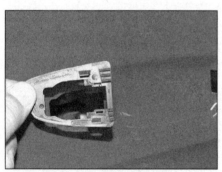

13.9b Recover the gasket

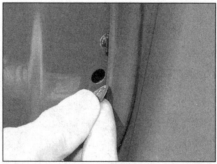

13.11 Remove the cover

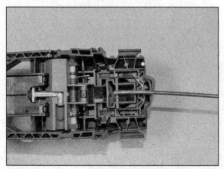

13.12a The hooked tool in position (shown with the handle frame removed from the door)

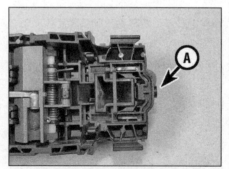

13.12b The position of the bracket after release (again shown removed from the door). Note the position of the peg (A).

13.12c Releasing the handle with the hooked tool

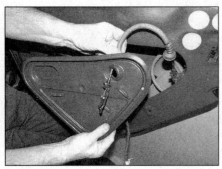

13.16 Remove the cable from the cover

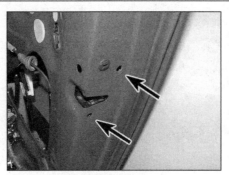

13.17 Remove the bolts

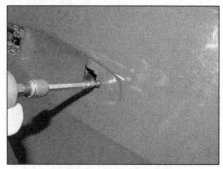

13.18a Remove the screw

13.18b Remove the lock and frame from
the door

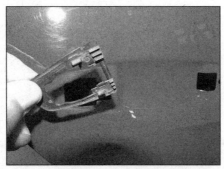

13.18c Recover the gasket

13.19a Remove the cover…

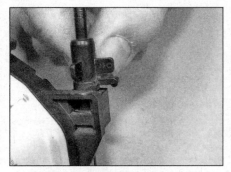

13.19b …release the cable outer…

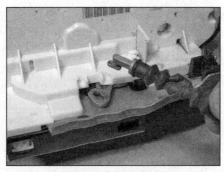

13.19c …and then the inner

15 Remove the door trim panel as described
in Section 12.
16 Remove the inner cover and then feed the
inner handle release cable through the cover
(see illustration).
17 Remove the mounting bolts from the end
of the door (see illustration).
18 Remove the single screw from the outer
panel. Reach into the door frame and remove
the lock and frame handle (see illustrations).
19 The release cables can now be
removed from the lock where required (see
illustrations).

Refitting

20 Refitting is a reversal of removal, but
on the rear door push in the peg (see illustration 12b) to lock the handle to the frame.

Note that it is also possible to unlock the outer
handle by removing the inner trim panel and
unlocking the frame by either guiding the
tool into position or by 'feeling' for the frame
unlock bracket and releasing it by hand.

13 After removing the smaller section of the
handle, unhook and remove the main handle.
Rear door lock
14 Remove the outer handle as described
above.

14 Door window glass and regulator –
removal and refitting

Removal

Front door window glass

1 Remove the door trim panel as described
in Section 12 and then remove the power
window switch from the panel as described in
Chapter 12 Section 5.
2 Remove the cover panel. Refit the switch,
turn on the ignition and move the window
glass up or down as required to access the
glass clamps (see illustrations).

14.2a Remove the loom grommet to
access the front clamp

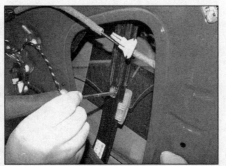

14.2b Push the locking peg open whilst
pulling up the glass

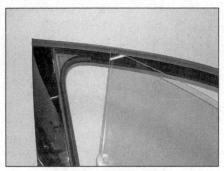

14.3 Lift out the glass

14.5 The glass clamp, showing the plastic roll pins

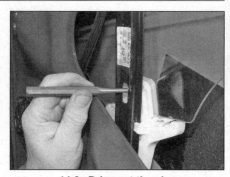

14.6a Drive out the pins

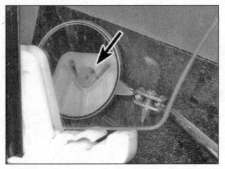

14.6b A view of the roll pins from the rear

14.7a Remove the screws

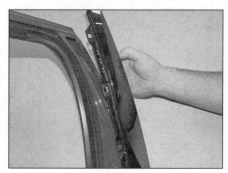

14.7b Remove the panel

3 Lift the rear of the window glass so that it is tilted. Lift it upwards (whilst rotating it towards the front of the door) and remove it from the outside of the door **(see illustration)**.

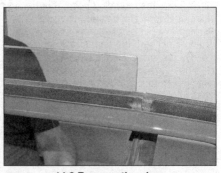

14.8 Remove the glass

Rear door window glass

4 Remove the door trim panel as described in Section 12 and then (where fitted) remove the power window switch from the panel as described in Chapter 12 Section 5.
5 Refit the switch (or winder handle) and lower the window glass until the glass clamp is visible **(see illustration)**.
6 The plastic roll pins must now be removed. There are two pins – an inner and outer. The can be removed by either screwing in a bolt and pulling out the centre pin (5 mm diameter bolt required), followed by the outer pin (8 mm diameter bolt required) or more simply by driving the pins through the glass **(see illustrations)**. An assistant will be required to support the glass directly behind the clamp if the pins are to be driven out.
7 Pull up and partially remove the glass guide

channel at the quarter light and at the front. At the front of the door remove the screws and release the trim panel **(see illustrations)**.
8 Pull up the glass clear of the front guide channel and remove it from the door **(see illustration)**.

Window motor and regulator

Note: *Removal of the front and rear window regulators and motors is essentially the same procedure, but with minor differences.*
9 Remove the door inner trim panel as described in Section 12 and tape the window up in the fully closed position **(see illustration)**.
10 Disconnect the wiring plug (on models with power windows) and then remove the motor **(see illustrations)**.
11 Depress the locking tabs and push the

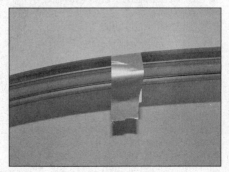

14.9 Tape the window up

14.10a Remove the screws...

14.10b ...and lift off the motor

14.11 Push the motor mounts into the door frame

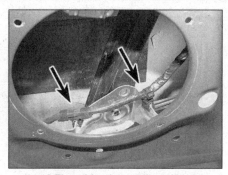

14.12 The wiring loom clipped to the regulator (front door only)

14.13a Remove the covers...

14.13b ...to access the bolts

14.13c Remove the regulator from the door

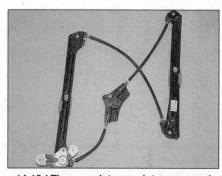

14.13d The complete regulator removed from the door

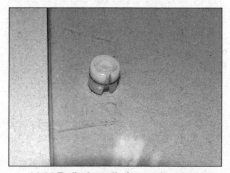

14.14 Refit the roll pins to the glass

motor mounts into the door frame **(see illustration)**.

12 If working on the front door, remove the loudspeaker by drilling out the rivets. This is necessary to access the wiring loom clipped to the regulator **(see illustration)**.

13 Where fitted remove the self adhesive covers from the regulator bolts. Remove the regulator bolts and then lower the regulator down and out of the door frame **(see illustrations)**.

Refitting

14 Refitting is a reversal of removal, noting the following:

● Fit the plastic roll pins to the glass before refitting the glass **(see illustration)**. Removing the inner weatherseal will also be required.

● Refit the self adhesive covers. These are important as the door mounted crash

sensor is an air pressure sensor. The door frame must be sealed so that little or no air escapes.

● Install the loudspeaker with new rivets.

15 Tailgate and support struts
– removal and refitting

Removal

Tailgate

1 Open the tailgate and and unclip the upper trim panel and both side panels **(see illustrations)**.

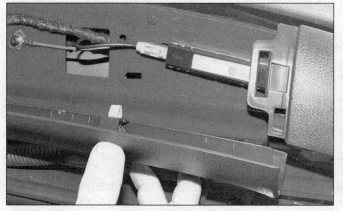

15.1a Remove the upper panel...

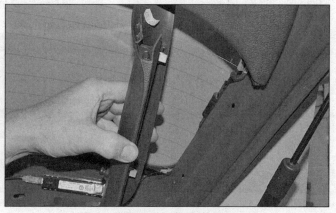

15.1b ...followed by both side panels

15.2a Remove the central fixings...

15.2b ...and the outer fixings

15.3a Unclip the panel...

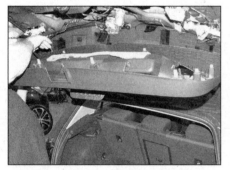

15.3b ...and remove it from the tailgate

15.4 Disconnect the hose

2 Open the compartment cover and remove the screws. Remove the screws from both grab handles **(see illustrations)**.

3 Carefully lever between the panel and the tailgate with a plastic trim tool. Work around the outside of the panel, and when all the clips are released, remove the panel **(see illustrations)**.

4 Remove the high level brake light as described in Chapter 12 Section 8 and then disconnect the screen washer hose **(see illustration)**.

5 Free the wiring grommets from the tailgate/ bodyshell **(see illustration)**. Work around the tailgate and disconnect the wiring plugs from all the electrical components. If the same tailgate is to be refitted tie cord to the wiring plugs (the cord will be used to pull the wiring loom back into the tailgate) Release the loom from the cable clips and pull it out the tailgate.

Repeat the procedure for the screen washer hose.

6 Using a suitable marker pen, draw around the outline of each hinge marking its correct position on the tailgate **(see illustration)**.

7 With the help of an assistant to support the tailgate, remove the support struts as described below.

Caution: The tailgate is heavy. At least one assistant will be required to remove it.

8 Unscrew and remove the bolts securing the hinges to the tailgate. Where necessary, recover the gaskets that are fitted between the hinge and vehicle body.

9 Inspect the hinges for signs of wear or damage and renew if necessary. The hinges are secured to the vehicle by nuts or bolts (depending on model), which can be accessed once the headlining rear cover strip has been removed.

Support struts

⚠ *Warning: The support struts are filled with a gas under pressure. They must not be opened and they and must be disposed of safely.*

10 With the help of an assistant, support the tailgate in the open position.

11 Using a small flat-bladed screwdriver lift the locking clip, and pull the gas support strut off its balljoint mounting on the tailgate **(see illustrations)**. Repeat the procedure on the lower strut mounting and remove the strut from the vehicle body. **Note:** *If the gas strut is to be re-used, the locking clip must not be taken all the way out, or the clip will be damaged.*

Refitting

Tailgate

12 Refitting is the reverse of removal, aligning the hinges with the marks made before removal. Tighten retaining bolts to the specified torque.

13 On completion, close the tailgate and check its alignment with the surrounding panels. If necessary slight adjustment can be made by unscrewing the retaining bolts and repositioning the tailgate on its hinges. If the tailgate buffers are in need of adjustment, continue as follows.

Support struts

14 Refitting is a reverse of the removal procedure, ensuring that the strut is securely retained by its retaining clips.

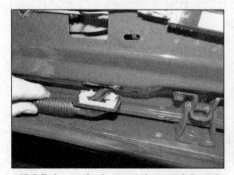

15.5 Release the loom at the conduit and pull it from the tailgate.

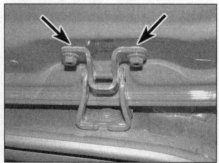

15.6 Mark the position of the hinges

15.11 Lift the locking clip upwards, then pull the strut off upper balljoint

16.2 Disconnect the wiring from the tailgate lock

16.3 Undo the lock retaining screws

16.5a Disconnect the wiring plug

16 Tailgate lock components – removal and refitting

Removal

Tailgate lock

1 Open up the tailgate and remove the trim panel as described in Section 15.
2 Disconnect the wiring from the lock **(see illustration)**.
3 Undo the retaining bolts and remove the lock from the lower edge of the tailgate **(see illustration)**.

Tailgate handle/release unit

4 Open up the tailgate and remove the trim panel as described in Section 15.
5 Disconnect the wiring connector and then undo the fixings holding the unit to the tailgate **(see illustrations)**.
6 The handle/release unit can now be withdrawn from the tailgate **(see illustration)**.

Refitting

7 Refitting is a reversal of removal, however, before refitting the trim panel, check the operation of the lock components.

17 Central locking components – description, removal and refitting

Description

1 The central locking system consists of the following main components. Note that the central locking and anti-theft alarm systems share some components (see Chapter 12 Section 22):
a) *Convenience system onboard supply control unit located next to the fusebox, behind the glovebox.*
b) *Door control unit fitted to the door frame.*
c) *Electric door lock actuators integrated in the door locks.*
d) *Fuel tank filler cap flap actuator located behind the rear wing liner.*
e) *Tailgate lock actuator located in the tailgate, together with the release button.*

16.5b Remove the tailgate handle/release unit fixings…

f) *Anti-theft alarm horn located in the plenum chamber.*
g) *Bonnet contact switch located on the bonnet lock.*
h) *Remote control transmitter on the ignition key fob.*

Removal

2 Before working on any electrical circuit, disconnect the battery negative lead (refer to Chapter 5A Section 3).

Convenience system control unit

Note: *The convenience control unit is often referred to as the BCM (Body Control Module). It controls the vehicle secondary systems – mirrors, central locking, wipers and lights to name but a few.*

17.4 Remove the BCM

16.6 …and withdraw the release handle from the tailgate

3 Remove the glovebox as described in Section 27.
4 Disconnect the wiring plug, unclip the module and remove it **(see illustration)**.

Door control unit

5 Remove the door trim panel as described in Section 12.
6 Disconnect the wiring plugs **(see illustration)** and remove the control unit.

Electric door lock actuator

7 Remove the door lock (see Section 13).

Fuel tank filler cap flap actuator

8 Jack up and support the rear of the vehicle (see *Jacking and vehicle support*). Remove the right-hand wheel and wing liner.
9 Open the fuel filler door and remove the

17.6 Disconnect the wiring plugs

17.9a Remove the screw...

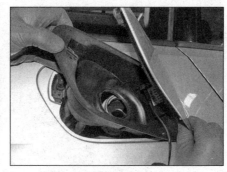

17.9b ...and lift out the surround

17.10 Remove the actuator

single screw. Remove the door and filler neck surround **(see illustrations)**.

10 Remove the load area side panel as described in Section 25 and disconnect the wiring plug. Reach up from inside the wheel arch, unclip the actuator and remove it **(see illustration)**.

Tailgate/boot lid lock actuator

11 Remove the tailgate handle/release unit as described in Section 16.

Bonnet contact switch

12 Remove the bonnet lock as described in Section 10.

13 On the lock, release the tab and push the switch from the slotted holes.

Remote control transmitter battery

14 Using a screwdriver or fingernail inserted in the slot, separate the transmitter unit cover from the key **(see illustrations)**.

15 Carefully prise out the battery, noting which way round it is fitted **(see illustrations)**.

Refitting

16 Refitting is a reversal of removal.

18 Mirrors and associated components – removal and refitting

Removal

Exterior mirror

1 Remove the door trim panel as described in Section 12.

2 Remove the loudspeaker by drilling out the rivets (see Chapter 12 Section 20).

17.14a Flip open the cover to...

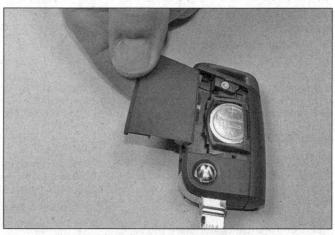

17.14b ...expose the battery

17.15a Remove the battery...

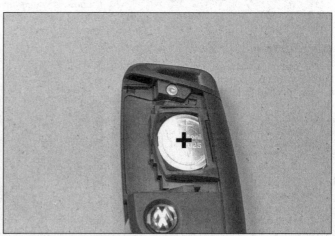

17.15b ...noting which way it is fitted

18.3a Disconnect the wiring plug

18.3b Release the cable clip

18.4a Unclip the cover...

3 Disconnect the wiring plug from the module. Release the cable clip **(see illustrations)** and grommet. Use a mirror and torch and note the routing of the wiring loom through the door. It is important that the loom does not foul the window glass when refitted.
4 Remove the cover and then unbolt the mirror from the door. Pull the wiring loom from the door as the mirror is removed **(see illustrations)**.

Mirror glass

5 Push the lower edge of the glass into the housing.
6 Insert an angled trim tool behind the glass.
7 Push in the base of the mirror glass whilst pulling the top out with the the trim tool **(see illustrations)**.
8 Disconnect the wiring plugs from the heating element and remove the glass **(see illustration)**.

Mirror housing

9 Remove the mirror glass as described in this Section.
10 Depress the locking tabs and slide the cover back to remove it **(see illustrations)**.
11 With the cover removed, remove the screws and unclip the front section of the housing **(see illustration)**.

Mirror switch

12 Refer to Chapter 12 Section 5.

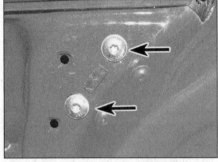
18.4b ...and remove the bolts

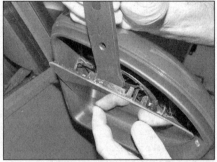
18.7a Insert the trim tool and...

18.7b ...release the mirror glass

18.8 Disconnect the wiring plugs with care

18.10a Depress the tabs and...

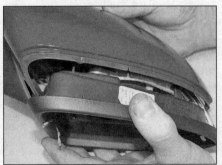
18.10b ...slide back the cover

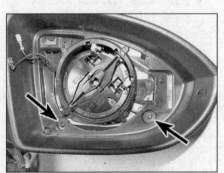
18.11 Remove the screws

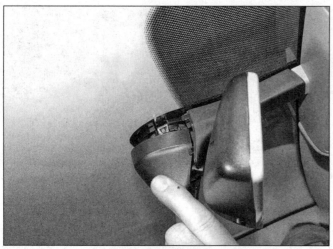

18.15 Unclip the cover

18.16 Release the mirror

Refitting

13 Refitting is the reverse of the relevant removal procedure. When refitting the mirror glass, press firmly at the centre taking care not to use excessive force, as the glass is easily broken.
Caution: Wear protective gloves and glasses to prevent personal injury.

Interior mirror

Removal

14 If rear view mirror is fitted with a rain sensor ensure the ignition is off (remove the key).
15 Using a plastic trim tool unclip the lower cover by spreading it open slightly **(see illustration)**.
16 Unclip the upper cover and remove it where possible. Alternatively remove the mirror and then remove the upper cover. Rotate the mirror anticlockwise in the housing to remove it **(see illustration)**.
17 On models fitted with an auto dimming mirror, disconnect the wiring plug as the mirror is removed.

Refitting

18 Refitting is a reversal of removal.

19 Windscreen and rear window glass – general information

1 These areas of glass are bonded in position with a special adhesive. Renewal of such fixed glass is a difficult, messy and time-consuming task, which is beyond the scope of the home mechanic. It is difficult, unless one has plenty of practice, to obtain a secure, waterproof fit. Furthermore, the task carries a high risk of breakage; this applies especially to the laminated glass windscreen. In view of this, owners are strongly advised to have this sort of work carried out by one of the many specialist windscreen fitters.

20 Sunroof – general information

1 Due to the complexity of the sunroof mechanism, considerable expertise is needed to repair, renew or adjust the sunroof components successfully. Removal of the roof first requires the headlining to be removed, which is a complex and tedious operation, and not a task to be undertaken lightly. Therefore, any problems with the sunroof should be referred to a Volkswagen dealer. On models with an electric sunroof, if the sunroof motor fails to operate, first check the relevant fuse. If the fault cannot be traced and rectified, the sunroof can be opened and closed manually using an Allen key to turn the motor spindle (a suitable key is supplied with the vehicle, and should be clipped onto the inside of the sunroof motor trim). To gain access to the motor, unclip the rear of the trim cover to open. Unclip the Allen key, and then insert it fully into the motor opening (against spring pressure). Rotate the key to move the sunroof to the required position.

21 Body exterior fittings – removal and refitting

Wheel arch liners and body under-panels

1 The various plastic covers fitted to the underside of the vehicle are secured in position by a mixture of screws, nuts and retaining clips and removal will be fairly obvious on inspection. Work methodically around the panel removing its retaining screws and releasing its retaining clips until the panel is free and can be removed from the underside of the vehicle. Most clips used on the vehicle are simply prised out of position. Remove the wheels to ease the removal of the wheel arch liners **(see illustration)**.
2 On refitting, renew any retaining clips that may have been broken on removal, and ensure that the panel is securely retained by all the relevant clips and screws.

Body trim strips and badges

3 The various body trim strips and badges are held in position with a special adhesive tape and locating lugs. Removal requires the trim/badge to be heated, to soften the adhesive, and then carefully lifted away from the surface. Due to the high risk of damage to the vehicle's paintwork during this operation, it is recommended that this task should be entrusted to a VW dealer.

22 Seats – removal and refitting ⚙

Note: *Refer to the warnings in Chapter 12 Section 23, on airbags.*

Removal

Front seats

Note: *The amount of wiring connectors under*

21.1 Removing the lower section of the front wheel arch liner

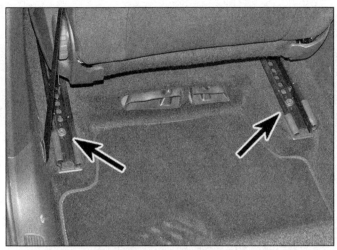

22.2 Seat rear mounting bolts

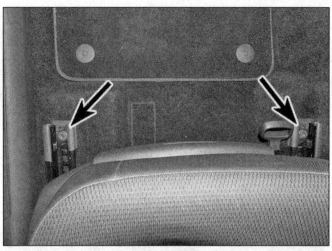

22.3a Remove the front bolts

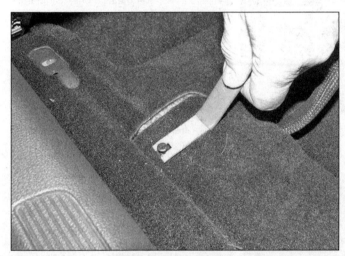

22.3b Open the cover...

22.3c ...and disconnect the wiring plugs

the seat will vary depending on the vehicle specification.

1 Disconnect the battery negative lead (refer to Section 5A Section 3).

2 Slide the seat forwards as far as possible and unscrew the rear mounting bolts (see illustration).

⚠ Warning: As a precaution against unintentional electrostatic discharge into the airbag, briefly touch part of the vehicle body before disconnecting the wiring.

3 Slide the seat to the rear and remove the front mounting bolts. Move the seat seat so that the rails are central and then move the seat back again.Open the cover and disconnect the wiring connectors (see illustrations). Volkswagen technicians fit an adapter to the airbag wiring connector as a safety precaution; however, wrap the wiring connectors with insulation tape or similar, to prevent any contact of the wiring.

4 Remove the headrests from the seat backs by releasing the safety catch. The safety catch is below the headrest guide, hidden by the seat fabric. Depress the catch through the fabric. Removing the headrest will give more room when removing the seat from the vehicle.

5 When removing the seat from the vehicle, do not lift the seat by the seat belt stalk or by the seat adjustment levers. If necessary, have an assistant help to remove the seat, as it is heavy, and surrounding trim panels may be otherwise damaged. Make sure that the seat runners do not damage the paintwork as the seat is withdrawn.

Rear seats

6 Remove the ISO fix covers, pull up the front of the seat squab and remove the squab (see illustrations).

22.6a Remove the covers and...

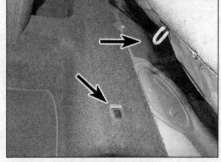

22.6b ...release the squab from the floor panel by pulling it up

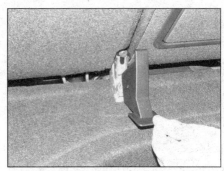

22.8a Unclip the bracket cover

22.8b Unbolt the bracket and...

22.8c ...remove it

22.8d On estate models lift up the floor covering...

22.8e ...and remove the cross rail to...

7 Open the tailgate and remove the parcel shelf.

8 Remove the cover, unbolt the clamp and remove it. Release the seat back catch from the single seat, lift up the seat back and remove it **(see illustrations)**.

9 Lift up and unhook the single seat and then remove it. Lift up the double seat and then unbolt the centre seat belt mounting **(see illustrations)**. Remove the seat

Refitting

10 Refitting is a reversal of removal, but tighten the mounting bolts to the specified torque where given.

23 Seat belt tensioning mechanisms – general information

1 All models covered in this manual are fitted with a front seat belt tensioner system incorporated in each of the inertia reels. Rear seat belt inertia reels with the tensioner system are only fitted to some models, other models having standard inertia reels.

2 The system is designed to instantaneously take up any slack in the seat belt in the case of a sudden frontal impact, therefore reducing the possibility of injury to the front seat occupants. The seat belt tensioner is triggered

22.8f ...access the bracket

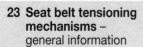

22.9a On estate models unhook the release cable...

22.9b ...and remove it

22.9c Release the seat back from the pivot...

22.9d ...and remove it

by a frontal impact above a predetermined force. Lesser impacts, including impacts from behind, will not trigger the system.

3 When the system is triggered, the explosive gas in the tensioner mechanism retracts and locks the seat belt. This prevents the seat belt moving and keeps the occupant firmly in position in the seat. Once the tensioner has been triggered, the seat belt will be permanently locked and the assembly must be renewed.

4 There is a risk of personal injury if the system is triggered inadvertently when working on the vehicle, and it is therefore strongly recommended that any work involving the seat belt inertia reels be entrusted to a Seat dealer. Note the following warnings before contemplating any work on the front seat belts.

 Warning: Do not expose the tensioner mechanism to temperatures in excess of 100°C.

 Warning: Before removing any components, disconnect the battery negative lead as described in Section.

Warning: If the tensioner mechanism is dropped, it must be renewed, even it has suffered no apparent damage.

Warning: Do not allow any solvents to come into contact with the tensioner mechanism.

Warning: Do not attempt to open the tensioner mechanism as it contains explosive gas.

Warning: Tensioners must be discharged before they are disposed of, but this task should be entrusted to a Volkswagen dealer.

Warning: Some of the bolts securing the seat belts are microencapsulated and need to be heated with a hot air blower before they are slackened. Microencapsulated means that the threads of the bolts are coated with a locking compound from new. New bolts will be required for refitting.

24 Seat belt components – removal and refitting

 Warning: Refer to Section before proceeding.

Front seat belt removal

1 Disconnect the battery negative lead (as described in Section 5A Section 3).

2 Remove the sill trim and the B-pillar trims with reference to Section 25.

3 Pull back the carpet, then unscrew and remove the seat belt lower anchor mounting bolt and remove the belt from the floor **(see illustration)**. On three door models remove the two bolts and slide the webbing off the bracket.

 Warning: As a precaution against unintentional electrostatic discharge, briefly touch part of the vehicle body before disconnecting the wiring.

4 Release the locking clip and disconnect the wiring connector from the inertia reel **(see illustrations)**.

5 Unscrew the bracket and remove the mounting bolt. Remove the inertia reel from the bottom of the B-pillar and on models fitted with a reversible pre-tensioner system, disconnect the wiring plug as the reel is removed **(see illustrations)**.

6 Undo the screws and remove the belt guide from the B-pillar **(see illustration)**.

7 Unscrew and remove the bolt securing the seat belt upper anchor to the height adjuster

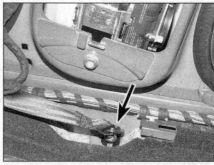

24.3 Remove the bolt

24.4a Release the locking peg...

24.4b ...and disconnect wiring plug

24.5a Unscrew the bracket...

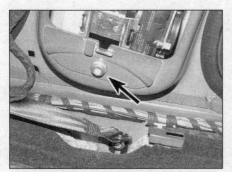

24.5b ...and remove the bolt

24.5c Disconnect the wiring plug as the inertia reel is removed (where fitted)

24.6 Front seat belt guide

24.7 Front seat belt upper anchor

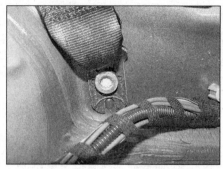

24.12 Remove the bolt

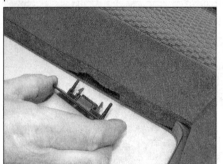

24.13 The lower mounting bolt

on the B-pillar (see illustration). The seat belt assembly can then be removed from the vehicle.
8 To remove the belt height adjustment, remove the securing bolt from the top of the adjuster and lift upwards to release from the pillar.

Front seat belt stalk removal

9 Remove the front seat as described in Section 22. On a clean surface, turn the seat over.
10 Unscrew and remove the bolt securing

the stalk to the seat, and remove the stalk. Discard the bolt – it must be replaced if loosened.

Rear seat belt removal

11 Remove the load area side trim panels and the sill panel as described in Section 25.
12 Where fitted disconnect the wiring plug and then remove the bolt (see illustration).
13 At the base of the C-pillar, unbolt and remove the lower mounting (see illustration) and then remove the belt and reel from the vehicle.

Rear centre belt removal

14 The reel is fitted into the centre rear seat back. Remove the seat as described in Section 22.
15 Place the seat on a protective surface and remove the rear cover to access the mounting bolt (see illustrations).

24.15a On models fitted with an armrest/ski hatch remove the locking catch covers…

24.15b …using a suitable hook (welding rod or similar) to release the cover

24.15c Unclip the trim main trim panel …

24.15d …and then remove the smaller panel (ski hatch models only)

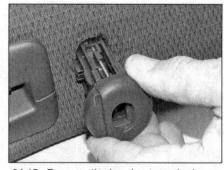

24.15e Remove the headrests and release the guides

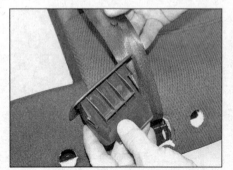

24.15f Unclip the seat belt guide. Note the position of the locking tabs

24.15g Release the seat back lock cover

24.15h Unclip and work free the seat fabric

24.16 Unbolt the reel

24.17 A detailed view of the headrest guide locking tabs

24.18 Unbolt the stalk

16 Partially remove the seat back cushion and then unbolt and remove the seat belt reel **(see illustration)**.

17 Note that if removing any of the upper covers/trim proves impossible, the locking tabs can be accessed if the seat cushion is partially removed first **(see illustration)**.

Rear seat belt stalks

18 Remove the rear seat squab. Unbolt and remove the stalk **(see illustration)**.

Refitting

19 Refitting is a reversal of the removal procedure, ensuring that all the seat belt units are located correctly and mounting bolts are securely tightened to their specified torque. Check all the trim panels are securely retained by all the relevant retaining clips. When refitting the B-pillar upper trim panels, ensure that the height adjustment peg engages correctly with the trim panel.

25 Interior trim – removal and refitting

 Warning: Refer to the warnings in Chapter 12 Section 23, on airbags.

Interior trim panels

1 The interior trim panels are secured using either screws or various types of trim fasteners, usually studs or clips.

2 Check that there are no other panels overlapping the one to be removed; usually there is a sequence that has to be followed, and this will only become obvious on close inspection.

3 Remove all obvious fasteners, such as screws. If the panel will not come free, it will be held by hidden clips or fasteners. These are usually situated around the edge of the panel and can be prised up to release them; note, however, that they can break quite easily so new ones should be available. The best way of releasing such clips, without the correct type of tool, is to use a large flat-bladed screwdriver. If a considerable amount of trim requires removal a wise investment will be a comprehensive set of plastic trim tools **(see illustration)**. Note in many cases that the adjacent sealing strip must be prised back to release a panel.

4 When removing a panel, never use excessive force or the panel may be damaged; always check carefully that all fasteners or other relevant components have been removed or released before attempting to withdraw a panel.

5 On models with side airbags, disconnect the battery negative lead (refer to Chapter 5A Section 3).

6 Refitting (except where noted) is the reverse of the removal procedure. Secure the fasteners by pressing them firmly into place and ensure that all disturbed components are correctly secured to prevent rattles.

A-pillar

Upper section

7 Starting from the top of the panel release the panel by working a long trim tool down the back of the panel and pushing the metal clips down the elongated slots in the pillar **(see illustrations)**. Where a curtain airbag is fitted the metal clips must be replaced.

8 Recover the retaining clips and replace then as required.

9 Refitting is a reversal of removal.

Quarter light panel

10 Remove the A-pillar upper trim panel as described above.

11 Release the panel **(see illustration)**.

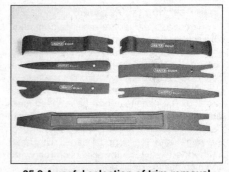

25.3 A useful selection of trim removal tools will avoid damage to the paintwork or trim panel

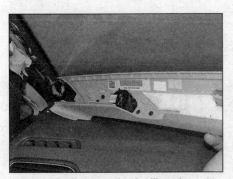

25.7a Remove the A-pillar trim

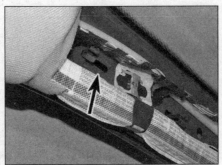

25.7b Note the elongated slots in the pillar

25.11 Release the quarter light panel

25.12a Remove the end panel...

25.12b ...and then the filler panel

25.14a Unclip the left-hand panel

25.14b Slide out the locking clip and...

25.14c ...remove the bonnet release handle

25.14d Remove the trim clip and...

A-pillar middle section (fascia filler panel)

12 Remove the facia end panel and then prise up the filler panel and remove it **(see illustrations)**.

Lower section (scuff panel)

13 Remove (or partially release) the doorstep/ sill panel as described below.

14 The left-hand panel can be simply unclipped. On the right-hand panel remove the bonnet release handle by sliding out the locking clip and removing the handle. Remove the trim clip. The panel can now be released **(see illustrations)**. Note however that removing this panel is difficult due to the interlock between the panel and the support panel. The best method is to pull the lower section rearward and then pull the panel up to release it.

Sill trim panel

15 The sill panel is the key panel. It must be

25.14e ...then remove the panel

removed to remove the lower A-pillar panel, the B-pillar panel and the C-pillar wheel arch panel (or side panel on 3 door models).

16 Remove the rear seat squab as described in Section 22 and then remove the single trim clip **(see illustration)**.

17 Working from the rear (and using a trim

25.16 Remove the trim clip

tool as required) pull up the sill panel from the rear doorstep (four door model) and then release the panel from the base of the B-pillar. Slide out the seat belt webbing as the panel is released. Continue along the front doorstep and then remove the panel **(see illustrations)**.

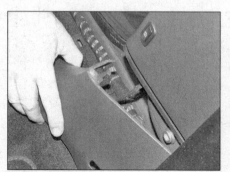

25.17a Release the panel from the base of the B-pillar...

25.17b ...and slide out the seat belt webbing

25.17c Prise up the panel from the door step

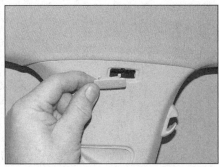

25.19a Remove the badge...

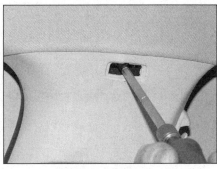

25.19b ...and the screw

25.20a Release the panel...

25.20b ...and then feed the seat belt webbing through the panel

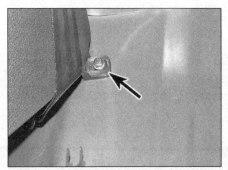

25.23 Remove the nut

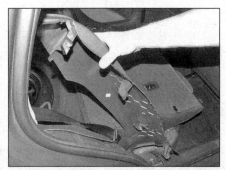

25.24 Remove the panel

B-pillar

Note: *The B-pillar trim is in two sections. In theory the upper section can be removed first, but in reality the simple solution is to remove the panels together and separate them after removal.*

18 Remove the door sill trim as described in this Section.

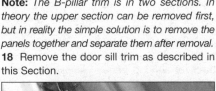

25.26a Carefully access the retaining clips

25.27 Remove the panel

19 Lower the seat belt height adjuster to the lowest position, remove the 'Airbag' badge and then remove the screw **(see illustrations)**.

20 Using a trim tool work the complete panel free from the pillar. Release the bottom first and then unhook the upper panel from the headlining **(see illustrations)**.

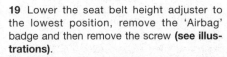

25.26b Remove the panel

25.28 Remove the roof panel

21 Feed the seatbelt buckle through the panel to remove it completely.

C-pillar

Note: *Access to the load area panels requires the removal of the lower C-pillar panel.*

22 Remove the rear seat squab as described in Section 22 and then remove the fixing from the sill panel **(see illustration 25.16)**.

23 Remove the single nut from the lower rear of the panel **(see illustration)**.

24 Lower the seat back by releasing the catches. Partially lift the rear off the sill panel and then release the lower section of the C-pillar from the wheel arch **(see illustration)**.

25 Removing the lower section gives access to the fixings for the rear shelf support. The shelf support must be removed (as described in the next subsection) before the upper C-pillar can be removed.

D-pillar

26 Unclip the roof panel as described below and then using a trim tool release the panel by levering directly on the metal retaining clips **(see illustrations)**.

Load area panels

Tailgate slam panel

27 Open the tailgate and prise up the panel **(see illustration)**.

Roof panel

28 Open the tailgate and prise off the panel **(see illustration)**.

Shelf support panel

29 Open the tailgate and remove the parcel

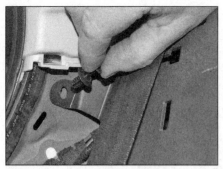

25.31a Remove the 'scrivet' at the front of the panel (hatchback)

25.31b Remove the hidden screw

25.31c On estate models a screw is hidden behind the seat back release handle...

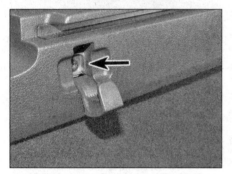

25.31d ...as well as behind the hook

25.31e Remove the rear screw (hatchback models)

25.31f Slide out the seat belt webbing as the panel is removed

shelf. Remove the D-pillar trim as described above.

30 Remove the tailgate slam panel as described above.

31 Remove the fixings and lift out the panel **(see illustrations)**. Where fitted disconnect the wiring plug from the load area lamp as the panel is removed. On estate models disconnect the seat back release cable.

Lower side panel

32 Remove the shelf support panel as described above and then remove the rear seatbacks as described in Section 22. Note that on estate models the lower side panel is bonded to the shelf support panel. Both are removed together.

33 Remove the load tie down brackets and the floor support panel. Remove the panel **(see illustrations)**.

Steering column shrouds

Note: *It is also possible to remove the shrouds with the steering wheel in position, but the column switches (apart from the key reader) can not be removed with the steering wheel in position.*

34 Remove the steering wheel as described in Chapter 10 Section 19.

35 Fully extend the column and then unclip the upper section from below the instrument panel **(see illustrations)**.

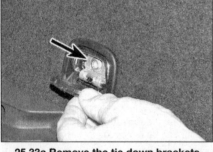

25.33a Remove the tie down brackets

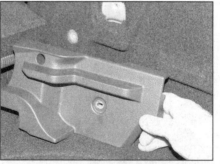

25.33b Remove the support bracket

25.33c Remove the side panel

25.35a Unclip the bellows...

25.35b ...and remove the upper shroud

25.36a Remove the upper screws and then...

25.36b ...remove the lower screw

25.37 Remove the lower shroud

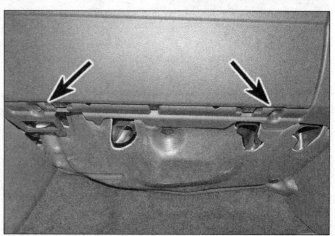

25.39 Remove the lower screws

36 Remove the upper screws and the lower screw **(see illustrations)**.
37 Manoeuvre the lower shroud past the lever to remove it **(see illustration)**.

Glovebox

38 Remove the facia end panel and then remove the centre console front lower side panel as described in Section 26.
39 Remove the glovebox lower fixings **(see illustration)**.
40 On models fitted with CD/DVD player in the glovebox, remove the unit **(see illustration)**.

41 With the CD/DVD player removed, remove the upper fixings. Note that a single screw is hidden behind the CD/DVD player or at the bottom of the storage compartment **(see illustration)**.
42 Remove the single screw from the end of the facia and pull the glovebox out from the

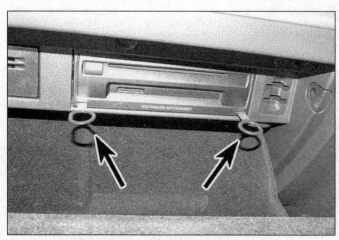

25.40 Audio unit removal keys will be required

25.41 Remove the screw

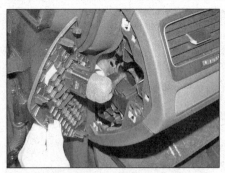

25.42a Remove the facia end panel...

25.42b ...disconnecting the PAD switch as the panel is removed

25.42c Remove the screw

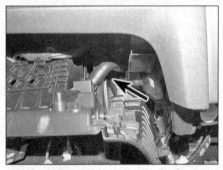

25.42d Disconnect the cooling hose

25.42e Unplug the glovebox wiring plug and...

25.42f ...unclip the wiring loom

facia. Disconnect the wiring plugs and the cooling hose as the glovebox is removed **(see illustrations)**.

43 Refitting is the reverse of removal.

Carpets

44 The passenger compartment floor carpet is in one piece and is secured at its edges by screws or clips, usually the same fasteners used to secure the various adjoining trim panels.

45 Carpet removal and refitting is reasonably straightforward but very time-consuming because all adjoining trim panels must be removed first, as must components such as the seats, the centre console and seat belt lower anchorages **(see illustration)**.

Headlining

46 The headlining is clipped to the roof and can be withdrawn only once all fittings such as the grab handles, sun visors, interior lights, sunroof (if fitted), and related upper trim panels have been removed.

47 To remove the sun visors and grab handles, the locking pegs have to be removed first and then the internal locking tabs can be released **(see illustrations)**.

25.45 Carpet removal is required to remove the heater module and evaporator

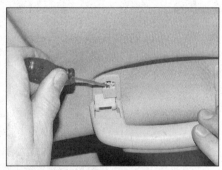

25.47a Remove the locking pegs...

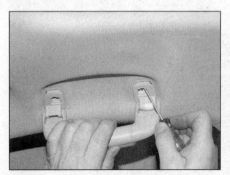

25.47b ...and release (with difficulty) the internal tabs

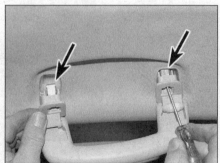

25.47c Remove the handle. Note the position of the tabs

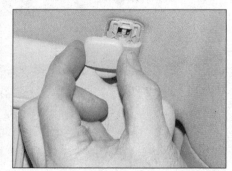

25.47d Unclip the cover to access the sunvisor mounting

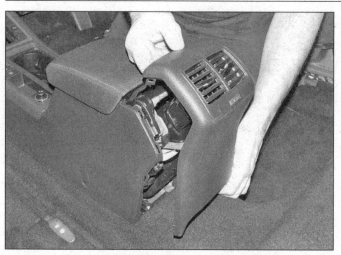

26.2 Remove the rear panel

26.3a Remove the footrest panel

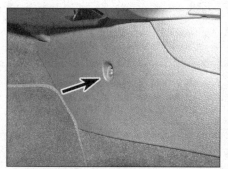

26.3b Unbolt, unclip and remove…

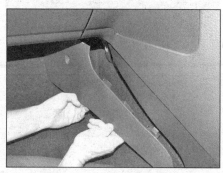

26.3c …both lower side panels

26.4 Remove the heater control panel trim

48 Note that headlining removal requires considerable skill and experience if it is to be carried out without damage and is therefore best entrusted to an expert.

26 Centre console – removal and refitting

Note: *There are two versions of the centre console fitted to the models covered by this manual: a basic version and a comfort version.*

Removal and refitting is essentially the same for both versions.

Removal

Note: *It is possible to remove the centre console with both front seats in position, however removal of the console is slightly easier if they are both removed first (as described in Section 22).*

1 Disconnect the battery (as described in Chapter 5A Section 3). If the front seats are not to be removed slide them back as far as possible.
2 On models with an armrest release the rear panel complete with the air distribution vents.

The panel is a tight fit and must be pulled up slightly before it can be released **(see illustration)**.
3 Remove the single fixing from the driver's foot rest panel. Remove the panel and then remove both front lower side panels **(see illustrations)**.
4 Move the gear lever to the rear and using a trim tool release the panel from the heater controls **(see illustration)**.
5 Unclip the gear lever gaiter panel. Prise up and remove the front storage compartment, disconnect the wiring plug and remove the compartment **(see illustrations)**.

26.5a Unclip the gaiter panel

26.5b Remove the storage compartment…

26.5c …and disconnect the wiring plugs as the compartment is removed

26.6a Remove the screw

26.6b Release the upper section and then...

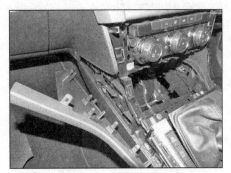

26.6c ...unclip the panel. Repeat the procedure for the other side

26.7 Remove the screws

6 Remove the screws (one per side) and remove both upper side panels. The front edges of the panels (close to the heater controls) must be carefully twisted over slightly to release them **(see illustrations)**.

7 Remove the screws at the front of the main switch panel **(see illustration)**.

8 With the screws removed, work along the panel and release the locking tabs. Lift up the front of the panel and disconnect the wiring plugs. Lift the panel over the gear lever gaiter and unhook it from the rear section of the console **(see illustrations)**.

9 Remove the covers and then remove the rear screws from the side of the main section. Remove the screws at the front **(see illustrations)**.

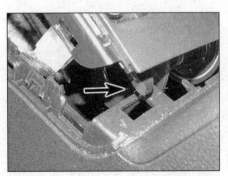

26.8a Release the locking tabs

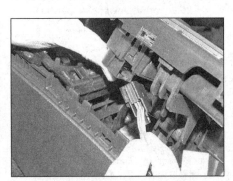

26.8b Disconnect the wiring plugs

26.8c Lift the front of the panel over the gear lever and...

26.8d ...unhook it at the rear. Note the peg

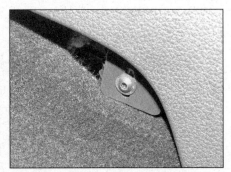

26.9a Remove the covers to access the screws

26.9b The left-hand side front screw

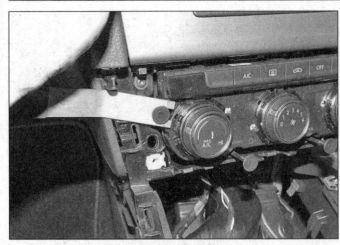

26.10a Release the fixings…

26.10b …pull the control panel out…

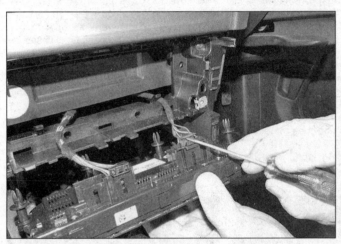

26.10c …and disconnect the wiring plugs

26.10d Remove the screws

10 Release the 'scrivet' type fixings from the heater control panel – the fixings are removed with the panel. Pull the panel forward and disconnect the wiring plugs. Remove the now exposed screws from the upper front section of the centre console (see illustrations).
11 On models fitted with an armrest, remove the rear mounting bolts. Lift up the rear of the console and then remove the console by pulling it up and backwards (see illustrations).

Refitting

12 Refitting is a reversal of removal.

26.11a Remove the screws

26.11b Removing the main section of the console

27.4a Unclip the left and...

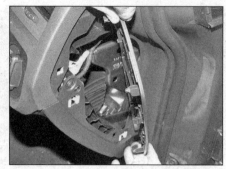

27.4b ...and the right facia end covers

27.5a Remove the compartment

27 Facia panel assembly –
removal and refitting

Note: *Refer to the warnings in Chapter 12 Section 23 for airbags.*

Note: *To avoid any damage to the facia panel, removal of the steering column (Chapter 10 Section 20) is highly recommended.*

Removal

1 Disconnect the battery negative lead (as described in Chapter 5A Section 3).
2 Slide the front seats fully rearward, or remove them completely as described in Section 22.

3 Remove the centre console as described in Section 26.
4 Prise out the trim panels from each end of the facia **(see illustrations)**. On the left-hand end disconnect the PAD (Passenger Airbag Disable) switch as the panel is removed.
5 Open and then remove the storage compartment on the driver's side by pulling it off the hinge mechanism. Remove the screws and lift out the panel **(see illustrations)**.
6 Remove the steering column shrouds as described in Section 25.
7 Remove the drivers airbag as described in Chapter 12 Section 24 and then remove the steering wheel (Chapter 10 Section 19).
8 Remove the steering column switch assembly, as described in Chapter 12 Section 5

and then remove the driver's knee airbag (Chapter 12 Section 24) and the steering column (Chapter 10 Section 20).
9 Remove the A-pillar upper, centre and lower trim panels, as described in Section 25.
10 Remove the glovebox as described in Section 25 and then disconnect the passenger airbag.
11 Remove the lighting switch as described in Chapter 12 Section 5 and then remove the trim panel complete with the headlight range adjuster **(see illustrations)**.
12 Prise out the hazard warning switch and then remove the centre vents. A special tool (VAG 3370) is available, but a similar pair of tools can be easily fabricated. The tool should be at least 140 mm in length, 10 mm wide and

27.5b Remove the screw from the end of the fascia...

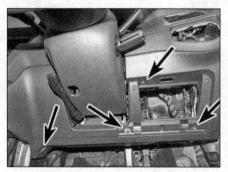

27.5c ...and from the front

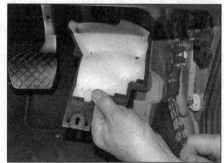

27.5d Remove the lower panel...

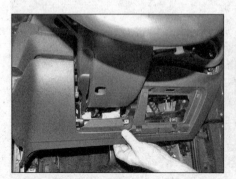

27.5e ...and then lift out the main panel

27.11a Remove the screw...

27.11b ...lift out the panel and disconnect the wiring plug

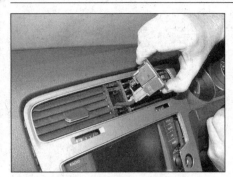

27.12a Release the hazard warning light switch...

27.12b ...and disconnect the wiring plug

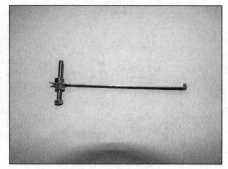

27.12c A suitable tool

with a right-angle up turn of 4 mm at one end. Place a felt tip pen mark at approximately 110 mm from the end **(see illustrations)**.

13 Insert the tools into the vents – one hole in and one hole up. Insert the tools to the depth of the felt pen mark and then angle them up to hook the upper rear section of the vents. A sharp tug on both tools will release the vents and the trim panel **(see illustrations)**.

14 Remove the Audio or SatNav unit, as described in Chapter 12 Section 19 and then remove the instrument panel (Chapter 12 Section 11).

15 Where fitted remove the sunlight sensor from the top of the facia. Disconnect the wiring plug as the sensor is removed and then tie a length of cord to the wiring plug as an aid for reassembly.

16 Unclip the diagnostic socket and

27.13a Partially release the lower section of the trim

27.13b Insert the tools through the vents and release the panel

disconnect the passenger side airbag wiring plug **(see illustrations)**.

17 Working logically from one side to the other, locate the facia cover screws. Unscrew

the retaining screws from the facia assembly **(see illustrations)**. As the facia is being removed, disconnect any loom retaining clips.

18 Make a final check that all the screws and

27.16a Unclip the diagnostic socket

27.16b Release the safety lock and disconnect the airbag wiring plug

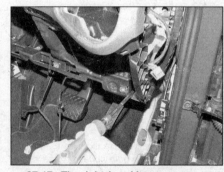

27.17a The right-hand lower screw...

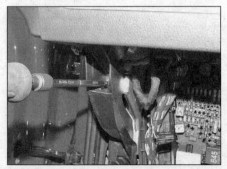

27.17b ...and the left-hand screw to the crossmember

27.17c Screws are fitted to both ends of the fascia

27.17d Remove the screws from the binnacle area

27.18a Remove the fascia

27.18b With the facia removed the crossmember is now accessible

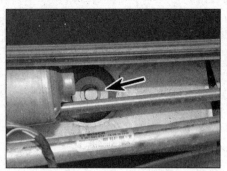

28.2 Remove the bolt hidden behind the wiper motor linkage

wiring have been removed and unclipped and then with the aid of an assistant remove the fascia panel (see illustrations).

Refitting

19 Refitting is a reversal of the removal procedure, noting the following points:

a) *Ensure the facia guides engage correctly with the clips on the bulkhead. As the facia is being fitted, check that all wiring is routed as noted during removal.*

b) *Insert all of the retaining screws hand-tight, then close both front doors and check that the facia is positioned centrally between the door trims. If it needs to be moved one way or another, place a wad of cloth between the facia and door trim, then close the door. This should move the facia as required. When central, fully tighten the securing screws.*

c) *On completion, reconnect the battery and check that all the electrical components and switches function correctly.*

28 Crossmember – removal and refitting

Note: *The most likely reason to remove the crossmember is to gain access to the heater*

28.5a Disconnect the wiring plugs from the BCM

28.5b Slide out the BCM

housing and in particular the air conditioning components. If this is the case then the AC system must be degassed by a garage equipped with an AC service station. Many garages and specialists will offer a mobile service at a reasonable cost.

Removal

1 Remove the facia panel as described in Section 27.

2 Remove the wiper arms and windscreen cowl panels as described in Chapter 12 Section 15. Remove the single bolt from the bulkhead (see illustration).

3 If not already removed, remove the air

distribution duct from the driver's footwell and the passenger footwell.

4 Unbolt and remove the crash protector from above the brake pedal.

5 Unplug and then unclip the BCM (Body Control Module) (see illustrations).

6 Unhook the main fusebox (see illustration) and lower it. Disconnect the wiring plugs at the rear if required.

7 Remove the 'scrivets' and remove both central air distribution ducts (see illustrations).

8 Remove the sound proofing from the top crossmember and then work along the crossmember unclipping the wiring loom as

28.6 Unhook the fusebox

28.7a Remove the scrivets and…

28.7b …and lift out the central air distribution ducts

28.8a Remove the sound proofing

28.8b Unclip the wiring loom and...

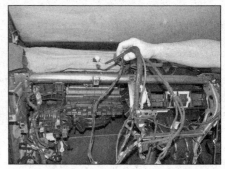

28.8c ...unclip it from the crossmember

required **(see illustrations)**. Note the position of the wiring loom and label the wiring plugs as required.

9 Unbolt the earth connector from the crossmember and then locate and remove the screws securing the heater/air distribution module to the crossmember **(see illustrations)**.

10 Fold back the carpet and unbolt the central support struts **(see illustration)**. Note that if the crossmember is being removed to access the heater/air distribution module, then completely remove the carpet and soundproofing at this point.

11 Mark the position of the crossmember in relation to the A-pillars **(see illustration)** and then unbolt the crossmember. Check that all sections of the wiring loom are unclipped from the crossmember and then with the aid of an assistant remove the crossmember.

28.9a Disconnect the main earth

28.9b Locate and remove the heater module fixings

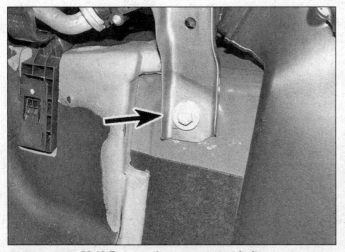

28.10 Remove the support strut bolts

28.11 Remove the crossmember

Chapter 12
Body electrical system

Contents

	Section number
12v Power outlets – removal and refitting	13
Aerials and filters – removal and refitting	21
Airbag system – general information and precautions	23
Airbag system components – removal and refitting	24
Anti-theft alarm system and engine immobiliser – general information	22
Audio unit – removal and refitting	19
Bulbs (exterior lights) – renewal	6
Bulbs (interior lights) – renewal	7
Electrical connectors	4
Electrical fault finding – general information	2
Exterior light units – removal and refitting	8
Fuses and relays – general information	3
General information and precautions	1

	Section number
Headlight beam adjustment components – removal and refitting	9
Headlight beam alignment – general information	10
Horn – removal and refitting	14
Instrument panel – removal and refitting	11
Loudspeakers – removal and refitting	20
Parking aid components – general information, removal and refitting	25
Rear wiper motor – removal and refitting	17
Service interval display – general information and resetting	12
Switches – removal and refitting	5
Washer system components – removal and refitting	18
Windscreen wiper motor and linkage – removal and refitting	16
Wiper arm – removal and refitting	15

Degrees of difficulty

Easy, suitable for novice with little experience 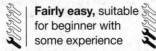	**Fairly easy,** suitable for beginner with some experience	**Fairly difficult,** suitable for competent DIY mechanic	**Difficult,** suitable for experienced DIY mechanic	**Very difficult,** suitable for expert DIY or professional

Specifications

System type . . . .   12 volt negative earth

Fuses . . . .   See *Wiring diagrams*

Bulbs	**Wattage**	**Type**
Approach light (in mirror)	LED	
Brake light*	21W	W21W
Brake light – High level	LED	
Cornering light	35W	H8
Cornering light (models with bi-Xenon bulbs)	55W	H7
Footwell light	5W	W5W
Front direction indicators	21W	H21W
Front direction indicator side repeater	LED	
Front foglight*	55W	H11
Front sidelight	55/15W	H15
Glovebox light	3W	W3W
Headlight:		
Halogen headlights		
Dipped beam	55W	H7
Main beam	55/15W	H15
Gas discharge headlights (Xenon)		
Dipped beam	35W	D1S
Main beam	55W	H7
Main/dipped (bi-Xenon models)	35W	D1S (H510)
Interior light	5W	W5W
Interior light (vanity mirror)	5W	Festoon
Load area light	10W	C10W
Number plate light	5W	W5W
Rear direction indicators	21W	WY21W
Rear foglight*	21W	W21W
Rear sidelight*	21W	W21W
Reversing light*	16W	W16W

*LED type on some models. Note also that some models have LED headlights, with no conventional bulbs

Torque wrench settings

	Nm	lbf ft
Crash sensor mounting bolt	9	7
Passenger airbag and bracket retaining screws	9	7
Wiper arm securing nut:		
Front	20	15
Rear	12	9

1 General information and precautions

⚠️ *Warning: Before carrying out any work on the electrical system, read through the precautions given in 'Safety first!' at the beginning of this manual, and in Chapter 5A Section 1.*

1 The electrical system is of 12-volt negative earth type. Power for the lights and all electrical accessories is supplied by a lead-acid type battery, which is charged by the alternator.

2 This Chapter covers repair and service procedures for the various electrical components not associated with the engine. Information on the battery, alternator and starter motor can be found in Chapter 5A.

3 It should be noted that prior to working on any component in the electrical system, the ignition and all electrical consumers must be switched off. Additionally, where stated, the battery must be disconnected, as described in Chapter 5A Section 3.

4 Some models are fitted with gas discharge headlight systems, which include automatic range control to reduce the possibility of dazzling oncoming drivers. Note the special precautions which apply to these systems as given in Section 6.

2 Electrical fault finding – general information

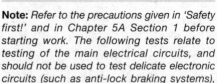

Note: *Refer to the precautions given in 'Safety first!' and in Chapter 5A Section 1 before starting work. The following tests relate to testing of the main electrical circuits, and should not be used to test delicate electronic circuits (such as anti-lock braking systems), particularly where an electronic control module is used.*

General

1 A typical electrical circuit consists of an electrical component; any switches, relays, motors, fuses, fusible links or circuit breakers related to that component, and the wiring and connectors which link the component to both the battery and the chassis. To help to pin-point a problem in an electrical circuit, wiring diagrams are included at the end of this Chapter. **Note:** *Many of the circuits are*

controlled by computerised systems (for instance, the windscreen wipers will only operate with the bonnet closed), so before assuming there are faults, it is worthwhile checking if specific conditions apply.

2 Before attempting to diagnose an electrical fault, first study the appropriate wiring diagram to obtain a complete understanding of the components included in the particular circuit concerned. The possible sources of a fault can be narrowed down by noting if other components related to the circuit are operating properly. If several components or circuits fail at one time, the problem is likely to be related to a shared fuse or earth connection.

3 Electrical problems usually stem from simple causes, such as loose or corroded connections, a faulty earth connection, a blown fuse, a melted fusible link, or a faulty relay (refer to Section 3 for details of testing relays). Visually inspect the condition of all fuses, wires and connections in a problem circuit before testing the components. Use the wiring diagrams to determine which terminal connections will need to be checked in order to pin-point the trouble spot.

4 The basic tools required for electrical fault finding include a circuit tester or voltmeter (a 12-volt bulb with a set of test leads can also be used for certain tests); a self-powered test light (sometimes known as a continuity tester); an ohmmeter (to measure resistance); a battery and set of test leads; and a jumper wire, preferably with a circuit breaker or fuse incorporated, which can be used to bypass suspect wires or electrical components. Before attempting to locate a problem with test instruments, use the wiring diagram to determine where to make the connections.

5 To find the source of an intermittent wiring fault (usually due to a poor or dirty connection, or damaged wiring insulation), a wiggle test can be performed on the wiring. This involves wiggling the wiring by hand to see if the fault occurs as the wiring is moved. It should be possible to narrow down the source of the fault to a particular section of wiring. This method of testing can be used in conjunction with any of the tests described in the following sub-Sections.

6 Apart from problems due to poor connections, two basic types of fault can occur in an electrical circuit – open-circuit, or short-circuit.

7 Open-circuit faults are caused by a break somewhere in the circuit, which prevents

current from flowing. An open-circuit fault will prevent a component from working, but will not cause the relevant circuit fuse to blow.

8 Short-circuit faults are caused by a short somewhere in the circuit, which allows the current flowing in the circuit to escape along an alternative route, usually to earth. Short-circuit faults are normally caused by a breakdown in wiring insulation, which allows a feed wire to touch either another wire, or an earthed component such as the bodyshell. A short-circuit fault will normally cause the relevant circuit fuse to blow.

Finding an open-circuit

9 To check for an open-circuit, connect one lead of a circuit tester or voltmeter to either the negative battery terminal or a known good earth.

10 Connect the other lead to a connector in the circuit being tested, preferably nearest to the battery or fuse.

11 Switch on the circuit, bearing in mind that some circuits are live only when the ignition switch is moved to a particular position.

12 If voltage is present (indicated either by the tester bulb lighting or a voltmeter reading, as applicable), this means that the section of the circuit between the relevant connector and the battery is problem-free.

13 Continue to check the remainder of the circuit in the same fashion.

14 When a point is reached at which no voltage is present, the problem must lie between that point and the previous test point with voltage. Most problems can be traced to a broken, corroded or loose connection.

Finding a short-circuit

15 To check for a short-circuit; first disconnect the load(s) from the circuit (loads are the components which draw current from a circuit, such as bulbs, motors, heating elements, etc).

16 Remove the relevant fuse from the circuit, and connect a circuit tester or voltmeter to the fuse connections.

17 Switch on the circuit, bearing in mind that some circuits are live only when the ignition switch is moved to a particular position.

18 If voltage is present (indicated either by the tester bulb lighting or a voltmeter reading, as applicable), this means that there is a short circuit.

19 If no voltage is present, but the fuse still blows with the load(s) connected, this indicates an internal fault in the load(s).

Finding an earth fault

20 The battery negative terminal is connected to earth – the metal of the engine/ transmission and the car body – and most systems are wired so that they only receive a positive feed, the current returning through the metal of the car body. This means that the component mounting and the body form part of that circuit. Loose or corroded mountings can therefore cause a range of electrical faults, ranging from total failure of a circuit, to a puzzling partial fault. In particular, lights may shine dimly (especially when another circuit sharing the same earth point is in operation), motors (e.g. wiper motors or the radiator cooling fan motor) may run slowly, and the operation of one circuit may have an apparently unrelated effect on another. Note that on many vehicles, earth straps are used between certain components, such as the engine/transmission and the body, usually where there is no metal-to-metal contact between components due to flexible rubber mountings, etc.

21 To check whether a component is properly earthed, disconnect the battery (refer to the warnings given in the Reference section at the rear of the manual) and connect one lead of an ohmmeter to a known good earth point. Connect the other lead to the wire or earth connection being tested. The resistance reading should be zero; if not, check the connection as follows.

22 If an earth connection is thought to be faulty, dismantle the connection and clean back to bare metal both the bodyshell and the wire terminal or the component earth connection mating surface. Be careful to remove all traces of dirt and corrosion, and then use a knife to trim away any paint, so that a clean metal-to-metal joint is made. On reassembly, tighten the joint fasteners securely; if a wire terminal is being refitted, use serrated washers between the terminal and the bodyshell to ensure a clean and secure connection. When the connection is remade, prevent the onset of corrosion in the future by applying a coat of petroleum jelly or silicone-based grease or by spraying on (at

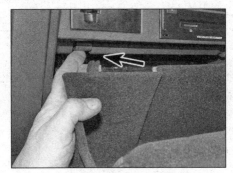
3.2a Lower the glovebox door to...

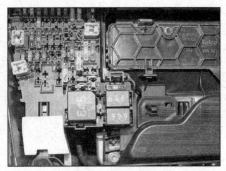
3.2b ...access the fusebox

regular intervals) a proprietary ignition sealer or a water dispersant lubricant.

3 Fuses and relays – general information

Fuses and fusible links

1 Fuses are designed to break a circuit when a predetermined current is reached, in order to protect the components and wiring, which could be damaged by excessive current flow. Any excessive current flow will be due to a fault in the circuit, usually a short-circuit (see Section 2).

2 The main fuses are located behind the glovebox. Release the retaining tabs and lower the glovebox door **(see illustrations)**.

3 To remove a fuse, first switch off the circuit concerned (or the ignition), and then pull the fuse out of its terminals **(see illustration)**.

4 The wire within the fuse should be visible; if the fuse has blown it will be broken or melted.

5 Always renew a fuse with one of the correct rating; never use a fuse with a different rating from that specified.

6 Refer to the wiring diagrams for details of the fuse ratings and the circuits protected. The fuse rating is stamped on the top of the fuse; the fuses are also colour-coded as follows.

Colour	Rating
Light brown	5A
Brown	7.5A
Red	10A
Blue	15A
Yellow	20A
White or clear	25A
Green	30A
Orange	40A

7 Never renew a fuse more than once without tracing the source of the trouble. If the new fuse blows immediately, find the cause before renewing it again; a short to earth as a result of faulty insulation is most likely. Where a fuse protects more than one circuit, try to isolate the fault by switching on each circuit in turn (where possible) until the fuse blows again. Always carry a supply of spare fuses of each relevant rating on the vehicle.

8 Additional fuses and relays are located in the fusebox located on the left-hand side of the engine compartment. Release the two securing clips and withdraw the cover to gain access to the fuses and relays **(see illustrations)**.

9 To renew a fusible link, first disconnect the battery negative terminal. Unscrew the retaining nuts then remove the blown link from the front of the engine compartment fusebox

3.3 Removing a fuse from the fusebox (under bonnet fusebox shown)

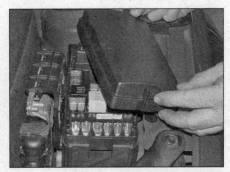
3.8a Lift off the cover...

3.8b ...to access the fuse and relay box in the engine compartment (note the fuse puller in the lid)

(see illustrations). Fit the new link to its terminals and reconnect the leads. Ensure the link and leads are correctly seated then refit the retaining nuts and tighten securely. Clip the cover back into position then reconnect the battery.

Relays

10 A relay is an electrically operated switch, which is used for the following reasons:

a) *A relay can switch a heavy current remotely from the circuit in which the current is flowing, allowing the use of lighter-gauge wiring and switch contacts.*

b) *A relay can receive more than one control input, unlike a mechanical switch.*

c) *A relay can have a timer function – for example, the intermittent wiper relay.*

11 Most of the relays are located on the relay plate behind the glovebox, however, additional relays are located in the engine compartment fusebox **(see illustration 3.8b).**

12 Access to the relays can be obtained after lowering the glovebox door **(see illustration 3.2b).** Identification details of the relays are given at the start of the wiring diagrams.

13 If a circuit or system controlled by a relay develops a fault, and the relay is suspect, operate the system. If the relay is functioning, it should be possible to hear it click as it is energised. If this is the case, the fault lies with the components or wiring of the system. If the relay is not being energised, then either the relay is not receiving a main supply or a switching voltage, or the relay itself is faulty. Testing is by the substitution of a known good unit, but be careful – while some relays are identical in appearance and in operation, others look similar but perform different functions.

14 To remove a relay, first ensure that the relevant circuit is switched off. The relay can then simply be pulled out from the socket, and pushed back into position.

4 Electrical connectors

1 Most electrical connections on these vehicles are made with multiwire plastic connectors. The mating halves of many connectors are secured with locking clips molded into the plastic connector shells. The mating halves of some large connectors, such as some of those under the instrument panel, are held together by a bolt through the center of the connector.

2 To separate a connector with locking clips, use a small screwdriver to pry the clips apart carefully, then separate the connector halves. Pull only on the shell, never pull on the wiring harness, as you may damage the individual wires and terminals inside the connectors. Look at the connector closely before trying to separate the halves. Often the locking clips

3.9a Remove the lid and front cover…

3.9b …to expose the fusible links

are engaged in a way that is not immediately clear. Additionally, many connectors have more than one set of clips.

3 Each pair of connector terminals has a male half and a female half. When you look at the end view of a connector in a diagram, be sure to understand whether the view shows the harness side or the component side of the connector. Connector halves are mirror images of each other, and a terminal shown on the right side end-view of one half will be on the left side end-view of the other half.

4 It is often necessary to take circuit voltage measurements with a connector connected. Whenever possible, carefully insert a small

straight pin (not your meter probe) into the rear of the connector shell to contact the terminal inside, then clip your meter lead to the pin. This kind of connection is called "backprobing." When inserting a test probe into a terminal, be careful not to distort the terminal opening. Doing so can lead to a poor connection and corrosion at that terminal later. Using the small straight pin instead of a meter probe results in less chance of deforming the terminal connector. "T" pins are a good choice as temporary meter connections. They allow for a larger surface area to attach the meter leads too.

5 Typical electrical connectors:

4.5a Most electrical connectors have a single release tab that you depress to release the connector

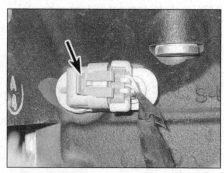
4.5b Some electrical connectors have a retaining tab which must be pried up to free the connector

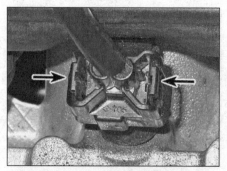
4.5c Some connectors have two release tabs that you must squeeze to release the connector

4.5d Some connectors use wire retainers that you squeeze to release the connector

4.5e Critical connectors often employ a sliding lock (1) that you must pull out before you can depress the release tab (2)

4.5f Here's another sliding-lock style connector, with the lock (1) and the release tab (2) on the side of the connector

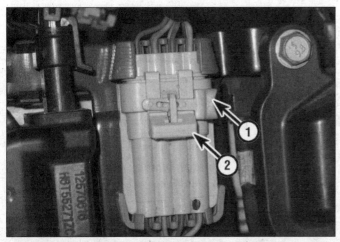

4.5g On some connectors the lock (1) must be pulled out to the side and removed before you can lift the release tab (2)

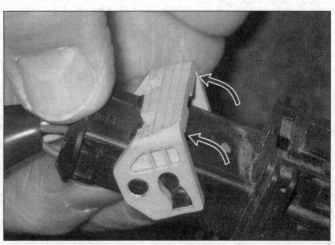

4.5h Some critical connectors, like the multi-pin connectors at the Electronic Control Module employ pivoting locks that must be flipped open

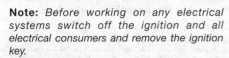

5 Switches –
removal and refitting

Note: *Before working on any electrical systems switch off the ignition and all electrical consumers and remove the ignition key.*

Ignition switch

1 Refer to Chapter 10 Section 21.

Wiper and indicator/ cruise switches

Note: *The switches are a single combined assembly. If any switch is faulty the entire switch assembly must be replaced.*
2 Check that the front wheels are pointing straight-ahead and the steering wheel is in its centre position, then remove the steering wheel as described in Chapter 10 Section 19.

3 Remove the steering column shrouds, as described in Chapter 11 Section 25.
4 Disconnect the wiring plugs from the electronic control unit/clockspring **(see illustration)**. The number varies according to the model specification.

5 Remove the single screw (Kostal units) or three screws (Valeo units) and unclip the clockspring and electronic control **(see illustration)**.
6 The clockspring must be kept in the same position whilst removed. Secure it with

5.4 Disconnect the wiring plugs. Note the clockspring secured with tape

5.5 Remove the clockspring

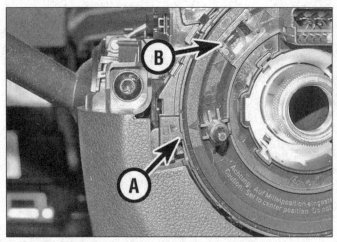

5.6 The alignment marks (A). Note that the connector must be visible (B)

5.7a Remove the screw (Kostal)...

tape and note the alignment marks (see illustration).

7 A Kostal or Valeo version of the switch may be fitted. Kostal switch assemblies have a single screw (below the column) and Valeo switches are clipped into position. Remove the screw and unclip the switch assembly as required (see illustrations).

8 Refitting is a reversal of removal.

Lighting switch

9 With the light switch in position O, press the switch centre inwards and turn it slightly to the right. Hold this position and pull the switch from the dash (see illustration). Removing the facia end panel makes this task slightly easier.

10 As the switch is withdrawn from the dash, disconnect the wiring plug (see illustration).

11 To refit the switch, first reconnect the wiring plug, then hold the switch and press the rotary part inwards and slightly to the right. Insert the switch into the dash, turn the rotary part to position O and release. Check the switch for correct operation.

Headlamp range control and instrument illumination switch

12 Remove the lighting switch as described in this section.

13 Remove the single screw and pull out the housing (see illustrations).

14 Disconnect the wiring plug and then unclip the switch from the housing (see illustration).

15 Refitting is a reversal of removal.

Air conditioning/heating switches

16 The switches are integral with the heater control panel, and cannot be removed separately. Refer to Chapter 3 Section 9 for details of heater control panel removal and refitting.

Heater blower motor switch

17 The switch is integral with the heater

5.7b ...and then slide off the switch assembly

5.9 Press the switch centre inwards and turn it slightly to the right to remove

5.10 Disconnect the wiring plug

5.13a Remove the screw...

5.13b ...and lift out the housing

5.14 Remove the switch from the housing

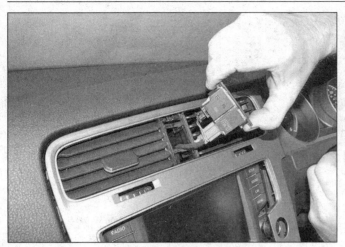

5.19a Remove the switch.

5.19b Disconnect the wiring plugs

control panel, and cannot be removed separately. Refer to Chapter 3 Section 9 for details of heater control panel removal and refitting.

Hazard warning

18 The switch is mounted centrally between the central air distribution vents.
19 Using a plastic trim tool inserted at each side of the switch, prise out the switch and disconnect the wiring plugs **(see illustrations)**.
20 Refitting is a reversal of removal.

Centre console mounted switches

21 The number of switches mounted on the centre console varies according to the trim level and the year of manufacture. The following switches are mounted to the centre console switch panel:
● Stop/start switch
● Parking aid switch
● Park assist steering switch
● TCS (Traction control) and ESP (Electronic Stability Programme) switch
● Electromechanical handbrake switch
22 The switches (apart from the handbrake and stop/start switch) are mounted either side of the gear lever. Only the complete row

of switches can be replaced, they can not be replaced individually.
23 Prise free gear lever gaiter and then using a trim tool, prise up the rear embellisher **(see illustrations)**.
24 Release the retaining clips and withdraw the appropriate row of switches from the panel **(see illustrations)**.
25 Where fitted the stop/start switch is removed in a similar manner.
26 The handbrake switch is removed after removal of the main switch panel (as described in Chapter 11 Section 26). Working

from the back of the panel release the switch **(see illustration)**.
27 Refitting is a reversal of removal.

Passenger airbag disable/ deactivation switch (PAD)

Caution: Disconnect the battery and wait several minutes before disconnecting the switch. Rear the warnings given in Section 23 when working on any part of the airbag system.
28 The switch is located in the fascia end panel.

5.23a Prise up the gaiter…

5.23b …and remove the trim (shown with complete panel removed)

5.24a Use a small screwdriver to release the tabs…

5.24b …and then remove the switch panel (shown with the complete panel removed for clarity)

5.26 Remove the switch

5.29a Remove the end panel

5.29b Disconnect the wiring plug...

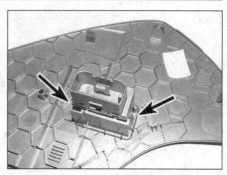

5.29c ...and compress the tangs to remove the switch

29 Using a trim tool prise of the end panel, disconnect the wiring plug and remove the switch (see illustrations).
30 Refitting is a reversal of removal.

Glovebox light switch

31 Fully open the glovebox, and release the operating arm from the damper.
32 Pull the switch out of the housing and disconnect the wiring plug.
33 Refitting is a reversal of removal.

Power window switch assembly

34 Remove the door trim panel as described in Chapter 11 Section 12.
35 Depress the locking tabs and remove the switch panel (see illustrations).
36 Refitting is a reversal of removal.

Mirror control/door lock switch

37 Remove the door trim panel as described in Chapter 11 Section 12.

5.35a Depress the tabs and...

38 Release the switch panel from the door trim panel (see illustrations). Note that the switches on all the doors are removed in the same manner.
39 Separate the switches from the housing as required (see illustration).
40 Refitting is a reversal of removal.

Handbrake 'on' warning switch

41 The warning switch is part of the handbrake switch and is removed with the switch.

Brake light switch

42 Refer to Chapter 9 Section 17.

Reversing light switch

43 Refer to Chapter 7A Section 6 for models fitted with manual transmissions. On models fitted with DSG transmissions, the switch is part of the selector mechanism.

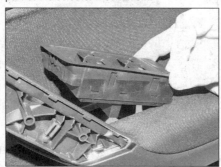

5.35b ...remove the switch panel

Courtesy light switches

44 The courtesy light switches are integrated into the door lock mechanisms and cannot be renewed independently. If the courtesy light switch is faulty, renew the door lock mechanism as described in Chapter 11 Section 13.

Luggage area light switch

45 The luggage compartment light switch is integrated into the tailgate lock mechanism, and cannot be renewed independently. If the luggage compartment light switch is faulty, renew the tailgate lock mechanism as described in Chapter 11 Section 16.

Interior monitoring deactivation switch

46 Carefully prise the switch from the B-pillar trim panel. Disconnect the wiring plug.
47 Refitting is a reversal of removal.

Rain and light sensor

48 The windscreen wipers/lights (depending on model) are automatically activated, when the sensor located in the interior mirror base detects droplets of water/darkness.
49 Unclip the outer cover and then slide up the inner cover.
50 Release the sensor and disconnect the wiring plug.
51 Refitting is a reversal of removal, but note that the windscreen must be thoroughly clean (or cleaned) before refitting the sensor.

5.38a Release...

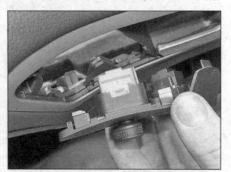

5.38b ...and remove the switch panel

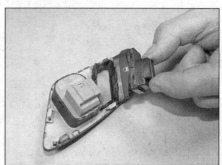

5.39 Remove the switches from the panel

6.2 Remove the cover

6.3a Remove the bulbholder

6.3b Remove the bulb from the bulbholder

6 Bulbs (exterior lights) – renewal

General

1 Whenever a bulb is renewed, note the following points:
a) *Switch off the ignition and all electrical consumers before commencing work.*
b) *Remember that if the light has just been in use the bulb may be extremely hot.*
c) *Always check the bulb contacts and holder, ensuring that there is clean metal-to-metal contact. Clean off any corrosion or dirt before fitting a new bulb.*
d) *Wherever bayonet-type bulbs are fitted ensure that the spring-tensioned arms bear firmly against the bulb contacts.*
e) *Always ensure that the new bulb is of the correct rating and that it is thoroughly clean before fitting it.*

Halogen headlight bulbs

Note: *The procedure for headlight bulb removal will vary, depending on the type of headlight fitted. For most models the easiest solution is to remove the appropriate front wheel (see 'Jacking and vehicle support') and then remove the wing liner. This will give access to the dipped beam and direction indicator. If working on the left-hand headlight, removing the screen washer reservoir filler neck improves access. The main beam and (daytime running/sidelight) bulb can be accessed from under the bonnet. Alternatively the headlight can be removed completely as described in Section 8.*

Headlight main beam

Note: *Do not touch the glass envelope of the bulb if it is to be re-used.*
Note: *The main beam bulb is also the daytime running light and sidelight.*

2 Open the bonnet and remove the cover from the rear of the headlight **(see illustration)**.
3 Reach inside the headlight, rotate the bulbholder and remove it complete with the the bulb. On the bench remove the bulb from the holder **(see illustrations)**.

4 When handling the new bulb, use a tissue or clean cloth to avoid touching the glass with the fingers; moisture and grease from the skin can cause blackening and rapid failure of this type of bulb. If the glass is accidentally touched, wipe it clean using methylated spirit.
5 Install the new bulb and refit the headlight cover.

Headlight dip beam

Note: *Do not touch the glass envelope of the bulb if it is to be re-used.*
6 Jack up and support the front of the vehicle. Remove the appropriate wheel and wing liner.
7 Reach up and remove the bulb cover. Rotate the bulbholder and remove the bulb. Remove the bulb from the holder **(see illustrations)**.

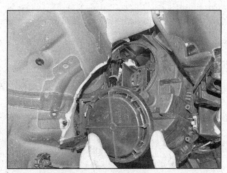

6.7a Remove the cover…

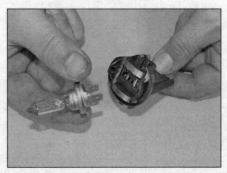

6.7c Remove the bulb

8 When handling the new bulb, use a tissue or clean cloth to avoid touching the glass with the fingers; moisture and grease from the skin can cause blackening and rapid failure of this type of bulb. If the glass is accidentally touched, wipe it clean using methylated spirit.
9 Fit the new bulb to the holder and then fit the bulbholder to the headlight.
10 Refit the headlight cover.

Front direction indicator

Note: *The direction indicator bulb is accessible after removing the appropriate wing liner.*
11 Reach up from the wheel arch and remove the cover **(see illustration)**. Note that access is restricted.
12 Turn the bulbholder anti-clockwise and

6.7b …and then remove the bulb with the bulbholder

6.11 Remove the cover

6.12 Remove the bulb and bulb holder

6.13 Remove the bulb

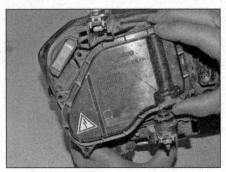

6.18 Remove the cover

6.19 Turn the bulb to remove it

6.20 Disconnect the wiring plug

remove it from the headlight complete with the bulb **(see illustration)**.

13 Pull the bulb to release it from the bulb holder **(see illustration)**.

14 Fit the new bulb to the bulb holder, then fit the bulb holder to the headlight and turn clockwise to secure.

Gas discharge headlights

 Warning: The headlight bulb contains gas at very high pressure, and it is recommended that gloves and eye protection be worn to prevent potential personal injury.

Note: *Do not touch the glass envelope of the bulb if it is to be re-used.*

15 Disconnect the battery as described in Chapter 5A Section 3 before proceeding.

16 Several versions of the gas discharge (Xenon) headlights are fitted to the range, but all use the same Bi-Xenon bulb. The bulb provides both main and dipped beam, with control either provided by a

mechanical shutter or by electronic control in conjunction with the cornering lights and LED lights.

Dipped/main beam

17 Remove the headlight as described in Section 8.

18 Remove the screws from the rear of the headlight and then remove the cover **(see illustration)**.

19 Turn the bulb anti-clockwise to remove it **(see illustration)**.

20 Pull out the bulb slightly, push down the retaining spring and disconnect the wiring plug **(see illustration)**.

21 When handling the new bulb, use a tissue or clean cloth to avoid touching the glass with the fingers; moisture and grease from the skin can cause blackening and rapid failure of this type of bulb. If the glass is accidentally touched, wipe it clean using methylated spirit.

22 Fit the new gas discharge bulb and wiring plug.

23 Refit the headlight cover and then refit the headlight.

Caution: After refitting a gas discharge headlamp, the basic setting of the Automatic Range Control system should be checked.

Daylight running (DLR) bulb

24 Remove the headlight as described in Section 8.

25 Remove the cover by turning it anti-clockwise and then pull the bulb straight out of the headlight. Note that access is difficult and the bulb is hidden above the cornering light bulb. Remove the bulb form the bulb holder.

26 Refitting is a reversal of removal.

Cornering light bulb

27 Remove the headlight (Section 8) and then remove the cover by turning it anti-clockwise.

28 Disconnect the wiring plug and push the bulb down to release it from the headlight. Remove the bulb **(see illustration)**.

29 Refitting is a reversal of removal.

Sidelight bulb

30 The DLR bulb performs the function of the sidelight on all gas discharge headlights.

Front direction indicator

31 Remove the headlight (Section 8) and then remove the cover by turning it anti-clockwise.

32 Remove the cover by turning it anti-clockwise.

33 Turn the bulb holder anti-clockwise to remove it – this is the bulb holder at the bottom of the headlight **(see illustration)**.

34 Remove the bulb from the bulb holder **(see illustration)**.

35 Refitting is a reversal of removal.

6.28 Remove the cornering light bulb

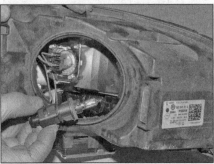

6.33 Rotate the bulb holder anti-clockwise to remove it

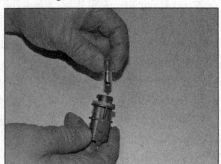

6.34 Remove the bulb

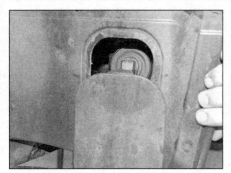

6.45 Remove the access panel

6.46a Disconnect the wiring plug...

6.46b ...and remove the bulb (shown with the wing liner removed for clarity)

LED Headlights

36 Some later models feature headlights that have no standard incandescent bulbs. All illumination is provide by LED type bulbs. Removal and refitting is similar to standard headlights. Note that the complete headlight does not need to be replaced if one of the LED modules fails.

37 Remove the headlight as described in Section 8.

38 If the lamps have not been replaced before then the covers must be broken free from the main body of the headlight. A break line is provided. Wearing suitable gloves, cut through the break line and remove the cover.

39 Release the wiring plugs, lift up the retaining clip and remove the LED module.

40 Replacement modules are supplied with a new rear cover, fixings and heat sink paste. Avoid skin contact with the paste – wear disposable gloves.

41 Apply the heat sink paste to the side contact surfaces of the new LED module and refit the module. Fit the retaining clip and reconnect the wiring plug.

42 Fit the new cover with the fixings supplied.

43 Refit the headlight as described in Section 8.

Front foglight

Note: *On some models the foglights have LED type bulbs. If the LEDs fail the complete lamp must be replaced.*

44 If not already done so, turn off the ignition and remove the vehicle key. Jack up and support the front of the vehicle (see *Jacking and vehicle support*). Either remove the appropriate front wheel or turn the steering to full lock.

45 Open the access panel **(see illustration)**.

46 Reach through the panel and disconnect the wiring plug. Rotate the bulbholder and remove the bulb **(see illustrations)**. The bulb and holder are a single item and replaced as such.

47 Fit the new bulb using a reversal of the removal procedure.

Direction indicator side repeater and approach light

48 The side repeater and approach lights are part of the door mirror. Both are LED style lamps and if faulty the complete lamp must replaced.

49 Remove the cover from the door mirror as described in Chapter 11 Section 18.

50 Disconnect the wiring plug, remove the screws and unclip the lamp. Remove the lamp **(see illustrations)**.

51 To remove the approach light, remove the mirror cover and mirror glass (as described in Chapter 11 Section 18) and then unclip the lamp from the housing **(see illustration)**. Disconnect the wiring plug.

Rear light cluster

Note: *Some models feature LED type lights in the rear lamps. If these fail the complete lamp must be replaced.*

Wing mounted lights

52 Remove the rear light cluster as described in Section 8.

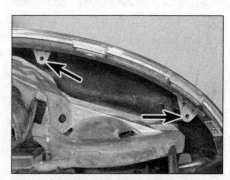

6.50a Remove the screws...

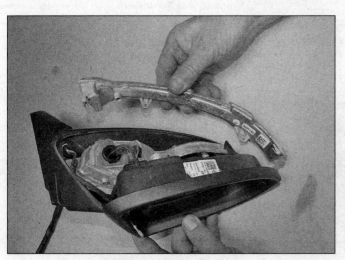

6.50b ...and lift out the lamp

6.51 Remove the approach lamp

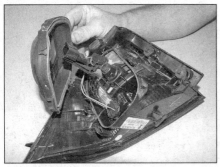

6.53a Remove the rear light cover...

6.53b ...and remove the relevant bulb

6.53c Remove the bulb from the holder

6.55 Open the cover

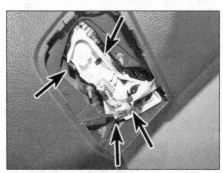

6.56a Release the locking tabs...

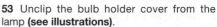

6.56b ...and remove the bulb holder
(shown with lamp removed for clarity)

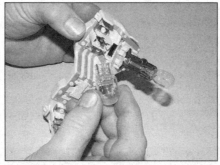

6.56c ...and remove the relevant bulb

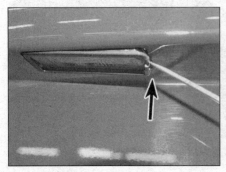

6.59 Remove the lamp

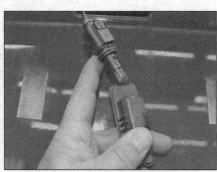

6.60a Remove the bulbholder and then...

6.60b ...remove the bulb

53 Unclip the bulb holder cover from the lamp (see illustrations).
54 Fit the new bulb using a reversal of the removal procedure.

Tailgate mounted lights

Note: *The tailgate lamp contains the rear side light and either the rear foglight or reversing light.*
55 Open the tailgate and remove the cover (see illustration).
56 Release the retaining clips and remove the bulb holder from the rear of the light unit. (see illustrations).
57 Fit the new bulb using a reversal of the removal procedure.

High-level brake light

Note: *The light is of LED design; therefore if faulty the complete unit must be renewed. Note that the LEDs are arranged in groups of four, and if just one group fails, the light still meets legal requirement. Failure of more than one group renders the light illegal.*
58 Remove the high-level light unit as described in Section 8.

Number plate light

59 Use a screwdriver and lever down the lamp (see illustration).
60 Remove the bulb holder and then remove the capless type bulb (see illustrations).
61 Fit the new bulb using a reversal of the removal procedure.

7.2 Remove the lens

7.3 Remove the bulb

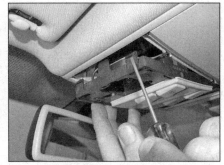
7.5 Unclip the lamp, lower it…

7.6 …and disconnect the wiring plugs

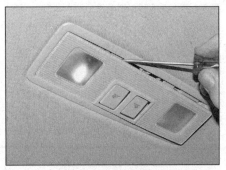
7.8a Unclip the lens…

7.8b …and remove it

7 Bulbs (interior lights) – renewal
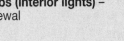

General

1 Whenever a bulb is renewed, note the following points:

a) Switch off the ignition and all electrical consumers before commencing work.

b) Remember that if the light has just been in use the bulb may be extremely hot.

c) Always check the bulb contacts and holder, ensuring that there is clean metal-to-metal contact between them. Clean off any corrosion or dirt before fitting a new bulb.

d) Wherever bayonet-type bulbs are fitted ensure that the live contact(s) bear firmly against the bulb contact.

e) Always ensure that the new bulb is of the correct rating and that it is completely clean before fitting it.

Front courtesy/reading light

Note: The design of the light varies according to the trim level and year of production. Removal for all variants is essentially the same procedure.

Note: Some models feature LED type lamps. If the light fails the complete lamp/lens must be replaced.

2 Using a small screwdriver, release the lens (see illustration).

3 Pull the wedge-type bulb from the contacts (see illustration).

4 Fit the new bulb(s) using a reversal of the removal procedure.

5 Unclip the lamp and lower it (see illustration).

6 Disconnect the wiring plugs (see illustration).

7 Refitting is a reversal of removal.

Rear courtesy/reading lights

Note: There are slight variation in the design of the rear light, depending on the year of production and if an anti-theft alarm system is fitted or not. Removal and refitting of the bulbs is essentially the same for all models.

8 Using a screwdriver, carefully release the locking lugs and remove the lens from the light unit (see illustrations).

9 Pull the wedge-type bulb from the light (see illustration).

10 If required remove the light unit by releaseing the two retaining clips and removing it from the headlining. Disconnect the wiring connector as it is removed (see illustrations).

11 Fit the new bulb and light unit using a reversal of the removal procedure.

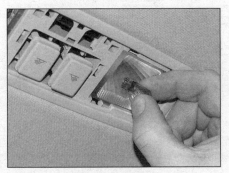
7.9 Pull out the bulb

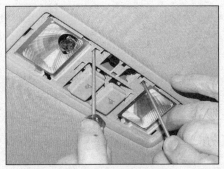
7.10a Release the locking tabs with a pair of small screwdrivers

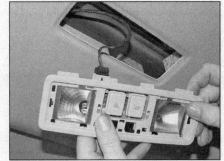
7.10b Remove the lamp

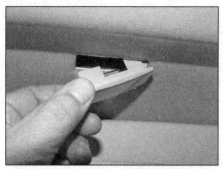

7.12a Prise out the vanity mirror light...

7.12b ...and remove the festoon-type bulb

7.17a Remove the lamp with a small
screwdriver...

7.17b ...and then remove the bulb

Vanity mirror lights

12 Carefully prise the light unit from its location in the headlining **(see illustrations)**. The festoon-type bulb is a push-fit in the spring contacts

13 Refitting is a reverse of the removal procedure.

Glovebox illumination light

14 Open the glovebox, then use a screwdriver to prise out the lens.

15 Disconnect the wiring plug and pull out the wedge-type bulb.

16 Fit the new bulb using a reversal of the removal procedure.

Luggage compartment light

17 Carefully prise the light unit from its location in the load area side panel **(see illustrations)**. The festoon-type bulb is a push-fit in the spring contacts.

18 Fit the new bulb using a reversal of the removal procedure.

Door entry light

19 Some models have an entry/warning light at the base of the door trim.

20 Prise off the cover complete with the lamp. Remove the wedge type bulb from the lamp.

21 Refitting is a reversal of removal.

Heater/ventilation control panel illumination

22 The control panel is illuminated by LEDs built into the panel. Consequently, if a fault develops, renewal of the panel is necessary.

Switch illumination

23 The switch illumination bulbs are integral with the switches. If a bulb fails, the complete switch must be renewed.

8 Exterior light units – removal and refitting

1 Before removing any light units, switch off the ignition and all electrical consumers, and then remove the ignition key.

Headlight

2 Remove the front bumper cover, as described in Chapter 11 Section 6. Note that if the bumper cover is fully protected, it is possible to remove the headlight by releasing the bumper cover at the appropriate side and then pulling the bumper away from the wing. With the aid of an assistant the headlight can be maneuvered past the bumper whilst the assistant manipulates the bumper out of the way.

3 Mark the position of the headlight mountings to ensure correct alignment on refitting

4 Remove the upper, lower and inboard mounting bolts **(see illustrations)**. If working on the left-hand headlight, unclip the bonnet release cable from the top cover.

8.4a Unbolt and then...

8.4b ...remove the top cover

8.4c Remove the front bolt...

8.4d ...and the side bolt

8.4e Slacken the rear bolt. There is no
need to remove it

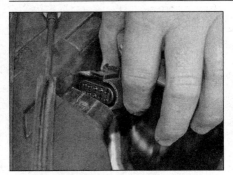

8.5a Disconnect the wiring plug...

8.5b ...and remove the headlight

8.12 Remove the wing liner

5 Pull the headlight forward and disconnect the wiring plug (see illustrations).

6 Refitting is a reversal of removal, but on completion, check that the headlight is aligned flush with the surrounding bodywork. If not, turn the eccentric adjustment bushing on the inside of the headlight as required. Finally, have the headlight alignment checked at the earliest opportunity.

Caution: After refitting a gas discharge headlamp, the basic setting of the Automatic Range Control system should be checked. Because of the requirement for specialised equipment, this can only be carried out by a Seat dealer or suitably equipped specialist. The headlight bulb contains gas at very high pressure, and it is recommended that gloves and eye protection be worn to prevent potential personal injury.

Gas discharge bulb control unit/ starter

7 Remove the headlight as described above.

8 Undo the retaining screws, and remove the control unit from the base of the headlight. Note that the electrical connections are automatically separated when the unit is removed.

9 Refitting is a reversal of removal.

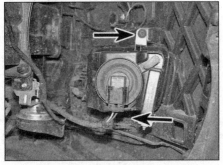

8.14 Remove the mounting bolts

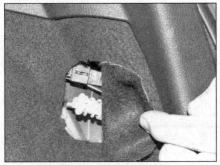

8.16 Open the access panel

Direction indicator side repeater

10 The lamp is removed as described in Section 6.

Front foglight

11 Jack up and support the front of the vehicle (see *Jacking and vehicle support*).

12 Remove the appropriate front wheel and then remove either the complete wing liner or the lower section (see illustration).

13 Disconnect the wiring plug.

14 Remove the mounting bolts and lift out the foglight (see illustration).

15 Refitting is a reversal of removal.

Rear wing mounted lights

16 Open the tailgate, and open the access panel (see illustration).

17 Reach through and remove the thumbwheel (see illustration).

18 Pull the lamp forward, disconnect the wiring plug and remove the lamp (see illustrations).

19 Refitting is a reversal of removal.

Tailgate mounted lights

20 Open the tailgate and then open the

8.17 Unscrew the thumb wheel (shown removed)

8.18a Pull the lamp out...

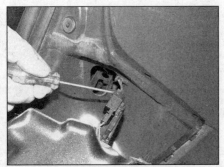

8.18b Release the safety catch and disconnect the wiring plug

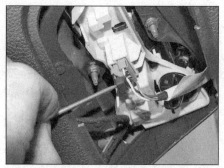
8.20a Release the safety catch...

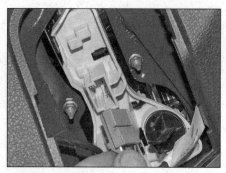
8.20b ...and disconnect the wiring plug

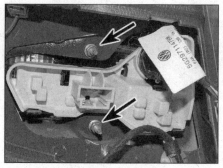
8.21a Remove the nuts...

8.21b ...and lift out the lamp

8.22a Lever out...

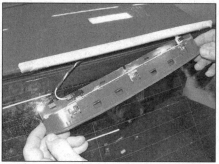
8.22b ...and remove the brake light

access panel. Disconnect the wiring plug **(see illustrations)**.

21 Unbolt the lamp and remove it **(see illustrations)**.

High level brake light

Note: *The light is of LED design; therefore if faulty the complete unit must be renewed. Note that the LEDs are arranged in groups of four, and if just one group fails, the light still meets legal requirement. Failure of more than one group renders the light illegal.*

22 Protect the top of the tailgate with masking tape and then using a broad trim tool lever out the lamp **(see illustrations)**.

23 Disconnect the screen washer hose and wiring plug **(see illustration)**.

8.23 Disconnect the screen washer hose

24 Fit the new light unit using a reversal of the removal procedure.

Rear number plate light

25 The procedure is described as part of the rear number plate light bulb renewal procedure in Section 6.

> **9** Headlight beam adjustment
> components – removal and
> refitting

Headlight adjustment switch

1 The switch is mounted in the same housing as the main lighting switch.

2 Removal and refitting of the switch assembly is covered in Section 5.

9.9 Release the control motor

Headlight range adjustment motor

Halogen headlights

3 Remove the headlight as described in Section 8.

4 Remove the cover from the rear of the headlight.

5 Rotate the motor clockwise (left-hand headlight) or anti-clockwise (right-hand headlight). Maintain tension on the motor and lower the height adjuster by turning it clockwise. Pull the motor downwards to remove it and disconnect the wiring plug.

6 Refitting is a reversal of removal, making sure the ball joint mounting is correctly located in the headlight reflector.

Gas discharge headlights (Xenon)

7 Remove the headlight as described in Section 8.

8 Unscrew the cover from the rear of the headlight.

9 Release the control motor by turning it clockwise (left-hand headlight) or anti-clockwise (right-hand headlight) **(see illustration)**.

10 Apply slight rearward tension to the motor and turn the height adjuster clockwise until the motor can be removed from the headlight.

11 Refitting is a reversal of removal, making sure the ball joint mounting is correctly located in the headlight reflector.

12 The automatic range adjustment should be checked with diagnostic equipment and adjusted as required. Consult a Volkswagen dealer or suitably equipped specialist.

11.2 Remove the lower panel

11.3 Remove the outer vent

11.4 Remove the panel

LED Headlight

13 Remove the headlight as described in Section 8.

14 Turn the adjustment screw at the top of the headlight fully anti-clockwise and then remove the bolt.

15 Remove the rear cover from the headlight and then remove the height adjuster and the operating shaft from below the adjuster.

16 Release the control motor by turning it clockwise (right-hand headlight) or anti-clockwise (left-hand headlight).

17 Lift up the motor and disconnect it from the ball/socket joint on the adjuster. Pull out the motor and disconnect the wiring plug.

18 Refitting is a reversal of removal, making sure the ball joint mounting is correctly located in the headlight reflector.

Automatic range control ECU

Note: *Although it is possible to remove and refit the ECU, the new unit will need to be coded before it will function correctly. This task can only be carried out by a Volkswagen dealer or suitably equipped specialist.*

19 The ECU is located behind the right-hand facia lower panel. Remove the panel as described in Chapter 11 Section 27.

20 Pull out the centre pins from the 'scrivets' and lower the module.

21 Release the locking lever and disconnect the wiring plug.

22 Refitting is a reversal of removal.

Vehicle level sender

23 Model fitted with gas discharge headlights (Xenon) have level sensors fitted to the front suspension arm and to the rear suspension. Removal and refitting is similar, regardless of the sensors location.

24 Chock the road wheels, then jack up the front (or rear) of the vehicle and support on axle stands (see *Jacking and vehicle support*). Remove the relevant wheel.

25 Disconnect the wiring plug and remove the upper mounting bolt. Remove the bolt from the lower suspension arm (front sensor) or the rear suspension trailing arm (or torsion beam on beam axle models). Remove the sensor.

26 Refitting is a reversal of removal, but note that the light leveling system will need calibrating using factory equipment.

10 Headlight beam alignment – general information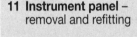

1 Accurate adjustment of the headlight beam is only possible using optical beam setting equipment and this work should be carried out by a Volkswagen dealer or suitably equipped workshop. All MOT stations will have this equipment.

2 For reference, the headlights can be manually adjusted using the adjuster assemblies fitted to the top of each light unit.

11 Instrument panel – removal and refitting

Removal

Note: *The instrument panel is a single complete unit. There are no replaceable parts fitted or available. If faulty it must be replaced. Note that the panel can not be simply swapped over from a donor vehicle as it contains firmware specific to the vehicle.*

1 Switch off the ignition and all electrical consumers and remove the ignition key. Release the steering wheel adjustment handle, pull the wheel out as far as possible, and set it in the lowest position. Note that the images show removal with the steering wheel removed for clarity, however the removal of the steering wheel is not essential.

2 Remove the steering column shrouds as described in Chapter 11 Section 25 and then remove the lower trim panel **(see illustration)**.

3 Remove the outer air distribution vent **(see illustration)** and then partially remove the central air distribution vents. Complete removal is not required (see Chapter 11 Section 27).

4 Unclip the instrument panel trim piece **(see illustration)**.

5 Remove the now exposed fixings **(see illustration)**.

6 Pull out the instrument panel and disconnect the wiring plug **(see illustrations)**. Remove the panel.

11.5 Remove the screws

11.6a Remove the panel...

11.6b ...and disconnect the wiring plug

Refitting

7 Refitting is a reversal of removal.

12 Service interval display – general information and resetting

1 All models are equipped with a Service Interval Display (SID). This is displayed on the information panel in the centre of the instrument panel. After all necessary maintenance work has been completed the SID should be reset.
2 Vehicles may be set to fixed or variable service intervals depending on the production number. It is possible to alter the service intervals using diagnostic equipment.
3 The reset procedure is part of routine maintenance as described in Chapter 1A Section 8 (petrol engines) or Chapter 1B Section 8 (diesel engines)

13 12v Power outlets – removal and refitting

Removal

Note: *A special tool is available that will allow the retaining sleeve of the power outlet to be easily removed (T40148). This is particularly useful on sockets that are illuminated.*
Note: *Several different versions are fitted throughout the range. Some have no illumination, some have a fixed non replaceable bulb, some have a replaceable bulb and others have a LED type bulb fitted. On the non-replaceable and LED versions the complete socket must be replaced if the bulb fails.*
1 Disconnect the battery (refer to Chapter 5A Section 3).
2 Remove the switch panel from the centre console as described in Chapter 11 Section 26.

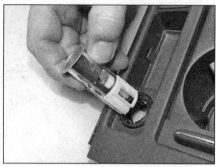
13.3a Remove the socket...

13.3b ...followed by the bezel

3 Release the retaining clips and push the centre element of the lighter out of the panel **(see illustrations)**. Note that without the special tool, considerable patience will be required to remove the socket.

Refitting

4 Refitting is a reversal of removal.

14 Horn – removal and refitting

Removal

1 Switch off the ignition and all electrical consumers and remove the ignition key.
2 Jack up and support the front of the vehicle (see *Jacking and vehicle support*). Remove the engine undershield and then release the front edge of the wing liner (or remove it completely). Twin horns are fitted, one at each side of the vehicle.
3 Reach up and disconnect the wiring plug and then unscrew the mounting bolt. Remove the horn together with the mounting bracket **(see illustration)**.
4 If required, unscrew the nut on the top of the horn to remove the bracket.

Refitting

5 Refitting is a reversal of removal.

15 Wiper arm – removal and refitting

Removal

1 Operate the wiper motor, then switch off so that the wiper arms return to the at-rest position. Alternatively, set the wiper blades to the service (vertical) position by turning on, then off the ignition and then operating the wiper single sweep function within 10 seconds of switching off the ignition. **Note:** *The wiper motor will only operate with the bonnet closed. If required, open the bonnet then use a screwdriver to close the bonnet catch.*
2 Use a piece of masking tape to the glass along the edge of the wiper blade to use as an alignment aid on refitting **(see illustration)**.
3 On the front wiper arms, prise off the wiper arm spindle nut cover, then slacken but do not completely remove the spindle nut. Lift the blade off the glass and carefully rock the wiper arm from side to side, until it releases

14.3 Disconnect the wiring plug

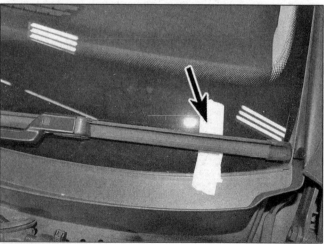
15.2 Mark the position of the blade on the glass

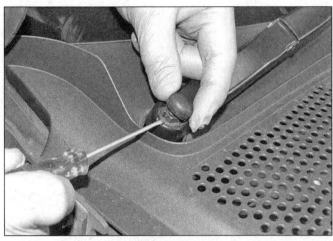

15.3a Remove the cover

15.3b Unscrew the spindle nut...

15.3c ...and remove the wiper arm

15.4a Lift up the cover and...

from the spindle. If necessary, use a small puller to release the arm from the spindle. Remove the spindle nut and the wiper arm **(see illustrations)**. Note: *If both windscreen wiper arms are to be removed at the same time mark them for identification; the arms are not interchangeable.*

4 On the rear wiper arms, unclip the spindle nut cover, then slacken but do not completely remove the spindle nut. Lift the blade off the

glass and carefully rock the wiper arm from side to side, until it releases from the spindle. Remove the spindle nut and wiper arm **(see illustrations)**.

5 If any of the arms are a tight fit on the spindle, the arm can be removed from the spindle using a small puller **(see illustration)**.

Refitting

6 Ensure that the wiper arm and spindle

splines are clean and dry, and then refit the arm to the spindle, aligning the wiper blade with the tape fitted on removal. Refit the spindle nut, tightening it securely, and clip the nut cover back in position.

Note: *Where the wipers were set to the service position in paragraph 1, they will only resume their normal position after actuating the wipers twice, or after starting a journey when the speed of the car is greater than 1 mph.*

15.4b ...remove the nut

15.5 Wiper arm pullers are available

16 Windscreen wiper motor and linkage – removal and refitting

Removal

1 Remove the wiper arms as described in Section 15.

2 Disconnect the battery (as described in Chapter 5A Section 3).

3 Pull off the rubber sealing strip from the plenum chamber cover. Remove the retaining

16.3a Remove the rubber seal...

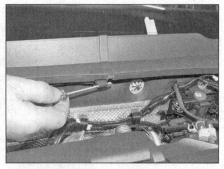

16.3b ...release...

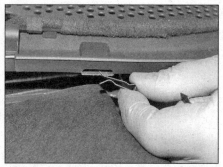

16.3c ...and remove the clips

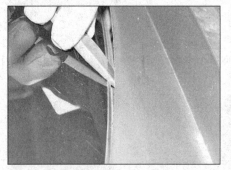

16.3d Work the panel free...

16.3e ...and remove it

16.4a Disconnect the wiring plug

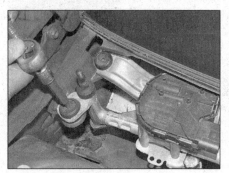

16.4b Remove the bolts...

16.4c ...and lift out the motor and linkage

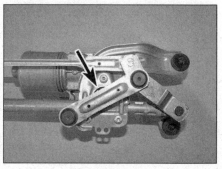

16.9 The crank arm (hidden) must be in line with the link rod

clips from the front of the cover and then remove the cover **(see illustrations)**. Note that the panel is a tight fit in the gutter at the base of the windscreen. Apply plenty of lubricant and slowly ease the panel free from the gutter. Release the screen washer hose as the panel is removed.

Caution: Do not use a screwdriver to lever between the cowling and windscreen, as this is likely to result in the windscreen cracking.

4 Disconnect the wiring plug, remove the bolts and lift out the wiper motor complete with the linkage **(see illustrations)**.

5 Where required, recover the washers and spacers from the motor mounting rubbers, noting their locations, then inspect the rubbers for signs of damage or deterioration, and renew if necessary.

6 If the motor requires replacement it can now be removed.

7 Lever off the link arm from the ball joints on the linkage and motor crank arm.

8 Unbolt the crank arm from the motor, remove the motor mounting bolts and remove the motor.

Refitting

9 Refitting is a reversal of removal, bearing in mind the following points.

a) When refitting the motor to the linkage the

17.3 Disconnect the wiring plug

motor crank arm must be fitted parallel with the link rod **(see illustration)**.

b) Ensure that the washers and spacers are fitted to the motor mounting rubbers as noted before removal.

c) Make sure the locating peg aligns with the grommet in the bulkhead, when refitting.

d) Refit the wiper arms as described in Section 15.

17 Rear wiper motor – removal and refitting

Removal

1 Remove the wiper arm as described in Section 15.

2 Open the tailgate, then remove the trim panel as described in Chapter 11 Section 15.

3 Release the locking clip and unplug the wiring connector from the motor **(see illustration)**.

4 Unscrew the three nuts securing the motor, and then withdraw the assembly **(see illustrations)**. Note the position of the rubber sealing ring and renew if necessary.

Refitting

5 Refitting is a reversal of removal, but ensure that the motor shaft rubber sealing ring/grommet is correctly refitted to prevent water leaks, and refit the wiper arm with reference to Section 15.

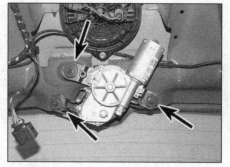
17.4a Remove the wiper motor securing nuts…

17.4b …and lift out the motor

18 Washer system components
– removal and refitting

Washer fluid reservoir

1 Switch off the ignition and all electrical consumers and remove the ignition key.
2 In the engine compartment, unclip the filler neck from above the headlight **(see illustration)**. On models with a headlight washer system, remove the bolt and lift the upper section of the reservoir away from the lower. Recover the seal. Note, that on models without headlight washers the filler neck and reservoir are designed as a single item – do not attempt to separate the neck form the reservoir.
3 Chock the rear wheels, then jack up the front of the vehicle and support it on axle stands (see *Jacking and vehicle support*). On models without headlight washers, remove the bumper cover as described in Chapter 11

Section 6. On models with headlight washers, remove the left-hand wheel and wing liner (there is no need to remove the bumper cover).
4 Disconnect the wiring plug from the washer pump (or pumps).
5 Note the position of the hoses, and then disconnect them from the washer pump. Position a suitable container beneath the reservoir to catch spilt fluid.
6 Where fitted, disconnect the wiring plug from the fluid level sender unit.
7 Release the retaining clips and disconnect the wiring loom from the side of the washer reservoir.
8 Remove the fixings then remove the reservoir from the vehicle **(see illustrations)**.
9 Refitting is a reversal of removal.

Washer fluid pump

10 Chock the rear wheels, then jack up the front of the vehicle and support it on axle stands (see *Jacking and vehicle support*).
11 Remove the left-hand wheel and wing liner. If working on a model with headlight washers remove the reservoir as described above.
12 Anticipate the loss off washer fluid by placing a large container beneath the pump and then disconnect the screen washer hoses **(see illustration)**.
13 Disconnect the wiring plug and then pull the pump(s) up and out of the reservoir **(see illustrations)**. Recover the sealing washer.

Windscreen washer jets

14 Open the bonnet, and unclip the washer

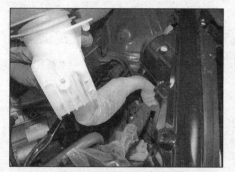
18.2 Unclip the filler neck

18.8a Remove the bolts…

18.8b …and remove the reservoir (model without headlight washers shown)

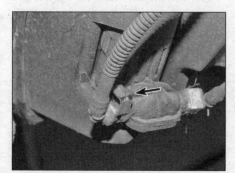
18.12 Lift up the locking clips to release the washer hose

18.13a Disconnect the wiring plug…

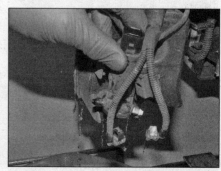
18.13b …and remove the washer pump

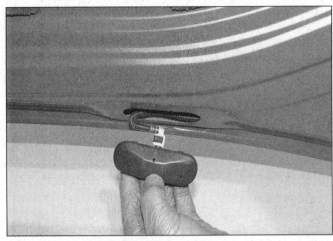

18.14a Unclip the washer jet...

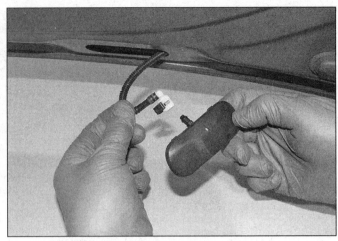

18.14b ...and disconnect the hose

18.22 The headlight washer jets are accessible form the rear

18.24 Remove the cylinder

jet. Release the securing clip and disconnect the washer tube (and wiring where applicable), then remove the washer jet (see illustrations).
15 If required the hose can be removed from the bonnet, by releasing the grommet and retaining clips.
16 Refitting is a reversal of removal. Note that the aim of the jet can be adjusted using a screwdriver and turning the eccentric shaft at the base of the washer jet.

Tailgate washer jet

17 Switch off the ignition and all electrical consumers and remove the ignition key.
18 Remove the high level brake light as described in Section 8.
19 Disconnect the washer jet from the brake light and then unclip the jet.
20 Refitting is a reversal of removal.

Headlight pop-up washer jet lift cylinder

21 Jack up and support the front of the vehicle – see *Jacking and vehicle support*.
22 Remove the wing liner and engine

undershield (see illustration). Place a container beneath the washer cylinder.
23 The aid of an assistant will now be required. If the washer system is functioning, have the assistant operate the washers and when the cylinder is extended the top cover can be removed. If the washers system is broken, then disconnect the fluid hose and use compressed air to lift the cylinder.
24 If not already done so, disconnect the screen washer hose. Reach up from below and release the cylinder locking clips (see illustration). Lower the cylinder from the bumper cover.
25 Refitting is a reversal of removal. Operate the washers several times to bleed any trapped air.

Headlight pop-up washer jets

26 Remove the pop-up cylinder as described above.
27 Depress the locking tabs and pull the jet out from the cylinder. Note that adjustment of the spray jet is not possible – they are preset during manufacture.
28 Refitting is a reversal of removal.

19 Audio unit –
removal and refitting

Note: *A variety of audio systems are fitted to the Golf range of vehicles. These range from a simple Radio/CD player through to an integrated navigation system (SatNav) and DVD player. The central display is the 'head' unit, with the main control module mounted in the glovebox. Some models have an additional amplifier mounted under the front left-hand seat. Steering wheel controls are fitted to most models. Models with SatNav and telephone integration also have a 'fishtail' roof mounted aerial. This Section only applies to standard-fit audio equipment.*

Head unit

Removal

1 Switch off the ignition and all electrical consumers, and remove the ignition key.

19.2 Remove the trim panel

19.3a Locate and then...

19.3b ...release the locking clips

19.3c Pull the head unit out from the fascia...

19.3d ...and disconnect the wiring plugs

19.7 The removal keys in position

2 Remove the trim panel as described in Chapter 11 Section 27 **(see illustration)**.
3 Release the locking clips at each corner of the unit, pull the head unit forward and disconnect the wiring plugs from the rear of the unit **(see illustrations)**.

Refitting

4 Refitting is a reversal of removal.

Control module/CD player

Removal

5 The control module (which is also the CD player and SD card player) is located in the glovebox. A set of removal keys will be required (T10057). These are widely available in the aftermarket.

6 Switch off the ignition and all electrical consumers, and remove the ignition key.
7 Open the glovebox and fit the removal keys **(see illustration)**.The pointed section of the keys should be to the outside.
8 With the keys locked in position, pull the unit forward, disconnecting the wiring plug(s) as the module is removed **(see illustrations)**.

Refitting

9 Refitting is a reversal of removal.

20 Loudspeakers – removal and refitting

1 Depending on the specification of the audio

unit fitted, speakers are fitted in a variety of locations:
● Front treble speakers – in A-pillar trims.
● Rear treble speakers – in door trim panels (5 door models) or rear side trim (3 door models).
● Rear bass speakers – in rear door trim panels (5 door models) or rear side trim (3 door models).
● Front bass speakers – in front doors.
● Subwoofer – in spare wheel well.
● Treble speakers
2 Switch off the ignition and all electrical consumers. Remove the ignition key.
3 To access the front treble speaker remove the A-pillar trim as described in Chapter 11 Section 25.

19.8a Release the module (aftermarket keys shown)...

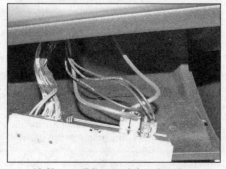

19.8b ...pull it out of the glovebox housing...

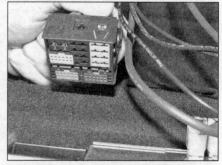

19.8c ...and disconnect the wiring plugs

20.4 The A-pillar mounted treble speaker

20.6 Drill out the pegs

20.10 Drill out the rivets

4 The speaker is bonded to the panel and if faulty the A-pillar panel must be replaced **(see illustration)**. Note that an aftermarket replacement that does not require panel replacement, maybe available.

5 To remove the rear treble speaker remove the door panel as described in Chapter 11 Section 12 (5 door models) or remove the side panel as described in Chapter 11 Section 25 (3 door models).

6 Disconnect the wiring plug. The speaker is held in place with heat melted pegs **(see illustration)**. Drill out the pegs and remove the speaker complete with the grille.

7 Refitting is a reversal of removal, but the replacement speaker must have the ends of the pegs melted to lock the speaker in place. An old soldering or hot air gun should be used, taking care not to damage the door (or trim) panel.

Front and rear bass speakers

8 Switch off the ignition and all electrical consumers, and remove the ignition key.

9 Remove the door trim panel as described in Chapter 11 Section 12. If working on the rear speaker of a 3 door model remove the rear side panel (Chapter 11 Section 25).

10 Disconnect the wiring plug from the loudspeaker, drill out the rivets **(see illustration)** and remove the speaker.

11 Refitting is a reversal of removal, but refit the speaker using new rivets.

Subwoofer

12 Switch off the ignition and all electrical consumers, and remove the ignition key.

13 Remove the load area floor and disconnect the wiring plug.

14 Remove the mounting bolt and lift out the subwoofer.

15 Refitting is a reversal of removal.

21 Aerials and filters – removal and refitting

Aerials

Roof mounted aerials

1 The aerial is mounted on the rear of the roof.

2 Partially lower the D-pillar panels as described in Chapter 11 Section 25.

3 Carefully lower the rear of the headlining, taking care not to damage it. Disconnect the wiring; note the fitted position of the wiring, as there may be more than one connector, depending on model.

4 Unscrew the securing nut and withdraw the aerial base from the roof. Hold the aerial base as the nut is being unscrewed to prevent the base from rotating and scratching the roof panel. Recover the rubber spacer.

5 Refitting is a reversal of removal, but make sure that the two guide lugs on the rubber spacer are correctly located in the aerial base.

Tailgate glass mounted aerial

6 The aerial is integrated into the tailgate glass. If faulty the glass must be replaced. This task is best left to a glazing specialist.

Amplifiers

7 The amplifiers and signal filters are mounted in the tailgate.

8 Remove the tailgate trim to access the amplifier.

9 Disconnect the wiring plug, remove the bolt and remove the amplifier from the tailgate.

10 Refitting is a reversal of removal.

22 Anti-theft alarm system and engine immobiliser – general information

Note: *This information is applicable only to the anti-theft alarm system fitted by VW as standard equipment.*

1 Models in the range are fitted with an anti-theft alarm system as standard equipment. The alarm has switches on all the doors (including the tailgate/boot lid), the bonnet and the ignition switch. If the tailgate, bonnet or any of the doors are opened whilst the alarm is set, the alarm horn will sound and the hazard warning lights will flash. Some models are equipped with an internal monitoring system, which will activate the alarm system if any movement in the cabin is detected.

2 The alarm is set using the key in the driver's or passenger's front door lock or with the central locking remote control transmitter.

The alarm system will then start to monitor its various switches approximately 30 seconds later.

3 All models are fitted with an immobiliser system, which is activated by the ignition switch. A transponder reading coil on the ignition switch reads a code contained within the ignition key. The system sends a signal to the engine management electronic control unit (ECU), which allows the engine to start if the code is correct. If an incorrect ignition key is used, the engine will not start.

4 If a fault is suspected with the alarm or immobiliser systems, the vehicle should be taken to a VW dealer for examination. They will have access to a special diagnostic tester that will quickly trace any fault present in the system.

23 Airbag system – general information and precautions

⚠ *Warning: Before carrying out any operations on the airbag system, disconnect the battery (Chapter 5A Section 3). When operations are complete, make sure no one is inside the vehicle when the battery is reconnected.*

⚠ *Warning: Note that the airbags must not be subjected to temperatures in excess of 90°C. When the airbag is removed, ensure that it is stored with the pad upwards to prevent possible inflation.*

⚠ *Warning: Do not allow any solvents or cleaning agents to contact the airbag assemblies. They must be cleaned using only a damp cloth.*

⚠ *Warning: The airbags and control unit are both sensitive to impact. If either is dropped or damaged they should be renewed.*

1 A driver's airbag, passengers airbag, side airbags and a knee airbag (driver's side only) are fitted as standard to the Golf range. Some models will also have rear side airbags fitted.

2 The airbag system is triggered in the event of a heavy frontal or side impact above a

24.6a One of the rear access points

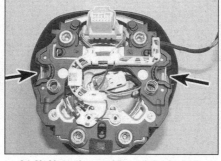

24.6b Note the position of the locking springs on the removed airbag

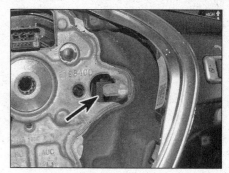

24.6c With the airbag removed, note the locking tabs on the steering wheel (one shown)

predetermined force, depending on the point of impact. The airbag is inflated within milliseconds and forms a safety cushion between the driver and the steering wheel, the passenger and the facia, and in the case of side impact, between front seat occupants and the sides of the cabin. This prevents contact between the upper body and cabin interior, and therefore greatly reduces the risk of injury. The airbag then deflates almost immediately.

3 Every time the ignition is switched on, the airbag control unit performs a self-test. The self-test takes approximately 3 seconds and during this time the airbag warning light on the facia is illuminated. After the self-test has been completed the warning light should go out. If the warning light fails to come on, remains illuminated after the initial 3-second period or comes on at any time when the vehicle is being driven, there is a fault in the airbag system. The vehicle should then be taken to a VW dealer or suitably equipped garage for examination at the earliest possible opportunity.

24 Airbag system components – removal and refitting

Note: *Refer to the warnings in Section 23 before carrying out the following operations.*
1 Disconnect the battery (refer to Chapter 5A Section 3) then continue as described under the relevant heading.
Caution: To prevent any discharge of static electricity into the airbag circuit, temporarily touch the vehicle bodywork before disconnecting the wiring from any airbag unit.

Driver's airbag

2 Set the front wheels to the straight-ahead position, and release the steering lock by inserting the ignition key.
3 Adjust the steering column to its lowest position by releasing the adjustment handle, then extend the steering wheel as far as possible. Lock the column in this position.
4 Remove the steering column upper trim as described in Chapter 11 Section 25.

5 Rotate the steering wheel so that one of the access holes in the rear of the steering wheel is in a convenient position.
6 Insert a torx head screwdriver (T25 is ideal) through the access hole and lift up the locking bar with the screwdriver **(see illustrations)**. Note that using a flat blade screwdriver may damage the wiring inside the steering wheel. Rotate the steering wheel to access the other hole and repeat the procedure.
7 Carefully withdraw the airbag module from the steering wheel, release the locking clip and disconnect the wiring connector **(see illustrations)**.

⚠️ *Warning: Position the airbag in a safe and secure place, away from the work area.*

8 When refitting make sure the steering wheel is in the straight-ahead position, then locate

the airbag module in position and reconnect the wiring. Carefully press in the module until both locking lugs are heard to engage. Reconnect the battery, ensuring that nobody is inside the vehicle as the lead is connected.

Passenger's airbag

9 Remove the passenger side glovebox with reference to Chapter 11 Section 25.
10 Release the locking clip and disconnect the wiring from the passenger's airbag **(see illustration)**.
11 Undo the mounting screws, then remove the airbag from under the facia **(see illustration)**.

⚠️ *Warning: Position the airbag in a safe and secure place, away from the work area.*

12 Refitting is a reversal of removal, but tighten the mounting screws to the specified

24.7a Release the locking tab and unplug the conector

24.7b Where fitted disconnect the wiring plugs from the steering wheels controls

24.10 Disconnect the wiring plug

24.11 The passenger airbag mounting screws

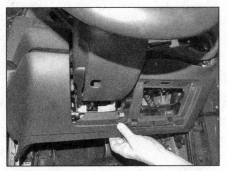

24.15 Remove the lower drivers side panel

24.16a Remove the bolts...

24.16b ...and disconnect the wiring plug as the airbag is lowered

torque. Reconnect the battery negative lead, ensuring that nobody is inside the vehicle as the lead is connected.

Front seat side impact airbags

13 The side impact air bags are integral with the seats. As seat upholstery removal requires considerable skill and experience, if it is to be carried out without damage, it is best entrusted to an expert.

Roof curtain and rear side airbags

14 This work involves removing the headlining and major dismantling of interior trim panels, and is best entrusted to a Volkswagen dealer.

Knee airbag

15 Remove the drivers side lower panel

as described in Chapter 11 Section 27 **(see illustration)**.
16 Remove the mounting bolts, lower the airbag and disconnect the wiring plug as the airbag is removed **(see illustrations)**.

Airbag control unit

17 The airbag control unit is located beneath the centre of the facia, under the heater housing **(see illustration)**.
18 Remove the trim from the passenger's side of the centre console with reference to Chapter 11 Section 26.
19 Remove the support bracket.
20 Release the locking lever and disconnect the wiring from the control unit.
21 Unscrew the nuts and remove the control unit from the vehicle.
22 Refitting is the reverse of removal

making sure the wiring connector is securely connected.

Airbag wiring contact unit

23 The airbag contact unit/clock spring is part of the steering column switch assembly, remove the contact unit as described in Section 5.

Passenger airbag on/ off switch

24 Remove the switch with reference to Section 5.

Crash sensors

25 Crash sensors are fitted to the front doors, the front bonnet slam panel and at the base of both C-pillars. Remove the appropriate trim panel (as described in Chapter 11 Section 25 for the rear sensors or the door trim panel as described in Chapter 11 Section 12 for the front sensors).
26 Disconnect the wiring plug from the crash sensor and then remove the fixings **(see illustrations)**.
27 To remove the front panel mounted sensor, remove the air filter housing (where necessary), disconnect the wiring plug and unbolt the sensor.
28 Refitting is a reversal of removal. Make sure that nobody is inside the vehicle when first switching on the ignition.

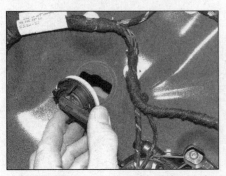

24.17 The control unit (shown with the heater housing removed)

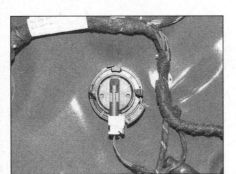

24.26a The front crash sensor

25 Parking aid components – general information, removal and refitting

General information

1 The parking aid system is available as a standard fitment on higher specification models, and optional on other models. Four ultrasound sensors are located in the rear and (where fitted) the front bumper. These measure the distance to the closest object behind or in front of the car, and inform the driver using acoustic signals from a warning buzzer. The nearer the object, the more frequent the acoustic signals.
2 The system includes a control unit and self-diagnosis program, and therefore, in the event of a fault, the vehicle should be taken to a Volkswagen dealer or suitably equipped garage.

24.26b Disconnect the wiring plug and rotate the sensor to remove it

24.26c The C-pillar sensor

25.5 The parking aid control module

25.9 The rear buzzer, fitted behind the right-hand panel

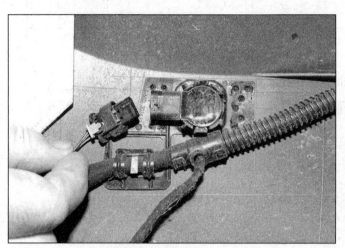

25.12 Disconnect the wiring plug...

25.13 and unclip the sensor

3 Switch off the ignition and all electrical consumers and remove the ignition key, before removing any electrical components.

Control unit

4 The parking aid control unit for the sensors is fitted next to the pedal assembly. Remove the drivers lower fascia panel **(see illustration 24.15)**.
5 Depress the locking lugs and disconnect the wiring plugs from the control unit **(see illustration)**.

6 Unclip the unit from the mounting bracket.
7 Refitting is a reversal of removal.

Warning buzzers

8 The warning buzzer for the front parking aid is fitted above the cabin fusebox. Lower the glovebox to access the buzzer.
9 The warning buzzer for the rear sensors is located behind the C-pillar trim. Remove the trim panel as described in Chapter 11 Section 25 for access **(see illustration)**.
10 Refitting is a reversal of removal.

Range/distance sensor

11 Remove the bumper cover as described in Chapter 11 Section 6 (front) or Chapter 11 Section 7 (rear).
12 Disconnect the wiring plug **(see illustration)**.
13 Remove the sensor **(see illustration)**.
14 Refitting is a reversal of removal. Press the sensor firmly into position until the retaining clips engage.

FUSE BOX IN ENGINE COMPARTMENT (SA)

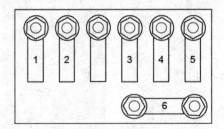

FUSE	VALUE	DESCRIPTION	OEM NAME
1	125 A	Supply for the fuses: SC2, SC4 - SC14, SC30 - SC42, SC47 - SC49, SC53, Terminal 15 voltage supply relay, Relay for power sockets, Starter relay 2	SA1
2	400 A	Alternator	SA2
3	80 A	Power steering control unit	SA3
4	80 A	Supply for fuses: SC15 - SC20, SC23 - SC28, SC43 - SC45	SA4
5	50 A	Radiator fan	SA5
6	125 A	Additional battery for coasting function or Not used	SA6

FUSE AND RELAY BOX IN ENGINE COMPARTMENT (SB)

VERSION 1

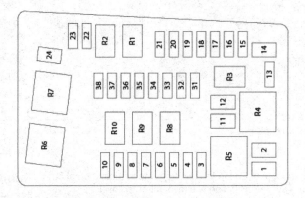

RELAY	VALUE	DESCRIPTION	OEM NAME
R1	-	Starter relay 1	R1
R2	-	Starter relay 2	R2
R3	-	Horn relay	R3
R4	-	High heat output relay (Only models with auxiliary air heater)	R4
R5	-	Main relay for Petrol engines or Terminal 30 voltage supply relay for Diesel engines	R5
R6	-	Automatic glow period control unit for Diesel engines	R6
R7	-	Low heat output relay (Only models with auxiliary air heater)	R7
R8	-	Fuel pump relay (Only for MPI petrol engine)	R8
R9	-	Not used	R9
R10	-	Not used	R10

Fuses and relays

VERSION 2

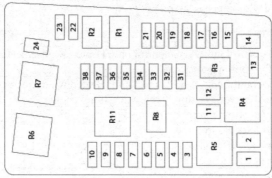

RELAY	VALUE	DESCRIPTION	OEM NAME
R1	-	Starter relay 1	R1
R2	-	Starter relay 2	R2
R3	-	Horn relay	R3
R4	-	High heat output relay (Only models with auxiliary air heater)	R4
R5	-	Main relay for Petrol engines or Terminal 30 voltage supply relay for Diesel engines	R5
R6	-	Automatic glow period control unit (Only models with Diesel engines)	R6
R7	-	Low heat output relay (Only models with auxiliary air heater)	R7
R8	-	Engine compartment current supply relay (According to equipment)	R8
R11	-	Heated windscreen relay (Only models with heated windscreen)	R11

FUSE	VALUE	DESCRIPTION	OEM NAME
1	40 A	ABS control unit, 20 A also used	SB1
2	60 A	ABS control unit, ABS hydraulic pump, 40 A also used	SB2
3	30 A	Engine control unit, 15 A also used	SB3
4	10 A	Oil level and oil temperature sender, Radiator fan control unit, Activated charcoal filter solenoid valve 1, 2, 3, Exhaust camshaft control valve 1, 2, 3, Valve for oil pressure control for Petrol engines	SB4
	5 A	Oil level and oil temperature sender, Radiator fan control unit, Exhaust gas recirculation cooler changeover valve, Low heat output relay, Charge pressure control solenoid valve for Diesel engines	
5	10 A	Fuel pressure regulating valve, Fuel metering valve for Diesel	SB5
6	5 A	Brake light switch	SB6
7	7.5 A	Fuel pressure regulating valve, Charge air cooling pump for Petrol engines	SB7
	10 A	Valve for oil pressure control, Solenoid valve for coolant circuit, Charge air cooling pump, Auxiliary pump for heating, Radiator blind control motor (According to equipment) for Diesel engines	
8	15 A	Lambda probe 1 before catalytic converter, Lambda probe 1 after catalytic converter, 10 A also used	SB8
9	20 A	Air mass meter, Ignition coils with output stage, Exhaust flap control unit, Sender 1 for secondary air pressure, Charge air cooling pump, Activated charcoal filter solenoid valve, Camshaft control valve 1, Exhaust camshaft control valve 1, 10 A also used for Petrol engines	SB9
	5 A	Air mass meter, Automatic glow period control unit, Heater element for crankcase breather for Diesel engines	
10	20 A	Fuel pump control unit, 10 A also used	SB10
11	40 A	Auxiliary air heater element	SB11
12	40 A	Auxiliary air heater element	SB12

Fuses and relays (continued)

13	30 A	Mechatronic unit for dual clutch gearbox	SB13
14	40 A	Heated windscreen relay or Not used	SB14
15	15 A	Horn relay	SB15
16	-	Not used	-
17	7.5 A	Engine control unit, ABS control unit, Heated windscreen control unit, Main relay for Petrol engines	SB17
		Engine control unit, ABS control unit, Heated windscreen control unit, Terminal 30 voltage supply relay for Diesel engines	
18	5 A	Battery monitor control unit, Data bus diagnostic interface	SB18
19	30 A	Wiper motor control unit	SB19
20	20 A	Alarm horn, 10 A also used	SB20
21	-	Not used	-
22	5 A	Engine control unit	SB22
23	30 A	Starter	SB23
24	40 A	Auxiliary air heater element	SB24
25	-	Not used	-
26	-	Not used	-
27	-	Not used	-
28	-	Not used	-
29	-	Not used	-
30	-	Not used	-
31	15 A	Vacuum pump for brakes, Vacuum pump relay or Not used	SB31
32	-	Not used	-
33	30 A	Auxiliary hydraulic pump 1 for gearbox oil	SB33
34	15 A	Axle differential lock control unit	**SB34**
35	-	Not used	-
36	-	Not used	-
37	20 A	Auxiliary heater control unit	SB37
38	-	Not used	-

Fuses and relays (continued)

FUSE AND RELAY BOX IN PASSENGER COMPARTMENT (SC)

FUSE/RELAY	VALUE	DESCRIPTION	OEM NAME
1	-	Not used	-
2	15 A	Steering column electronics control unit or Not used	SC2
3	-	Not used	-
4	10 A	Onboard supply control unit (Anti-theft alarm system)	SC4
5	5 A	Data bus diagnostic interface	SC5
6	5 A	Anti-theft alarm sensor or Selector lever	SC6
7	10 A	Heater and air conditioning controls, Heater control unit, Climatronic control unit, Air conditioning system control unit, Selector lever, Remote control receiver for auxiliary coolant heater, Heated rear window relay	SC7
8	10 A	Rotary light switch, Electromechanical parking brake button, Rain and light sensor, Diagnostic connection, Anti-theft alarm sensor	SC8
9	1 A	Steering column electronics control unit, 1 A also used or Not used	SC9
10	10 A	Display unit for front information display and operating unit control unit, Control unit for navigation system, TV tuner, CD player	SC10
11	25 A	Control unit for front belt tensioner or All-wheel drive control unit 15 A also used	SC11
12	20 A	Control unit 1 for information electronics, 5 A also used	SC12
13	15 A	Electronically controlled damping control unit	SC13
14	40 A	Fresh air blower control unit, 30 A also used	SC14
15	10 A	Control unit for electronics steering column lock	SC15
16	7.5 A	Two-way signal amplifier for mobile telephone / data services, Aerial amplifier 3, Voltage converter for USB charge module, USB hub, Chip card reader for Hatchback	SC16
		Two-way signal amplifier for mobile telephone / data services, Storage compartment with interface for mobile telephone, Chip card reader, Voltage converter for USB charge module, USB hub for Variant	
17	7.5 A	Control unit in dash panel insert, Dash panel insert and Emergency call module control unit and communication unit (According to equipment), 5 A also used	SC17
18	7.5 A	Reversing camera, Rear lid handle release button	SC18
19	7.5 A	Interface for entry and start system	SC19

Fuses and relays (continued)

20	7.5 A	Control unit for fuel tank leak detection, Relay for reducing agent metering system or Not used for Hatchback	SC20
		Relay for reducing agent metering system or Not used for Variant	
21	15 A	All-wheel drive control unit or Not used	SC21
22	15 A	Trailer detector control unit or Not used	SC22
23	40 A	Onboard supply control unit (Front right headlight)	SC23
24	30 A	Sliding sunroof adjustment control unit for Hatchback	SC24
		Sliding sunroof adjustment control unit, Sunroof roller blind control unit for Variant	
25	30 A	Driver control unit, Rear left door control unit for LHD or Front passenger door control unit, Rear right window regulator motor for RHD	SC25
26	30 A	Onboard supply control unit (Front seat heating)	SC26
27	30 A	Digital sound package control unit	SC27
28	20 A	Trailer detector control unit	SC28
29	-	Not used	-
30	25 A	Control unit for front left belt tensioner or Not used for Hatchback	SC30
		Control unit for front left belt tensioner, Terminal 15 relief relay or Not used for Variant	
31	40 A	Onboard supply control unit (Front left headlight)	SC31
32	10 A	Front camera for driver systems, Adaptive cruise control unit, Parking aid control unit, Park assist steering control unit, Blind spot monitor control units (according to equipment), 7.5 A also used	SC32
33	5 A	Airbag control unit, Front passenger side airbag deactivated warning lamp	SC33
34	7.5 A	Rotary light switch, Interior mirror, Relay for power sockets, Terminal 15 relief relay, Reversing light switch, Pressure sender for refrigerant circuit, Air quality sensor, TCS and ESP button, Electromechanical parking brake button for Hatchback	SC34
		Rotary light switch, Interior mirror, Relay for power sockets, Reversing light switch, Pressure sender for refrigerant circuit, Air quality sensor, Electromechanical parking brake button, DC/AC converter with socket 12 V, Terminal 15 relief relay, Switch module 1 in centre console for Variant	
35	10 A	Diagnostic connection, Headlight range control and instrument illumination regulator, Control unit for cornering light and headlight range control, Left and right headlight control motors	SC35
36	10 A	Front right headlight, 5 A also used	SC36
37	10 A	Front left headlight, 5 A also used	SC37
38	20 A	Trailer detector control unit	SC38
39	30 A	Driver control unit, Rear left door control unit for RHD or Front passenger door control unit, Rear right window regulator motor for LHD	SC39
40	20 A	Cigarette lighter, 12 V sockets	SC40
41	25 A	Control unit for right headlight belt tensioner or Steering column electronics control unit 1 A also used	SC41
42	40 A	Onboard supply control unit (Central locking)	SC42
43	30 A	Onboard supply control unit	SC43
44	15 A	Trailer detector control unit	SC44
45	15 A	Driver seat lumbar support adjustment switch, Driver seat adjustment operating unit	SC45
46	30 A	DC/AC converter with socket 12 V - 230 V or Not used	SC46
47	15 A	Rear window wiper motor	SC47
48	10 A	Engine sound generator control unit or Not used	SC48
49	5 A	Clutch position sender, Starter relay 1 and 2	SC49
50	-	Not used	-
51	25 A	Control unit for front right belt tensioner or Not used	SC51

Fuses and relays (continued)

52	-	Not used	SC52
53	30 A	Heated rear window relay	SC53
R1	-	Relay for reducing agent metering system or Not used	R1
R2	-	Terminal 15 relief relay	R2
R3	-	Not used	R3
R4	-	Terminal 15 voltage supply relay	R4
R5	-	Heated rear window relay	R5
R6	-	Relay for power sockets	R6

Fuses and relays (continued)

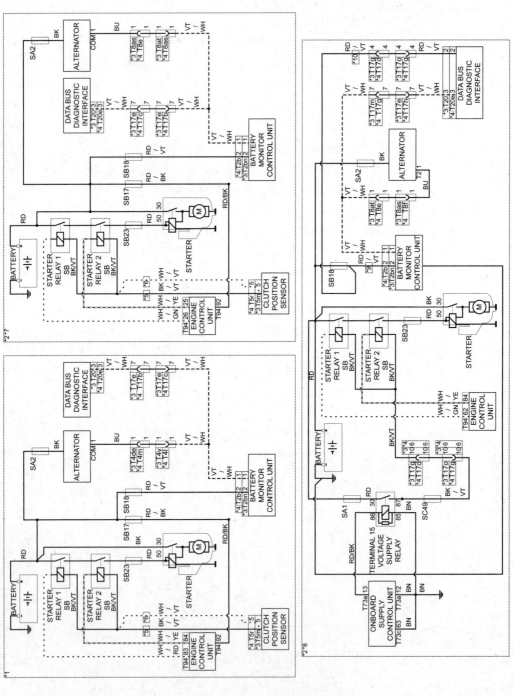

*1 Petrol engines
*2 Diesel engines
*3 Hatchback
*4 Variant
*5 Up to April 2014
*6 From May 2014
*7 Up to October 2014
*8 From November 2014
*9 With start / stop system
*10 Without start / stop system

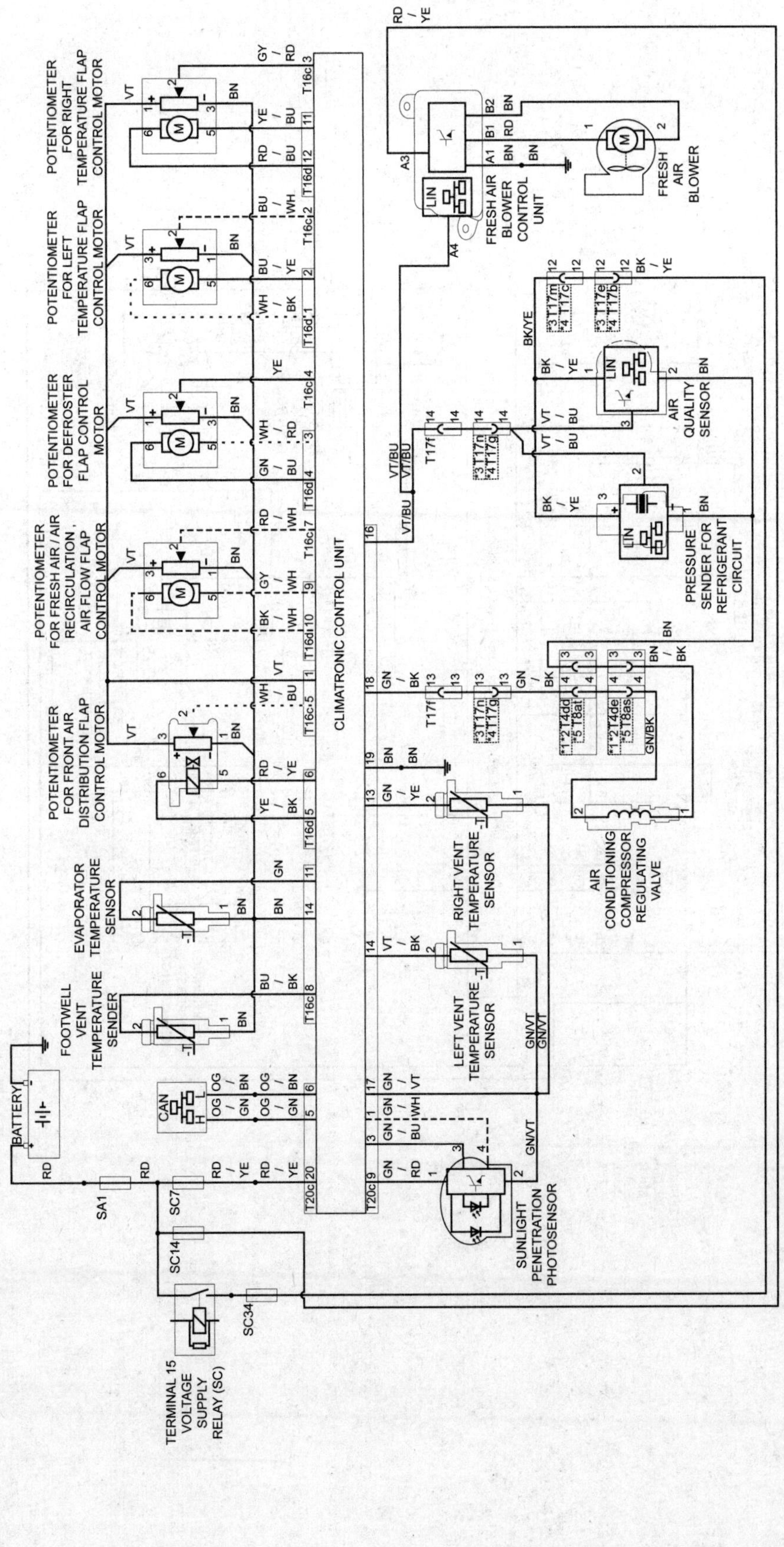

POTENTIOMETER FOR RIGHT TEMPERATURE FLAP CONTROL MOTOR

POTENTIOMETER FOR LEFT TEMPERATURE FLAP CONTROL MOTOR

POTENTIOMETER FOR DEFROSTER FLAP CONTROL MOTOR

POTENTIOMETER FOR FRESH AIR / AIR RECIRCULATION / AIR FLOW FLAP CONTROL MOTOR

POTENTIOMETER FOR FRONT AIR DISTRIBUTION FLAP CONTROL MOTOR

EVAPORATOR TEMPERATURE SENSOR

FOOTWELL VENT TEMPERATURE SENDER

BATTERY

CAN

TERMINAL 15 VOLTAGE SUPPLY RELAY (SC)

SA1   SC7   SC14   SC34

CLIMATRONIC CONTROL UNIT

FRESH AIR BLOWER CONTROL UNIT

FRESH AIR BLOWER

AIR QUALITY SENSOR

PRESSURE SENDER FOR REFRIGERANT CIRCUIT

AIR CONDITIONING COMPRESSOR REGULATING VALVE

RIGHT VENT TEMPERATURE SENSOR

LEFT VENT TEMPERATURE SENSOR

SUNLIGHT PENETRATION PHOTOSENSOR

Heating and cooling - Automatic air conditioning

*1 Only for 1.2 L engine
*2 Only for 1.4 L engine
*3 Hatchback
*4 Variant
*5 According to equipment to other engines

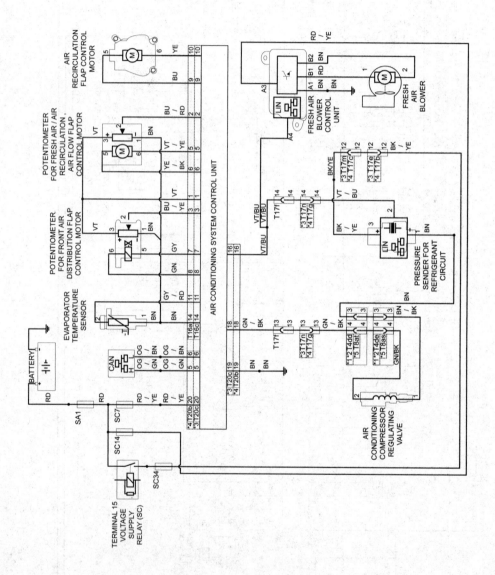

Heating and air conditioning - Manual air conditioning

*1 Only for 1.2 L engine
*2 Only for 1.4 L engine
*3 Hatchback
*4 Variant
*5 According to equipment to other engines

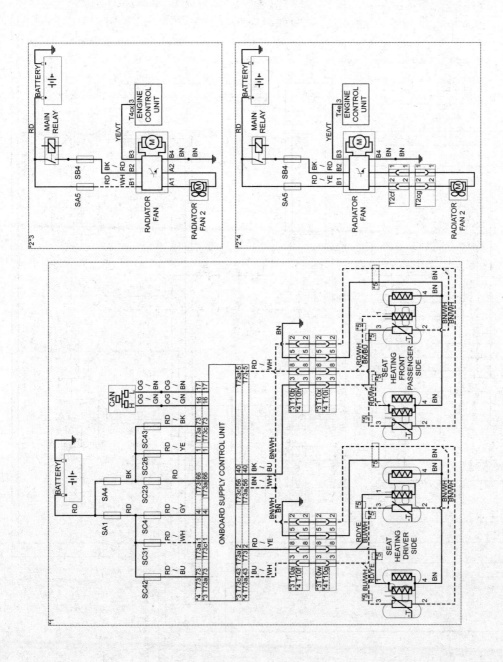

Heated seats and blower motor

*1 Heated seats
*2 Cooling fan
*3 Hatchback
*4 Variant
*5 According to equipment

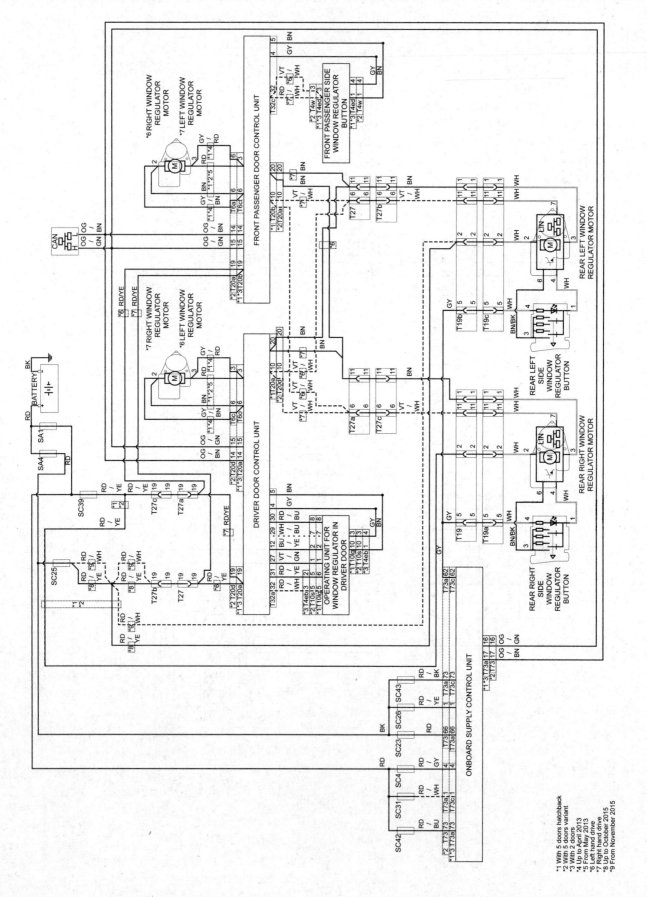

Power windows

*1 With 5 doors hatchback
*2 With 5 doors variant
*3 With 2 doors
*4 Up to April 2013
*5 From May 2013
*6 Left hand drive
*7 Right hand drive
*8 Up to October 2015
*9 From November 2015

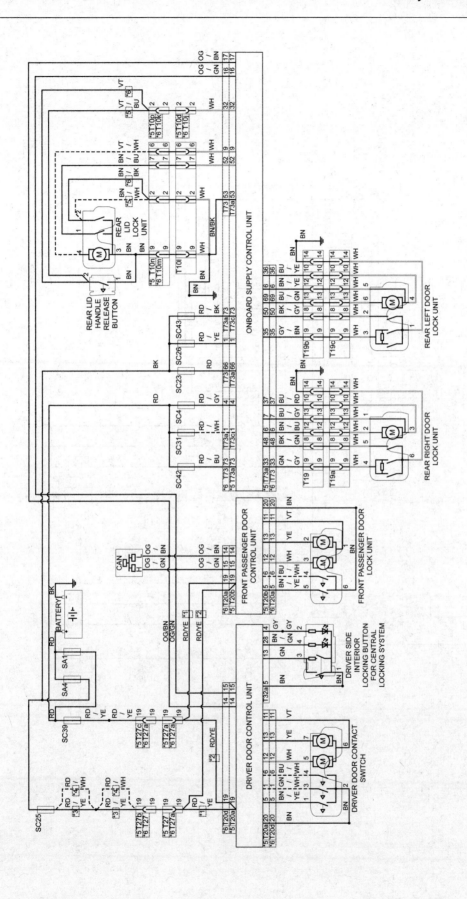

Central locking - not Keyless

*1 Left hand drive
*2 Right hand drive
*3 Up to October 2015
*4 From November 2015
*5 Hatchback
*6 Variant

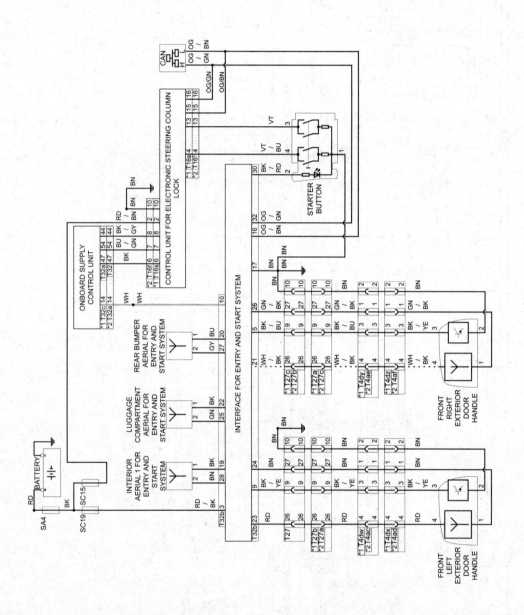

Central locking - Keyless

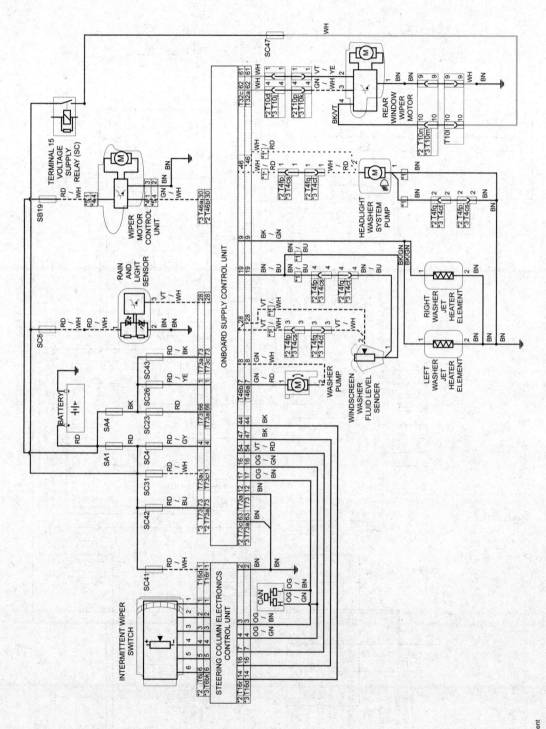

Washers and wipers

*1 According to equipment
*2 Hatchback
*3 Variant
*4 Left hand drive
*5 Right hand drive

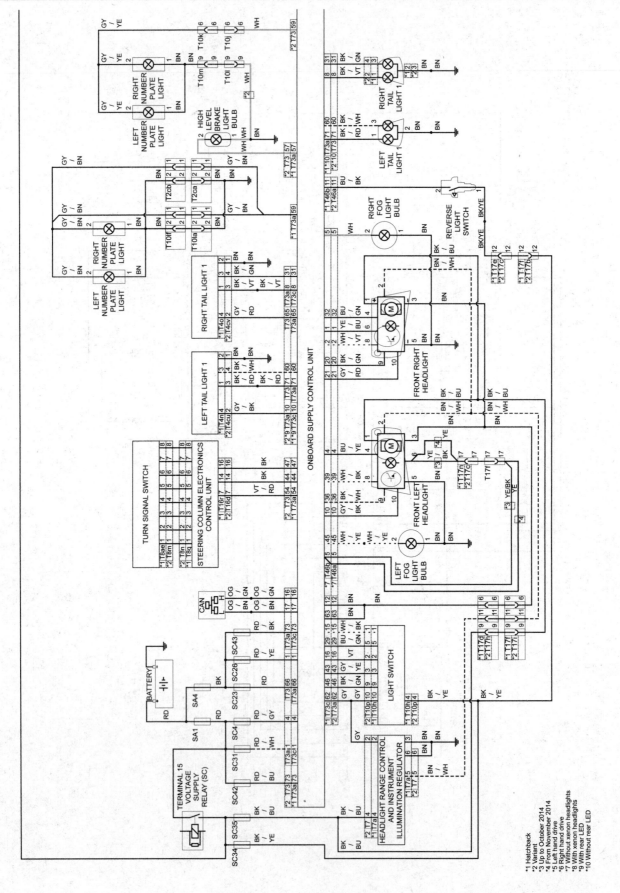

Exterior lighting - Part 1

*1 Hatchback
*2 Variant
*3 Up to October 2014
*4 From November 2014
*5 Left hand drive
*6 Right hand drive
*7 Without xenon headlights
*8 With xenon headlights
*9 With rear LED
*10 Without rear LED

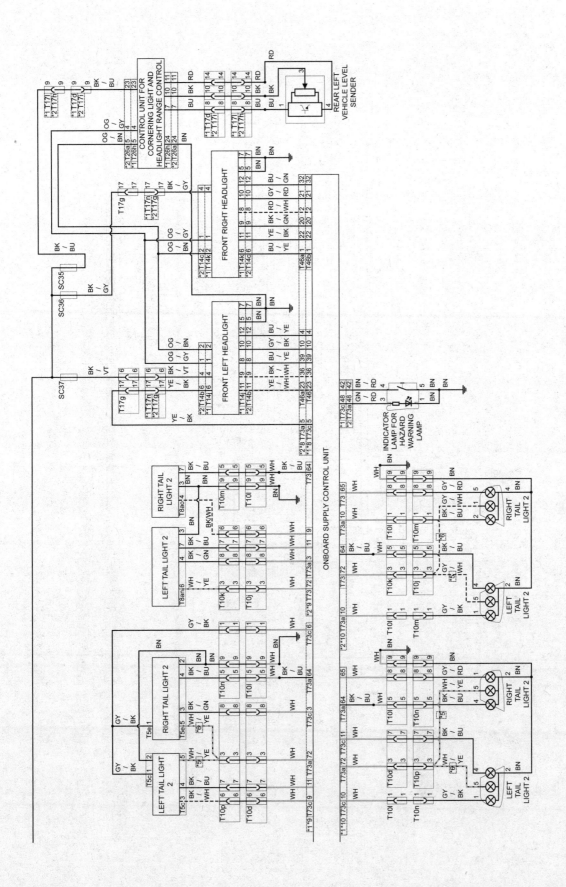

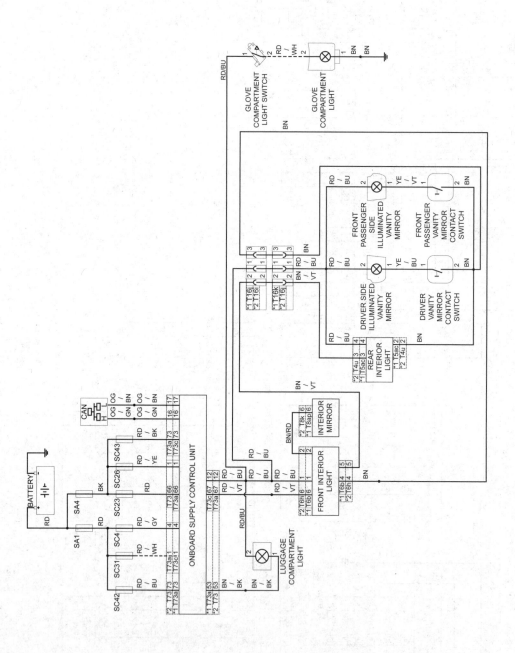

Interior lighting

*1 Hatchback
*2 Variant

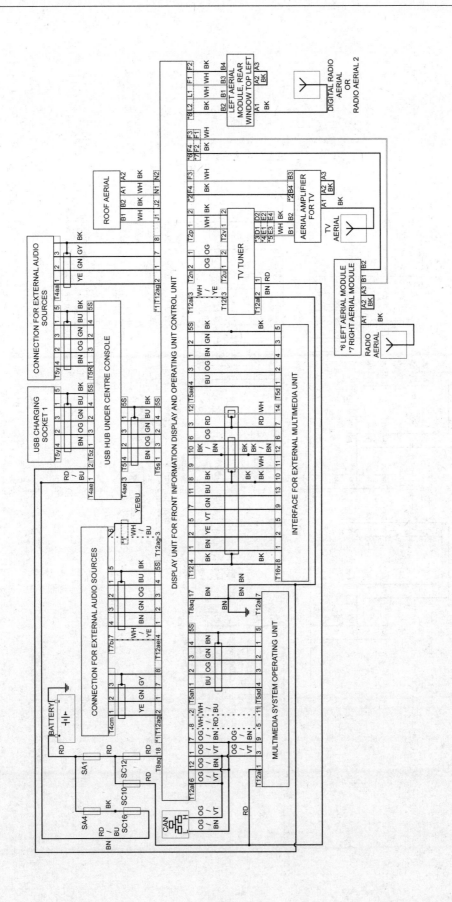

Sound system

*1 According to equipment
*2 Only models with TV tuner
*3 Aerial amplifier 1
*4 Aerial amplifier 2
*5 Aerial amplifier 3
*6 Only models without TV receiver
*7 Only models without digital audio
*8 Only models with digital audio

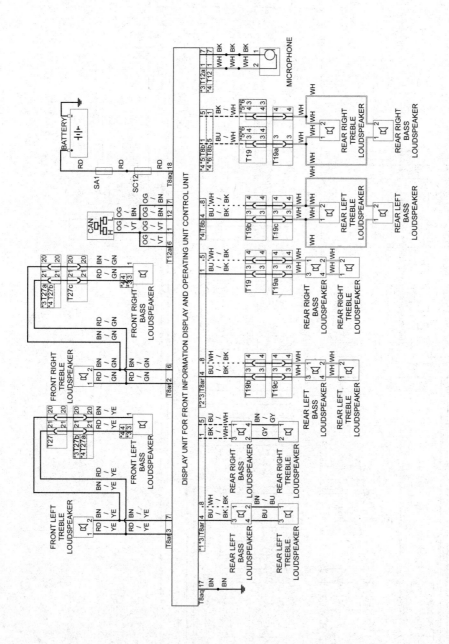

Speakers

*1 Only models with 2 doors
*2 Only models with 5 doors
*3 Hatchback
*4 Variant
*5 Up to April 2015
*6 From May 2015

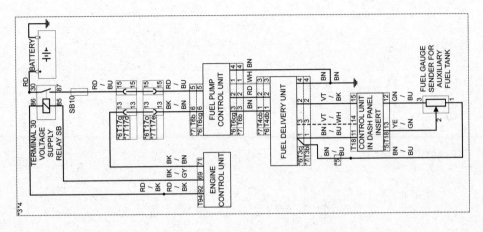

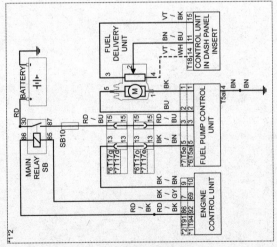

Fuel pump

*1 Engine: 1.2 L petrol, 1.4 L petrol
*2 Engine: 2.0 L petrol
*3 Engine: 1.6 L diesel
*4 Engine: 2.0 L diesel
*5 All-wheel drive models
*6 Hatchback
*7 Variant

Notes

Reference REF•1

Dimensions and weights . . . . **REF•1**
Conversion factors . . . . **REF•2**
Buying spare parts . . . . **REF•3**
Disconnecting the battery . . . . **REF•3**
General repair procedures . . . . **REF•4**
Vehicle identification numbers . . . . **REF•5**
Jacking and vehicle support . . . . **REF•5**
Tools and working facilities . . . . **REF•6**
MOT test checks . . . . **REF•8**
Fault finding . . . . **REF•12**
Index . . . . **REF•21**

Dimensions and weights

Note: *All figures and dimensions are approximate and may vary according to model. Refer to manufacturer's data for exact figures.*

Dimensions
Length . . . . 4255 mm
Width . . . . 1799 mm
Height . . . . 1452 mm
Wheelbase . . . . 2637 mm
Turning circle . . . . 10.9 M

Weights
Kerb weight . . . . 1130 kg
Maximum gross vehicle weight . . . . 1720 kg
Maximum roof rack load . . . . 75 kg

Towing weights

Maximum towing weights	Unbraked trailer	Braked trailer
Petrol engines	610 to 690 kg	1100 to 1600 kg
Diesel engines	640 to 690 kg	1000 to 1600 kg

Conversion factors

Length (distance)

Inches (in)	x 25.4	= Millimetres (mm)	x 0.0394	= Inches (in)
Feet (ft)	x 0.305	= Metres (m)	x 3.281	= Feet (ft)
Miles	x 1.609	= Kilometres (km)	x 0.621	= Miles

Volume (capacity)

Cubic inches (cu in; in^3)	x 16.387	= Cubic centimetres (cc; cm^3)	x 0.061	= Cubic inches (cu in; in^3)
Imperial pints (Imp pt)	x 0.568	= Litres (l)	x 1.76	= Imperial pints (Imp pt)
Imperial quarts (Imp qt)	x 1.137	= Litres (l)	x 0.88	= Imperial quarts (Imp qt)
Imperial quarts (Imp qt)	x 1.201	= US quarts (US qt)	x 0.833	= Imperial quarts (Imp qt)
US quarts (US qt)	x 0.946	= Litres (l)	x 1.057	= US quarts (US qt)
Imperial gallons (Imp gal)	x 4.546	= Litres (l)	x 0.22	= Imperial gallons (Imp gal)
Imperial gallons (Imp gal)	x 1.201	= US gallons (US gal)	x 0.833	= Imperial gallons (Imp gal)
US gallons (US gal)	x 3.785	= Litres (l)	x 0.264	= US gallons (US gal)

Mass (weight)

Ounces (oz)	x 28.35	= Grams (g)	x 0.035	= Ounces (oz)
Pounds (lb)	x 0.454	= Kilograms (kg)	x 2.205	= Pounds (lb)

Force

Ounces-force (ozf; oz)	x 0.278	= Newtons (N)	x 3.6	= Ounces-force (ozf; oz)
Pounds-force (lbf; lb)	x 4.448	= Newtons (N)	x 0.225	= Pounds-force (lbf; lb)
Newtons (N)	x 0.1	= Kilograms-force (kgf; kg)	x 9.81	= Newtons (N)

Pressure

Pounds-force per square inch (psi; lbf/in^2; lb/in^2)	x 0.070	= Kilograms-force per square centimetre (kgf/cm^2; kg/cm^2)	x 14.223	= Pounds-force per square inch (psi; lbf/in^2; lb/in^2)
Pounds-force per square inch (psi; lbf/in^2; lb/in^2)	x 0.068	= Atmospheres (atm)	x 14.696	= Pounds-force per square inch (psi; lbf/in^2; lb/in^2)
Pounds-force per square inch (psi; lbf/in^2; lb/in^2)	x 0.069	= Bars	x 14.5	= Pounds-force per square inch (psi; lbf/in^2; lb/in^2)
Pounds-force per square inch (psi; lbf/in^2; lb/in^2)	x 6.895	= Kilopascals (kPa)	x 0.145	= Pounds-force per square inch (psi; lbf/in^2; lb/in^2)
Kilopascals (kPa)	x 0.01	= Kilograms-force per square centimetre (kgf/cm^2; kg/cm^2)	x 98.1	= Kilopascals (kPa)
Millibar (mbar)	x 100	= Pascals (Pa)	x 0.01	= Millibar (mbar)
Millibar (mbar)	x 0.0145	= Pounds-force per square inch (psi; lbf/in^2; lb/in^2)	x 68.947	= Millibar (mbar)
Millibar (mbar)	x 0.75	= Millimetres of mercury (mmHg)	x 1.333	= Millibar (mbar)
Millibar (mbar)	x 0.401	= Inches of water (inH$_2$O)	x 2.491	= Millibar (mbar)
Millimetres of mercury (mmHg)	x 0.535	= Inches of water (inH$_2$O)	x 1.868	= Millimetres of mercury (mmHg)
Inches of water (inH$_2$O)	x 0.036	= Pounds-force per square inch (psi; lbf/in^2; lb/in^2)	x 27.68	= Inches of water (inH$_2$O)

Torque (moment of force)

Pounds-force inches (lbf in; lb in)	x 1.152	= Kilograms-force centimetre (kgf cm; kg cm)	x 0.868	= Pounds-force inches (lbf in; lb in)
Pounds-force inches (lbf in; lb in)	x 0.113	= Newton metres (Nm)	x 8.85	= Pounds-force inches (lbf in; lb in)
Pounds-force inches (lbf in; lb in)	x 0.083	= Pounds-force feet (lbf ft; lb ft)	x 12	= Pounds-force inches (lbf in; lb in)
Pounds-force feet (lbf ft; lb ft)	x 0.138	= Kilograms-force metres (kgf m; kg m)	x 7.233	= Pounds-force feet (lbf ft; lb ft)
Pounds-force feet (lbf ft; lb ft)	x 1.356	= Newton metres (Nm)	x 0.738	= Pounds-force feet (lbf ft; lb ft)
Newton metres (Nm)	x 0.102	= Kilograms-force metres (kgf m; kg m)	x 9.804	= Newton metres (Nm)

Power

Horsepower (hp)	x 745.7	= Watts (W)	x 0.0013	= Horsepower (hp)

Velocity (speed)

Miles per hour (miles/hr; mph)	x 1.609	= Kilometres per hour (km/hr; kph)	x 0.621	= Miles per hour (miles/hr; mph)

Fuel consumption*

Miles per gallon, Imperial (mpg)	x 0.354	= Kilometres per litre (km/l)	x 2.825	= Miles per gallon, Imperial (mpg)
Miles per gallon, US (mpg)	x 0.425	= Kilometres per litre (km/l)	x 2.352	= Miles per gallon, US (mpg)

Temperature

Degrees Fahrenheit = (°C x 1.8) + 32   Degrees Celsius (Degrees Centigrade; °C) = (°F - 32) x 0.56

It is common practice to convert from miles per gallon (mpg) to litres/100 kilometres (l/100km), where mpg x l/100 km = 282

Spare parts are available from many sources, including maker's appointed garages, accessory shops, and motor factors. To be sure of obtaining the correct parts, it will sometimes be necessary to quote the vehicle identification number. If possible, it can also be useful to take the old parts along for positive identification. Items such as starter motors and alternators may be available under a service exchange scheme – any parts returned should be clean.

Our advice regarding spare parts is as follows.

Officially appointed garages

This is the best source of parts which are peculiar to your car, and which are not otherwise generally available (eg, badges, interior trim, certain body panels, etc). It is also the only place at which you should buy parts if the car is still under warranty.

Accessory shops

These are very good places to buy materials and components needed for the maintenance of your car (oil, air and fuel filters, light bulbs, drivebelts, greases, brake pads, touch-up paint, etc). Components of this nature sold by a reputable shop are usually of the same standard as those used by the car manufacturer.

Besides components, these shops also sell tools and general accessories, usually have convenient opening hours, charge lower prices, and can often be found close to home. Some accessory shops have parts counters where components needed for almost any repair job can be purchased or ordered.

Motor factors

Good factors will stock all the more important components which wear out comparatively quickly, and can sometimes supply individual components needed for the overhaul of a larger assembly (eg, brake seals and hydraulic parts, bearing shells, pistons, valves). They may also handle work such as cylinder block reboring, crankshaft regrinding, etc.

Engine reconditioners

These specialise in engine overhaul and can also supply components. It is recommended that the establishment is a member of the Federation of Engine Re-Manufacturers, or a similar society.

Tyre and exhaust specialists

These outlets may be independent, or members of a local or national chain. They frequently offer competitive prices when compared with a main dealer or local garage, but it will pay to obtain several quotes before making a decision. When researching prices, also ask what extras may be added – for instance fitting a new valve, balancing the wheel and tyre disposal all both commonly charged on top of the price of a new tyre.

Other sources

Beware of parts or materials obtained from market stalls, car boot sales, on-line auctions or similar outlets. Such items are not invariably sub-standard, but there is little chance of compensation if they do prove unsatisfactory. In the case of safety-critical components such as brake pads, there is the risk not only of financial loss, but also of an accident causing injury or death.

Second-hand components or assemblies obtained from a car breaker can be a good buy in some circumstances, but this sort of purchase is best made by the experienced DIY mechanic.

Disconnecting the battery

Caution: After reconnecting the battery, the safety function of the electric windows will not be re-instated until the windows have been reprogrammed. This could potentially cause severe pinching injuries.
Several of the systems require battery power to be available at all times (permanent live). This is either to ensure their continued operation (such as the clock), or to maintain electronic memory settings which would otherwise be erased. Whenever the battery is to be disconnected, first note the following points, to ensure there are no unforeseen consequences:

a) *Firstly, on any vehicle with central door locking, it is a wise precaution to remove the key from the ignition, and to keep it with you. This avoids the possibility of the key being locked inside the car, should the central locking engage when the battery is reconnected.*

b) *If a security-coded audio unit is fitted, and the unit and/or the battery is disconnected, the unit will not function until the correct security code has been entered. Therefore, if you do not know the correct security code for the radio/ CD unit, do not disconnect either of the battery terminals, or remove the radio/ CD unit from the vehicle. The code appears on a code card supplied with the car when new. Details for entering*

the code appear in the vehicle handbook. Should the code have been misplaced or forgotten, on production of proof of ownership, a VW dealer or in-car entertainment specialist may be able to help.

c) *The engine management system ECU is of the 'self-learning' type, meaning that, as it operates, it adapts to changes in operating conditions, and stores the optimum settings found (this is especially true for idle speed settings). When the battery is disconnected, these 'learned' settings are lost, and the ECU reverts to the base factory settings. When the engine is restarted, it may idle and run roughly until the ECU has 'relearned' the best settings. To further this 'learning' process, take the car for a road test of at least 15 minutes' duration, covering as many engine speeds and loads as possible, and concentrating on the 2000 to 4000 rpm range. On completion, let the engine idle for at least 10 minutes, turning the steering wheel occasionally and switching on high-current-draw equipment such as the heater fan or heated rear window. If the engine does not regain its normal performance, have the system checked for faults by a VW dealer.*

d) *On vehicles equipped with an original*

equipment anti-theft alarm system, before disconnecting the battery, de-activate the alarm system, otherwise the alarm will be triggered.

e) *After the battery has been reconnected, the warning lights for the ESP and electro-mechanical steering will light up and stay on. They will extinguish if you drive briefly in a straight line at a speed of 9 to 13 mph.*

Devices known as 'memory-savers' or 'code-savers' can be used to avoid some of the above problems. Precise details of use vary according to the device used. Typically, it is plugged into the cigarette lighter socket, and is connected by its own wiring to a spare battery; the vehicle battery is then disconnected from the electrical system, leaving the memory-saver to pass sufficient current to maintain audio unit security codes, and other memory values, and also to run permanently-live circuits such as the clock.

⚠️ *Warning: Some of these devices allow a considerable amount of current to pass, which can mean that many of the vehicle's systems are still operational when the main battery is disconnected. If a memory-saver is used, ensure that the circuit concerned is actually 'dead' before carrying out any work on it.*

Whenever servicing, repair or overhaul work is carried out on the car or its components, observe the following procedures and instructions. This will assist in carrying out the operation efficiently and to a professional standard of workmanship.

Joint mating faces and gaskets

When separating components at their mating faces, never insert screwdrivers or similar implements into the joint between the faces in order to prise them apart. This can cause severe damage which results in oil leaks, coolant leaks, etc upon reassembly. Separation is usually achieved by tapping along the joint with a soft-faced hammer in order to break the seal. However, note that this method may not be suitable where dowels are used for component location.

Where a gasket is used between the mating faces of two components, a new one must be fitted on reassembly; fit it dry unless otherwise stated in the repair procedure. Make sure that the mating faces are clean and dry, with all traces of old gasket removed. When cleaning a joint face, use a tool which is unlikely to score or damage the face, and remove any burrs or nicks with an oilstone or fine file.

Make sure that tapped holes are cleaned with a pipe cleaner, and keep them free of jointing compound, if this is being used, unless specifically instructed otherwise.

Ensure that all orifices, channels or pipes are clear, and blow through them, preferably using compressed air.

Oil seals

Oil seals can be removed by levering them out with a wide flat-bladed screwdriver or similar implement. Alternatively, a number of self-tapping screws may be screwed into the seal, and these used as a purchase for pliers or some similar device in order to pull the seal free.

Whenever an oil seal is removed from its working location, either individually or as part of an assembly, it should be renewed.

The very fine sealing lip of the seal is easily damaged, and will not seal if the surface it contacts is not completely clean and free from scratches, nicks or grooves. If the original sealing surface of the component cannot be restored, and the manufacturer has not made provision for slight relocation of the seal relative to the sealing surface, the component should be renewed.

Protect the lips of the seal from any surface which may damage them in the course of fitting. Use tape or a conical sleeve where possible. Where indicated, lubricate the seal lips with oil before fitting and, on dual-lipped seals, fill the space between the lips with grease.

Unless otherwise stated, oil seals must be fitted with their sealing lips toward the lubricant to be sealed.

Use a tubular drift or block of wood of the appropriate size to install the seal and, if the seal housing is shouldered, drive the seal down to the shoulder. If the seal housing is unshouldered, the seal should be fitted with its face flush with the housing top face (unless otherwise instructed).

Screw threads and fastenings

Seized nuts, bolts and screws are quite a common occurrence where corrosion has set in, and the use of penetrating oil or releasing fluid will often overcome this problem if the offending item is soaked for a while before attempting to release it. The use of an impact driver may also provide a means of releasing such stubborn fastening devices, when used in conjunction with the appropriate screwdriver bit or socket. If none of these methods works, it may be necessary to resort to the careful application of heat, or the use of a hacksaw or nut splitter device. Before resorting to extreme methods, check that you are not dealing with a left-hand thread!

Studs are usually removed by locking two nuts together on the threaded part, and then using a spanner on the lower nut to unscrew the stud. Studs or bolts which have broken off below the surface of the component in which they are mounted can sometimes be removed using a stud extractor.

Always ensure that a blind tapped hole is completely free from oil, grease, water or other fluid before installing the bolt or stud. Failure to do this could cause the housing to crack due to the hydraulic action of the bolt or stud as it is screwed in.

For some screw fastenings, notably cylinder head bolts or nuts, torque wrench settings are no longer specified for the latter stages of tightening, "angle-tightening" being called up instead. Typically, a fairly low torque wrench setting will be applied to the bolts/nuts in the correct sequence, followed by one or more stages of tightening through specified angles.

When checking or retightening a nut or bolt to a specified torque setting, slacken the nut or bolt by a quarter of a turn, and then retighten to the specified setting. However, this should not be attempted where angular tightening has been used.

Locknuts, locktabs and washers

Any fastening which will rotate against a component or housing during tightening should always have a washer between it and the relevant component or housing.

Spring or split washers should always be renewed when they are used to lock a critical component such as a big-end bearing retaining bolt or nut. Locktabs which are folded over to retain a nut or bolt should always be renewed.

Self-locking nuts can be re-used in non-critical areas, providing resistance can be felt when the locking portion passes over the bolt or stud thread. However, it should be noted that self-locking stiffnuts tend to lose their effectiveness after long periods of use, and should then be renewed as a matter of course.

Split pins must always be replaced with new ones of the correct size for the hole.

When thread-locking compound is found on the threads of a fastener which is to be re-used, it should be cleaned off with a wire brush and solvent, and fresh compound applied on reassembly.

Special tools

Some repair procedures in this manual entail the use of special tools such as a press, two or three-legged pullers, spring compressors, etc. Wherever possible, suitable readily-available alternatives to the manufacturer's special tools are described, and are shown in use. In some instances, where no alternative is possible, it has been necessary to resort to the use of a manufacturer's tool, and this has been done for reasons of safety as well as the efficient completion of the repair operation. Unless you are highly-skilled and have a thorough understanding of the procedures described, never attempt to bypass the use of any special tool when the procedure described specifies its use. Not only is there a very great risk of personal injury, but expensive damage could be caused to the components involved.

Environmental considerations

When disposing of used engine oil, brake fluid, antifreeze, etc, give due consideration to any detrimental environmental effects. Do not, for instance, pour any of the above liquids down drains into the general sewage system, or onto the ground to soak away. Many local council refuse tips provide a facility for waste oil disposal, as do some garages. You can find your nearest disposal point by calling the Environment Agency on 08708 506 506 or by visiting www.oilbankline.org.uk.

Note: It is illegal and anti-social to dump oil down the drain. To find the location of your local oil recycling bank, call 08708 506 506 or visit www.oilbankline.org.uk.

Modifications are a continuing and unpublicised process in vehicle manufacture, quite apart from major model changes. Spare parts manuals and lists are compiled upon a numerical basis, the individual vehicle identification numbers being essential to correct identification of the component concerned.

When ordering spare parts, always give as much information as possible. Quote the car model, year of manufacture and registration, chassis and engine numbers as appropriate.

The Vehicle Identification Number (VIN) plate is visible from the outside of the vehicle, through the left-hand lower corner of the windscreen, and is also stamped on the top of the right-hand inner wing in the engine compartment (see illustrations).

The Vehicle Data Sticker is located in the below the tailgate slam panel. Removal of the slam panel will be required (see illustration). It contains the VIN, vehicle type, engine power, transmission type, engine and transmission codes, paint number, interior equipment, optional extras, and PR numbers (for maintenance schedule).

The Type plate and factory plate is located at the bottom of the front, left-hand door B-pillar, and is visible with the door open. It contains the gross vehicle weight, front axle weight and rear axle weight.

The Engine Number is stamped into the front left-hand end of the cylinder block, next to the engine-to-transmission joint. 2.0 litre petrol engines also have the engine number stamped into the block behind the oil filter. Additional identification stickers are located on the timing belt cover (see illustrations).

Engine codes

Petrol engines

1.2 litre	CJZA, CJZB and CYVA
1.4 litre	CPTA, CHPA, CMBA, CXSA, CPVA, CZEA and CZDA
2.0 litre	CHHA, CHHB, CJXE and CXDA

Diesel engines

1.6 litre	CLHA, CLHB, CRKA, CRKB, CXXA, CXXB and DBKA
2.0 litre	CKFC, CRBA, CRBC, CRLB, CRMB and CUNA

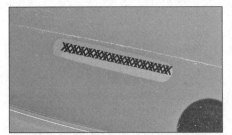

Vehicle Identification Number (VIN) located on the left-hand front edge of the windscreen

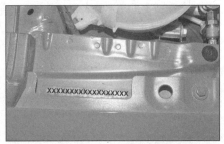

Vehicle Identification Number (VIN) located on the top of the right-hand inner wing

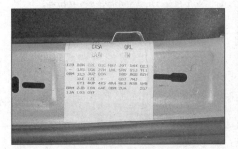

The data sticker, with details of the trim level, paint code etc

Engine code behind the oil filter on the 2.0 litre petrol engine

Engine code sticker on the top of the timing belt cover

Jacking and vehicle support

The jack supplied with the vehicle tool kit should only be used for changing the roadwheels – see Wheel changing at the front of this book. When carrying out any other kind of work, raise the vehicle using a hydraulic (or 'trolley') jack, and always supplement the jack with axle stands positioned under the vehicle jacking points.

When using a hydraulic jack or axle stands, always position the jack head or axle stand head under one of the relevant jacking points.

To raise the front and/or rear of the vehicle, use the jacking/support points at the front and rear ends of the door sills, indicated by the triangular depressions in the sill panel (see illustration). Position a block of wood with a groove cut in it on the jack head to prevent the vehicle weight resting on the sill edge; align the sill edge with the groove in the wood so that the vehicle weight is spread evenly over the surface of the block. Supplement the jack with axle stands (also with slotted blocks of wood) positioned as close as possible to the jacking points (see illustrations).

Do not jack the vehicle under any other part of the sill, sump, floor pan, or any of the steering or suspension components. With the vehicle raised, an axle stand should be positioned beneath the vehicle jack location point on the sill.

⚠️ *Warning:Never work under, around, or near a raised car, unless it is supported in at least two places.*

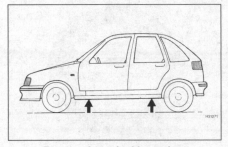

Front and rear jacking points

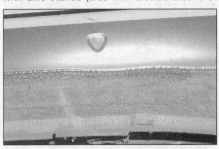

The jacking points are indicated by an arrow on the sill

Use an axle stand with a suitable block of wood

Introduction

A selection of good tools is a fundamental requirement for anyone contemplating the maintenance and repair of a motor vehicle. For the owner who does not possess any, their purchase will prove a considerable expense, offsetting some of the savings made by doing-it-yourself. However, provided that the tools purchased meet the relevant national safety standards and are of good quality, they will last for many years and prove an extremely worthwhile investment.

To help the average owner to decide which tools are needed to carry out the various tasks detailed in this manual, we have compiled three lists of tools under the following headings: *Maintenance and minor repair, Repair and overhaul,* and *Special.* Newcomers to practical mechanics should start off with the *Maintenance and minor repair* tool kit, and confine themselves to the simpler jobs around the vehicle. Then, as confidence and experience grow, more difficult tasks can be undertaken, with extra tools being purchased as, and when, they are needed. In this way, a *Maintenance and minor repair* tool kit can be built up into a *Repair and overhaul* tool kit over a considerable period of time, without any major cash outlays. The experienced do-it-yourselfer will have a tool kit good enough for most repair and overhaul procedures, and will add tools from the *Special* category when it is felt that the expense is justified by the amount of use to which these tools will be put.

Maintenance and minor repair tool kit

The tools given in this list should be considered as a minimum requirement if routine maintenance, servicing and minor repair operations are to be undertaken. We recommend the purchase of combination spanners (ring one end, open-ended the other); although more expensive than open-ended ones, they do give the advantages of both types of spanner.

- [ ] *Combination spanners:*
  Metric - 8 to 19 mm inclusive
- [ ] *Adjustable spanner - 35 mm jaw (approx.)*
- [ ] *Spark plug spanner (with rubber insert) - petrol models*
- [ ] *Spark plug gap adjustment tool - petrol models*
- [ ] *Set of feeler gauges*
- [ ] *Brake bleed nipple spanner*
- [ ] *Screwdrivers:*
  Flat blade - 100 mm long x 6 mm dia
  Cross blade - 100 mm long x 6 mm dia
  Torx - various sizes (not all vehicles)
- [ ] *Combination pliers*
- [ ] *Hacksaw (junior)*
- [ ] *Tyre pump*
- [ ] *Tyre pressure gauge*
- [ ] *Oil can*
- [ ] *Oil filter removal tool (if applicable)*
- [ ] *Fine emery cloth*
- [ ] *Wire brush (small)*
- [ ] *Funnel (medium size)*
- [ ] *Sump drain plug key (not all vehicles)*

Repair and overhaul tool kit

These tools are virtually essential for anyone undertaking any major repairs to a motor vehicle, and are additional to those given in the *Maintenance and minor repair* list. Included in this list is a comprehensive set of sockets. Although these are expensive, they will be found invaluable as they are so versatile - particularly if various drives are included in the set. We recommend the half-inch square-drive type, as this can be used with most proprietary torque wrenches.

The tools in this list will sometimes need to be supplemented by tools from the *Special* list:

- [ ] *Sockets to cover range in previous list (including Torx sockets)*
- [ ] *Reversible ratchet drive (for use with sockets)*
- [ ] *Extension piece, 250 mm (for use with sockets)*
- [ ] *Universal joint (for use with sockets)*
- [ ] *Flexible handle or sliding T "breaker bar" (for use with sockets)*
- [ ] *Torque wrench (for use with sockets)*
- [ ] *Self-locking grips*
- [ ] *Ball pein hammer*
- [ ] *Soft-faced mallet (plastic or rubber)*
- [ ] *Screwdrivers:*
  Flat blade - long & sturdy, short (chubby), and narrow (electrician's) types
  Cross blade – long & sturdy, and short (chubby) types
- [ ] *Pliers:*
  Long-nosed
  Side cutters (electrician's)
  Circlip (internal and external)
- [ ] *Cold chisel - 25 mm*
- [ ] *Scriber*
- [ ] *Scraper*
- [ ] *Centre-punch*
- [ ] *Pin punch*
- [ ] *Hacksaw*
- [ ] *Brake hose clamp*
- [ ] *Brake/clutch bleeding kit*
- [ ] *Selection of twist drills*
- [ ] *Steel rule/straight-edge*
- [ ] *Allen keys (inc. splined/Torx type)*
- [ ] *Selection of files*
- [ ] *Wire brush*
- [ ] *Axle stands*
- [ ] *Jack (strong trolley or hydraulic type)*
- [ ] *Light with extension lead*
- [ ] *Universal electrical multi-meter*

Sockets and reversible ratchet drive

Brake bleeding kit

Torx key, socket and bit

Hose clamp

Angular-tightening gauge

Special tools

The tools in this list are those which are not used regularly, are expensive to buy, or which need to be used in accordance with their manufacturers' instructions. Unless relatively difficult mechanical jobs are undertaken frequently, it will not be economic to buy many of these tools. Where this is the case, you could consider clubbing together with friends (or joining a motorists' club) to make a joint purchase, or borrowing the tools against a deposit from a local garage or tool hire specialist.

The following list contains only those tools and instruments freely available to the public, and not those special tools produced by the vehicle manufacturer specifically for its dealer network. You will find occasional references to these manufacturers' special tools in the text of this manual. Generally, an alternative method of doing the job without the vehicle manufacturers' special tool is given. However, sometimes there is no alternative to using them. Where this is the case and the relevant tool cannot be bought or borrowed, you will have to entrust the work to a dealer.

- [ ] *Angular-tightening gauge*
- [ ] *Valve spring compressor*
- [ ] *Valve grinding tool*
- [ ] *Piston ring compressor*
- [ ] *Piston ring removal/installation tool*
- [ ] *Cylinder bore hone*
- [ ] *Balljoint separator*
- [ ] *Coil spring compressors (where applicable)*
- [ ] *Two/three-legged hub and bearing puller*
- [ ] *Impact screwdriver*
- [ ] *Micrometer and/or vernier calipers*
- [ ] *Dial gauge*
- [ ] *Tachometer*
- [ ] *Fault code reader*
- [ ] *Cylinder compression gauge*
- [ ] *Hand-operated vacuum pump and gauge*
- [ ] *Clutch plate alignment set*
- [ ] *Brake shoe steady spring cup removal tool*
- [ ] *Bush and bearing removal/installation set*
- [ ] *Stud extractors*
- [ ] *Tap and die set*
- [ ] *Lifting tackle*

Buying tools

Reputable motor accessory shops and superstores often offer excellent quality tools at discount prices, so it pays to shop around.

Remember, you don't have to buy the most expensive items on the shelf, but it is always advisable to steer clear of the very cheap tools. Beware of 'bargains' offered on market stalls, on-line or at car boot sales. There are plenty of good tools around at reasonable prices, but always aim to purchase items which meet the relevant national safety standards. If in doubt, ask the proprietor or manager of the shop for advice before making a purchase.

Care and maintenance of tools

Having purchased a reasonable tool kit, it is necessary to keep the tools in a clean and serviceable condition. After use, always wipe off any dirt, grease and metal particles using a clean, dry cloth, before putting the tools away. Never leave them lying around after they have been used. A simple tool rack on the garage or workshop wall for items such as screwdrivers and pliers is a good idea. Store all normal spanners and sockets in a metal box. Any measuring instruments, gauges, meters, etc, must be carefully stored where they cannot be damaged or become rusty.

Take a little care when tools are used. Hammer heads inevitably become marked, and screwdrivers lose the keen edge on their blades from time to time. A little timely attention with emery cloth or a file will soon restore items like this to a good finish.

Working facilities

Not to be forgotten when discussing tools is the workshop itself. If anything more than routine maintenance is to be carried out, a suitable working area becomes essential.

It is appreciated that many an owner-mechanic is forced by circumstances to remove an engine or similar item without the benefit of a garage or workshop. Having done this, any repairs should always be done under the cover of a roof.

Wherever possible, any dismantling should be done on a clean, flat workbench or table at a suitable working height.

Any workbench needs a vice; one with a jaw opening of 100 mm is suitable for most jobs. As mentioned previously, some clean dry storage space is also required for tools, as well as for any lubricants, cleaning fluids, touch-up paints etc, which become necessary.

Another item which may be required, and which has a much more general usage, is an electric drill with a chuck capacity of at least 8 mm. This, together with a good range of twist drills, is virtually essential for fitting accessories.

Last, but not least, always keep a supply of old newspapers and clean, lint-free rags available, and try to keep any working area as clean as possible.

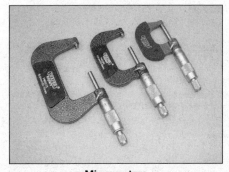

Micrometers

Dial test indicator ("dial gauge")

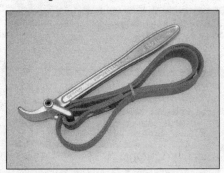

Oil filter removal tool (strap wrench type)

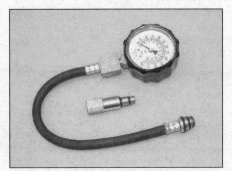

Compression tester

Bearing puller

This is a guide to getting your vehicle through the MOT test. Obviously it will not be possible to examine the vehicle to the same standard as the professional MOT tester. However, working through the following checks will enable you to identify any problem areas before submitting the vehicle for the test.

It has only been possible to summarise the test requirements here, based on the regulations in force at the time of printing. Test standards are becoming increasingly stringent, although there are some exemptions for older vehicles.

An assistant will be needed to help carry out some of these checks.

The checks have been sub-divided into four categories, as follows:

1 Checks carried out **FROM THE VEHICLE INTERIOR**

2 Checks carried out **WITH THE VEHICLE ON THE GROUND**

3 Checks carried out **WITH THE VEHICLE RAISED AND THE WHEELS FREE TO TURN**

4 Checks carried out on **YOUR VEHICLE'S EXHAUST EMISSION SYSTEM**

1 Checks carried out **FROM THE VEHICLE INTERIOR**

Handbrake (parking brake)

☐ Test the operation of the handbrake. Excessive travel (too many clicks) indicates incorrect brake or cable adjustment.

☐ Check that the handbrake cannot be released by tapping the lever sideways. Check the security of the lever mountings.

☐ If the parking brake is foot-operated, check that the pedal is secure and without excessive travel, and that the release mechanism operates correctly.

☐ Where applicable, test the operation of the electronic handbrake. The brake should engage and disengage without excessive delay. If the warning light does not extinguish, or a warning message is displayed when the brake is disengaged, this could indicate a fault which will need further investigation.

Footbrake

☐ Depress the brake pedal and check that it does not creep down to the floor, indicating a master cylinder fault. Release the pedal, wait a few seconds, then depress it again. If the pedal travels nearly to the floor before firm resistance is felt, brake adjustment or repair is necessary. If the pedal feels spongy, there is air in the hydraulic system which must be removed by bleeding.

☐ Check that the brake pedal is secure and in good condition. Check also for signs of fluid leaks on the pedal, floor or carpets, which would indicate failed seals in the brake master cylinder.

☐ Check the servo unit (when applicable) by operating the brake pedal several times, then keeping the pedal depressed and starting the engine. As the engine starts, the pedal will move down. If not, the vacuum hose or the servo itself may be faulty.

Steering wheel and column

☐ Examine the steering wheel for fractures or looseness of the hub, spokes or rim.

☐ Move the steering wheel from side to side and then up and down. Check that the steering wheel is not loose on the column, indicating wear or a loose retaining nut. Continue moving the steering wheel as before, but also turn it slightly from left to right.

☐ Check that the steering wheel is not loose on the column, and that there is no abnormal movement of the steering wheel, indicating wear in the column support bearings or couplings.

☐ Check that the ignition lock (where fitted) engages and disengages correctly.

☐ Steering column adjustment mechanisms (where fitted) must be able to lock the column securely in place with no play evident.

Windscreen, mirrors and sunvisor

☐ The windscreen must be free of cracks or other significant damage within the 'swept area' of the windscreen. This is the area swept by the windscreen wipers. A second test area, known as 'Zone A', is the part of the swept area 290 mm wide, centred on the steering wheel centre line. Any damage in Zone A that cannot be contained in a 10 mm diameter circle, or any damage in the remainder of the swept area that cannot be contained in a 40 mm diameter circle, may cause the vehicle to fail the test.

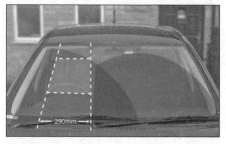
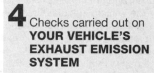

☐ Any items that may obscure the drivers view, such as stickers, sat-navs, anything hanging from the interior mirror, should be removed prior to the test.

☐ Vehicles registered after 1st August 1978 must have a drivers side mirror, and either an interior mirror, or a passenger's side mirror. Cameras (or indirect vision devices) may replace the mirrors, but they must function correctly.

☐ The driver's sunvisor must be capable of being stored in the "up" position.

Seat belts, seats and supplementary restraint systems (SRS)

Note: *The following checks are applicable to all seat belts, front and rear.*

☐ Examine the webbing of all the belts (including rear belts if fitted) for cuts, serious fraying or deterioration. Fasten and unfasten each belt to check the buckles. If applicable, check the retracting mechanism. Check the security of all seat belt mountings accessible from inside the vehicle, ensuring any height adjustable mountings lock securely in place.

☐ Where the seat belt is attached to a seat, the frame and mountings of the seat form part of the belt mountings, and are to be inspected as such.

☐ Any airbag, or SRS warning light must extinguish a few seconds after the ignition is switched on. Failure to do so indicates a fault which must be investigated.

☐ Seat belts with pre-tensioners, once activated, have a "flag" or similar showing on the seat belt stalk. This, in itself, is a reason for test failure.

☐ Check that the original airbag(s) is/are present, and not obviously defective.

☐ The seats themselves must be securely attached and the backrests must lock in the upright position. The driver's seat must also be able to slide forwards/rearwards, and lock in several positions.

Doors

☐ Both front doors must be able to be opened and closed from outside and inside, and must latch securely when closed.

☐ The rear doors must open from the outside.

☐ Examine all door hinges, catches and striker plates for missing, deteriorated, or insecure parts that could effect the opening and closing of the doors.

Speedometer

☐ The vehicle speedometer must be present, and appear operative. The figures on the speedometer must be legible, and illuminated when the lights are switched on.

2 Checks carried out WITH THE VEHICLE ON THE GROUND

Vehicle identification

☐ Number plates must be in good condition, secure and legible, with letters and numbers correctly spaced – spacing at (A) should be 33 mm and at (B) 11 mm. At the front, digits must be black on a white background and at the rear

black on a yellow background. Other background designs (such as honeycomb) are not permitted.

☐ The VIN plate and/or homologation plate must be permanently displayed and legible.

Electrical equipment

☐ Switch on the ignition and check the operation of the horn.

☐ Check the windscreen washers and wipers, examining the wiper blades; renew damaged or perished blades. The wiper blades must clear a large enough area of the windscreen to provide an 'adequate' view of the road, and be able to be parked in a position where they will not affect the drivers' view.

☐ On vehicles first used from 1st September 2009, the headlight washers (where fitted) must operate correctly.

☐ Check the operation of the stop-lights. This includes any lights that appear to be connected – Eg. high-level lights.

☐ Check the operation of the sidelights and number plate lights. The lenses and reflectors must be secure, clean and undamaged.

☐ Check the operation and alignment of the headlights. The headlight reflectors must not be tarnished and the lenses must be undamaged. Where plastic lenses are fitted, check they haven't deteriorated to the extent where they affect the light ouput or beam image. It's often possible to restore the plastic lens using a suitable polish or aftermarket treatment.

☐ Where HID or LED headlights are fitted, check the operation of the cleaning and self-levelling functions.

☐ The headlight main beam warning lamp must be functional.

☐ On vehicles first used from 1st March 2018, the daytime running lights (where fitted) must operate correctly.

☐ Switch on the ignition and check the operation of the direction indicators (including the instrument panel tell-tale) and the hazard warning lights. Operation of the sidelights and stop-lights must not affect the indicators – if it does, the cause is usually a bad earth at the rear light cluster. Indicators should flash at a rate of between 60 and 120 times per minute – faster or slower than this could indicate a fault with the flasher unit or a bad earth at one of the light units.

☐ The hazard warning lights must operate with the ignition on and off.

☐ Check the operation of the rear foglight(s), including the warning light on the instrument panel or in the switch. Note that the foglight

must be positioned in the centre or driver's side of the vehicle. If only the passenger's side illuminates, the test will fail.

☐ The warning lights must illuminate in accordance with the manufacturers' design (this includes any warning messages). For most vehicles, the ABS and other warning lights should illuminate when the ignition is switched on, and (if the system is operating properly) extinguish after a few seconds. Refer to the owner's handbook.

☐ On vehicles first used from 1st September 2009, the reversing lights must operate correctly when reverse gear is selected.

☐ Check the vehicle battery for security and leakage.

☐ Check the visible/accessible vehicle wiring is adequately supported, with no evidence of damage or deterioration that could result in a short-circuit.

Footbrake

☐ Examine the master cylinder, brake pipes and servo unit for leaks, loose mountings, corrosion or other damage. If ABS is fitted, this unit should also be examined for signs of leaks or corrosion.

☐ The fluid reservoir must be secure and the fluid level must be between the upper (A) and lower (B) markings.

☐ Check the fluid in the reservoir for signs of contamination.

☐ Inspect both front brake flexible hoses for cracks or deterioration of the rubber. Turn the steering from lock to lock, and ensure that the hoses do not contact the wheel, tyre, or any part of the steering or suspension mechanism. With the brake pedal firmly depressed, check the hoses for bulges or leaks under pressure.

Steering and suspension

☐ Have your assistant turn the steering wheel from side to side slightly, up to the point where the steering gear just begins to transmit this movement to the roadwheels. Check for excessive free play between the steering wheel and the steering gear, indicating wear or insecurity of the steering column joints, the column-to-steering gear coupling, or the steering gear itself. With a standard (380 mm diameter) steering wheel, there should be no more than 13 mm of free play for rack-and-pinion systems, and no more than 75 mm for non-rack-and-pinion designs.

☐ Have your assistant turn the steering

wheel more vigorously in each direction, so that the roadwheels just begin to turn. As this is done, examine all the steering joints, linkages, fittings and attachments. Renew any component that shows signs of wear or damage. On vehicles with hydraulic power steering, check the security and condition of the steering pump, drivebelt and hoses.

☐ Note that all movement checks on power steering systems are carried out with the engine running.

☐ Check that the vehicle is standing level, and at approximately the correct ride height.

Exhaust system

☐ Start the engine. With your assistant holding a rag over the tailpipe, check the entire system for leaks. Repair or renew leaking sections.

3 Checks carried out
WITH THE VEHICLE RAISED AND THE WHEELS FREE TO TURN

Jack up the front and rear of the vehicle, and securely support it on axle stands. Position the stands clear of the suspension assemblies. Ensure that the wheels are clear of the ground and that the steering can be turned from lock to lock.

Steering mechanism

☐ Have your assistant turn the steering from lock to lock. Check that the steering turns smoothly, and that no part of the steering mechanism, including a wheel or tyre, fouls any brake hose or pipe or any part of the body structure.

☐ Examine the steering rack rubber gaiters for damage or insecurity of the retaining clips. If power steering is fitted, check for signs of damage or leakage of the fluid hoses, pipes or connections. Also check for excessive stiffness or binding of the steering, a missing split pin or locking device, or severe corrosion of the body structure within 30 cm of any steering component attachment point.

☐ Check the track rod end ball joint dust covers. Any covers that are missing, seriously damaged, deteriorated or insecure, may fail inspection.

Front and rear suspension and wheel bearings

☐ Starting at the front right-hand side, grasp the roadwheel at the 3 o'clock and 9 o'clock positions and rock gently but firmly. Check for free play or insecurity at the wheel bearings, suspension balljoints, or suspension mountings, pivots and attachments.

☐ Now grasp the wheel at the 12 o'clock and 6 o'clock positions and repeat the previous inspection. Spin the wheel, and check for roughness or tightness of the front wheel bearing.

☐ If excess free play is suspected at a component pivot point, this can be confirmed by using a large screwdriver or similar tool and levering between the mounting and the component attachment. This will confirm whether the wear is in the pivot bush, its retaining bolt, or in the mounting itself (the bolt holes can often become elongated).

☐ Carry out all the above checks at the other front wheel, and then at both rear wheels.

Springs and shock absorbers

☐ Examine the suspension struts (when applicable) for serious fluid leakage, corrosion, or damage to the casing. Also check the security of the mounting points.

☐ If coil springs are fitted, check that the spring ends locate in their seats, and that the spring is not corroded, cracked or broken.

☐ If leaf springs are fitted, check that all leaves are intact, that the axle is securely attached to each spring, and that there is no deterioration of the spring eye mountings, bushes, and shackles.

☐ The same general checks apply to vehicles fitted with other suspension types, such as torsion bars, hydraulic displacer units, etc. Ensure that all mountings and attachments are secure, that there are no signs of excessive wear, corrosion or damage, and (on hydraulic types) that there are no fluid leaks or damaged pipes.

☐ Check any suspension and anti-roll bar link ball joint dust covers. Any covers that are missing, seriously damaged, deteriorated or insecure, may fail inspection.

☐ Examine each shock absorber for signs of leakage, corrosion of the casing, missing, detached or worn pivots and/or rubber bushes.

Driveshafts
(fwd vehicles only)

☐ Rotate each front wheel in turn and inspect the inner and outer joint gaiters for splits or damage. Also check that each driveshaft is straight and undamaged.

Braking system

☐ If possible without dismantling, check brake pad wear and disc condition. Ensure that the friction lining material has not worn excessively, (A) and that the discs are not fractured, pitted, scored or badly worn (B). As a general rule, if the friction material is less than 1.5 mm thick, the inspection will fail.

☐ Examine all the rigid brake pipes underneath the vehicle, and the flexible hose(s) at the rear. Look for corrosion, chafing or insecurity of the pipes, and for signs of bulging under pressure, chafing, splits or deterioration of the flexible hoses.

☐ Look for signs of fluid leaks at the brake calipers or on the brake backplates. Repair or renew leaking components.

☐ Slowly spin each wheel, while your assistant depresses and releases the footbrake. Ensure that each brake is operating and does not bind when the pedal is released.

□ Examine the handbrake mechanism, checking for frayed or broken cables, excessive corrosion, or wear or insecurity of the linkage. Check that the mechanism works on each relevant wheel, and releases fully, without binding.

□ Check the ABS sensors' wiring for signs of damage, deterioration or insecurity.

□ It is not possible to test brake efficiency without special equipment, but a road test can be carried out later to check that the vehicle pulls up in a straight line.

Fuel and exhaust systems

□ Inspect the fuel tank (including the filler cap), fuel pipes, hoses and unions. All components must be secure and free from leaks. Locking fuel caps must lock securely and the key must be provided for the MOT test.

□ Examine the exhaust system over its entire length, checking for any damaged, broken or missing mountings, security of the retaining clamps and rust or corrosion.

□ If the vehicle was originally equipped with a catalytic converter or particulate filter, one must be fitted.

Wheels and tyres

□ Examine the sidewalls and tread area of each tyre in turn. Check for cuts, tears, lumps, bulges, separation of the tread, and exposure of the ply or cord due to wear or damage. Check that the tyre bead is correctly seated on the wheel rim, that the valve is sound and properly seated, and that the wheel is not distorted or damaged.

□ Check that the tyres are of the correct size for the vehicle, that they are of the same size and type on each axle, and that the pressures are correct. The vehicle will fail the test if the tyres are obviously under-inflated.

□ Check the tyre tread depth. The legal minimum at the time of writing is 1.6 mm over the central three-quarters of the tread width. Abnormal tread wear may indicate incorrect front wheel alignment or wear in steering or suspension components.

□ Check that all wheel bolts/nuts are present.

□ If the spare wheel is fitted externally or in a separate carrier beneath the vehicle, check that mountings are secure and free of excessive corrosion.

Body corrosion

□ Check the condition of the entire vehicle structure for signs of corrosion in load-bearing areas. (These include chassis box sections, side sills, cross-members, pillars, and all suspension, steering, braking system and seat belt mountings and anchorages.) Any corrosion which has seriously reduced the thickness of a load-bearing area (or is within 30 cm of safety-related components such as steering or suspension) is likely to cause the vehicle to fail. In this case professional repairs are likely to be needed.

□ Damage or corrosion which causes sharp or otherwise dangerous edges to be exposed will also cause the vehicle to fail.

Towbars

□ Check the condition of mounting points (both beneath the vehicle and within boot/hatchback areas) for signs of corrosion, ensuring that all fixings are secure and not worn or damaged. There must be no excessive play in detachable tow ball arms or quick-release mechanisms.

□ Examine the security and condition of the towbar electrics socket. If the later 13-pin socket is fitted, the MOT tester will check its' wiring functions/connections are correct.

General leaks

□ The vehicle will fail the test if there is a fluid leak of any kind that poses an environmental risk.

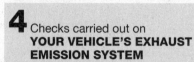

4 Checks carried out on **YOUR VEHICLE'S EXHAUST EMISSION SYSTEM**

Petrol models

□ The engine should be warmed up, and running well (ignition system in good order, air filter element clean, etc).

□ Before testing, run the engine at around 2500 rpm for 20 seconds. Let the engine drop to idle, and watch for smoke from the exhaust. If the idle speed is too high, or if dense blue or black smoke emerges for more than 5 seconds, the vehicle will fail. Typically, blue smoke signifies oil burning (engine wear); black smoke means unburnt fuel (dirty air cleaner element, or other fuel system fault).

□ An exhaust gas analyser for measuring carbon monoxide (CO) and hydrocarbons (HC) is now needed. If one cannot be hired or borrowed, have a local garage perform the check.

CO emissions (mixture)

□ The MOT tester has access to the CO limits for all vehicles from 1st August 1992. The CO level is measured at idle speed, and at 'fast idle' (2500 to 3000 rpm). The following limits are given as a general guide:

At idle speed – Less than 0.3% CO
At 'fast idle' – Less than 0.2% CO
Lambda reading – 0.97 to 1.03

□ If the CO level is too high, this may point to poor maintenance, a fuel injection system problem, faulty lambda (oxygen) sensor or catalytic converter. Try an injector cleaning treatment, and check the vehicle's ECU for fault codes.

HC emissions

□ The MOT tester has access to HC limits for all vehicles. The HC level is measured at 'fast idle' (2500 to 3000 rpm). The following limits are given as a general guide:

At 'fast idle' – Less than 200 ppm

□ Excessive HC emissions are typically caused by oil being burnt (worn engine), or by a blocked crankcase ventilation system ('breather'). If the engine oil is old and thin, an oil change may help. If the engine is running badly, check the vehicle's ECU for fault codes.

Diesel models

□ If the vehicle was fitted with a DPF (Diesel Particulate Filter) when it left the factory, it will fail the test if the MOT tester can see smoke of any colour emitting from the exhaust, or finds evidence that the filter has been tampered with.

□ The only emission test for diesel engines is measuring exhaust smoke density, using a calibrated smoke meter.

□ This test involves accelerating the engine to its maximum unloaded speed a minimum of once, and a maximum of 6 times. With the smoke meter connected, the engine is accelerated quickly to its maximum speed. If the smoke level is at or below the limit specified, the vehicle will pass. If the level is more than the specified limit then two further accelerations are carried out, and an average of the readings calculated. If the vehicle is still over the limit, a further three accelerations are carried out, with the average of the last three calculated after each check.

Note: *On engines with a timing belt, it is VITAL that the belt is in good condition before the test is carried out.*

Vehicles registered after 1st July 2008
Smoke level must not exceed 1.5m-1 – Turbo-charged and non-Turbocharged engines

Vehicles registered before 1st July 2008
Smoke level must not exceed 2.5m-1 – Non-turbo vehicles
Smoke level must not exceed 3.0m-1 – Turbocharged vehicles:

□ If excess smoke is produced, try fitting a new air cleaner element, or using an injector cleaning treatment. If the engine is running badly, where applicable, check the vehicle's ECU for fault codes. Also check the vehicle's EGR system, where applicable. At high mileages, the injectors may require professional attention.

Engine

- ☐ Engine fails to rotate when attempting to start
- ☐ Engine rotates, but will not start
- ☐ Engine difficult to start when cold
- ☐ Engine difficult to start when hot
- ☐ Starter motor noisy or excessively rough in engagement
- ☐ Engine starts, but stops immediately
- ☐ Engine idles erratically
- ☐ Engine misfires at idle speed
- ☐ Engine misfires throughout the driving speed range
- ☐ Engine hesitates on acceleration
- ☐ Engine stalls
- ☐ Engine lacks power
- ☐ Engine backfires
- ☐ Oil pressure warning light illuminated with engine running
- ☐ Engine runs-on after switching off
- ☐ Engine noises

Cooling system

- ☐ Overheating
- ☐ Overcooling
- ☐ External coolant leakage
- ☐ Internal coolant leakage
- ☐ Corrosion

Fuel and exhaust systems

- ☐ Excessive fuel consumption
- ☐ Fuel leakage and/or fuel odour

Clutch

- ☐ Pedal travels to floor – no pressure or very little resistance
- ☐ Clutch fails to disengage (unable to select gears)
- ☐ Clutch slips (engine speed increases, with no increase in vehicle speed)
- ☐ Judder as clutch is engaged
- ☐ Noise when depressing or releasing clutch pedal

Manual transmission

- ☐ Noisy in neutral with engine running
- ☐ Noisy in one particular gear
- ☐ Difficulty engaging gears
- ☐ Vibration
- ☐ Jumps out of gear
- ☐ Lubricant leaks

DSG transmissions

- ☐ Fluid leakage
- ☐ General gear selection problems

Braking system

- ☐ Vehicle pulls to one side under braking
- ☐ Noise (grinding or high-pitched squeal) when brakes applied)
- ☐ Brakes binding
- ☐ Excessive brake pedal travel
- ☐ Brake pedal feels spongy when depressed
- ☐ Excessive brake pedal effort required to stop vehicle
- ☐ Judder felt through brake pedal or steering wheel when braking
- ☐ Rear wheels locking under normal braking

Driveshafts

- ☐ Clicking or knocking noise on turns (at slow speed on full-lock)

Suspension and steering

- ☐ Vehicle pulls to one side
- ☐ Excessive pitching and/or rolling around corners, or during braking
- ☐ Lack of power assistance
- ☐ Wandering or general instability
- ☐ Excessively stiff steering
- ☐ Excessive play in steering
- ☐ Wheel wobble and vibration
- ☐ Tyre wear excessive

Electrical system

- ☐ Battery will not hold a charge for more than a few days
- ☐ Ignition/no-charge warning light remains illuminated with engine running
- ☐ Ignition/no-charge warning light fails to come on
- ☐ Lights inoperative
- ☐ Instrument readings inaccurate or erratic
- ☐ Horn inoperative, or unsatisfactory in operation
- ☐ Windscreen/tailgate wipers inoperative, or unsatisfactory in operation
- ☐ Windscreen/tailgate washers inoperative, or unsatisfactory in operation
- ☐ Electric windows inoperative, or unsatisfactory in operation
- ☐ Central locking system inoperative, or unsatisfactory in operation

Introduction

The vehicle owner who does his or her own maintenance according to the recommended service schedules should not have to use this section of the manual very often. Modern component reliability is such that, provided those items subject to wear or deterioration are inspected or renewed at the specified intervals, sudden failure is comparatively rare. Faults do not usually just happen as a result of sudden failure, but develop over a period of time. Major mechanical failures in particular are usually preceded by characteristic symptoms over hundreds or even thousands of miles. Those components that do occasionally fail without warning are often small and easily carried in the vehicle.

With any fault-finding, the first step is to decide where to begin investigations. Sometimes this is obvious, but on other occasions, a little detective work will be necessary. The owner who makes half a dozen haphazard adjustments or component renewals may be successful in curing a fault (or its symptoms). However, will be none the wiser if the fault recurs, and ultimately may have spent more time and money than was necessary. A calm and logical approach will be found to be more satisfactory in the long run. Always take into account any warning signs or abnormalities that may have been noticed in the period preceding the fault – power loss, high or low gauge readings, unusual smells, etc – and remember that failure of components such as fuses or spark plugs may only be pointers to some underlying fault.

The pages which follow provide an easy-reference guide to the more common problems which may occur during the operation of the vehicle. These problems and their possible causes are grouped under headings denoting various components or systems, such as Engine, Cooling system, etc. The general Chapter which deals with the problem is also shown in brackets; refer to the relevant part of that Chapter for system-specific information. Whatever the fault, certain basic principles apply. These are as follows:

Verify the fault. This is simply a matter of being sure that you know what the symptoms are before starting work. This is particularly important if you are investigating a fault for someone else, who may not have described it very accurately.

Do not overlook the obvious. For example, if the vehicle will not start, is there petrol in the tank? (Do not take anyone else's word on this particular point, and do not trust the fuel gauge either!) If an electrical fault is indicated, look for loose or broken wires before digging out the test gear.

Cure the disease, not the symptom. Substituting a flat battery with a fully-charged one will get you off the hard shoulder, but if the underlying cause is not attended to, the new battery will go the same way. Similarly, changing oil-fouled spark plugs for a new set will get you moving again, but remember that the reason for the fouling (if it was not simply an incorrect grade of plug) will have to be established and corrected.

Do not take anything for granted. Particularly, do not forget that a new component may itself be defective (especially if it's been rattling around in the boot for months). Also do not leave components out of a fault diagnosis sequence just because they are new or recently fitted. When you do finally diagnose a difficult fault, you will probably realise that all the evidence was there from the start.

Diesel fault diagnosis

The majority of starting problems on small diesel engines are electrical in origin. The mechanic who is familiar with petrol engines but less so with diesel may be inclined to view the diesel's injectors and pump in the same light as the spark plugs and distributor, but this is generally a mistake.

When investigating complaints of difficult starting for someone else, make sure that the correct starting procedure is understood and is being followed. Some drivers are unaware of the significance of the preheating warning light – many modern engines are sufficiently forgiving for this not to matter in mild weather, but with the onset of winter, problems begin.

As a rule of thumb, if the engine is difficult to start but runs well when it has finally got going, the problem is electrical (battery, starter motor or preheating system). If poor performance is combined with difficult starting, the problem is likely to be in the fuel system. The low-pressure (supply) side of the fuel system should be checked before suspecting the injectors and high-pressure pump. The most common fuel supply problem is air getting into the system, and any pipe from the fuel tank forwards must be scrutinised if air leakage is suspected. Normally the pump is the last item to suspect, since unless it has been tampered with, there is no reason for it to be at fault.

Engine

Engine fails to rotate when attempting to start

☐ Battery terminal connections loose or corroded (Weekly checks).
☐ Battery discharged or faulty (Chapter 5A Section 2).
☐ Broken, loose or disconnected wiring in the starting circuit (Chapter 5A Section 7).
☐ Defective starter solenoid or switch (Chapter 5A Section 8).
☐ Defective starter motor (Chapter 5A Section 8).
☐ Starter pinion or flywheel ring gear teeth loose or broken (Chapter 2A Section 15, Chapter 2B Section 12, Chapter 2B Section 12).
☐ Engine earth strap broken or disconnected (Chapter 12 Section 2).

Engine rotates, but will not start

☐ Fuel tank empty.
☐ Battery discharged (engine rotates slowly) (Chapter 5A Section 2).
☐ Battery terminal connections loose or corroded (Weekly checks).
☐ Ignition components damp or damaged – petrol models (Chapter 1A Section 29 and Chapter 5B Section 3).
☐ Broken, loose or disconnected wiring in the ignition circuit – petrol models (Chapter 5B Section 2 and Chapter 12 Section 2).
☐ Worn, faulty or incorrectly gapped spark plugs – petrol models (Chapter 1A Section 29).
☐ Fuel injection system fault (Chapter 4A Section 4 and Chapter 4B Section 4).
☐ Air in fuel system – diesel models (Chapter 4B Section 11).
☐ Major mechanical failure (eg, timing belt) (Chapter 2A Section 7, Chapter 2B Section 6 or Chapter 2C Section 7).

Engine difficult to start when cold

☐ Battery discharged (Chapter 5A Section 2).
☐ Battery terminal connections loose or corroded (Weekly checks).
☐ Worn, faulty or incorrectly gapped spark plugs – petrol models (Chapter 1A Section 29).
☐ Fuel injection system fault (Chapter 4A Section 4 and Chapter 4B Section 5).
☐ Other ignition system fault – petrol models (Chapter 5B Section 2).
☐ Preheating system fault – diesel models (Chapter 5C Section 2).
☐ Low cylinder compressions (Chapter 2A Section 2, Chapter 2A Section 2 or Chapter 2C Section 2).

Engine difficult to start when hot

☐ Air filter element dirty or clogged (Chapter 1A Section 28 or Chapter 1B Section 28).
☐ Fuel injection system fault (Chapter 4A Section 4 and Chapter 4B Section 4).
☐ Low cylinder compressions (Chapter 2A Section 2, Chapter 2B Section 3, or Chapter 2C Section 2).

Starter motor noisy or excessively rough in engagement

☐ Starter pinion or flywheel ring gear teeth loose or broken (Chapter 2A Section 15, Chapter 2B Section 12, Chapter 2C Section 14 and Chapter 5A Section 8).
☐ Starter motor mounting bolts loose or missing (Chapter 5A Section 8).
☐ Starter motor internal components worn or damaged (Chapter 5A Section 8).

Engine starts, but stops immediately

☐ Loose or faulty electrical connections in the ignition circuit – petrol models (Chapter 5B Section 2 and Chapter 12 Section 2).
☐ Vacuum leak at the throttle body or inlet manifold – petrol models (Chapter 4A Section 8).

☐ Blocked injector/fuel injection system fault - petrol models (Chapter 4A Section 4 or Chapter 12 Section 2).
☐ Faulty injector(s) – diesel models (Chapter 4B Section 5).
☐ Air in fuel system – diesel models (Chapter 4B Section 11).

Engine idles erratically

☐ Air filter element clogged (Chapter 4A Section 3 or Chapter 4B Section 3).
☐ Vacuum leak at the throttle body, inlet manifold or associated hoses – petrol models (Chapter 4A).
☐ Worn, faulty or incorrectly gapped spark plugs – petrol models (Chapter 1A Section 29).
☐ Uneven or low cylinder compressions (Chapter 2A Section 2, Chapter 2B Section 3 or Chapter 2C Section 2.
☐ Camshaft lobes worn (Chapter 2A Section 9, Chapter 2B Section 8, or Chapter 2C Section 9
☐ Timing belt (or chain) incorrectly tensioned (Chapter 2A Section 7, Chapter 2B Section 2 or Chapter 2C Section 7)
☐ Blocked injector/fuel injection system fault (Chapter 4A Section 4 or Chapter 4B Section 5. Faulty injector(s) – diesel models (Chapter 4B Section 5).

Engine misfires at idle speed

☐ Worn, faulty or incorrectly gapped spark plugs – petrol models (Chapter 1A Section 29).
☐ Faulty spark plug HT leads – petrol models (Chapter Section).
☐ Vacuum leak at the throttle body, inlet manifold or associated hoses (Chapter 4A).
☐ Blocked injector/fuel injection system fault (Chapter 4A Section 4 or Chapter 4B Section 5).
☐ Faulty injector(s) – diesel models (Chapter 4B Section 5).
☐ Uneven or low cylinder compressions (Chapter 2A Section 2, Chapter 2B Section 3 or Chapter 2C Section 2).
☐ Disconnected, leaking, or perished crankcase ventilation hoses (Chapter 4C or Chapter 4D)

Engine misfires throughout the driving speed range

☐ Fuel filter choked (Chapter 4A Section 5 or Chapter 1B Section 29)
☐ Fuel pump faulty, or delivery pressure low (Chapter 4A Section 5 or Chapter 4B Section 10).
☐ Fuel tank vent blocked, or fuel pipes restricted (Chapter 4A Section 6 or Chapter 4B Section 9).
☐ Vacuum leak at the throttle body, inlet manifold or associated hoses – petrol models (Chapter 4A).
☐ Worn, faulty or incorrectly gapped spark plugs – petrol models (Chapter 1A Section 29).
☐ Faulty injector(s) – diesel models (Chapter 4B Section 5).
☐ Faulty ignition coil – petrol models (Chapter 5B Section 3).
☐ Uneven or low cylinder compressions (Chapter 2A Section 2, Chapter 2A Section 2 or Chapter 2C Section 2).
☐ Blocked injector/fuel injection system fault (Chapter 4A Section 4 or Chapter 4B Section 5).

Engine hesitates on acceleration

☐ Worn, faulty or incorrectly gapped spark plugs – petrol models (Chapter 1A Section 29).
☐ Vacuum leak at the throttle body, inlet manifold or associated hoses – petrol models (Chapter 4A Section 8).
☐ Blocked injector/fuel injection system fault (Chapter 4A Section 4 or Chapter 4B Section 4).
☐ Faulty injector(s) – diesel models (Chapter 4B Section 5).

Engine (continued)

Engine stalls

- [ ] Vacuum leak at the throttle body, inlet manifold or associated hoses – petrol models (Chapter 4A Section 8).
- [ ] Fuel filter choked (Chapter 1B Section 29).
- [ ] Fuel pump faulty, or delivery pressure low – petrol models (Chapter 4A Section 5).
- [ ] Fuel tank vent blocked, or fuel pipes restricted (Chapter 4A Section 6 or Chapter 4B Section 9).
- [ ] Blocked injector/fuel injection system fault (Chapter 4A Section 4 or Chapter 4B Section 4).
- [ ] Faulty injector(s) – diesel models (Chapter 4B Section 5).
- [ ] Air in fuel system – diesel models (Chapter 4B Section 11).

Engine lacks power

- [ ] Timing belt (or chain) incorrectly fitted or tensioned (Chapter 2A Section 7, Chapter 2B Section 2 or Chapter 2C Section 7).
- [ ] Fuel filter choked (Chapter 1B Section 29).
- [ ] Fuel pump faulty, or delivery pressure low – petrol models (Chapter 4A Section 5).
- [ ] Uneven or low cylinder compressions (Chapter 2A Section 2, Chapter 2B Section 3 or Chapter 2C Section 2).
- [ ] Worn, faulty or incorrectly gapped spark plugs – petrol models (Chapter 1A Section 29).
- [ ] Vacuum leak at the throttle body, inlet manifold or associated hoses – petrol models (Chapter 4A Section 8).
- [ ] Blocked injector/fuel injection system fault (Chapter 4A Section 4 or Chapter 4B Section 5).
- [ ] Turbocharger fault (Chapter 4C Section 4 or Chapter 4D Section 5).
- [ ] Brakes binding (Chapter 9 Section 5 or Chapter 9 Section 9).
- [ ] Clutch slipping (Chapter 6A Section 5).

Engine backfires

- [ ] Timing belt (or chain) incorrectly fitted or tensioned (Chapter 2A Section 7, Chapter 2B Section 6 or Chapter 2C Section 7).
- [ ] Vacuum leak at the throttle body, inlet manifold or associated hoses – petrol models (Chapter 4A Section 8).
- [ ] Blocked injector/fuel injection system fault (Chapter 4A Section 4 or Chapter 4B Section 4).

Oil pressure warning light illuminated with engine running

- [ ] Low oil level, or incorrect oil grade (Weekly checks).
- [ ] Faulty oil pressure warning light switch (Chapter 2A Section 19, Chapter 2B Section 15 or Chapter 2C Section 18).
- [ ] Worn engine bearings and/or oil pump (Chapter 2A Section 14, Chapter 2B Section 14 or Chapter 2C Section 13).
- [ ] Oil pick-up strainer clogged (Chapter 2A Section 14, Chapter 2A Section 14 or Chapter 2C Section 13).

Engine runs-on after switching off

- [ ] Excessive carbon build-up in engine (Chapter 2A Section 12, Chapter 2B Section 10 or Chapter 2C Section 11).
- [ ] High engine operating temperature (Chapter 3).
- [ ] Fuel injection system fault – petrol models (Chapter 4A Section 4).
- [ ] Fuel injection system fault - diesel models (Chapter 4B Section 4).

Engine noises

Pre-ignition (pinking) or knocking during acceleration or under load

- [ ] Ignition system fault – petrol models (Chapter 1A Section 29 and Chapter 5B Section 2).
- [ ] Incorrect grade of spark plug – petrol models (Chapter 1A Section 29).
- [ ] Vacuum leak at the throttle body, inlet manifold or associated hoses – petrol models (Chapter 4A Section 8).
- [ ] Excessive carbon build-up in engine (Chapter 2A Section 12, Chapter 2B Section 10 or Chapter 2B Section 10).
- [ ] Blocked injector/fuel injection system fault – petrol models (Chapter 4A Section 4).

Whistling or wheezing noises

- [ ] Leaking inlet manifold or throttle body gasket – petrol models (Chapter 4A Section 8).
- [ ] Leaking exhaust manifold gasket or pipe-to-manifold joint (Chapter 4C Section 6 or Chapter 4D Section 9).
- [ ] Leaking turbocharger air ducts (Chapter 4C Section 5 or Chapter 4D Section 7).
- [ ] Leaking vacuum hose (Chapter 9 Section 11 or Chapter 9 Section 20).
- [ ] Blowing cylinder head gasket (Chapter 2A Section 12, Chapter 2B Section 10 or Chapter 2C Section 11).

Tapping or rattling noises

- [ ] Worn valve gear or camshaft (Chapter 2A Section 4, Chapter 2B Section 8 or Chapter 2C Section 9).
- [ ] Ancillary component fault (coolant pump, alternator, etc) (Chapter 3 Section 7 and Chapter 5A Section 5).

Knocking or thumping noises

- [ ] Worn big-end bearings (regular heavy knocking, perhaps worsening under load) (Chapter 2D Section 14).
- [ ] Worn main bearings (rumbling and knocking, perhaps less under load) (Chapter 2D Section 14).
- [ ] Piston slap (most noticeable when cold) (Chapter 2D Section 12).
- [ ] Ancillary component fault (coolant pump, alternator, etc) (Chapter 3 Section 7 or Chapter 5A Section 5) etc.

Cooling system

Overheating

- ☐ Insufficient coolant in system (Weekly checks).
- ☐ Thermostat faulty (Chapter 3 Section 4).
- ☐ Radiator core blocked, or grille restricted (Chapter 3 Section 3).
- ☐ Electric cooling fan or thermoswitch faulty (Chapter 3 Section 5).
- ☐ Pressure cap faulty (Chapter 3 Section 1).
- ☐ Ignition system fault – petrol engines (Chapter 1A Section 29 or Chapter 5B Section 2).
- ☐ Airlock in cooling system (Chapter 1A Section 33 or Chapter 1B Section 33).

Overcooling

- ☐ Thermostat faulty (Chapter 3 Section 4).
- ☐ Inaccurate temperature sensor unit (Chapter 3 Section 6).

External coolant leakage

- ☐ Deteriorated or damaged hoses or hose clips (Chapter 3 Section 2).

- ☐ Radiator core or heater matrix leaking (Chapter 3 Section 3 or Chapter 3 Section 9).
- ☐ Pressure cap faulty (Chapter 3 Section 1).
- ☐ Water pump seal leaking (Chapter 3 Section 7).
- ☐ Boiling due to overheating (Chapter 0 Section 5).
- ☐ Core plug leaking (Chapter 2D Section 7).

Internal coolant leakage

- ☐ Leaking cylinder head gasket (Chapter 2A Section 12, Chapter 2B Section 10 or Chapter 2C Section 11).
- ☐ Cracked cylinder head or cylinder bore (Chapter 2D Section 7).

Corrosion

- ☐ Infrequent draining and flushing (Chapter 1A Section 33 or Chapter 1B Section 33).
- ☐ Incorrect coolant mixture or inappropriate coolant type (Chapter 1A Section 33 or Chapter 1B Section 33).

Fuel and exhaust systems

Excessive fuel consumption

- ☐ Air filter element dirty or clogged (Chapter 1A Section 28 or Chapter 1B Section 28).
- ☐ Fuel injection system fault (Chapter 4A Section 9 or Chapter 4B Section 4).
- ☐ Ignition system fault – petrol models (Chapter 1A Section 29 and Chapter 5B Section 3).
- ☐ Faulty injector(s) – diesel models (Chapter 4B Section 5).
- ☐ Tyres under-inflated (Weekly checks).

Fuel leakage and/or fuel odour

- ☐ Damaged or corroded fuel tank, pipes or connections (Chapter 4A Section 6 or Chapter 4B Section 9)
- ☐ Excessive noise or fumes from exhaust system (Chapter 4C Section 6 or Chapter 4D Section 9).
- ☐ Leaking exhaust system or manifold joints (Chapter 4C Section 4, Chapter 4C Section 6, Chapter 4D Section 5 or Chapter 4D Section 9).
- ☐ Leaking, corroded or damaged silencers or pipe (Chapter 4C Section 6 or Chapter 4D Section 9).
- ☐ Broken mountings causing body or suspension contact (Chapter 4C Section 6 or Chapter 4D Section 9).

Clutch

Pedal travels to floor – no pressure or very little resistance

- ☐ Hydraulic fluid level low/air in hydraulic system (Weekly checks).
- ☐ Broken clutch release bearing or fork (Chapter 6A Section 6).
- ☐ Broken diaphragm spring in clutch pressure plate (Chapter 6A Section 5).

Clutch fails to disengage (unable to select gears)

- ☐ Clutch disc sticking on transmission input shaft splines (Chapter 6A Section 5).
- ☐ Clutch disc sticking to flywheel or pressure plate (Chapter 6A Section 5).
- ☐ Faulty pressure plate assembly (Chapter 6A Section 5).
- ☐ Clutch release mechanism worn or incorrectly assembled (Chapter 6A Section 6).

Clutch slips (engine speed increases, with no increase in vehicle speed)

- ☐ Clutch disc linings excessively worn (Chapter 6A Section 5).
- ☐ Clutch disc linings contaminated with oil or grease (Chapter 6A Section 5).

- ☐ Faulty pressure plate or weak diaphragm spring (Chapter 6A Section 5).

Judder as clutch is engaged

- ☐ Clutch disc linings contaminated with oil or grease (Chapter 6A Section 5).
- ☐ Clutch disc linings excessively worn (Chapter Section).
- ☐ Faulty or distorted pressure plate or diaphragm spring (Chapter 6A Section 5).
- ☐ Worn or loose engine or transmission mountings (Chapter 2A Section 17, Chapter 2B Section 17 or Chapter 2C Section 16).
- ☐ Clutch disc hub or transmission input shaft splines worn (Chapter 6A Section 5).

Noise when depressing or releasing clutch pedal

- ☐ Worn clutch release bearing (Chapter 6A Section 6).
- ☐ Worn or dry clutch pedal bushes (Chapter 6A Section 3).
- ☐ Faulty pressure plate assembly (Chapter 6A Section 5).
- ☐ Pressure plate diaphragm spring broken (Chapter 6A Section 5).
- ☐ Broken clutch disc cushioning springs (Chapter 6A Section 5).

Manual transmission

Noisy in neutral with engine running

☐ Input shaft bearings worn (noise apparent with clutch pedal released, but not when depressed) (Chapter 7A Section 5).*
☐ Clutch release bearing worn (noise apparent with clutch pedal depressed, possibly less when released) (Chapter 6A Section 6).

Noisy in one particular gear

☐ Worn, damaged or chipped gear teeth (Chapter 7A Section 5).*

Difficulty engaging gears

☐ Clutch fault (Chapter 6A Section 5).
☐ Worn or damaged gear linkage (Chapter 7A Section 2).
☐ Incorrectly adjusted gear linkage (Chapter 7A Section 2).
☐ Worn synchroniser units (Chapter 7A Section 5).*

Vibration

☐ Lack of oil (Chapter 7A Section 4).
☐ Worn bearings (Chapter 7A Section 5).*

Jumps out of gear

☐ Worn or damaged gear linkage (Chapter 7A Section 2).
☐ Incorrectly adjusted gear linkage (Chapter 7A Section 2).
☐ Worn synchroniser units (Chapter 7A Section 5).*
☐ Worn selector forks (Chapter 7A Section 5).*

Lubricant leaks

☐ Leaking housing joint (Chapter 7A Section 5).*
☐ Leaking input shaft oil seal (Chapter 6A Section 4).*

Although the corrective action necessary to remedy the symptoms described is beyond the scope of the home mechanic, the above information should be helpful in isolating the cause of the condition. This should enable the owner can communicate clearly with a professional mechanic.

DSG transmissions

Fluid leakage

Note: *Due to the complexity of the DSG transmissions, it is difficult for the home mechanic to properly diagnose and service this unit. For problems other than the following, the vehicle should be taken to a dealer service department or automatic transmission specialist. Do not be too hasty in removing the transmission if a fault is suspected, as most of the testing is carried out with the unit still fitted.*

☐ To determine the source of a leak, first remove all built-up dirt and grime from the transmission housing and surrounding areas using a degreasing agent, or by steam-cleaning. Drive the vehicle at low speed, so airflow will not blow the leak far from its source. Raise and support the vehicle, and determine where the leak is coming from.

General gear selection problems

☐ Chapter 7B Section 4 deals with checking and adjusting the selector cable on transmissions.

Braking system

Vehicle pulls to one side under braking

Note: *Before assuming that a brake problem exists, make sure that the tyres are in good condition and correctly inflated, that the front wheel alignment is correct, and that the vehicle is not loaded with weight in an unequal manner. Apart from checking the condition of all pipe and hose connections, any faults occurring on the anti-lock braking system should be referred to a Volkswagen dealer or suitably equipped garage for diagnosis.*

☐ Worn, defective, damaged or contaminated brake pads on one side (Chapter 9 Section 4 and Chapter 9 Section 8).

☐ Seized or partially seized brake caliper piston (Chapter 9 Section 5 or Chapter 9 Section 9).

☐ Brake caliper mounting bolts loose (Chapter 9 Section 5 or Chapter 9 Section 9)Worn or damaged steering or suspension components (Chapter 10).

Noise (grinding or high-pitched squeal) when brakes applied)

☐ Brake pad friction lining material worn down to metal backing (Chapter 9 Section 4 or Chapter 9 Section 8).

☐ Excessive corrosion of brake disc. This may be apparent after the vehicle has been standing for some time (Chapter 9 Section 6).

☐ Foreign object (stone chipping, etc.) trapped between brake disc and shield (Chapter 9 Section 6).

Brakes binding

☐ Seized brake caliper piston(s) (Chapter 9 Section 5 or Chapter 9 Section 9).

☐ Incorrectly adjusted handbrake mechanism (Chapter 9 Section 14).

☐ Faulty master cylinder (Chapter 9 Section 13).

Excessive brake pedal travel

☐ Faulty master cylinder (Chapter 9 Section 13).

☐ Air in hydraulic system (Chapter 9 Section 2).

☐ Faulty vacuum servo unit (Chapter 9 Section 11).

Brake pedal feels spongy when depressed

☐ Air in hydraulic system (Chapter 9 Section 2).

☐ Deteriorated flexible rubber brake hoses (Chapter 9 Section 3).

☐ Master cylinder mounting nuts loose (Chapter 9 Section 13).

☐ Faulty master cylinder (Chapter 9 Section 13).

Excessive brake pedal effort required to stop vehicle

☐ Faulty vacuum servo unit (Chapter 9 Section 11).

☐ Faulty brake vacuum pump – petrol models (Chapter 9 Section 20).

☐ Faulty brake vacuum pump - diesel models (Chapter 2C Section 13).

☐ Disconnected, damaged or insecure brake servo vacuum hose (Chapter 9 Section 11).

☐ Primary or secondary hydraulic circuit failure (Chapter 9 Section 1).

☐ Seized brake caliper piston(s) (Chapter 9 Section 5 or Chapter 9 Section 9).

☐ Brake pads incorrectly fitted (Chapter 9 Section 4 or Chapter 9 Section 8).

☐ Incorrect grade of brake pads fitted (Chapter 9 Section 4 or Chapter 9 Section 8).

☐ Brake pads contaminated (Chapter 9 Section 4 or Chapter 9 Section 8).

Judder felt through brake pedal or steering wheel when braking

☐ Excessive run-out or distortion of discs (Chapter 9 Section 6).

☐ Brake pads worn (Chapter 9 Section 4 or Chapter 9 Section 8).

☐ Brake caliper mounting bolts loose (Chapter 9 Section 5 or Chapter 9 Section 9).

☐ Wear in suspension or steering components or mountings (Chapter 10).

Rear wheels locking under normal braking

☐ Rear brake pads contaminated (Chapter 9 Section 8).

☐ ABS system fault (Chapter 9 Section 18).

Driveshafts

Clicking or knocking noise on turns (at slow speed on full-lock)

☐ Lack of constant velocity joint lubricant, possibly due to damaged gaiter (Chapter 8 Section 3).

☐ Worn outer constant velocity joint (Chapter 8 Section 4).

☐ Vibration when accelerating or decelerating (Chapter 8 Section 4).

☐ Worn inner constant velocity joint (Chapter 8 Section 4).

☐ Bent or distorted driveshaft (Chapter 8 Section 4).

Suspension and steering

Vehicle pulls to one side

Note: *Before diagnosing suspension or steering faults, be sure that the trouble is not due to incorrect tyre pressures, mixtures of tyre types, or binding brakes.*

☐ Defective tyre (Weekly checks).
☐ Excessive wear in suspension or steering components (Chapter 10).
☐ Incorrect front wheel alignment (Chapter 10 Section 25).
☐ Accident damage to steering or suspension components (Chapter 10).

Excessive pitching and/or rolling around corners, or during braking

☐ Defective shock absorbers (Chapter 10 Section 4 or Chapter 10 Section 15).
☐ Broken or weak spring and/or suspension component (Chapter 10).
☐ Worn or damaged anti-roll bar or mountings – where applicable (Chapter 10 Section 7 or Chapter 10 Section 16).

Lack of power assistance

☐ Faulty rack-and-pinion steering gear (Chapter 10 Section 22).

Wandering or general instability

☐ Incorrect front wheel alignment (Chapter 10 Section 25).
☐ Worn steering or suspension joints, bushes or components (Chapter 10).
☐ Roadwheels out of balance (Chapter 0 Section 5).
☐ Faulty or damaged tyre (Weekly checks).
☐ Wheel bolts loose (refer to Chapter 10 Section 0 for correct torque).
☐ Defective shock absorbers (Chapter 10 Section 4 or Chapter 10 Section 15).

Excessively stiff steering

☐ Lack of steering gear lubricant (Chapter 10 Section 22).
☐ Seized track rod end balljoint or suspension balljoint (Chapter 10 Section 6 or Chapter 10 Section 24).
☐ Incorrect front wheel alignment (Chapter 10 Section 25).
☐ Steering rack or column bent or damaged (Chapter 10 Section 22 or Chapter 10 Section 20).

Excessive play in steering

☐ Worn steering column intermediate shaft universal joint (Chapter 10 Section 20).

☐ Worn steering track rod end balljoints (Chapter Section).
☐ Worn rack-and-pinion steering gear (Chapter 10 Section 22).
☐ Worn steering or suspension joints, bushes or components (Chapter 10).

Wheel wobble and vibration

☐ Front roadwheels out of balance (vibration felt mainly through the steering wheel) (Chapter 1A Section 20, Chapter 1B Section 19 and Chapter 10 Section 1).
☐ Rear roadwheels out of balance (vibration felt throughout the vehicle) (Chapter 1A Section 20, Chapter 1B Section 19, and Chapter 10).
☐ Roadwheels damaged or distorted (Chapter 1A Section 27, Chapter 1B Section 26 and Chapter 10).
☐ Faulty or damaged tyre (Weekly checks).
☐ Worn steering or suspension joints, bushes or components (Chapter 1A Section 20, Chapter 1B Section 19 and Chapter 10).
☐ Wheel bolts loose (Chapter 0 Section 5).

Tyre wear excessive

Tyres worn on inside or outside edges

☐ Tyres under-inflated (wear on both edges) (Weekly checks).
☐ Incorrect camber or castor angles (wear on one edge only) (Chapter 0 Section 5).
☐ Worn steering or suspension joints, bushes or components (Chapter 1A Section 20, Chapter 1B Section 19 and Chapter 10).
☐ Excessively hard cornering.Accident damage.

Tyre treads exhibit feathered edges

☐ Incorrect toe setting (Chapter 10 Section 25).

Tyres worn in centre of tread

☐ Tyres over-inflated (Weekly checks).

Tyres worn on inside and outside edges

☐ Tyres under-inflated (Weekly checks).

Tyres worn unevenly

☐ Tyres/wheels out of balance (Chapter 1A Section 20 or Chapter 1B Section 19).
☐ Excessive wheel or tyre run-out (Chapter 1A Section 20, Chapter 1B Section 19 and Chapter 10).
☐ Worn shock absorbers (Chapter 10 Section 4 and Chapter 10 Section 15).
☐ Faulty tyre (Weekly checks).

Electrical system

Battery will not hold a charge for more than a few days

Note: *For problems associated with the starting system, refer to the faults listed under 'Engine' earlier in this Section.*

☐ Battery defective internally (Chapter 5A Section 2).
☐ Battery terminal connections loose or corroded (Weekly checks).
☐ Auxiliary drivebelt worn or incorrectly adjusted (Chapter 1A Section 30 or Chapter 1B Section 30).
☐ Alternator not charging at correct output (Chapter 5A Section 4).
☐ Alternator or voltage regulator faulty (Chapter 5A Section 4).
☐ Short-circuit causing continual battery drain (Chapter 12 Section 2)

Ignition/no-charge warning light remains illuminated with engine running

☐ Auxiliary drivebelt broken, worn, or incorrectly adjusted (Chapter 1A Section 30 or Chapter 1B Section 30).
☐ Alternator brushes worn, sticking, or dirty (Chapter 5A Section 6).
☐ Alternator brush springs weak or broken (Chapter 5A Section 6).
☐ Internal fault in alternator or voltage regulator (Chapter 5A Section 6).
☐ Broken, disconnected, or loose wiring in charging circuit (Chapter 12 Section 2).

Electrical system (continued)

Ignition/no-charge warning light fails to come on

- [ ] Warning light LED defective (Chapter 12 Section 11).
- [ ] Broken, disconnected, or loose wiring in warning light circuit (Chapter 12 Section 2).
- [ ] Alternator faulty (Chapter 5A Section 4).

Lights inoperative

- [ ] Bulb blown or LED unit faulty (Chapter 12 Section 6 and Chapter 12 Section 7).
- [ ] Corrosion of bulb or bulbholder contacts (Chapter 12 Section 6).
- [ ] Blown fuse (Chapter 12 Section 3).
- [ ] Faulty relay (Chapter 12 Section 3).
- [ ] Broken, loose, or disconnected wiring (Chapter 12 Section 2).
- [ ] Faulty switch (Chapter 12 Section 5).

Instrument readings inaccurate or erratic

Fuel or temperature gauges give no reading

- [ ] Faulty gauge sender unit (Chapter 4A Section 5 or Chapter 4B Section 8).
- [ ] Wiring open-circuit (Chapter 12 Section 2).
- [ ] Faulty gauge (Chapter 12 Section 11).

Fuel or temperature gauges give continuous maximum reading

- [ ] Faulty gauge sender unit (Chapter 4A Section 5 or Chapter 4B Section 8).
- [ ] Wiring short-circuit (Chapter 12 Section 2).
- [ ] Faulty gauge (Chapter 12 Section 11).

Horn inoperative, or unsatisfactory in operation

Horn operates all the time

- [ ] Horn push either earthed or stuck down (Chapter 12 Section 5).
- [ ] Horn cable-to-horn push earthed (Chapter 12 Section 2).

Horn fails to operate

- [ ] Blown fuse (Chapter 12 Section 3).
- [ ] Cable or cable connections loose, broken or disconnected (Chapter 12 Section 2).
- [ ] Faulty horn (Chapter 12 Section 14).

Horn emits intermittent or unsatisfactory sound

- [ ] Cable connections loose (Chapter 12 Section 2).
- [ ] Horn mountings loose (Chapter 12 Section 14).
- [ ] Faulty horn (Chapter 12 Section 14).

Windscreen/tailgate wipers inoperative, or unsatisfactory in operation

Wipers fail to operate, or operate very slowly

- [ ] Bonnet not closed (built-into the electronic control system) (Chapter 11 Section 10).
- [ ] Wiper blades stuck to screen, or linkage seized or binding (Weekly checks and Chapter 12 Section 15).
- [ ] Blown fuse (Chapter 12 Section 3).
- [ ] Cable or cable connections loose, broken or disconnected (Chapter 12 Section 2).
- [ ] Faulty relay (Chapter 12 Section 3).
- [ ] Faulty wiper motor (Chapter 12 Section 16).

Wiper blades sweep over too large or too small an area of the glass

- [ ] Wiper arms incorrectly positioned on spindles (Chapter 12 Section 15).
- [ ] Excessive wear of wiper linkage (Chapter 12 Section 16).
- [ ] Wiper motor or linkage mountings loose or insecure (Chapter 12 Section 16).

Wiper blades fail to clean the glass effectively

- [ ] Wiper blade rubbers worn or perished (Weekly checks).
- [ ] Wiper arm tension springs broken, or arm pivots seized (Chapter 12 Section 15).
- [ ] Insufficient windscreen washer additive to adequately remove road film (Weekly checks).

Windscreen/tailgate washers inoperative, or unsatisfactory in operation

One or more washer jets inoperative

- [ ] Blocked washer jet (Chapter Chapter 1A Section 24 or Chapter 1B Section 23).
- [ ] Disconnected, kinked or restricted fluid hose (Chapter 12 Section 18).
- [ ] Insufficient fluid in washer reservoir (*Weekly checks*).

Washer pump fails to operate

- [ ] Broken or disconnected wiring or connections (Chapter 12 Section 2).
- [ ] Blown fuse (Chapter 12 Section 3).
- [ ] Faulty washer switch (Chapter 12 Section 5).
- [ ] Faulty washer pump (Chapter 12 Section 18).

Electric windows inoperative, or unsatisfactory in operation

Window glass will only move in one direction

- [ ] Faulty switch (Chapter 12 Section 5).

Window glass slow to move

- [ ] Regulator seized or damaged, or in need of lubrication (Chapter 11 Section 14).
- [ ] Door internal components or trim fouling regulator (Chapter 11 Section 12).
- [ ] Faulty motor (Chapter 11 Section 14).

Window glass fails to move

- [ ] Blown fuse (Chapter 12 Section 3).
- [ ] Faulty relay (Chapter 12 Section 3).
- [ ] Broken or disconnected wiring or connections (Chapter 12 Section 2).
- [ ] Faulty motor (Chapter 11 Section 14).

Central locking system inoperative, or unsatisfactory in operation

Complete system failure

- [ ] Blown fuse (Chapter 12 Section 3).
- [ ] Faulty relay (Chapter 12 Section 3).
- [ ] Broken or disconnected wiring or connections (Chapter 12 Section 2).
- [ ] Faulty control unit (Chapter 11 Section 17).

Latch locks but will not unlock, or unlocks but will not lock

- [ ] Faulty control unit (Chapter 11 Section 17).
- [ ] Broken or disconnected latch operating rods or levers (Chapter 11 Section 13).
- [ ] Faulty relay (Chapter 12 Section 3).

One actuator fails to operate

- [ ] Broken or disconnected wiring or connections (Chapter 12 Section 2).
- [ ] Faulty actuator (Chapter 11 Section 13).
- [ ] Broken, binding or disconnected latch operating rods or levers (Chapter 11 Section 13).
- [ ] Fault in door lock (Chapter 11 Section 13).

Note: *References throughout this index are in the form* "**Chapter number**" • "**Page number**". *So, for example, 2C•15 refers to page 15 of Chapter 2C.*

A

ABS (anti-lock braking system)
Components – 9•15
Front wheel sensor – 9•15
General information and precautions – 9•14
Hydraulic unit and electronic control – 9•15
Rear wheel sensor – 9•15
Reluctor rings – 9•16
**Absolute pressure (altitude) sensor
(diesel engines)** – 4B•6
Aerial
Aerials and filters – 12•24
Amplifiers – 12•24
Roof mounted aerial – 12•24
Tailgate glass mounted aerial – 12•24
Air conditioning
Air conditioning/heating switches – 12•6
Ambient temperature sensor (A/C) – 3•18
Evaporator – 3•18
Evaporator temperature sensor – 3•17
Receiver/drier – 3•20
Refrigerant pressure sensor – 3•20
System components – 3•17
System general information and precautions – 3•17
Air filter
Assembly removal (diesel engines) – 4B•4
Element renewal (diesel models) – 1B•13
Element renewal (petrol models) – 1A•15
Housing and inlet system (petrol engines) – 4A•5
Airbags
Airbag unit check – 1A•14, 1B•12
Airbag wiring contact unit – 12•26
Control unit – 12•26
Crash sensors – 12•26
Driver's airbag – 12•25
Front seat side impact airbags – 12•26
Knee airbag – 12•26
Passenger airbag on/off switch – 12•26
Passenger airbag – 12•25
Passenger airbag disable/deactivation switch (PAD) – 12•7
System components – 12•25
System general information and precautions – 12•24
Alternator
Brush holder/regulator module renewal – 5A•5
Charging system testing – 5A•4
Removal – 5A•4
Antifreeze mixture check
Diesel models – 1B•10, 1B•16
Petrol models – 1A•11, 1A•18
**Anti-theft alarm system and engine
immobiliser** – 12•24
Audio
Audio head unit – 12•22
Audio unit – 12•22
Control module/CD player – 12•23

Auxiliary drivebelt
Check
Diesel models – 1B•10
Petrol models – 1A•11
Renewal
Diesel models – 1B•15
Petrol models – 1A•17
Auxiliary heater – 3•16

B

Balancer shafts (2.0 litre direct injection petrol engine) – 2B•13
Bass speakers (front and rear) – 12•24
Battery
Battery check – 1A•13, 1B•12
Disconnection/removal – 5A•3
Terminals – 0•16
Testing and charging – 5A•2
Body exterior fittings – 11•20
Body trim strips and badges – 11•20
Bonnet
Contact switch – 11•18
Lock – 11•7
Release cable – 11•6
Removal/adjustment – 11•5
Boost pressure
Controller (diesel engines) – 4D•6
Control solenoid valve (diesel engines) – 4D•6
Control valve (diesel engines) – 4B•8
Position sensor (diesel engines) – 4B•8
Sensor
Diesel engines – 4D•6
Petrol engines – 4A•10
Braking system
Brake (and clutch) fluid level – 0•13
Brake (and clutch) fluid renewal – 1A•17, 1B•15
Brake light switch – 9•14, 12•8
Brake pad check – 1A•10, 1B•8
Brake pedal assembly – 9•11
Brake vacuum pump testing/removal – 9•16
Disc inspection/removal – 9•7
Front brake disc shield – 9•9
Front brake pads – 9•4
Front caliper removal/overhaul – 9•7
Hydraulic circuit check – 1A•12, 1B•10
Hydraulic pipes and hoses renewal – 9•4
Hydraulic system bleeding – 9•3
Master cylinder removal/overhaul – 9•13
Rear brake caliper removal/overhaul – 9•11
Rear brake pads renewal – 9•9
Servo non-return valve testing/removal – 9•12
Vacuum servo unit testing/removal – 9•12
Bulbs
Exterior lights – 12•9
Interior lights – 12•13
Wing mounted light bulbs – 12•11
Buying spare parts – REF•3

Note: *References throughout this index are in the form "**Chapter number**" • "**Page number**". So, for example, 2C•15 refers to page 15 of Chapter 2C.*

C

Camshaft(s)
Camshaft and hydraulic tappets (1.6 litre and 2.0 litre diesel engine) – 2C•10
Camshaft cover (1.6 litre and 2.0 litre diesel engine) – 2C•5
Camshaft housing (1.2 and 1.4 litre petrol engine) – 2A•6
Camshaft oil seals
  1.2 litre and 1.4 litre petrol engine – 2A•12
  1.6 litre and 2.0 litre diesel engine – 2C•12
Camshaft position sensor
  Diesel engines – 4B•8
  Petrol engines – 4A•10
Camshafts/camshaft cover (2.0 litre direct injection petrol engine) – 2B•14
Camshafts inspection (1.2 and 1.4 litre petrol engine) – 2A•12
Carpets – 11•30
Catalytic converter general information (petrol engines) – 4C•7
Catalytic converter/particulate filter (diesel engines) – 4D•6
Central locking components – 11•17
Centre console mounted switches – 12•7
Centre console – 11•31
Charge air boost pressure sensor (diesel engines) – 4B•6
Charge air temperature sensors (diesel engines) – 4B•6
Clutch
  Friction disc and pressure plate (manual transmission) – 6A•4
  Hydraulic system bleeding – 6A•2
  Pedal and master cylinder (manual transmission) – 6A•2
  Pedal switch (diesel engines) – 4B•6
  Release bearing and lever (manual transmission) – 6A•5
  Slave cylinder (manual transmission) – 6A•3
Compression and leakdown tests (1.6 litre and 2.0 litre diesel engine) – 2C•4
Compression test description and interpretation (1.2 and 1.4 litre petrol engine) – 2A•4
Compressor (A/C) – 3•19
Condenser (A/C) – 3•19
Convenience system control unit – 11•17
Conversion factors – REF•2
Coolant level – 0•13
Coolant pump – 3•10
Coolant renewal
  Diesel models – 1B•15
  Petrol models – 1A•18
Coolant temperature sensor – 3•10
Cooling fan temperature sensor – 3•9
Cooling system
  Draining
    Diesel models – 1B•16
    Petrol models – 1A•18
  Electrical sensors testing/removal – 3•9
  Filling
    Diesel models – 1B•16
    Petrol models – 1A•18
  Flushing
    Diesel models – 1B•16
    Petrol models – 1A•18
  Hoses renewal – 3•3
  Thermostat – 3•6
Courtesy light switches – 12•8
Crankcase emission system
  Petrol engines – 4C•3
  Diesel engines – 4D•2
Crankshaft inspection – 2D•13
Crankshaft oil seals
  1.2 litre and 1.4 litre petrol engine – 2A•18
  1.6 litre and 2.0 litre diesel engine – 2C•18
  2.0 litre direct injection petrol engine – 2B•15

Crankshaft position sensor (petrol engines – 4A•11
Crankshaft pulley
  1.2 litre and 1.4 litre petrol engine – 2A•8
  1.6 litre and 2.0 litre diesel engine – 2C•6
  2.0 litre direct injection petrol engine – 2B•8
Crankshaft refitting – 2D•15
Crankshaft removal – 2D•10
Crossmember – 11•36
Cylinder block/crankcase inspection – 2D•10
Cylinder compression test (2.0 litre direct injection petrol engine) – 2B•5
Cylinder head
  Head and valves inspection – 2D•7
  Dismantling – 2D•6
  Reassembly – 2D•8
  Removal/inspection (1.2 and 1.4 litre petrol engine) – 2A•13
  Removal (2.0 litre direct injection petrol engine) – 2B•17
  Removal/inspection (1.6 litre and 2.0 litre diesel engine) – 2C•12

D

Diesel engine management system component – 4B•5
Diesel engines general information and precautions – 4B•2
Dimensions and weights – REF•1
Direction indicator side repeater – 12•15
Direction indicator side repeater and approach light bulb – 12•11
Disconnecting the battery – REF•3
Door control unit – 11•17
Door entry light bulb – 12•14
Door handle and lock components – 11•11
Door inner trim panel – 11•9
Door removal/adjustment – 11•8
Door window glass/regulator – 11•13
Driveshaft
  Gaiter check – 1A•12, 1B•11
  Gaiter renewal – 8•3
  Overhaul general information – 8•8
  Removal – 8•2
DSG transmission
  6 speed transmission clutch (OD9) – 6B•1
  7 speed transmission clutch (OCW) – 6B•2
  Emergency release of selector lever – 7B•6
  Oil renewal – 1A•12, 1B•13, 7B•6
  Overhaul general information – 7B•5
  Removal – 7B•3
  Selector lever housing and cable removal/adjustment – 7B•5
  Spigot bearing renewal – 7B•7

E

Exhaust Gas Recirculation
  EGR control valves (diesel engines) – 4D•3
  EGR cooler (diesel engines) – 4D•3
  EGR exhaust control flap (diesel engines) – 4D•4
Electric cooling fans – 3•8
Electric cooling pump – 3•13
Electric door lock actuator – 11•17
Electrical system
  Connectors – 12•4
  Fault finding general information – 12•2
  General information and precautions – 12•2
  System check – 0•16
Electronic control unit/ECU
  Diesel engines – 4B•7
  Petrol engines – 4A•11
Engine and transmission removal – 2D•3
Engine assembly and valve timing marks (1.6 litre and 2.0 litre diesel engine) – 2C•4
Engine assembly and valve timing marks (1.2 and 1.4 litre petrol engine) – 2A•5

Note: *References throughout this index are in the form "Chapter number"* • *"Page number". So, for example, 2C•15 refers to page 15 of Chapter 2C.*

Engine initial start-up after overhaul – 2D•17
Engine management self-diagnosis memory fault check – 1A•14, 1B•13
Engine mountings
    1.2 litre and 1.4 litre petrol engine – 2A•21
    2.0 litre direct injection petrol engine – 2B•21
    1.6 litre and 2.0 litre diesel engine – 2C•20
Engine oil and filter renewal (diesel models) – 1B•6
Engine oil and filter renewal (petrol models) – 1A•7
Engine oil cooler/filter housing
    1.2 litre and 1.4 litre petrol engine – 2A•22
    1.6 litre and 2.0 litre diesel engine – 2C•22
Engine oil level – 0•12
Engine overhaul
    General information – 2D•2
    Preliminary information – 2D•6
    Reassembly sequence – 2D•14
Engine speed/TDC sensor (diesel engines) – 4B•6
Engine valve timing marks setting TDC (2.0 litre direct injection petrol engine) – 2B•4
Evaporative loss emission control system component (petrol engines) – 4C•2
Exhaust Gas Recirculation (EGR) system components (diesel engines) – 4D•3
Exhaust system
    Check – 1A•10, 1B•9
    Component renewal
        Petrol engines – 4C•6
        Diesel engines – 4D•8
Exterior light units – 12•14
Exterior mirror – 11•18

F
Facia panel assembly – 11•34
Fault finding – REF•12
Flywheel
    1.6 litre and 2.0 litre diesel engine – 2C•17
    1.2 and 1.4 litre petrol engine – 2A•17
    2.0 litre direct injection petrol engine – 2B•18
Footwell temperature sensor – 3•17
Fresh/circulating air flap and positioning motor – 3•16
Front anti-roll bar drip link – 10•12
Front anti-roll bar – 10•11
Front bumper cover – 11•4
Front courtesy/reading light bulb – 12•13
Front direction indicator bulb – 12•9
Front door lock and support bracket – 11•12
Front door lock cylinder and handle – 11•11
Front door window glass and regulator – 11•13
Front fog light
    Bulb – 12•11
    Removal – 12•15
Front hub bearings renewal – 10•6
Front suspension
    Lower arm balljoint – 10•11
    Lower arm removal/overhaul – 10•9
    Strut removal/overhaul – 10•7
Front wheel bearing housing (swivel hub) – 10•5
Fuel filter
    Renewal (diesel engines) – 1B•14, 4B•11
    Fuel injection system (petrol engines)
    System depressurisation – 4A•16
    Testing – 4A•18
Fuel injectors/fuel rail – 4A•7
Fuel lift pump and gauge sender unit
    Petrol engines – 4A•13
    Diesel engines – 4B•11
Fuel pipes and connections – 4A•3

Fuel pipes and connectors (diesel engines) – 4B•2
Fuel pressure regulating valve (diesel engines) – 4B•7
Fuel pressure regulator (petrol engines) – 4A•13
Fuel pressure sensor
    Diesel engines – 4B•7
    Petrol engines – 4A•13
Fuel rail (diesel engines) – 4B•14
Fuel system bleeding (diesel engines) – 4B•14
Fuel system components (petrol engines) – 4A•6
Fuel tank
    Diesel engines – 4B•12
    Filler cap flap actuator – 11•17
    Petrol engines – 4A•15
Fuel temperature sensor (diesel engines) – 4B•5
Fuses and relays general information – 12•3

G
Gas discharge headlights
    Bulb control unit/starter – 12•15
    Cornering light bulb – 12•10
    Dipped main beam bulbs – 12•10
    Front direction indicator bulb – 12•10
    Headlights bulbs – 12•10
    Sidelight bulb – 12•10
General repair procedures – REF•4
Glovebox
    Illumination light bulb – 12•14
    Light switch – 12•8
    Removal – 11•29
Glow plug control unit (diesel engines) – 5C•2
Glow plugs testing/removal (diesel engines) – 5C•1

H
Halogen headlight bulbs – 12•9
Handbrake
    Handbrake 'on' warning switch – 12•8
    Control switch – 9•14
    Control unit – 9•14
    Motor – 9•13
Hazard warning switch – 12•7
Headlamp range control and instrument illumination switch – 12•6
Headlight
    Adjustment switch – 12•16
    Automatic range control ECU – 12•17
    Beam adjustment – 1A•12, 1B•10
    Beam adjustment components – 12•16
    Beam alignment – 12•17
    Dip beam bulb – 12•9
    Main beam bulb – 12•9
    Pop-up washer jet lift cylinder – 12•22
    Pop-up washer jets – 12•22
    Range adjustment motor – 12•16
    Removal – 12•14
Headlining – 11•30
Heater blower motor
    Removal – 3•16
    Series resistor – 3•16
    Switch – 12•6
Heater matrix – 3•14
Heater unit – 3•15
Heater/ventilation control panel illumination bulb – 12•14
Heating and ventilation system
    Components – 3•13
    General information – 3•13
    Vents – 3•17
High level brake light – 12•16
High pressure fuel pump (petrol engines) – 4A•12

Note: *References throughout this index are in the form "**Chapter number**" • "**Page number**". So, for example, 2C•15 refers to page 15 of Chapter 2C.*

High pressure fuel pump (diesel engines) – 4B•13
High pressure injectors (petrol engines) – 4A•7
High-level brake light bulb – 12•12
Hinge and lock lubrication – 1A•14, 1B•12
Horn – 12•18
Hose and fluid leak check – 1A•11, 1B•9
Hydraulic tappets operational check (2.0 litre direct injection petrol engine) – 2B•18
Hydraulic tappets/roller rocker fingers (1.2 and 1.4 litre petrol engine) – 2A•12

I

Identifying leaks – 0•10
If your car won't start – 0•6
Ignition system (petrol engines)
    HT coil(s) – 5B•2
    Ignition switch – 12•5
    Ignition switch/lock cylinder housing – 10•21
    Ignition switch/lock cylinder – 10•21
    Testing – 5B•2
Ignition timing checking and adjusting – 5B•2
Injector seals (petrol engines) – 4A•8
Injectors checking/removal (diesel engines) – 4B•8
Inlet air temperature sensor (diesel engines) – 4B•6
Inlet air temperature/pressure sensor (petrol engines) – 4A•10
Inlet manifold and associated components (petrol engines) – 4A•16
Inlet manifold (diesel engines) – 4B•10
Instrument panel – 12•17
Intercooler
    General information (petrol engines) – 4C•6
    Removal (diesel engines) – 4D•6
Interior mirror – 11•20
Interior monitoring deactivation switch – 12•8
Interior trim – 11•25

J

Jacking and vehicle support – REF•5
Jump starting – 0•7

K

Knock sensor (petrol engines) – 4A•11

L

LED headlight removal – 12•17
LED headlights bulbs – 12•11
Lighting switch – 12•6
Load area panels – 11•27
Loudspeakers – 12•23
Low pressure injectors (2.0 litre petrol engines) – 4A•9
Lubricants and fluids – 0•17
Luggage area light switch – 12•8
Luggage compartment light bulb – 12•14

M

Main and big-end bearings inspection – 2D•14
Maintenance
    Bodywork and underframe – 11•2
    Schedule (diesel models) – 1B•3
    Schedule (petrol models) – 1A•3
    Upholstery and carpets – 11•2
Major body damage repair – 11•4
Manual transmission
    Reversing light and neutral switches testing/removal – 7A•7
    Gear change housing and cable removal/adjustment – 7A•2
    Oil draining, refilling and level checking – 7A•6
    Oil level check
    Diesel models – 1B•11

Petrol models – 1A•12
Overhaul general information – 7A•7
Removal – 7A•3
Mass airflow sensor (diesel engines) – 4B•6
Minor body damage repair – 11•2
Mirrors
    Associated components – 11•18
    Glass – 11•19
    Housing – 11•19
Mirror control/door lock switch – 12•8
    Switch – 11•19
MOT test checks – REF•8
Multi-link rear suspension – 10•13

N

Number plate light bulb – 12•12

O

Oil cooler (2.0 litre direct injection petrol engine) – 2B•21
Oil level/temperature sender
    1.2 litre and 1.4 litre petrol engine) – 2A•23
    1.6 litre and 2.0 litre diesel engine) – 2C•23
Oil pressure components
    Switches and oil control valves (2.0 litre direct injection petrol engine) – 2B•20
    Warning light switch (1.2 and 1.4 litre petrol engine) – 2A•22
    Warning light switch/ regulating valve (1.6 litre and 2.0 litre diesel engine) – 2C•23
Oil pump
Oil pump and drivebelt (1.6 litre and 2.0 litre diesel engine) – 2C•16
    Removal
    1.2 litre and 1.4 litre petrol engines – 2A•16
    2.0 litre direct injection petrol engine – 2B•20
Oxygen (lambda) sensors (petrol engines) – 4A•11

P

Parking aid components
    Components – 12•26
    Control unit – 12•27
    Range/distance sensor – 12•27
    Warning buzzers – 12•27
Particulate filter ash deposit mass check (diesel models) – 1B•16
Piston rings refitting – 2D•14
Piston/connecting rod assemblies
    Removal – 2D•9
    Inspection – 2D•11
    Refitting – 2D•16
Pollen filter element renewal – 1A•12, 1B•10
Power outlets (12 volt) – 12•18
Power window switch assembly – 12•8
Puncture repair kit – 0•9

R

Radiators – 3•4
Rain and light sensor – 12•8
Rear anti-roll bar and drop link – 10•18
Rear brake
    Caliper removal/overhaul – 9•11
    Brake pads renewal – 9•9
Rear bumper cover – 11•5
Rear coil spring – 10•16
Rear courtesy/reading light bulb – 12•13
Rear door
    Handle – 11•12
    Lock – 11•13
    Window glass – 11•14

Note: *References throughout this index are in the form "**Chapter number**" • "**Page number**". So, for example, 2C•15 refers to page 15 of Chapter 2C.*

Rear hub/wheel bearings – 10•13
Rear light cluster bulbs – 12•11
Rear number plate light – 12•16
Rear shock absorber – 10•17
Rear subframe (multi-link suspension) – 10•19
Rear track control rod – 10•14
Rear trailing arm and bracket removal/overhaul – 10•15
Rear transverse links – 10•14
Rear wheel bearing housing/stub axle – 10•13
Rear wing mounted lights – 12•15
Rear wiper motor – 12•20
Receiver/drier (A/C) – 3•20
Refrigerant pressure sensor (A/C) – 3•20
Regular Maintenance
   Diesel models – 1B•6
   Petrol models – 1A•7
Remote control transmitter battery – 11•18
Resetting the service interval display – 1A•10, 1B•9, 12•18
Reversing light switch – 12•8
Road test and exhaust emissions check – 1A•14, 1B•13
Routine maintenance component location
   Petrol models – 1A•4
   Diesel models – 1B•4

S

Safety First – 0•5
Screen washer fluid level – 0•14
Seat belts
   Components – 11•23
   Front seat belt – 11•23
   Front seat belt stalk – 11•24
   Rear centre belt – 11•24
   Rear seat belt – 11•24
   Rear seat belt stalks – 11•25
   Seat belt tensioning mechanisms – 11•22
Seats – 11•20
Service interval display resetting – 12•18
Side vent temperature sensors – 3•17
Sill trim panel – 11•26
Spark plug renewal (petrol models) – 1A•16
Starter and starting system
Starter motor – 5A•6
Starter motor testing/overhaul – 5A•7
Starting system testing – 5A•6
Steering and suspension
   Check – 1A•13, 1B•11
Steering column – 10•19
Steering column shrouds – 11•28
Steering gear assembly removal/overhaul – 10•22
Steering gear gaiters and track rods – 10•23
Steering wheel – 10•19
Subwoofer – 12•24
Sump
   Removal
     1.2 and 1.4 litre petrol engine – 2A•14
     1.6 litre and 2.0 litre diesel engine – 2C•15
     2.0 litre direct injection petrol engine – 2B•19
Sunlight sensor – 3•17
Sunroof
   Check and lubrication – 1A•14, 1B•13
   General information – 11•20
Switch illumination bulbs – 12•14

T

Tailgate
   Handle/release unit – 11•17
   Lock – 11•17
   Lock components – 11•17

Tailgate and support struts – 11•15
Tailgate/boot lid lock actuator – 11•18
Tailgate mounted light bulbs – 12•12
Tailgate mounted lights – 12•15
Tailgate washer jet – 12•22
Temperature flap control motor – 3•16
Throttle body
   Petrol engines – 4A•6
Throttle pedal/position sensor
   Diesel engines – 4B•5
   Petrol engines – 4A•10
Throttle valve housing/module (diesel engines) – 4B•5
Timing belt
   Belt and tensioner roller (diesel models) – 1B•15
   Covers
     1.2 and 1.4 litre petrol engine – 2A•9
     1.6 litre and 2.0 litre diesel engine – 2C•6
     Idler pulley – 2A•12
   Belt removal
     1.2 litre and 1.4 litre petrol engine – 2A•9
     1.6 litre and 2.0 litre diesel engine – 2C•8
   Renewal (petrol models) – 1A•17
   Tensioner and sprockets
     1.2 litre and 1.4 litre petrol engine – 2A•11
     1.6 litre and 2.0 litre diesel engine – 2C•9
Timing chain
   Chain and balancer shaft (2.0 litre direct injection petrol engine) – 2B•9
   Covers (2.0 litre direct injection petrol engine) – 2B•6
Tools and working facilities – REF•6
Torsion beam axle
   Removal – 10•13, 10•18
Towing – 0•9
Track rod end – 10•24
Turbocharger
   Turbocharger and exhaust manifold (diesel engines) – 4D•4
   Charge control system components (diesel engines) – 4D•6
   General information (diesel engines) – 4D•4
   Removal (petrol engines) – 4C•4
Tyres
   Condition and pressure – 0•15, 0•17
   Tread wear patterns – 0•15

U

Underbody protection check – 1A•12, 1B•11
Underbonnet check points – 0•11

V

Vanity mirror light bulb – 12•14
Vehicle identification numbers – REF•5
Vehicle level sender – 12•17

W

Washer system components
   Pump – 12•21
   Reservoir – 12•21
Wheel alignment and steering angles – 10•25
Wheel arch liners and body under-panels – 11•20
Wheel changing – 0•8
Window motor and regulator – 11•14
Windscreen and rear window glass general information – 11•20
Windscreen washer jets – 12•21
Windscreen wiper motor and linkage – 12•19
Windscreen/tailgate/headlight washer system check – 1A•14, 1B•13
Wiper and indicator/cruise switches – 12•5
Wiper arm – 12•18
Wiper blades – 0•14
Wiring diagrams 12•28 to 12•47 – 12•28

Preserving Our Motoring Heritage

< The Model J Duesenberg Derham Tourster. Only eight of these magnificent cars were ever built – this is the only example to be found outside the United States of America

Almost every car you've ever loved, loathed or desired is gathered under one roof at the Haynes Motor Museum. Over 300 immaculately presented cars and motorbikes represent every aspect of our motoring heritage, from elegant reminders of bygone days, such as the superb Model J Duesenberg to curiosities like the bug-eyed BMW Isetta. There are also many old friends and flames. Perhaps you remember the 1959 Ford Popular that you did your courting in? The magnificent 'Red Collection' is a spectacle of classic sports cars including AC, Alfa Romeo, Austin Healey, Ferrari, Lamborghini, Maserati, MG, Riley, Porsche and Triumph.

A Perfect Day Out

Each and every vehicle at the Haynes Motor Museum has played its part in the history and culture of Motoring. Today, they make a wonderful spectacle and a great day out for all the family. Bring the kids, bring Mum and Dad, but above all bring your camera to capture those golden memories for ever. You will also find an impressive array of motoring memorabilia, a comfortable 70 seat video cinema and one of the most extensive transport book shops in Britain. The Pit Stop Cafe serves everything from a cup of tea to wholesome, home-made meals or, if you prefer, you can enjoy the large picnic area nestled in the beautiful rural surroundings of Somerset.

> John Haynes O.B.E., Founder and Chairman of the museum at the wheel of a Haynes Light 12.

< Graham Hill's Lola Cosworth Formula 1 car next to a 1934 Riley Sports.

The Museum is situated on the A359 Yeovil to Frome road at Sparkford, just off the A303 in Somerset. It is about 40 miles south of Bristol, and 25 minutes drive from the M5 intersection at Taunton.
Open 9.30am - 5.30pm (10.00am - 4.00pm Winter) 7 days a week, *except Christmas Day, Boxing Day and New Years Day*
Special rates available for schools, coach parties and outings Charitable Trust No. 292048